Data Mining for Business Analytics

AN INDIAN ADAPTATION

Data Mining for Business Analytics

Concepts, Techniques, and Applications in Python

AN INDIAN ADAPTATION

Galit Shmueli

Professor, National Tsing Hua University's Institute of Service Science
Hsinchu City, Taiwan

Peter C. Bruce

President and Founder
Institute for Statistics Education, U.S.

Peter Gedeck, PHD

Senior Data Scientist at Collaborative Drug Discovery
Burlingame, California, U.S.

Nitin R. Patel

Chairman and Cofounder of Cytel, Inc.
Cambridge, Massachusetts

O. P. Wali

Professor, IT and Knowledge Management
Indian Institute of Foreign Trade

WILEY

Data Mining for Business Analytics

Concepts, Techniques, and Applications in Python

WILEY INDIA ADAPTATION

Authors: Galit Shmueli, Peter C. Bruce, Peter Gedeck, Nitin R. Patel, and O.P. Wali

Published by Wiley India Pvt. Ltd.,
4436/7, Ansari Road, Daryaganj, New Delhi-110002.

Printed at: S.D.R.Printers

First Edition: 2023
Reprint: 2024

ISBN: 978-93-5746-167-2
ISBN: 978-93-5746-166-5 (ebk)

Other Wiley Editorial Offices:
John Wiley & Sons, Inc. 111 River Street, Hoboken, NJ 07030, USA
Wiley-VCH Verlag GmbH, Pappellaee 3, D-69469 Weinheim, Germany
John Wiley & Sons Australia Ltd, 42 McDougall Street, Milton, Queensland 4064, Australia
John Wiley & Sons (Asia) Pte Ltd, 1 Fusionpolis Walk #07-01 Solaris, South Tower Singapore 138628
John Wiley & Sons Canada Ltd, 22 Worcester Road, Etobicoke, Ontario, Canada, M9W ILI

Edition: 2023

www.wileyindia.com

The beginning of wisdom is this:
Get wisdom, and whatever else you get, get insight.

רֵאשִׁית חָכְמָה, קְנֵה חָכְמָה; וּבְכָל-קִנְיָנְךָ, קְנֵה בִינָה.

– Proverbs 4:7

In memory of Professor Ayala Cohen (1940–2019)
who combined wisdom, insight, enthusiasm, and care

Peter Gedeck dedicates this book to his son, Victor

Foreword by Gareth James

The field of statistics has existed in one form or another for 200 years, and by the second half of the 20th century had evolved into a well-respected and essential academic discipline. However, its prominence expanded rapidly in the 1990s with the explosion of new, and enormous, data sources. For the first part of this century, much of this attention was focused on biological applications, in particular, genetics data generated as a result of the sequencing of the human genome. However, the last decade has seen a dramatic increase in the availability of data in the business disciplines, and a corresponding interest in business-related statistical applications.

The impact has been profound. Ten years ago, when I was able to attract a full class of MBA students to my new statistical learning elective, my colleagues were astonished because our department struggled to fill most electives. Today, we offer a Masters in Business Analytics, which is the largest specialized masters program in the school and has application volume rivaling those of our MBA programs. Our department's faculty size and course offerings have increased dramatically, yet the MBA students are still complaining that the classes are all full. Google's chief economist, Hal Varian, was indeed correct in 2009 when he stated that "the sexy job in the next 10 years will be statisticians."

This demand is driven by a simple, but undeniable, fact. Business analytics solutions have produced significant and measurable improvements in business performance, on multiple dimensions and in numerous settings, and as a result, there is a tremendous demand for individuals with the requisite skill set. However, training students in these skills is challenging given that, in addition to the obvious required knowledge of statistical methods, they need to understand business-related issues, possess strong communication skills, and be comfortable dealing with multiple computational packages. Most statistics texts concentrate on abstract training in classical methods, without much emphasis on practical, let alone business, applications.

This book has by far the most comprehensive review of business analytics methods that I have ever seen, covering everything from classical approaches such as linear and logistic regression, through to modern methods like neural networks, bagging and boosting, and even much more business specific procedures such as social network analysis and text mining. If not the bible, it is at the least a definitive manual on the subject. However, just as important as the list of topics, is the way that they are all presented in an applied fashion using business applications. Indeed the last chapter is entirely dedicated to 10 separate cases where business analytics approaches can be applied.

In this latest edition, the authors have added support for Python, a programming language that is rapidly gaining popularity among data scientists. The book provides detailed descriptions and code involving applications of Python in numerous business settings, ensuring that the reader will actually be able to apply their knowledge to real-life problems. I'm confident that this book will be an indispensable tool for any business analytics course using Python.

We recently introduced a business analytics course into our required MBA core curriculum and I intend to make heavy use of this book in developing the syllabus. I'm confident that it will be an indispensable tool for any such course.

GARETH JAMES
Marshall School of Business, University of Southern California, 2019

Foreword by Ravi Bapna

Data is the new gold—and mining this gold to create business value in today's context of a highly networked and digital society requires a skillset that we haven't traditionally delivered in business or statistics or engineering programs on their own. For those businesses and organizations that feel overwhelmed by today's Big Data, the phrase *you ain't seen nothing yet* comes to mind. Yesterday's three major sources of Big Data—the 20+ years of investment in enterprise systems (ERP, CRM, SCM, etc.), the 3 billion plus people on the online social grid, and the close to 5 billion people carrying increasingly sophisticated mobile devices—are going to be dwarfed by tomorrow's smarter physical ecosystems fueled by the Internet of Things (IoT) movement.

The idea that we can use sensors to connect physical objects such as homes, automobiles, roads, even garbage bins and streetlights, to digitally optimized systems of governance goes hand in glove with bigger data and the need for deeper analytical capabilities. We are not far away from a smart refrigerator sensing that you are short on, say, eggs, populating your grocery store's mobile app's shopping list, and arranging a Task Rabbit to do a grocery run for you. Or the refrigerator negotiating a deal with an Uber driver to deliver an evening meal to you. Nor are we far away from sensors embedded in roads and vehicles that can compute traffic congestion, track roadway wear and tear, record vehicle use and factor these into dynamic usage-based pricing, insurance rates, and even taxation. This brave new world is going to be fueled by analytics and the ability to harness data for competitive advantage.

Business Analytics is an emerging discipline that is going to help us ride this new wave. This new Business Analytics discipline requires individuals who are grounded in the fundamentals of business such that they know the right questions to ask, who have the ability to harness, store, and optimally process vast datasets from a variety of structured and unstructured sources, and who can then use an array of techniques from machine learning and statistics to uncover new insights for decision-making. Such individuals are a rare commodity today, but their creation has been the focus of this book for a decade now. This book's forte is that it relies on explaining the core set of concepts required for today's business analytics professionals using real-world data-rich cases in a hands-on manner, without sacrificing academic rigor. It provides a modern day foundation for Business Analytics, the notion of linking the x's to the y's of interest in a predictive sense. I say this with the confidence of someone who was probably the first adopter of the zeroth edition of this book (Spring 2006 at the Indian School of Business).

After the publication of the R edition in 2018, the new Python edition is an important addition. Python is gaining in popularity among analytics professionals, and the two open source languages constitute the primary statistical modeling and machine learning programming environments in data science.

I look forward to using the book in multiple fora, in executive education, in MBA classrooms, in MS-Business Analytics programs, and in Data Science bootcamps. I trust you will too!

RAVI BAPNA
Carlson School of Management, University of Minnesota, 2019

Preface to the Indian Adaptation

The digital transformation of organizations is a widespread phenomenon. It is happening alongside huge advances in computational science, pace in global connectivity, and data usage across the globe. Massive data is getting generated, accessed, and processed to support decision making in all spheres. This has given huge impetus to the science of data mining. It has brought together different disciplines to dig out every possible insight from the data. As a result, the application of data mining is becoming ubiquitous under the broader umbrella of Artificial Intelligence. However, many stakeholders of this ecosystem prefer the use of efficient, latest, and open access technology resources as enablers of this empowerment for them, their organizations or their clients. This has made languages like R, Python etc., or applications, in the open-source category, very popular among the analysts and this is growing day by day. In this context, this book addresses this need of putting together the host of methods used for data processing, analysis and problem-solving. It also brings ready-to-use algorithms in Python to prepare learners for data analysis supported with cases and examples from a variety of domains.

Data Mining for Business Analytics Concepts, Techniques, and Applications in Python has seen adoption across students and practitioners and in many courses, ranging from dedicated data mining classes to more general business analytics courses. The focus of the book is on data mining concepts, techniques, and application of algorithms in Python to generate insights from data for problem solving. The content structure has been designed to enable learners to learn approaches and techniques in a systematic way, from simple to advanced methods, descriptive to predictive, and from quantitative to qualitative methods.

This Indian adaptation has reset the content to fit the local context with examples and cases in the local context while retaining examples, exercises, and cases of generic and global nature to make the learning process comprehensive but easier for learners of Indian sub-continent. Examples have been included to build the local flavor so that cognitive and analytical capacities are spared more to focus on the concept, method, and nuances of problem solving. Examples cut across different functional areas of organizations, private as well as public, offline, and digital, to bring a sufficient variety of use scenarios for effective learning outcomes.

NEW IN THE INDIAN ADAPTATION

1. Examples which are more appropriate to Indian scenario have been added:
   - Service Feedback and Usage Data
   - Time Series Indices of Industrial Production of India
   - Service Feedback and Usage
   - Fruit Variety Classification
   - Predicting Online Buying Behavior
   - Fruit Variety
   - Customer Recommendation Behavior
   - Rating Behavior Towards Online Quick Food Service Providers in Indian Cities
   - Rule for Cross Category Purchases in Online Store
   - State-Wise Virus Recoveries
2. Case studies more relevant to Indian scenario have been added:
   - Predicting Tourist Travel Packages
   - Predicting Attrition
   - Attitude Towards Therapy Suggestions in COVID-19 Times
3. Content has been modified and updated to fit the Indian curriculum, including Predictive Power and Overfitting, Building a Predictive Model, Basic Charts, Multidimensional Visualization, Data Summaries, Reducing the Number of Categories in Categorical Variables, Evaluating Predictive Performance, *k*-NN Classifier, Advantages and Shortcomings of the Naive Bayes Classifier, Classification Trees, Avoiding Overfitting, Classification Rules from Trees, Random Forests, Boosted Trees, Advantages and Weaknesses of a Tree, Evaluating Classification Performance, and Uplift (Persuasion) Modeling.
4. Addition of new end-of-chapter problems.

RESOURCES

The resources of the original US edition can be obtained from Dr. Shmueli at https://www.dataminingbook.com/user/register

The following resources of the adapted edition can be obtained from https://www.wileyindia.com/Instructor_Manuals/Register/login.php/

- Solutions to new problems
- Datasets to new examples, problems, and case studies
- Solutions to new case studies

Preface to the Python Edition

This textbook first appeared in early 2007 and has been used by numerous students and practitioners and in many courses, including our own experience teaching this material both online and in person for more than 15 years. The first edition, based on the Excel add-in Analytic Solver Data Mining (previously XLMiner), was followed by two more Analytic Solver editions, a JMP edition, an R edition, and now this Python edition, with its companion website, www.dataminingbook.com.

This new Python edition, which relies on the free and open-source Python programming language, presents output from Python, as well as the code used to produce that output, including specification of the appropriate packages and functions, the dominant one being scikit-learn. Unlike computer-science or statistics-oriented textbooks, the focus in this book is on data mining concepts, and how to implement the associated algorithms in Python. We assume a basic familiarity with Python.

For this Python edition, a new co-author, Peter Gedeck comes on board bringing extensive data science experience in business. In addition to providing Python code and output, this edition also incorporates updates and new material based on feedback from instructors teaching MBA, MS, undergraduate, diploma, and executive courses, and from their students as well. Importantly, this edition includes for the first time an extended section on Data Ethics (Section 2.9).

A note about the book's title: The first two editions of the book used the title *Data Mining for Business Intelligence*. Business Intelligence today refers mainly to reporting and data visualization ("what is happening now"), while Business Analytics has taken over the "advanced analytics," which include predictive analytics and data mining. In this new edition, we therefore use the updated terms.

This Python edition includes the material that was recently added in the third edition of the original (Analytic Solver based) book:

- Social network analysis
- Text mining
- Ensembles
- Uplift modeling
- Collaborative filtering

Since the appearance of the (Analytic Solver based) second edition, the landscape of the courses using the textbook has greatly expanded: whereas initially, the book was used mainly in semester-long elective MBA-level courses, it is now used in a variety of courses in Business Analytics degrees and certificate programs, ranging from undergraduate programs, to post-graduate and executive education programs. Courses in such programs also vary in their duration and coverage. In many cases, this textbook is used across multiple courses. The book is designed to continue supporting the general "Predictive Analytics" or "Data Mining" course as well as supporting a set of courses in dedicated business analytics programs.

A general "Business Analytics," "Predictive Analytics," or "Data Mining" course, common in MBA and undergraduate programs as a one-semester elective, would cover Parts I–III, and choose a subset of methods from Parts IV and V. Instructors can choose to use cases as team assignments, class discussions, or projects. For a two-semester course, Part VI might be considered, and we recommend introducing the new Part VII (Data Analytics).

For a set of courses in a dedicated business analytics program, here are a few courses that have been using our book:

Predictive Analytics—Supervised Learning: In a dedicated Business Analytics program, the topic of Predictive Analytics is typically instructed across a set of courses. The first course would cover Parts I–IV and instructors typically choose a subset of methods from Part IV according to the course length. We recommend including the Chapter 13 on ensembles in such a course, as well as "Part VII: Data Analytics."

Predictive Analytics—Unsupervised Learning: This course introduces data exploration and visualization, dimension reduction, mining relationships, and clustering (Parts III and V). If this course follows the Predictive Analytics: Supervised Learning course, then it is useful to examine examples and approaches that integrate unsupervised and supervised learning, such as the new part on "Data Analytics."

Forecasting Analytics: A dedicated course on time series forecasting would rely on Part VI.

Advanced Analytics: A course that integrates the learnings from Predictive Analytics (supervised and unsupervised learning). Such a course can focus on Part VII: Data Analytics, where social network analytics and text mining are introduced. Some instructors choose to use the Cases (Chapter 21) in such a course.

In all courses, we strongly recommend including a project component, where data are either collected by students according to their interest or provided by the instructor (e.g., from the many data mining competition datasets available). From our experience and other instructors' experience, such projects enhance the learning and provide students with an excellent opportunity to understand the strengths of data mining and the challenges that arise in the process.

GALIT SHMUELI, PETER C. BRUCE, PETER GEDECK, AND NITIN R. PATEL
2019

Acknowledgments

We thank the many people who assisted us in improving the book from its inception as *Data Mining for Business Intelligence* in 2006 (using XLMiner, now Analytic Solver), through the recent editions now called *Data Mining for Business Analytics*, including two later XLMiner editions, a JMP edition, an R edition, and now for the first time, a Python edition.

Anthony Babinec, who has been using earlier editions of this book for years in his data mining courses at Statistics.com, provided us with detailed and expert corrections. Dan Toy and John Elder IV greeted our project with early enthusiasm and provided detailed and useful comments on initial drafts. Ravi Bapna, who used an early draft in a data mining course at the Indian School of Business and later at University of Minnesota, has provided invaluable comments and helpful suggestions since the book's start.

Many of the instructors, teaching assistants, and students using earlier editions of the book have contributed invaluable feedback both directly and indirectly, through fruitful discussions, learning journeys, and interesting data mining projects that have helped shape and improve the book. These include MBA students from the University of Maryland, MIT, the Indian School of Business, National Tsing Hua University, and Statistics.com. Instructors from many universities and teaching programs, too numerous to list, have supported and helped improve the book since its inception. Scott Nestler has been a helpful friend of this book project from the beginning.

Kuber Deokar, instructional operations supervisor at Statistics .com, has been unstinting in his assistance, support, and detailed attention. We also thank Anuja Kulkarni, assistant teacher at Statistics .com. Valerie Troiano has shepherded many instructors and students through the Statistics.com courses that have helped nurture the development of these books.

Colleagues and family members have been providing ongoing feedback and assistance with this book project. Boaz Shmueli and Raquelle Azran gave detailed editorial comments and suggestions on the first two editions; Bruce McCullough and Adam Hughes did the same for the first edition. Noa Shmueli provided careful proofs of the third edition. Ran Shenberger offered design tips. Che Lin and Boaz Shmueli provided feedback on Deep Learning. Ken Strasma, founder of the microtargeting firm HaystaqDNA and director of targeting for the 2004 Kerry campaign and the 2008 Obama campaign, provided the scenario and data for the section on uplift modeling. We also thank Jen Golbeck, director of the Social Intelligence Lab at the University of Maryland and author of *Analyzing the Social Web*, whose book inspired our presentation in the chapter on social network analytics. Randall Pruim contributed extensively to the chapter on visualization. Inbal Yahav, co-author of the R edition, helped improve the social network analytics and text mining chapters.

Marietta Tretter at Texas A&M shared comments and thoughts on the time series chapters, and Stephen Few and Ben Shneiderman provided feedback and suggestions on the data visualization chapter and overall design tips.

Susan Palocsay and Mia Stephens have provided suggestions and feedback on numerous occasions, as have Margret Bjarnadottir, and, specifically for this Python edition, Mohammad Salehan. We also thank Catherine Plaisant at the University of Maryland's Human–Computer Interaction Lab, who helped out in a major way by contributing exercises and illustrations to the data visualization chapter. Gregory Piatetsky-Shapiro, founder of KDNuggets.com, has been generous with his time and counsel in the early years of this project.

We thank colleagues at the MIT Sloan School of Management for their support during the formative stage of this book—Dimitris Bertsimas, James Orlin, Robert Freund, Roy Welsch, Gordon Kaufmann, and Gabriel Bitran. As teaching assistants for the data mining course at Sloan, Adam Mersereau gave detailed comments on the notes and cases that were the genesis of this book, Romy Shioda helped with the preparation of several cases and exercises used here, and Mahesh Kumar helped with the material on clustering.

Colleagues at the University of Maryland's Smith School of Business: Shrivardhan Lele, Wolfgang Jank, and Paul Zantek provided practical advice and comments. We thank Robert Windle, and University of Maryland MBA students Timothy Roach, Pablo Macouzet, and Nathan Birckhead for invaluable datasets. We also thank MBA students Rob Whitener and Daniel Curtis for the heatmap and map charts.

Anand Bodapati provided both data and advice. Jake Hofman from Microsoft Research and Sharad Borle assisted with data access. Suresh Ankolekar and Mayank Shah helped develop several cases and provided valuable pedagogical comments. Vinni Bhandari helped write the Charles Book Club case.

We would like to thank Marvin Zelen, L. J. Wei, and Cyrus Mehta at Harvard, as well as Anil Gore at Pune University, for thought-provoking discussions on the relationship between statistics and data mining. Our thanks to Richard Larson of the Engineering Systems Division, MIT, for sparking many stimulating ideas on the role of data mining in modeling complex systems. Over two decades ago, they helped us develop a balanced philosophical perspective on the emerging field of data mining.

Lastly, we thank the folks at Wiley for the decade-long successful journey of this book. Steve Quigley at Wiley showed confidence in this book from the beginning and helped us navigate through the publishing process with great speed. Curt Hinrichs' vision, tips, and encouragement helped bring this book to the starting gate. Sarah Keegan, Mindy Okura-Marszycki, Jon Gurstelle, Kathleen Santoloci, and Katrina Maceda greatly assisted us in pushing ahead and finalizing this Python edition. We are also especially grateful to Amy Hendrickson, who assisted with typesetting and making this book beautiful.

Contents

PART V MINING RELATIONSHIPS AMONG RECORDS 363

CHAPTER 14 Association Rules and Collaborative Filtering 365

CHAPTER 15 Cluster Analysis 397

PART

I

Preliminaries

CHAPTER 1

Introduction

1.1 | WHAT IS BUSINESS ANALYTICS?

Business Analytics (BA) is the practice and art of bringing quantitative data to bear on decision-making. The term means different things to different organizations.

Consider the role of analytics in helping newspapers survive the transition to a digital world. One tabloid newspaper with a working-class readership in Britain had launched a web version of the paper, and did tests on its home page to determine which images produced more hits: cats, dogs, or monkeys. This simple application, for this company, was considered analytics. By contrast, the *Washington Post* has a highly influential audience that is of interest to big defense contractors: it is perhaps the only newspaper where you routinely see advertisements for aircraft carriers. In the digital environment, the *Post* can track readers by time of day, location, and user subscription information. In this fashion, the display of the aircraft carrier advertisement in the online paper may be focused on a very small group of individuals—say, the members of the House and Senate Armed Services Committees who will be voting on the Pentagon's budget.

Business Analytics, or more generically, *analytics*, include a range of data analysis methods. Many powerful applications involve little more than counting, rule-checking, and basic arithmetic. For some organizations, this is what is meant by analytics.

The next level of business analytics, now termed *Business Intelligence* (BI), refers to data visualization and reporting for understanding "what happened and what is happening." This is done by use of charts, tables, and dashboards to display, examine, and explore data. BI, which earlier consisted mainly of generating static reports, has evolved into more user-friendly and effective tools and practices, such as creating interactive dashboards that allow the user not only to access real-time data, but also to directly interact with it. Effective dashboards are those that tie directly into company data, and give managers a tool to quickly see what might not readily be apparent in a large complex database. One such tool for industrial operations managers displays customer orders in a single two-dimensional display, using color and bubble size as added variables, showing customer name, type of product, size of order, and length of time to produce.

Business Analytics now typically includes BI as well as sophisticated data analysis methods, such as statistical models and data mining algorithms used for exploring data, quantifying and explaining relationships between measurements, and predicting new records. Methods like regression models are used to describe and quantify "on average" relationships (e.g., between advertising and sales), to predict new records (e.g., whether a new patient will react positively to a medication), and to forecast future values (e.g., next week's web traffic).

Readers familiar with earlier editions of this book may have noticed that the book title has changed from *Data Mining for Business Intelligence* to *Data Mining for Business Analytics* in this edition. The change reflects the more recent term BA, which overtook the earlier term BI to denote advanced analytics. Today, BI is used to refer to data visualization and reporting.

WHO USES PREDICTIVE ANALYTICS?

The widespread adoption of predictive analytics, coupled with the accelerating availability of data, has increased organizations' capabilities throughout the economy.

A few examples:

Credit scoring: One long-established use of predictive modeling techniques for business prediction is credit scoring. A credit score is not some arbitrary judgment of credit-worthiness; it is based mainly on a predictive model that uses prior data to predict repayment behavior.

Future purchases: A more recent (and controversial) example is Target's use of predictive modeling to classify sales prospects as "pregnant" or "not-pregnant." Those classified as pregnant could then be sent sales promotions at an early stage of pregnancy, giving Target a head start on a significant purchase stream.

Tax evasion: The US Internal Revenue Service found it was 25 times more likely to find tax evasion when enforcement activity was based on predictive models, allowing agents to focus on the most-likely tax cheats (Siegel, 2013).

The Business Analytics toolkit also includes statistical experiments, the most common of which is known to marketers as A/B testing. These are often used for pricing decisions:

- Orbitz, the travel site, found that it could price hotel options higher for Mac users than Windows users.
- Staples online store found it could charge more for staplers if a customer lived far from a Staples store.

Beware the organizational setting where analytics is a solution in search of a problem: a manager, knowing that business analytics and data mining are hot areas, decides that her organization must deploy them too, to capture that hidden value that must be lurking somewhere. Successful use of analytics and data mining requires both an understanding of the business context where value is to be captured, and an understanding of exactly what the data mining methods do.

1.2 | WHAT IS DATA MINING?

In this book, data mining refers to business analytics methods that go beyond counts, descriptive techniques, reporting, and methods based on business rules. While we do introduce data visualization, which is commonly the first step into more advanced analytics, the book focuses mostly on the more advanced data analytics tools. Specifically, it includes statistical and machine-learning methods that inform decision-making, often in an automated fashion. Prediction is typically an important component, often at the individual level. Rather than "what is the relationship between advertising and sales," we might be interested in "what specific advertisement, or recommended product, should be shown to a given online shopper at this moment?" Or we might be interested in clustering customers into different "personas" that receive different marketing treatment, then assigning each new prospect to one of these personas.

The era of Big Data has accelerated the use of data mining. Data mining methods, with their power and automaticity, have the ability to cope with huge amounts of data and extract value.

1.3 | DATA MINING AND RELATED TERMS

The field of analytics is growing rapidly, both in terms of the breadth of applications, and in terms of the number of organizations using advanced analytics. As a result, there is considerable overlap and inconsistency of definitions.

The term *data mining* itself means different things to different people. To the general public, it may have a general, somewhat hazy and pejorative meaning of digging through vast stores of (often personal) data in search of something interesting. One major consulting firm has a "data mining department," but its responsibilities are in the area of studying and graphing past data in search of general trends. And, to confuse matters, their more advanced predictive models are the responsibility of an "advanced analytics department." Other terms that organizations use are *predictive analytics*, *predictive modeling*, and *machine learning.*

Data mining stands at the confluence of the fields of statistics and machine learning (also known as *artificial intelligence*). A variety of techniques for exploring data and building models have been around for a long time in the world of statistics: linear regression, logistic regression, discriminant analysis, and principal components analysis, for example. But the core tenets of classical statistics—computing is difficult and data are scarce—do not apply in data mining applications where both data and computing power are plentiful.

This gives rise to Daryl Pregibon's description of data mining as "statistics at scale and speed" (Pregibon, 1999). Another major difference between the fields of statistics and machine learning is the focus in statistics on inference from a sample to the population regarding an "average effect"—for example, "a $1 price increase will reduce average demand by 2 boxes." In contrast, the focus in machine learning is on predicting individual records—"the predicted demand for person *i* given a $1 price increase is 1 box, while for person *j* it is 3 boxes." The emphasis that classical statistics places on inference (determining whether a pattern or interesting result might have happened by chance in our sample) is absent from data mining.

In comparison to statistics, data mining deals with large datasets in an open-ended fashion, making it impossible to put the strict limits around the question being addressed that inference would require. As a result, the general approach to data mining is vulnerable to the danger of *overfitting*, where a model is fit so closely to the available sample of data that it describes not merely structural characteristics of the data, but random peculiarities as well. In engineering terms, the model is fitting the noise, not just the signal.

In this book, we use the term *machine learning* to refer to algorithms that learn directly from data, especially local patterns, often in layered or iterative fashion. In contrast, we use *statistical models* to refer to methods that apply global structure to the data. A simple example is a linear regression model (statistical) vs. a k-nearest-neighbors algorithm (machine learning). A given record would be treated by linear regression in accord with an overall linear equation that applies to *all* the records. In k-nearest neighbors, that record would be classified in accord with the values of a small number of nearby records.

Lastly, many practitioners, particularly those from the IT and computer science communities, use the term *machine learning* to refer to all the methods discussed in this book.

1.4 | BIG DATA

Data mining and Big Data go hand in hand. *Big Data* is a relative term—data today are big by reference to the past, and to the methods and devices available to deal with them. The challenge Big Data presents is often characterized by the four Vs—volume, velocity, variety, and veracity. *Volume* refers to the amount of data. *Velocity* refers to the flow rate—the speed at which it is being generated and changed. *Variety* refers to the different types of data being generated (currency, dates, numbers, text, etc.). *Veracity* refers to the fact that data is being generated by organic distributed processes (e.g., millions of people signing up for services or free downloads) and not subject to the controls or quality checks that apply to data collected for a study.

Most large organizations face both the challenge and the opportunity of Big Data because most routine data processes now generate data that can be stored and, possibly, analyzed. The scale can be visualized by comparing the data in a traditional statistical analysis (say, 15 variables and 5000 records) to the Walmart database. If you consider the traditional statistical study to be the size of a period at the end of a sentence, then the Walmart database is the size of a football field. And that probably does not include other data associated with Walmart—social media data, for example, which comes in the form of unstructured text.

If the analytical challenge is substantial, so can be the reward:

- OkCupid, the online dating site, uses statistical models with their data to predict what forms of message content are most likely to produce a response.
- Telenor, a Norwegian mobile phone service company, was able to reduce subscriber turnover 37% by using models to predict which customers were most likely to leave, and then lavishing attention on them.
- Allstate, the insurance company, tripled the accuracy of predicting injury liability in auto claims by incorporating more information about vehicle type.

The above examples are from Eric Siegel's book *Predictive Analytics* (2013, Wiley).

Some extremely valuable tasks were not even feasible before the era of Big Data. Consider web searches, the technology on which Google was built. In early days, a search for "Ricky Ricardo Little Red Riding Hood" would have yielded various links to the *I Love Lucy* TV show, other links to Ricardo's career as a band leader, and links to the children's story of Little Red Riding Hood. Only once the Google database had accumulated sufficient data (including records of what users clicked on) would the search yield, in the top position, links to the specific *I Love Lucy* episode in which Ricky enacts, in a comic mixture of Spanish and English, Little Red Riding Hood for his infant son.

1.5 | DATA SCIENCE

The ubiquity, size, value, and importance of Big Data has given rise to a new profession: the *data scientist. Data science* is a mix of skills in the areas of statistics, machine learning, math, programming, business, and IT. The term itself is thus broader than the other concepts we discussed above, and it is a rare individual who combines deep skills in all the constituent areas. In their book *Analyzing the Analyzers* (Harris et al., 2013), the authors describe the skill sets of most data scientists as resembling a "T"—deep in one area (the vertical bar of the T), and shallower in other areas (the top of the T).

At a large data science conference session (Strata+Hadoop World, October 2014), most attendees felt that programming was an essential skill, though there was a sizable minority who felt otherwise. And, although Big Data is the motivating power behind the growth of data science, most data scientists do not actually spend most of their time working with terabyte-size or larger data.

Data of the terabyte or larger size would be involved at the deployment stage of a model. There are manifold challenges at that stage, most of them IT and programming issues related to data-handling and tying together different components of a system. Much work must precede that phase. It is that earlier piloting and prototyping phase on which this book focuses—developing the statistical and machine learning models that will eventually be plugged into a deployed system. What methods do you use with what sorts of data and problems? How do the methods work? What are their requirements, strengths, and weaknesses? How do you assess their performance?

1.6 | WHY ARE THERE SO MANY DIFFERENT METHODS?

As can be seen in this book or any other resource on data mining, there are many different methods for prediction and classification. You might ask yourself why they coexist, and whether some are better than others. The answer is that each method has advantages and disadvantages. The usefulness of a method can depend on factors such as the size of the dataset, the types of patterns that exist in the data, whether the data meet some underlying assumptions of the method, how noisy the data are, and the particular goal of the analysis. A small illustration is shown in Figure 1.1, where the goal is to find a combination of *household income level* and *household lot size* that separates buyers (blue solid circles) from nonbuyers (orange hollow circles) of riding mowers. The first

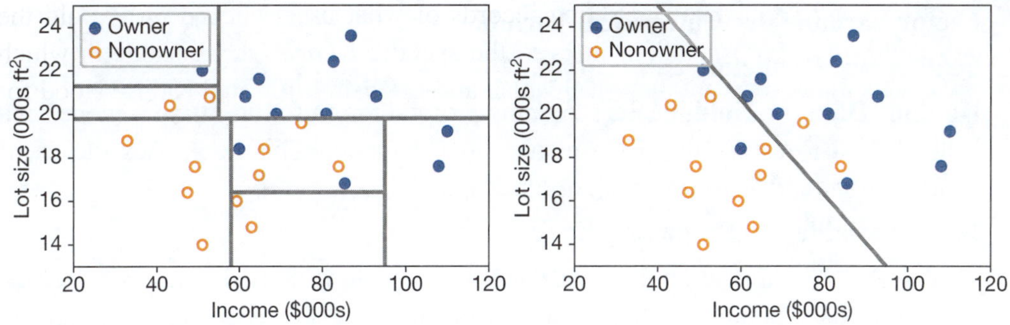

FIGURE 1.1 TWO METHODS FOR SEPARATING OWNERS FROM NONOWNERS

method (left panel) looks only for horizontal and vertical lines to separate buyers from nonbuyers, whereas the second method (right panel) looks for a single diagonal line.

Different methods can lead to different results, and their performance can vary. It is therefore customary in data mining to apply several different methods and select the one that appears most useful for the goal at hand.

1.7 | TERMINOLOGY AND NOTATION

Because of the hybrid parentry of data mining, its practitioners often use multiple terms to refer to the same thing. For example, in the machine learning (artificial intelligence) field, the variable being predicted is the output variable or target variable. To a statistician, it is the dependent variable or the response. Here is a summary of terms used:

Algorithm A specific procedure used to implement a particular data mining technique: classification tree, discriminant analysis, and the like.

Attribute see **Predictor**.

Case see **Observation**.

Categorical Variable A variable that takes on one of several fixed values, for example, a flight could be on-time, delayed, or canceled.

Confidence A performance measure in association rules of the type "IF A and B are purchased, THEN C is also purchased." Confidence is the conditional probability that C will be purchased IF A and B are purchased.

Confidence also has a broader meaning in statistics (*confidence interval*), concerning the degree of error in an estimate that results from selecting one sample as opposed to another.

Dependent Variable see **Response**.

Estimation see **Prediction**.

Factor Variable see **Categorical Variable**

Feature see **Predictor**.

Holdout Data (or **Holdout Set**) A sample of data not used in fitting a model, but instead used to assess the performance of that model. This book uses the terms *validation set* and *test set* instead of *holdout set*.

Input Variable see **Predictor**.

Model An algorithm as applied to a dataset, complete with its settings (many of the algorithms have parameters that the user can adjust).

Observation The unit of analysis on which the measurements are taken (a customer, a transaction, etc.), also called *instance*, *sample*, *example*, *case*, *record*, *pattern*, or *row*. In spreadsheets, each row typically represents a record; each column, a variable. Note that the term "sample" here is different from its usual meaning in statistics, where it refers to a collection of observations.

Outcome Variable see **Response**.

Output Variable see **Response**.

***P* (*A* | *B*)** The conditional probability of event A occurring given that event B has occurred, read as "the probability that A will occur given that B has occurred."

Prediction The prediction of the numerical value of a continuous output variable; also called *estimation*.

Predictor A variable, usually denoted by X, used as an input into a predictive model, also called a *feature*, *input variable*, *independent variable*, or from a database perspective, a *field*.

Profile A set of measurements on an observation (e.g., the height, weight, and age of a person).

Record see **Observation**.

Response A variable, usually denoted by Y, which is the variable being predicted in supervised learning, also called *dependent variable*, *output variable*, *target variable*, or *outcome variable*.

Sample In the statistical community, "sample" means a collection of observations. In the machine learning community, "sample" means a single observation.

Score A predicted value or class. *Scoring new data* means using a model developed with training data to predict output values in new data.

Success Class The class of interest in a binary outcome (e.g., *purchasers* in the outcome *purchase/no purchase*).

Supervised Learning The process of providing an algorithm (logistic regression, regression tree, etc.) with records in which an output variable of interest is known and the algorithm "learns" how to predict this value with new records where the output is unknown.

Target see **Response**.

Test Data (or **Test Set**) The portion of the data used only at the end of the model building and selection process to assess how well the final model might perform on new data.

Training Data (or **Training Set**) The portion of the data used to fit a model.

Unsupervised Learning An analysis in which one attempts to learn patterns in the data other than predicting an output value of interest.

Validation Data (or **Validation Set**) The portion of the data used to assess how well the model fits, to adjust models, and to select the best model from among those that have been tried.

Variable Any measurement on the records, including both the input (X) and the output (Y) variables.

1.8 | ROAD MAPS TO THIS BOOK

The book covers many of the widely used predictive and classification methods as well as other data mining tools. Figure 1.2 outlines data mining from a process perspective and where the topics in this book fit in. Chapter numbers are indicated beside the topic. Table 1.1 provides a different perspective: it organizes data mining procedures according to the type and structure of the data.

Order of Topics

The book is divided into five parts: Part I (Chapters 1 and 2) gives a general overview of data mining and its components. Part II (Chapters 3 and 4) focuses on the early stages of data exploration and dimension reduction.

Part III (Chapter 5) discusses performance evaluation. Although it contains only one chapter, we discuss a variety of topics, from predictive performance metrics to misclassification costs. The principles covered in this part are crucial for the proper evaluation and comparison of supervised learning methods.

Part IV includes eight chapters (Chapters 6–13), covering a variety of popular supervised learning methods (for classification and/or prediction). Within this part, the topics are generally organized according to the level of sophistication of the algorithms, their popularity, and ease of understanding. The final chapter introduces ensembles and combinations of methods.

Part V focuses on unsupervised mining of relationships. It presents association rules and collaborative filtering (Chapter 14) and cluster analysis (Chapter 15).

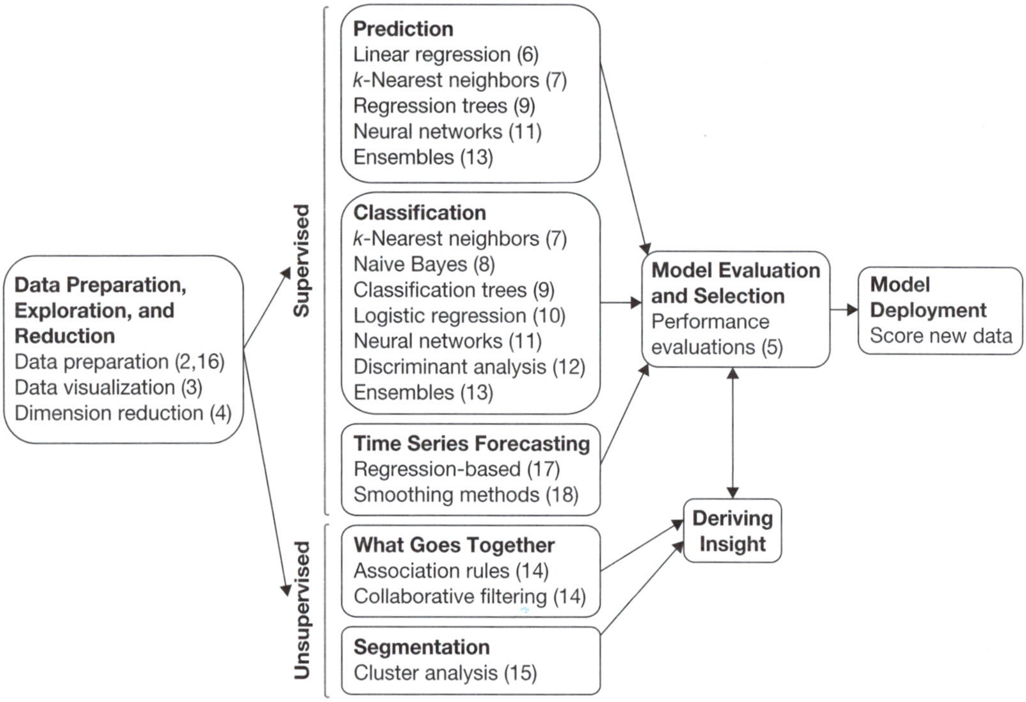

FIGURE 1.2 DATA MINING FROM A PROCESS PERSPECTIVE. NUMBERS IN PARENTHESES INDICATE CHAPTER NUMBERS

TABLE 1.1 ORGANIZATION OF DATA MINING METHODS IN THIS BOOK, ACCORDING TO THE NATURE OF THE DATA[a]

	Supervised		Unsupervised
	Continuous response	**Categorical response**	**No response**
Continuous predictors	Linear regression (6) *k*-Nearest neighbors (7) Neural nets (11) Ensembles (13)	*k*-Nearest neighbors (7) Logistic regression (10) Neural nets (11) Discriminant analysis (12) Ensembles (13)	Principal components (4) Collaborative filtering (14) Cluster analysis (15)
Categorical predictors	Linear regression (6) Regression trees (9) Neural nets (11) Ensembles (13)	Naïve Bayes (8) Classification trees (9) Logistic regression (10) Neural nets (11) Ensembles (13)	Association rules (14) Collaborative filtering (14)

[a]Numbers in parentheses indicate chapter number.

Part VI includes three chapters (Chapters 16–18), with the focus on forecasting time series. The first chapter covers general issues related to handling and understanding time series. The next two chapters present two popular forecasting approaches: regression-based forecasting and smoothing methods.

Part VII (Chapters 19 and 20) presents two broad data analytics topics: social network analysis and text mining. These methods apply data mining to specialized data structures: social networks and text.

Finally, Part VIII includes a set of cases.

Although the topics in the book can be covered in the order of the chapters, each chapter stands alone. We advise, however, to read Parts I–III before proceeding to chapters in Parts IV and V. Similarly, Chapter 16 should precede other chapters in Part VI.

USING PYTHON AND JUPYTER NOTEBOOKS

Python is a powerful, general purpose programming language that can be used for many applications ranging from short scripts to enterprise applications. There is a large and growing number of free, open-source libraries and tools for scientific computing. For more information about Python and its use visit www.python.org.

To facilitate a hands-on data mining experience, this book uses Jupyter notebooks (see example in Figure 1.3). They provide an interactive computational environment, in which you can easily combine code execution, rich text, and plots.

The Python language is widely used in academia and industry and had gained wide popularity for data mining and data analysis owing to the availability of well maintained packages for data analysis, data visualization, and machine learning. It has extensive coverage of statistical and data mining techniques for classification, prediction, mining associations and text, forecasting, and data exploration and reduction. It offers a variety of supervised data mining tools: neural nets, classification and regression trees, *k*-nearest-neighbor classification, naive Bayes, logistic regression, linear regression, and discriminant analysis, all for predictive modeling. Python's packages also cover unsupervised algorithms: association rules, collaborative filtering, principal components analysis, *k*-means clustering, and hierarchical clustering, as well as visualization tools and data-handling utilities. Often, the same method is implemented in multiple packages, as we will discuss throughout the book. The illustrations, exercises, and cases in this book are written in relation to Python.

Download: To download Python and Jupyter notebooks, we recommend that you use *anaconda*. Visit `www.anaconda.com` and follow the instructions there.

Installation: Install anaconda and the anaconda-navigator. The anaconda-navigator can also be used to install and update individual packages.

Use: You can start Jupyter notebooks from the anaconda-navigator or from the command line.

For up-to-date and more comprehensive instructions see `www.dataminingbook.com`.

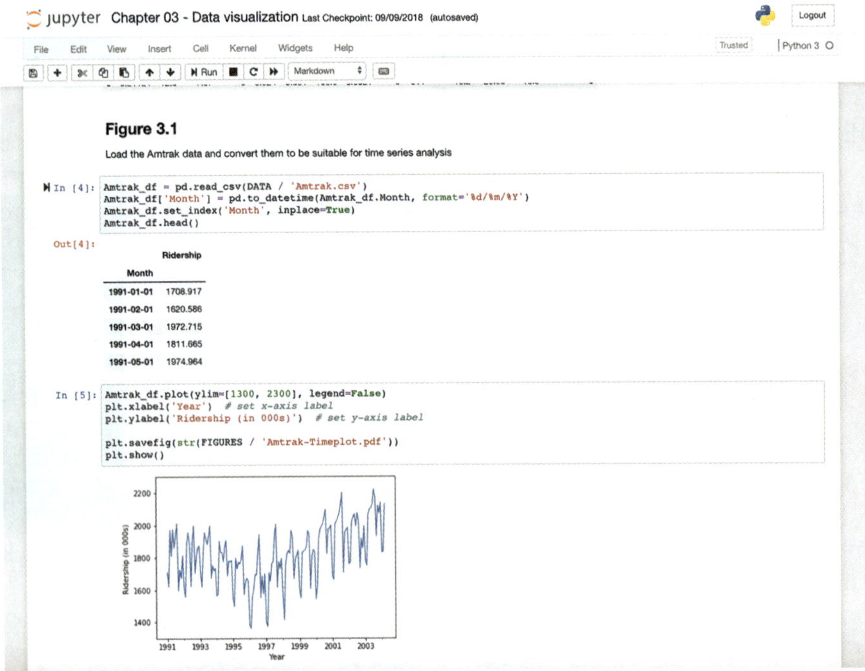

FIGURE 1.3 JUPYTER NOTEBOOK

CHAPTER 2

Overview of the Data Mining Process

In this chapter, we give an overview of the steps involved in data mining, starting from a clear goal definition and ending with model deployment. The general steps are shown schematically in Figure 2.1. We also discuss issues related to data collection, cleaning, and preprocessing. We introduce the notion of data partitioning, where methods are trained on a set of training data and then their performance is evaluated on a separate set of validation data, as well as explain how this practice helps avoid overfitting. Finally, we illustrate the steps of model building by applying them to data.

FIGURE 2.1 SCHEMATIC OF THE DATA MODELING PROCESS

2.1 | INTRODUCTION

In Chapter 1, we saw some very general definitions of data mining. In this chapter, we introduce the variety of methods sometimes referred to as *data mining*. The core of this book focuses on what has come to be called *predictive analytics*, the tasks of classification and prediction as well as pattern discovery, which have become key elements of a "business analytics" function in most large firms. These terms are described and illustrated below.

Not covered in this book to any great extent are two simpler database methods that are sometimes considered to be data mining techniques: (1) OLAP (online analytical processing) and (2) SQL (structured query language). OLAP and SQL searches on databases are descriptive in nature and are based on business rules set by the user (e.g., "find all credit card customers in a certain zip code with annual charges > $20,000, who own their home and who pay the entire amount of their monthly bill at least 95% of the time"). Although SQL queries are often used to obtain the data in data mining, they do not involve statistical modeling or automated algorithmic methods.

2.2 | CORE IDEAS IN DATA MINING

Classification

Classification is perhaps the most basic form of data analysis. The recipient of an offer can respond or not respond. An applicant for a loan can repay on time, repay late, or declare bankruptcy. A credit card transaction can be normal or fraudulent. A packet of data traveling on a network can be benign or threatening. A bus in a fleet can be available for service or unavailable. The victim of an illness can be recovered, still be ill, or be deceased.

A common task in data mining is to examine data where the classification is unknown or will occur in the future, with the goal of predicting what that classification is or will be. Similar data where the classification is known are used to develop rules, which are then applied to the data with the unknown classification.

Prediction

Prediction is similar to classification, except that we are trying to predict the value of a numerical variable (e.g., amount of purchase) rather than a class (e.g., purchaser or nonpurchaser). Of course, in classification we are trying to predict a class, but the term *prediction* in this book refers to the prediction of the value of a continuous variable. (Sometimes in the data mining literature, the terms *estimation* and *regression* are used to refer to the prediction of the value of a continuous variable, and *prediction* may be used for both continuous and categorical data.)

Association Rules and Recommendation Systems

Large databases of customer transactions lend themselves naturally to the analysis of associations among items purchased, or "what goes with what." *Association rules*, or *affinity analysis*, is designed to find such general associations patterns between items in large databases. The rules can then be used in a variety of ways. For example, grocery stores can use such information for product placement. They can use the rules for weekly promotional offers or for bundling products. Association rules derived from a hospital database on patients' symptoms during consecutive hospitalizations can help find "which symptom is followed by what other symptom" to help predict future symptoms for returning patients.

Online recommendation systems, such as those used on Amazon.com and Netflix.com, use *collaborative filtering*, a method that uses individual users' preferences and tastes given their historic purchase, rating, browsing, or any other measurable behavior indicative of preference, as well as other users' history. In contrast to *association rules* that generate rules general to an entire population, collaborative filtering generates "what goes with what" at the individual user level. Hence, collaborative filtering is used in many recommendation systems that aim to deliver personalized recommendations to users with a wide range of preferences.

Predictive Analytics

Classification, prediction, and to some extent, association rules and collaborative filtering constitute the analytical methods employed in *predictive analytics*. The term predictive analytics is sometimes used to also include data pattern identification methods such as clustering.

Data Reduction and Dimension Reduction

The performance of data mining algorithms is often improved when the number of variables is limited, and when large numbers of records can be grouped into homogeneous groups. For example, rather than dealing with thousands of product types, an analyst might wish to group them into a smaller number of groups and build separate models for each group. Or a marketer might want to classify customers into different "personas," and must therefore group customers into homogeneous groups to define the personas. This process of consolidating a large number of records (or cases) into a smaller set is termed *data reduction*. Methods for reducing the number of cases are often called *clustering*.

Reducing the number of variables is typically called *dimension reduction*. Dimension reduction is a common initial step before deploying data mining methods, intended to improve predictive power, manageability, and interpretability.

Data Exploration and Visualization

One of the earliest stages of engaging with a dataset is exploring it. Exploration is aimed at understanding the global landscape of the data, and detecting unusual values. Exploration is used for data cleaning and manipulation as well as for visual discovery and "hypothesis generation."

Methods for exploring data include looking at various data aggregations and summaries, both numerically and graphically. This includes looking at each variable separately as well as looking at relationships among variables. The purpose is to discover patterns and exceptions. Exploration by creating charts and dashboards is called *Data Visualization* or *Visual Analytics*. For numerical variables, we use histograms and boxplots to learn about the distribution of their values, to detect outliers (extreme observations), and to find other information that is relevant to the analysis task. Similarly, for categorical variables, we use bar charts. We can also look at scatter plots of pairs of numerical variables to learn about possible relationships, the type of relationship, and again, to detect outliers. Visualization can be greatly enhanced by adding features such as color and interactive navigation.

Supervised and Unsupervised Learning

A fundamental distinction among data mining techniques is between supervised and unsupervised methods. *Supervised learning algorithms* are those used in classification and prediction. We must have data available in which the value of the outcome of interest (e.g., purchase or no purchase) is known. Such data are also called "labeled data," since they contain the label (outcome value) for each record. These *training data* are the data from which the classification or prediction algorithm "learns," or is "trained," about the relationship between predictor variables and the outcome variable. Once the algorithm has learned from the training data, it is then applied to another sample of labeled data (the *validation data*) where the outcome is known but initially hidden, to see how well it does in comparison to other models. If many different models are being tried out, it is prudent to save a third sample, which also includes known outcomes (the *test data*) to use with the model finally selected to predict how well it will do. The model can then be used to classify or predict the outcome of interest in new cases where the outcome is unknown.

Simple linear regression is an example of a supervised learning algorithm (although rarely called that in the introductory statistics course where you probably first encountered it). The Y variable is the (known) outcome variable and the X variable is a predictor variable. A regression line is drawn to minimize the sum of squared deviations between the actual Y values and the values predicted by this line. The regression line can now be used to predict Y values for new values of X for which we do not know the Y value.

Unsupervised learning algorithms are those used where there is no outcome variable to predict or classify. Hence, there is no "learning" from cases where such an outcome variable is known. Association rules, dimension reduction methods, and clustering techniques are all unsupervised learning methods.

Supervised and unsupervised methods are sometimes used in conjunction. For example, unsupervised clustering methods are used to separate loan applicants into several risk-level groups. Then, supervised algorithms are applied separately to each risk-level group for predicting propensity of loan default.

SUPERVISED LEARNING REQUIRES GOOD SUPERVISION

In some cases, the value of the outcome variable (the "label") is known because it is an inherent component of the data. Web logs will show whether a person clicked on a link or not. Bank records will show whether a loan was paid on time or not. In other cases, the value of the known outcome must be supplied by a human labeling process to accumulate enough data to train a model. E-mail must be labeled as spam or legitimate, documents in legal discovery must be labeled as relevant or irrelevant. In either case, the data mining algorithm can be led astray if the quality of the supervision is poor.

Gene Weingarten reported in the January 5, 2014 *Washington Post* magazine how the strange phrase "defiantly recommend" is making its way into English via auto-correction. "Defiantly" is closer to the common misspelling *definatly* than is *definitely*, so Google.com, in the early days, offered it as a correction when users typed the misspelled word "definatly." In the ideal supervised learning model, humans guide the auto-correction process by rejecting *defiantly* and substituting *definitely*. Google's algorithm would then learn that this is the best first-choice correction of "definatly." The problem was that too many people were lazy, just accepting the first correction that Google presented. All these acceptances then cemented "defiantly" as the proper correction.

2.3 | THE STEPS IN DATA MINING

This book focuses on understanding and using data mining algorithms (Steps 4–7 below). However, some of the most serious errors in analytics projects result from a poor understanding of the problem—an understanding that must be developed before we get into the details of algorithms to be used. Here is a list of steps to be taken in a typical data mining effort:

1. *Develop an understanding of the purpose of the data mining project*: How will the stakeholder use the results? Who will be affected by the results? Will the analysis be a one-shot effort or an ongoing procedure?
2. *Obtain the dataset to be used in the analysis*: This often involves sampling from a large database to capture records to be used in an analysis. How well this sample reflects the records of interest affects the ability of the data mining results to generalize to records outside of this sample. It may also involve pulling together data from different databases or sources. The databases could be internal (e.g., past purchases made by customers) or external (credit ratings). While data mining deals with very large databases, usually the analysis to be done requires only thousands or tens of thousands of records.

3. *Explore, clean, and preprocess the data*: This step involves verifying that the data are in reasonable condition. How should missing data be handled? Are the values in a reasonable range, given what you would expect for each variable? Are there obvious outliers? The data are reviewed graphically: for example, a matrix of scatterplots showing the relationship of each variable with every other variable. We also need to ensure consistency in the definitions of fields, units of measurement, time periods, and so on. In this step, new variables are also typically created from existing ones. For example, "duration" can be computed from start and end dates.
4. *Reduce the data dimension, if necessary*: Dimension reduction can involve operations such as eliminating unneeded variables, transforming variables (e.g., turning "money spent" into "spent > \$100" vs. "spent ≤ \$100"), and creating new variables (e.g., a variable that records whether at least one of several products was purchased). Make sure that you know what each variable means and whether it is sensible to include it in the model.
5. *Determine the data mining task (classification, prediction, clustering, etc.)*: This involves translating the general question or problem of Step 1 into a more specific data mining question.
6. *Partition the data (for supervised tasks)*: If the task is supervised (classification or prediction), randomly partition the dataset into three parts: training, validation, and test datasets.
7. *Choose the data mining techniques to be used (regression, neural nets, hierarchical clustering, and so on).*
8. *Use algorithms to perform the task*: This is typically an iterative process—trying multiple variants, and often using multiple variants of the same algorithm (choosing different variables or settings within the algorithm). Where appropriate, feedback from the algorithm's performance on validation data is used to refine the settings.
9. *Interpret the results of the algorithms*: This involves making a choice as to the best algorithm to deploy, and where possible, testing the final choice on the test data to get an idea as to how well it will perform. (Recall that each algorithm may also be tested on the validation data for tuning purposes; in this way, the validation data become a part of the fitting process and are likely to underestimate the error in the deployment of the model that is finally chosen.)
10. *Deploy the model*: This step involves integrating the model into operational systems and running it on real records to produce decisions or actions. For example, the model might be applied to a purchased list of possible customers,

and the action might be "include in the mailing if the predicted amount of purchase is > $10." A key step here is "scoring" the new records, or using the chosen model to predict the outcome value ("score") for each new record.

The foregoing steps encompass the steps in SEMMA, a methodology developed by the software company SAS:

Sample	Take a sample from the dataset; partition into training, validation, and test datasets.
Explore	Examine the dataset statistically and graphically.
Modify	Transform the variables and impute missing values.
Model	Fit predictive models (e.g., regression tree, neural network).
Assess	Compare models using a validation dataset.

IBM SPSS Modeler (previously SPSS-Clementine) has a similar methodology, termed CRISP-DM (CRoss-Industry Standard Process for Data Mining). All these frameworks include the same main steps involved in predictive modeling.

2.4 | PRELIMINARY STEPS

Organization of Datasets

Datasets are mostly always constructed and displayed so that variables are in columns and records are in rows. We will illustrate this with purchase details of August 2019 and patronizing behavior of Allwin superstore chain customers in various cities of India. Nine variables are recorded for 1100 customers in datasets *ALLWIN SUMMER-19* I.*csv* and *ALLWIN SUMMER-19* II.*csv*. *ALLWIN SUMMER-19* I.*csv* has data in the original measurement type where *ALLWIN SUMMER-19* II.*csv* has variable measurements coded as shown in Table 2.1. The name of the store chain is being masked for confidentiality reasons. The spreadsheet is organized so that each row represents a customer—the row represents the purchase details of customer who is a local resident of Delhi and buys quite frequently (>5 times a month) from a superstore chain located in Delhi and buys promoted products offered under the scheme by the store. Prime members do not pay any membership fee but are required to patronize chain stores regularly or buy specific promoted products to gather loyalty points, which help earn gifts as well as certain service benefits like product financing, payment in installments, extended warranties on certain white goods, etc. In supervised learning situations, one of these variables will be the outcome variable, typically listed in the first or last column (in this case it can be Promo_Item_Purchase, in the last column).

The retail industry in India has evolved a lot in the last two decades. As per some think tank outfits, the Indian retail market is one of the fastest growing worldwide and is the fifth largest retail destination globally. The factors attributed to the growth are economic growth, increasing consumerism, and growing disposable income. The industry is projected to reach around USD 1,750 billion by 2026. The growth is likely to come from cities spread across all regions of the country. The upward changes in consumption expenditure are likely to influence positively growth of the retail industry. Of the total retail market, food and groceries comprise the largest share, followed by apparel and footwear.

There has been growing competition for unorganized as well as organized retailers from e-tailers and online platform companies like Amazon, Flipkart, Meesho, etc. In India, these platform-based retailers facilitate sellers to sell their products on their platforms. In the face of this competition, organized retailers have been responding through various strategies to sustain and grow their business, which are executed through loyalty programs, attractive promotions, and other marketing tactics to counter the onslaught of retail e-commerce platforms.

Some of the techniques to sustain customer loyalty include point programs, spend programs, tiered programs, paid programs – VIP member clubs, value-based programs, partnered programs, hybrid loyalty programs, and so on. New innovative ways keep on hitting the retail market. The point program is one of the most popular methods used by these organized retailers. It follows the tactic of spend more, earn more points, and monetize more to get more.

Allwin is a progressive retail store chain, established almost a decade before, with a footprint in most of the major cities of India. Like other major organized retail players in India, Allwin also has a regular rollout of loyalty programs. In August 2019, it rolled out a promotional drive, Allwin Summer-19, that could allow customers to earn points on the purchase of six promoted products during the month of August 2019 which could be redeemed for gifts, extended warranties on specific items, and discounts on various brands of partner firms.

Allwin has an analytics team that operates centrally from a major metro city in India and feeds store managers all over the country with insights for new strategies and operations to supplement marketing and sales efforts. One of the key deliverables of the analytics team is to develop an effective predictive model that can help refine loyalty programs to achieve desired outcomes.

Let's look at how Allwin Summer-19 has succeeded based on August 2019 data from select stores in select cities. We will use select customer profile and purchase behavior variables to predict the value of Promo_Item_Purchase, which means number of distinct items purchased out of six products on promotion captured in *ALLWIN SUMMER-19* II.*csv* of 1100 customers. The description of all variables used is given in

Table 2.1 and a sample of datasets used is given in Table 2.2 (I) and Table 2.2 (II). The data in *Allwin Summer-19* I.*csv* is in tabular form with categorical values of variables whereas variables in *Allwin Summer-19* II.*csv* have been coded into numbers except for StoreLocation as shown in Table 2.1.

TABLE 2.1 DESCRIPTION OF VARIABLES IN ALLWIN SUMMER-19 DATASET

Card_ID	Autogenerated Customer ID for each customer based on Mobile Nos provided by customers during first transaction
StoreLocation	Name of city where store is located
Monthly Visit Frequency	Frequency of customer visit to store categorized in 1–2, 3–5 and >5 times which has been coded as 1, 2 and 3 respectively
Customer_Gender	Female coded 1 and Male coded 2
Local_Resident	Customer could be local resident (Coded "Yes") or non-local (Coded "No")
Store_Distance	Customer residence distance from store in kilometers - <1 (Coded 1), 1–3 (Coded 2), 3–5 (Coded 3) and >5 (Coded 4)
Avg Basket-Items	Average number of items purchased in one visit - 1–4 (Coded 1), 5–8 (Coded 2), 9–12 (Coded 3), 13–16 (Coded 4) and > 16 (Coded 5)
Avg Basket-Value	Average cutomer spend in one visit - Small size (Coded 1), Mid size (Coded 2), and Large size (Coded 3)
Promo_Item_Purchase	No of distinct promoted items purchase out of 6 items put on promotion in August 2019

TABLE 2.2 (I) FIRST TEN RECORDS IN THE ALLWIN SUMMER-19 DATASET (BASE TABULAR FORM CATEGORICAL)

Card_ID	Store Location	Monthly Visit Frequency	Customer_ Gender	Local_ Resident	Store_ Distance	Avg Basket-Value	Avg Basket-Items	Promo_ Item_ Purchase
150474	Delhi	>5 Times	Male	Yes	<1 Km	Large Basket	1-4	5
183509	Delhi	>5 Times	Male	Yes	<1 Km	Large Basket	5-8	5
102910	Jaipur	>5 Times	Male	Yes	<1 Km	Large Basket	13-16	5
101593	Delhi	>5 Times	Male	Yes	<1 Km	Large Basket	13-16	5
140156	Delhi	>5 Times	Male	Yes	<1 Km	Large Basket	>16	5
123930	Delhi	>5 Times	Male	No	<1 Km	Large Basket	1-4	5
175003	Delhi	>5 Times	Male	No	<1 Km	Large Basket	5-8	5
124312	Jaipur	>5 Times	Male	No	<1 Km	Large Basket	5-8	5
111608	Banglore	3-5Times	Male	Yes	<1 Km	Large Basket	1-4	5

TABLE 2.2 (II) FIRST TEN RECORDS IN THE ALLWIN SUMMER-19 DATASET (BASE TABULAR FORM NUMERIC CODED)

Card_ID	Store Location	Monthly Visit Frequency	Customer_ Gender	Local_ Resident	Store_ Distance	Avg Basket-Value	Avg Basket-Items	Promo_ Item_ Purchase
150474	Delhi	3	2	1	1	3	1	5
183509	Delhi	3	2	1	1	3	2	5
102910	Jaipur	3	2	1	1	3	4	5
101593	Delhi	3	2	1	1	3	4	5
140156	Delhi	3	2	1	1	3	5	5
123930	Delhi	3	2	0	1	3	1	5
175003	Delhi	3	2	0	1	3	2	5
124312	Jaipur	3	2	0	1	3	2	5
111608	Banglore	2	2	1	1	3	1	5

Loading and Looking at the Data in Python

The pandas package supports loading data in a large number of file formats. However, we will typically want to have the data available as a csv (comma separated values) file. If the data are in an xlsx (or xls) file, we can save that same file in Excel as a csv file: go to File > Save as > Save as type: CSV (Comma delimited) (*.csv) > Save.
Note: When dealing with .csv files in Excel, beware of two things:

- Opening a .csv file in Excel strips off leading 0's, which corrupts zip code data.
- Saving a .csv file in Excel saves only the digits that are displayed; if you need precision to a certain number of decimals, you need to ensure they are displayed before saving.

Once we have Python and pandas installed on our machine and the *ALLWIN SUMMER*-19 II.*csv* file saved as a csv file, we can run the code in Table 2.3 to load the data into Python.

Data from a csv file is stored in pandas as a data frame (e.g., *allwin_df*). If our csv file has column headers, these headers get automatically stored as the column names of our data. A data frame is the fundamental object which is particularly useful for data handling and manipulation. A data frame has rows and columns. The rows are the observations for each case (e.g., buying transaction), and the columns are the variables of interest (e.g., Customer_Gender, Avg_Basket-Items). The codes in Table 2.3 walks you through some basic steps you will want to perform prior to doing any analysis: finding the size and dimension of your data (number of rows and columns), viewing all the data, displaying only selected rows and columns, and computing summary statistics for variables of interest. Note that comments are preceded by the # symbol.

TABLE 2.3 WORKING WITH FILES IN pandas

To start, open Anaconda-Navigator and launch a 'jupyter' notebook. It opens a new browser window. Navigate to the directory where your csv file is saved and open a new Python notebook. You can change the name from 'Untitled' to a more descriptive title, e.g. Allwin.
Paste the code into the input area and execute it using the *Run* button. The notebook will output the result of the last statement in each input field. If you like to see additional output use the *print* function. We will exclude it in most code samples to improve clarity.

code for loading and creating subsets from the data

```
# Import required packages
import pandas as pd

# Load data
allwin_df = pd.read_csv('ALLWIN SUMMER-19 II.csv')
allwin_df.shape  # find the dimension of data frame
allwin_df.head()  # show the first five rows
print(allwin_df)  # show all the data

# Rename columns: replace spaces with '_' to allow dot notation
allwin_df = allwin_df.rename(columns={'Monthly Visit Frequency':'Monthly_Visit_Frequency'}) # explicit
allwin_df.columns = [s.strip().replace(' ', '_') for s in allwin_df.columns] # all columns

# Practice showing the first four rows of the data
allwin_df.loc[0:3]  # loc[a:b] gives rows a to b, inclusive
allwin_df.iloc[0:4]  # iloc[a:b] gives rows a to b-1

# Different ways of showing the first 10 values in column StoreLocation
allwin_df['StoreLocation'].iloc[0:10]
allwin_df.iloc[0:10]['StoreLocation']
allwin_df.iloc[0:10].StoreLocation  # use dot notation if the column name has no spaces

# Show the fifth row of the first 10 columns
allwin_df.iloc[4][0:10]
allwin_df.iloc[4, 0:10]
allwin_df.iloc[4:5, 0:10]  # use a slice to return a data frame

# Use pd.concat to combine non-consecutive columns into a new data frame.
# The axis argument specifies the dimension along which the
# concatenation happens, 0=rows, 1=columns.
pd.concat([allwin_df.iloc[4:6,0:2], allwin_df.iloc[4:6,4:6]], axis=1)

# To specify a full column, use:
allwin_df.iloc[:,0:1]

allwin_df. Monthly_Visit_Frequency
# show the first 10 rows of the specified column
allwin_df ['Monthly_Visit_Frequency][0:10]
# show length of first column
print('Number of rows ', len(allwin_df ['Monthly_Visit_Frequency']))
```

(*Continued*)

TABLE 2.3 WORKING WITH FILES IN pandas (*Continued*)

```
# Descriptive statistics
# show mean of column
print('Mean of Monthly_Visit_Frequency', allwin_df ['Monthly_Visit_Frequency'].mean())
# show summary statistics for each column
allwin_df.describe()
```

In Python, it is useful to use *slices* of data frames or lists. A *slice* returns an object usually containing a portion of a sequence, such as a subset of rows and columns from a data frame. For example, `Store_Distance[0:4]` is a slice of variable Store_Distance containing the first five records. Note that Python uses 0-indexing, which means that indices start at 0 and not at 1. `pandas` uses two methods[1] to access rows in a data frame: *loc* and *iloc*. The *loc* method is more general and allows accessing rows using labels. The *iloc* method on the other hand only allows using integer numbers. To specify a range of rows, use the slice notation, for example, 0:9. In general, Python excludes the end index in the slice and the *iloc* method conforms with this convention. The *loc* method, however, includes it, so be careful when using these methods.

Python Imports

In Table 2.3, we imported the Python package `pandas` to use it for data handling. We will use a few other packages in the remainder of this chapter. Use the following lines to import all the required packages.

import required functionality for this chapter

```
import numpy as np
import pandas as pd

from sklearn.model_selection import train_test_split
from sklearn.metrics import r2_score

from sklearn.linear_model import LinearRegression
```

The abbreviations pd, np, and sm are commonly used in the data science community.

[1]*Method* and *function* are slightly different in object-oriented programming. For simplicity consider a method as a function that is closely associated with an object (e.g., a data frame) and has access to its data.

Sampling from a Database

Typically, we perform data mining on less than the complete database. Data mining algorithms will have varying limitations on what they can handle in terms of the numbers of records and variables, limitations that may be specific to computing power and capacity as well as software limitations. Even within those limits, many algorithms will execute faster with smaller samples.

Accurate models can often be built with as few as several thousand records. Hence, we will want to sample a subset of records for model building. Table 2.4 provides code for sampling in pandas.

TABLE 2.4 SAMPLING IN pandas

code for sampling and over/under-sampling

```
# random sample of 5 observations
allwin_df.sample(5)

# oversample records with Store_Distance more than 2
weights = [0.8 if Store_Distance > 2 else 0.2 for Store_Distance in allwin_df.Store_Distance]
allwin_df.sample(5, weights=weights)
```

Oversampling Rare Events in Classification Tasks

If the event we are interested in classifying is rare, for example, customers purchasing a product in response to a mailing, or fraudulent credit card transactions, sampling a random subset of records may yield so few events (e.g., purchases) that we have little information on them. We would end up with lots of data on nonpurchasers and non-fraudulent transactions but little on which to base a model that distinguishes purchasers from nonpurchasers or fraudulent from non-fraudulent. In such cases, we would want our sampling procedure to overweight the rare class (purchasers or frauds) relative to the majority class (nonpurchasers, non-frauds) so that our sample would end up with a healthy complement of purchasers or frauds.

Assuring an adequate number of responder or "success" cases to train the model is just part of the picture. A more important factor is the costs of misclassification. Whenever the response rate is extremely low, we are likely to attach more importance to identifying a responder than to identifying a non-responder. In direct-response advertising (whether by traditional mail, e-mail, or web advertising), we may encounter only one or two responders for every hundred records—the value of finding such a customer far outweighs the costs of reaching him or her. In trying to identify fraudulent transactions, or customers unlikely to repay debt, the costs of failing to find the fraud or the non-paying customer are likely to exceed the cost of more detailed review of a legitimate transaction or customer.

If the costs of failing to locate responders are comparable to the costs of misidentifying responders as non-responders, our models would usually achieve highest overall accuracy if they identified everyone as a non-responder (or almost everyone, if it is easy to identify a few responders without catching many nonresponders). In such a case, the misclassification rate is very low—equal to the rate of responders—but the model is of no value.

More generally, we want to train our model with the asymmetric costs in mind so that the algorithm will catch the more valuable responders, probably at the cost of "catching" and misclassifying more non-responders as responders than would be the case if we assume equal costs. This subject is discussed in detail in Chapter 5.

Preprocessing and Cleaning the Data

Types of Variables There are several ways of classifying variables. Variables can be numerical or text (character/string). They can be continuous (able to assume any real numerical value, usually in a given range), integer (taking only integer values), categorical (assuming one of a limited number of values), or date. Categorical variables can be either coded as numerical (1, 2, 3) or text (payments current, payments not current, bankrupt). Categorical variables can be unordered (called *nominal variables*) with categories such as Delhi, Kolkata, and Mumbai; or they can be ordered (called *ordinal variables*) with categories such as high value, low value, and nil value.

Continuous variables can be handled by most data mining routines with the exception of the naive Bayes classifier, which deals exclusively with categorical predictor variables. The machine learning roots of data mining grew out of problems with categorical outcomes; the roots of statistics lie in the analysis of continuous variables. Sometimes, it is desirable to convert continuous variables to categorical variables. This is done most typically in the case of outcome variables, where the numerical variable is mapped to a decision (e.g., credit scores above a certain threshold mean "grant credit," a medical test result above a certain threshold means "start treatment").

For the Allwin Summer-19 II data, Table 2.5 presents some `pandas` statements to review the variables and determine what type (class) `pandas` thinks they are, and to determine the number of levels in a categorical variable.

Handling Categorical Variables Categorical variables can also be handled by most data mining routines, but often require special handling. If the categorical variable is ordered (age group, degree of nearness to store, etc.), we can sometimes code the categories numerically (1, 2, 3, ...) and treat the variable as if it were a continuous variable. The smaller the number of categories, and the less they represent equal increments of value, the more problematic this approach becomes, but it often works well enough.

Nominal categorical variables, however, often cannot be used as is. In many cases, they must be decomposed into a series of binary variables, called *dummy variables*.

TABLE 2.5 REVIEWING VARIABLES IN pandas

code for reviewing variables

```
allwin_df.columns  # print a list of variables

# StoreLocation needs to be converted to a categorical variable
allwin_df.StoreLocation = allwin_df.StoreLocation.astype('category')
allwin_df.StoreLocation.cat.categories  # Show number of categories
allwin_df.StoreLocation.dtype  # Check type of converted variable
```

Partial Output

```
>allwin_df.columns
Index(['Card__ID', 'StoreLocation', 'Monthly_Visit_Frequency',
       'Customer_Gender', 'Local_Resident', 'Store_Distance',
       'Avg_Basket-Value', 'Avg_Basket-Items', 'Promo_Item_Purchase'],
      dtype='object')

>allwin_df.StoreLocation.cat.categories
Index(['Banglore', 'Chennai', 'Delhi', 'Jaipur', 'Mumbai'], dtype='object')

>allwin_df.StoreLocation.dtype
CategoricalDtype(categories=['Banglore', 'Chennai', 'Delhi', 'Jaipur', 'Mumbai'],
                 ordered=False)
```

For example, a single categorical variable that can have possible values of "student," "unemployed," "employed," or "retired" would be split into four separate dummy variables:

Student—Yes/No

Unemployed—Yes/No

Employed—Yes/No

Retired—Yes/No

In many cases, only three of the dummy variables need to be used; if the values of three are known, the fourth is also known. For example, given that these four values are the only possible ones, we can know that if a person is neither student, unemployed, nor employed, he or she must be retired. In some routines (e.g., linear regression and logistic regression), you should not use all four variables—the redundant information will cause the algorithm to fail. Note, also, that typical methods of creating dummy variables will leave the original categorical variable intact; obviously you should not use both the original variable and the dummies. The code to create binary dummies from all categorical variables in the allwin_df is given in Table 2.6 (here only StoreLocation is categorical).

TABLE 2.6 CREATING DUMMY VARIABLES IN pandas

code for creating binary dummies (indicators)

```
# use drop_first=True to drop the first dummy variable
allwin_df = pd.get_dummies(allwin_df, prefix_sep='_', drop_first=True)
allwin_df.columns
allwin_df.loc[:, 8:12]
```

Partial Output

	StoreLocation_Chennai	StoreLocation_Delhi	StoreLocation_Jaipur	StoreLocation_Mumbai
0	0	1	0	0
1	0	1	0	0
2	0	0	1	0
3	0	1	0	0
4	0	1	0	0

Variable Selection More is not necessarily better when it comes to selecting variables for a model. Other things being equal, parsimony, or compactness, is a desirable feature in a model. For one thing, the more variables we include and the more complex the model, the greater the number of records we will need to assess relationships among the variables. Fifteen records may suffice to give us a rough idea of the relationship between Y and a single predictor variable X. If we now want information about the relationship between Y and 15 predictor variables $X_1, \dots, X_{15}$, 15 records will not be enough (each estimated relationship would have an average of only one record's worth of information, making the estimate very unreliable). In addition, models based on many variables are often less robust, as they require the collection of more variables in the future, are subject to more data quality and availability issues, and require more data cleaning and preprocessing.

How Many Variables and How Much Data? Statisticians give us procedures to learn with some precision how many records we would need to achieve a given degree of reliability with a given dataset and a given model. These are called "power calculations" and are intended to assure that an average population effect will be estimated with sufficient precision from a sample. Data miners' needs are usually different, because the focus is not on identifying an average effect but rather on predicting individual records. This purpose typically requires larger samples than those used for statistical inference. A good rule of thumb is to have 10 records for every predictor variable. Another rule, used by Delmaster and Hancock (2001, p. 68) for classification procedures, is to have at least $6 \times m \times p$ records, where m is the number of outcome classes and p is the number of variables.

In general, compactness or parsimony is a desirable feature in a data mining model. Even when we start with a small number of variables, we often end up with many more after creating new variables (such as converting a categorical variable into a set of dummy variables). Data visualization and dimension reduction methods help reduce the number of variables so that redundancies and information overlap are reduced.

Even when we have an ample supply of data, there are good reasons to pay close attention to the variables that are included in a model. Someone with domain knowledge (i.e., knowledge of the business process and the data) should be consulted, as knowledge of what the variables represent is typically critical for building a good model and avoiding errors. For example, suppose we're trying to predict the total purchase amount spent by customers, and we have a few predictor columns that are coded $X_1, X_2, X_3, \ldots$, where we don't know what those codes mean. We might find that X_1 is an excellent predictor of the total amount spent. However, if we discover that X_1 is the amount spent on shipping, calculated as a percentage of the purchase amount, then obviously a model that uses shipping amount cannot be used to predict purchase amount, because the shipping amount is not known until the transaction is completed. Another example is if we are trying to predict loan default at the time a customer applies for a loan. If our dataset includes only information on approved loan applications, we will not have information about what distinguishes defaulters from non-defaulters among denied applicants. A model based on approved loans alone can therefore not be used to predict defaulting behavior at the time of loan application, but rather only once a loan is approved.

Outliers The more data we are dealing with, the greater the chance of encountering erroneous values resulting from measurement error, data-entry error, or the like. If the erroneous value is in the same range as the rest of the data, it may be harmless. If it is well outside the range of the rest of the data (e.g., a misplaced decimal), it may have a substantial effect on some of the data mining procedures we plan to use.

Values that lie far away from the bulk of the data are called *outliers*. The term *far away* is deliberately left vague because what is or is not called an outlier is an arbitrary decision. Analysts use rules of thumb such as "anything over three standard deviations away from the mean is an outlier," but no statistical rule can tell us whether such an outlier is the result of an error. In this statistical sense, an outlier is not necessarily an invalid data point, it is just a distant one.

The purpose of identifying outliers is usually to call attention to values that need further review. We might come up with an explanation looking at the data—in the case of a misplaced decimal, this is likely. We might have no explanation, but know that the value is wrong—a temperature of 178°F for a sick person. Or, we might conclude that the value is within the realm of possibility and leave it alone. All these are judgments best made by someone with *domain knowledge*, knowledge of the particular application being considered: direct mail, mortgage finance, and so on, as opposed to technical knowledge of statistical or data mining procedures. Statistical procedures can do little beyond identifying the record as something that needs review.

If manual review is feasible, some outliers may be identified and corrected. In any case, if the number of records with outliers is very small, they might be treated as missing data. How do we inspect for outliers? One technique is to sort the records by the first column (e.g., using the `pandas` method *sort_values()* such as `df.sort_values(by=['col1'])`), then review the data for very large or very small values in that column. Then repeat for each successive column. Another option is to examine the minimum and maximum values of each column using `pandas`'s *min()* and *max()* methods. For a more automated approach that considers each record as a unit, rather than each column in isolation, clustering techniques (see Chapter 14) could be used to identify clusters of one or a few records that are distant from others. Those records could then be examined.

Missing Values Typically, some records will contain missing values. If the number of records with missing values is small, those records might be omitted. However, if we have a large number of variables, even a small proportion of missing values can affect a lot of records. Even with only 30 variables, if only 5% of the values are missing (spread randomly and independently among cases and variables), almost 80% of the records would have to be omitted from the analysis. (The chance that a given record would escape having a missing value is $0.95^{30} = 0.215$.)

An alternative to omitting records with missing values is to replace the missing value with an imputed value, based on the other values for that variable across all records. For example, if among 30 variables, household income is missing for a particular record, we might substitute the mean household income across all records. Doing so does not, of course, add any information about how household income affects the outcome variable. It merely allows us to proceed with the analysis and not lose the information contained in this record for the other 29 variables. Note that using such a technique will understate the variability in a dataset. However, we can assess variability and the performance of our data mining technique using the validation data, and therefore this need not present a major problem. One option is to replace missing values using fairly simple substitutes (e.g., mean, median). More sophisticated procedures do exist—for example, using linear regression, based on other variables, to fill in the missing values. These methods have been elaborated mainly for analysis of medical and scientific studies, where each patient or subject record comes at great expense. In data mining, where data are typically plentiful, simpler methods usually suffice. Table 2.7 shows some Python code to illustrate the use of the median to replace missing values. Since the data are complete to begin with, the first step is an artificial one of creating some missing records for illustration purposes. The median is used for imputation, rather than the mean, to preserve the integer nature of the counts for Store_Distance.

TABLE 2.7 MISSING DATA

code for imputing missing data with median

```
# To illustrate missing data procedures, we first convert a few entries for
# Store_Distance to NA's. Then we impute these missing values using the median of the
# remaining values.
missingRows = allwin_df.sample(10).index
allwin_df.loc[missingRows, 'Store_Distance'] = np.nan
print('Number of rows with valid Store_Distance values after setting to NAN: ',
      allwin_df['Store_Distance'].count())

# remove rows with missing values
reduced_df = allwin_df.dropna()
print('Number of rows after removing rows with missing values: ', len(reduced_df))

# replace the missing values using the median of the remaining values.
medianStore_Distance = allwin_df['Store_Distance'].median()
allwin_df.Store_Distance = allwin_df.Store_Distance.fillna(value=medianStore_Distance)
print('Number of rows with valid Store_Distance values after filling NA values: ',
      allwin_df['Store_Distance'].count())
```

Output

```
Number of rows with valid Store_Distance values after setting to NAN:  1061
Number of rows after removing rows with missing values:  1061
Number of rows with valid Store_Distance values after filling NA values:  1099 Number of rows
```

Some datasets contain variables that have a very large number of missing values. In other words, a measurement is missing for a large number of records. In that case, dropping records with missing values will lead to a large loss of data. Imputing the missing values might also be useless, as the imputations are based on a small number of existing records. An alternative is to examine the importance of the predictor. If it is not very crucial, it can be dropped. If it is important, perhaps a proxy variable with fewer missing values can be used instead. When such a predictor is deemed central, the best solution is to invest in obtaining the missing data.

Significant time may be required to deal with missing data, as not all situations are susceptible to automated solutions. In a messy dataset, for example, a "0" might mean two things: (1) the value is missing, or (2) the value is actually zero. In the credit industry, a "0" in the "past due" variable might mean a customer who is fully paid up, or a customer with no credit history at all—two very different situations. Human judgment may be required for individual cases or to determine a special rule to deal with the situation.

Normalizing (Standardizing) and Rescaling Data Some algorithms require that the data be normalized before the algorithm can be implemented effectively. To normalize a variable, we subtract the mean from each value and then divide by the standard deviation. This operation is also sometimes called *standardizing*. `pandas` has no custom method for this, however, the operation can be easily performed using the methods *mean* and *std*; `(df-df.mean())/df.std()`. In effect, we are expressing each value as the "number of standard deviations away from the mean," also called a *z-score*. An alternative is the class *StandardScaler()*, which is one of a number different transformers available in `scikit-learn`. You can use the methods *fit()* or *fit_transform()* to train the transformer on the training set and the method *transform()* to apply on the validation set. The result of the transformation is no longer a `pandas` dataframe, however, you can convert it back into one easily. Table 2.8 demonstrates both approaches.

Normalizing is one way to bring all variables to the same scale. Another popular approach is rescaling each variable to a [0, 1] scale. This is done by subtracting the minimum value and then dividing by the range. Subtracting the minimum shifts the variable origin to zero. Dividing by the range shrinks or expands the data to the range [0, 1]. In `pandas`, use the expression `(df-df.min())/(df.max()-df.min())`. The corresponding `scikit-learn` transformer is *MinMaxScaler*.

TABLE 2.8 NORMALIZING AND RESCALING DATA

code for normalizing and rescaling a data frame

```
from sklearn.preprocessing import MinMaxScaler, StandardScaler
df = allwin_df.copy()

# Normalizing a data frame

# pandas:
norm_df = (allwin_df - allwin_df.mean()) / allwin_df.std()

# scikit-learn:
scaler = StandardScaler()
norm_df = pd.DataFrame(scaler.fit_transform(allwin_df),
                       index=allwin_df.index, columns=allwin_df.columns)
# the result of the transformation is a numpy array, we convert it into a dataframe

# Rescaling a data frame

# pandas:
norm_df = (allwin_df - allwin_df.min()) / (allwin_df.max() - allwin_df.min())

# scikit-learn:
scaler = MinMaxScaler()
norm_df = pd.DataFrame(scaler.fit_transform(allwin_df),
                       index=allwin_df.index, columns=allwin_df.columns)
```

To consider why normalizing or scaling to [0, 1] might be necessary, consider the case of clustering. Clustering typically involves calculating a distance measure that reflects how far each record is from a cluster center or from other records. With multiple variables, different units will be used: days, dollars, counts, and so on. If the dollars are in the thousands and everything else is in the tens, the dollar variable will come to dominate the distance measure. Moreover, changing units from, say, days to hours or months, could alter the outcome completely.

2.5 | PREDICTIVE POWER AND OVERFITTING

In supervised learning, a key question presents itself: How well will our prediction or classification model perform when we apply it to new data? We are particularly interested in comparing the performance of various models so that we can choose the one we think will do the best when it is implemented in practice. A key concept is to make sure that our chosen model generalizes beyond the dataset that we have at hand. To assure generalization, we use the concept of *data partitioning* and try to avoid *overfitting*. These two important concepts are described next.

Overfitting

The more variables we include in a model, the greater the risk of overfitting the particular data used for modeling. What is overfitting?

In Table 2.9, we show hypothetical data about advertising expenditures in one time period and sales in a subsequent time period. A scatter plot of the data is shown in Figure 2.2. We could connect up these points with a smooth but complicated function, one that interpolates all these data points perfectly and leaves no error (residuals). This can be seen in Figure 2.3. However, we can see that such a curve is unlikely to be accurate, or even useful, in predicting future sales on the basis of advertising expenditures. For instance, it is hard to believe that increasing expenditures from \$400 to \$500 will actually decrease revenue.

TABLE 2.9

Advertising	Sales
239	514
364	789
602	550
644	1386
770	1394
789	1440
911	1354

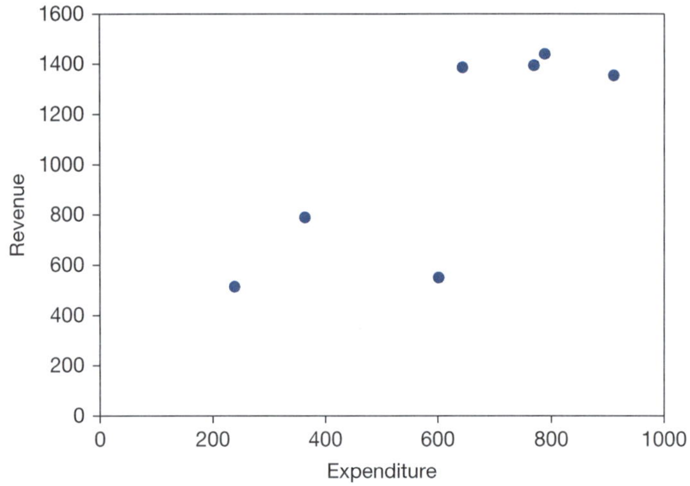

FIGURE 2.2 SCATTER PLOT FOR ADVERTISING AND SALES DATA

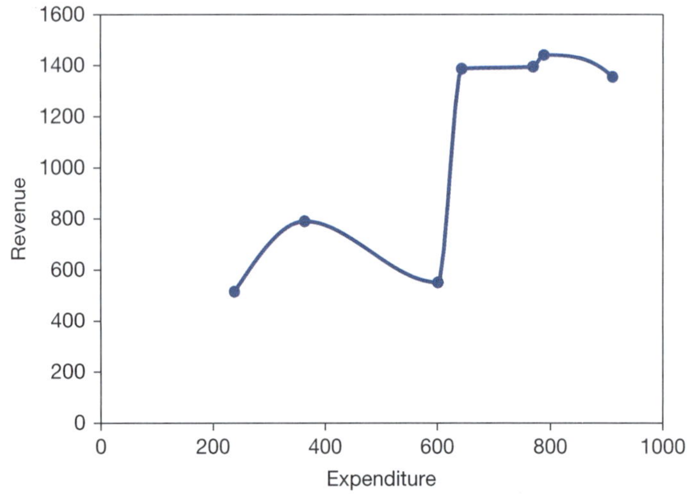

FIGURE 2.3 OVERFITTING: THIS FUNCTION FITS THE DATA WITH NO ERROR

A basic purpose of building a model is to represent relationships among variables in such a way that this representation will do a good job of predicting future outcome values on the basis of future predictor values. Of course, we want the model to do a good job of describing the data we have, but we are more interested in its performance with future data.

In the hypothetical advertising example, a simple straight line might do a better job than the complex function in terms of predicting future sales on the basis of advertising. Instead, we devised a complex function that fit the data perfectly, and in doing so, we overreached. We ended up modeling some variation in the data that is nothing more than chance variation. We mistreated the noise in the data as if it were a signal.

Similarly, we can add predictors to a model to sharpen its performance with the data at hand. Consider a database of 100 individuals, half of whom have contributed to a charitable cause. Information about income, family size, and zip code might do a fair job of predicting whether or not someone is a contributor. If we keep adding additional predictors, we can improve the performance of the model with the data at hand and reduce the misclassification error to a negligible level. However, this low error rate is misleading, because it probably includes spurious effects, which are specific to the 100 individuals, but not beyond that sample.

For example, one of the variables might be height. We have no basis in theory to suppose that tall people might contribute more or less to charity, but if there are several tall people in our sample and they just happened to contribute heavily to charity, our model might include a term for height—the taller you are, the more you will contribute. Of course, when the model is applied to additional data, it is likely that this will not turn out to be a good predictor.

If the dataset is not much larger than the number of predictor variables, it is very likely that a spurious relationship like this will creep into the model. Continuing with our charity example, with a small sample just a few of whom are tall, whatever the contribution level of tall people may be, the algorithm is tempted to attribute it to their being tall. If the dataset is very large relative to the number of predictors, this is less likely to occur. In such a case, each predictor must help predict the outcome for a large number of cases, so the job it does is much less dependent on just a few cases, which might be flukes.

Somewhat surprisingly, even if we know for a fact that a higher-degree curve is the appropriate model, if the model-fitting dataset is not large enough, a lower-degree function (that is not as likely to fit the noise) is likely to perform better in terms of predicting new values. Overfitting can also result from the application of many different models, from which the best performing model is selected.

Creation and Use of Data Partitions

At first glance, we might think it best to choose the model that did the best job of classifying or predicting the outcome variable of interest with the data at hand. However, when we use the same data both to develop the model and to assess its performance, we introduce an "optimism" bias. This is because when we choose the model that works best with the data, this model's superior performance comes from two sources:

- A superior model
- Chance aspects of the data that happen to match the chosen model better than they match other models

The latter is a particularly serious problem with techniques (such as trees and neural nets) that do not impose linear or other structure on the data, and thus end up overfitting it.

To address the overfitting problem, we simply divide (partition) our data and develop our model using only one of the partitions. After we have a model, we try it out on another partition and see how it performs, which we can measure in several ways. In a classification model, we can count the proportion of held-back records that were misclassified. In a prediction model, we can measure the residuals (prediction errors) between the predicted values and the actual values. This evaluation approach in effect mimics the deployment scenario, where our model is applied to data that it hasn't "seen."

We typically deal with two or three partitions: a training set, a validation set, and sometimes an additional test set. Partitioning the data into training, validation, and test sets is done either randomly according to predetermined proportions or by specifying which records go into which partition according to some relevant variable (e.g., in time-series forecasting, the data are partitioned according to their chronological order). In most cases, the partitioning should be done randomly to minimize the chance of getting a biased partition. Note the varying nomenclature—the training partition is nearly always called "training" but the names for the other partitions can vary and overlap.

Training Partition The training partition, typically the largest partition, contains the data used to build the various models we are examining. The same training partition is generally used to develop multiple models.

Validation Partition The validation partition (sometimes called the *test partition*) is used to assess the predictive performance of each model so that you can compare models and choose the best one. In some algorithms (e.g., classification and regression trees, *k*-nearest neighbors), the validation partition may be used in an automated fashion to tune and improve the model.

Test Partition The test partition (sometimes called the *holdout* or *evaluation partition*) is used to assess the performance of the chosen model with new data.

Why have both a validation and a test partition? When we use the validation data to assess multiple models and then choose the model that performs best with the validation data, we again encounter another (lesser) facet of the overfitting problem—chance aspects of the validation data that happen to match the chosen model better than they match other models. In other words, by using the validation data to choose one of several models, the performance of the chosen model on the validation data will be overly optimistic.

The random features of the validation data that enhance the apparent performance of the chosen model will probably not be present in new data to which the model is applied. Therefore, we may have overestimated the accuracy of our model. The more models we test, the more likely it is that one of them will be particularly effective in modeling the noise in the validation data. Applying the model to the test data, which it has not seen before, will provide an unbiased estimate of how well the model will perform with new data. Figure 2.4 shows the three data partitions and their use in the data mining process. When we are concerned mainly with finding the best model and less with exactly how well it will do, we might use only training and validation partitions. Table 2.10 shows Python code to partition the Allwin Summer-19 II data into two sets (training and validation) or into three sets (training, validation, and test). This is done by first drawing a random sample of records into the training set, then assigning the remaining records as validation. In the case of three partitions, the validation records are chosen randomly from the data after excluding the records already sampled into the training set.

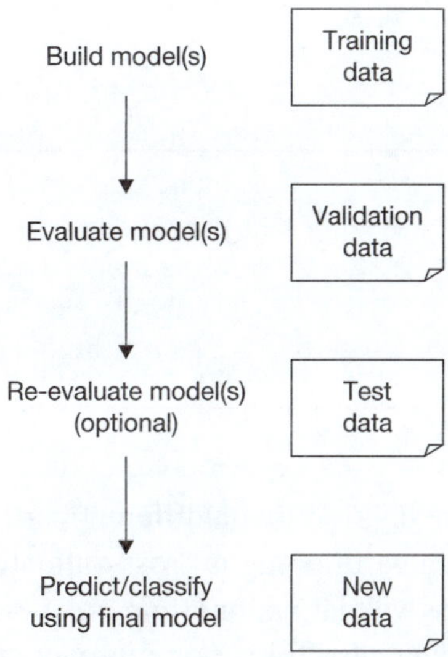

FIGURE 2.4 THREE DATA PARTITIONS AND THEIR ROLE IN THE DATA MINING PROCESS

Note that with some algorithms, such as nearest-neighbor algorithms, records in the validation and test partitions, and in new data, are compared to records in the training data to find the nearest neighbor(s). As *k*-nearest neighbors is discussed in this book, the use of two partitions is an essential part of the classification or prediction process, not merely a way to improve or assess it. Nonetheless, we can still interpret the error in the validation data in the same way that we would interpret error from any other model.

Cross-Validation When the number of records in our sample is small, data partitioning might not be advisable as each partition will contain too few records for model building and performance evaluation. Furthermore, some data mining methods are sensitive to

TABLE 2.10 DATA PARTITIONING IN PYTHON

code for partitioning the allwin data into training, validation (and test) sets

```
# random_state is set to a defined value to get the same partitions when re-running
# the code
# training (60%) and validation (40%)
trainData, validData = train_test_split(allwin_df, test_size=0.40, random_state=1)

print('Training : ', trainData.shape)
print('Validation : ', validData.shape)
print()

# training (50%), validation (30%), and test (20%)
trainData, temp = train_test_split(allwin_df, test_size=0.5, random_state=1)
validData, testData = train_test_split(temp, test_size=0.4, random_state=1)

print('Training : ', trainData.shape)
print('Validation : ', validData.shape)
print('Test : ', testData.shape)
```

Output

```
Training   :  (659, 12)
Validation :  (440, 12)

Training   :  (549, 12)
Validation :  (330, 12)
Test       :  (220, 12)
```

small changes in the training data, so that a different partitioning can lead to different results. An alternative to data partitioning is cross-validation, which is especially useful with small samples. Cross-validation, or *k-fold cross-validation*, is a procedure that starts with partitioning the data into "folds," or non-overlapping subsamples. Often we choose $k = 5$ folds, meaning that the data are randomly partitioned into five equal parts, where each fold has 20% of the observations. A model is then fit k times. Each time, one of the folds is used as the validation set and the remaining $k = 1$ folds serve as the training set. The result is that each fold is used once as the validation set, thereby producing predictions for every observation in the dataset. We can then combine the model's predictions on each of the k validation sets in order to evaluate the overall performance of the model. In Python, cross-validation is achieved using the *cross_val_score()* or the more general *cross_validate* function, where argument `cv` determines the number of folds. Sometimes cross-validation is built into a data mining algorithm, with the results of the cross-validation used for choosing the algorithm's parameters (see, e.g., Chapter 9).

2.6 | BUILDING A PREDICTIVE MODEL

Let us go through the steps typical to many data mining tasks using a familiar procedure: multiple linear regression. This will help you understand the overall process before we begin tackling new algorithms.

Modeling Process

We now describe in detail the various model stages using the Allwin example.

1. *Determine the purpose*: Let's assume that the purpose of our data mining project is to predict the value of Allwin for new records.
2. *Obtain the data*: We will use the Allwin data. The dataset in question is small enough that we do not need to sample from it—we can use it in its entirety.
3. *Explore, clean, and preprocess the data*: Let's look first at the description of the variables, also known as the "data dictionary," to be sure that we understand them all. These descriptions are available in Table 2.2. The variable names and descriptions in this dataset all seem fairly straightforward, but this is not always the case. Often, variable names are cryptic and their descriptions may be unclear or missing.

   It is useful to pause and think about what the variables mean and whether they should be included in the model. For example, considering AvgBasket-Value as the target variable, AvgBasket-Items as a predictor, there could be a circular relationship between the two variables. Similarly considering a variable like No_of_Gifts_Earned, as a predictor of Promo_Item_Purchase, there is again possible circularity in the model. If we want to predict promoted items purchased with No_of_Gifts_Earned as a predictor, yet No_of_Gifts_Earned itself is determined by the number of promoted items purchased might be a very good predictor in a numerical sense, but would it be useful if we wanted to apply our model? For this reason, we have excluded the No_of_Gifts_Earned variable from the dataset and analysis.

   It is also useful to check for outliers that might be errors. For example, suppose that the column AvgBasket-Items looked like the one in Table 2.11, after sorting the data in descending order based on frequency. We can tell right away that the 6 is in error—it is unlikely that a category level can have a value of 6. Since all other values are between 1 and 5, the decimal was probably misplaced and the value should be from 1 to 5. Hence, corrections or imputation is required before we proceed further.

   Lastly, we create dummy variables for categorical variables. Here we have one categorical variable: StoreLocation, which has five categories.

TABLE 2.11 OUTLIER IN ALLWIN SUMMER-19

AvgBasket-Items	Frequency
1	289
2	279
3	0
4	284
5	248
6	1

4. *Reduce the data dimension*: The ALLWIN SUMMER-19 dataset has been prepared for presentation with fairly low dimension—it has only 9 variables including row identifier, and the single categorical variable considered has only five categories (and hence adds four dummy variables when used in a linear regression model). If we had many more variables, at this stage we might want to apply a variable reduction technique, such as condensing multiple categories into a smaller number, or applying principal components analysis to consolidate multiple similar numerical variables into a smaller number of variables.
5. *Determine the data mining task*: The specific task is to predict the Promo_Item_Purchase using other predictor variables. This is a supervised prediction task. For simplicity, we excluded several additional variables present in the original dataset, which have many categories. We therefore use all the numerical variables (which are actually numerically coded categorical values in the csv dataset) and the dummies created for the remaining categorical variables.
6. *Partition the data (for supervised tasks)*: In this case we divide the data into two partitions: training and validation (see Table 2.10). The training partition is used to build the model, and the validation partition is used to see how well the model does when applied to new data. We need to specify the percent of the data used in each partition. *Note*: Although not used in our example, a test partition might also be used.
7. *Choose the technique*: In this case, it is multiple linear regression. Having divided the data into training and validation partitions, we can build a multiple linear regression model with the training data. We want to predict the Promo_Item_Purchase on the basis of all the other predictors.
8. *Use the algorithm to perform the task*: In Python, we use the `scikit-learn` *LinearRegression* method to predict house value with the training data, then use the same model to predict values for the validation data. Chapter 6 on linear

regression goes into more detail. Table 2.12 shows the predicted values for the first few records in the training data along with the actual values and the residuals (prediction errors). Note that the predicted values are often called the *fitted values*, since they are for the records to which the model was fit. The results for the validation data are shown in Table 2.13. The prediction errors for the training and validation data are compared in Table 2.14.

TABLE 2.12 PREDICTIONS (FITTED VALUES) FOR A SAMPLE OF TRAINING DATA

code for fitting a regression model to training data (Allwin)

```
# getting data and preprocessing
allwin_df = pd.read_csv('ALLWIN SUMMER-19 II.csv')
allwin_df.columns = [s.strip().replace(' ', '_') for s in allwin_df.columns]
allwin_df = pd. get_dummies(allwin_df, prefix_sep='_', drop_first=True)

# create list of predictors and outcome
excludeColumns =allwin_df.loc[:, allwin_df.columns!='Promo_Item_Purchase']
outcome = 'Promo_Item_Purchase'

# partition data
X = excludeColumns
y = allwin_df[outcome]
# partition data
train_X, valid_X, train_y, valid_y = train_test_split(X, y, test_size=0.4,
random_state=1)
model = LinearRegression()

model.fit(train_X, train_y)
train_pred = model.predict(train_X)
train_results = pd.DataFrame({
'Promo_Item_Purchase': train_y,
'predicted': train_pred,
'residual': train_y - train_pred
})
train_results.head()
```

Output

```
    Promo_Item_Purchase predicted   residual
699                   1  1.353075  -0.353075
 68                   5  3.289766   1.710234
318                   1  1.739319  -0.739319
291                   1  1.818594  -0.818594
 46                   5  3.101646   1.898354

Predictions: [2.39705255 1.35467062 2.59084725 3.6836085 1.85552925 3.31597857
 0.70924156 3.49935788 1.33843865]
```

TABLE 2.13 **PREDICTIONS FOR A SAMPLE OF VALIDATION DATA**

code for applying the regression model to predict validation set (ALLWIN SUMMER-19)

```
valid_pred = model.predict(valid_X)
valid_results = pd.DataFrame({
    'Promo_Purchase': valid_y,
    'predicted': valid_pred,
    'residual': valid_y - valid_pred
})
valid_results.head()
```

Output

```
     Promo_Item_Purchase   predicted    residual
834                    1   0.3681831   0.6318169
499                    1   1.7186773  -0.7186773
12                     5   3.5487097   1.4512903
156                    5   3.5741609   1.4258391
769                    1   0.1779552   0.8220448
857                    1   0.2863699   0.7136301
```

Prediction error can be aggregated in several ways. Five common measures are shown in Table 2.14. The first is *mean error (ME)*, simply the average of the residuals (errors). In both cases, it is quite small relative to the units of Promo_Purchase, indicating that, on balance, predictions average about right—our predictions are "unbiased." Of course, this simply means that the positive and negative errors balance out. It tells us nothing about how large these errors are.

The *root-mean-squared error (RMSE)* is more informative of the error magnitude: it takes the square root of the average squared error, so it gives an idea of the typical error (whether positive or negative) in the same scale as that used for the original outcome variable. The RMSE for the validation data, which the model is seeing for the first time in making these predictions, is in the same range as for the training data, which were used in training the model. Normally, we expect the validation set error to be higher than for the training set. Here they are practically the same, within the expected variation, which is a good indication the model is not overfitting the data. The other measures are discussed in Chapter 5.

9. *Interpret the results*: At this stage, we would typically try other prediction algorithms (e.g., regression trees) and see how they do error-wise. We might also try different "settings" on the various models (e.g., we could use the *best subsets* variable selection approach in multiple linear regression to choose a reduced

TABLE 2.14 PREDICTION ERROR METRICS FOR TRAINING AND VALIDATION DATA

code for computing model evaluation metrics

```
# import the utility function regressionSummary
from dmba import regressionSummary

# training set
regressionSummary(train_results.Promo_Item_Purchase, train_results.predicted)

# validation set
regressionSummary(valid_results.Promo_Item_Purchase, valid_results.predicted)
```

Output

```
# training set
Regression statistics

                      Mean Error (ME) : -0.0000
       Root Mean Squared Error (RMSE) :  0.9153
            Mean Absolute Error (MAE) :  0.7821
          Mean Percentage Error (MPE) : 15.5193
Mean Absolute Percentage Error (MAPE) : 58.5637

# validation set
Regression statistics

                      Mean Error (ME) : -0.0000
       Root Mean Squared Error (RMSE) :  0.9570
            Mean Absolute Error (MAE) :  0.8503
          Mean Percentage Error (MPE) : 17.0941
Mean Absolute Percentage Error (MAPE) : 63.8665
```

set of variables that might perform better with the validation data). After choosing the best model—typically, the model with the lowest error on the validation data while also recognizing that "simpler is better"—we use that model to predict the output variable in fresh data. These steps are covered in more detail in the analysis of cases.

10. *Deploy the model*: After the best model is chosen, it is applied to new data to predict Promo_Item_Purchase for customers where this value is unknown. This was, of course, the original purpose. Predicting the output value for new records is called *scoring*. For predictive tasks, scoring produces predicted numerical values. For classification tasks, scoring produces classes and/or propensities. Table 2.15 shows an example of a data frame with nine customers data (using *ALLWIN SUMMER-19* II-*Prediction.csv*) to be scored using our regression model. Note that all the required predictor columns are present, and the output column is absent.

TABLE 2.15 **DATA FRAME WITH NINE RECORDS TO BE SCORED**

```
allwin_P = pd.read_csv('ALLWIN SUMMER-19 II-Prediction.csv')
allwin_P.columns = [s.strip().replace(' ', '_') for s in allwin_P.columns]
allwin_P = pd. get_dummies(allwin_P, prefix_sep='_', drop_first=True)
excludeColumns =allwin_P.loc[:, allwin_P.columns!='Promo_Item_Purchase']
print('Predictions: ', model.predict(excludeColumns))
```

Output

```
Predictions: [2.39705255 1.35467062 2.59084725 3.6836085 1.85552925 3.31597857
 0.70924156 3.49935788 1.33843865]
```

2.7 | USING PYTHON FOR DATA MINING ON A LOCAL MACHINE

An important aspect of the data mining process is that the heavy-duty analysis does not necessarily require a huge number of records. The dataset to be analyzed may have millions of records, of course, but in applying multiple linear regression or applying a classification tree, the use of a sample of 20,000 is likely to yield as accurate an answer as that obtained when using the entire dataset. The principle involved is the same as the principle behind polling: If sampled judiciously, 2000 voters can give an estimate of the entire population's opinion within one or two percentage points. (See "How Many Variables and How Much Data" in Section 2.4 for further discussion.)

Therefore, in most cases, the number of records required in each partition (training, validation, and test) can be accommodated within the memory limit allowed of your local machine.

When we apply Big Data analytics in Python, it might be useful to remove unused objects (function *del*) and call the garbage collection (function *gc.collect()*) afterwards. In general, this is not necessary.

2.8 | AUTOMATING DATA MINING SOLUTIONS

In most supervised data mining applications, the goal is not a static, one-time analysis of a particular dataset. Rather, we want to develop a model that can be used on an ongoing basis to predict or classify new records. Our initial analysis will be in prototype mode, while we explore and define the problem and test different models. We will follow all the steps outlined earlier in this chapter.

At the end of that process, we will typically want our chosen model to be deployed in automated fashion. For example, the US Internal Revenue Service (IRS) receives several hundred million tax returns per year—it does not want to have to pull each tax return out into an Excel sheet or other environment separate from its main database to determine the predicted probability that the return is fraudulent. Rather, it would prefer that determination to be made as part of the normal tax filing environment and process.

Music streaming services, such as Pandora or Spotify, need to determine "recommendations" for next songs quickly for each of millions of users; there is no time to extract the data for manual analysis.

In practice, this is done by building the chosen algorithm into the computational setting in which the rest of the process lies. A tax return is entered directly into the IRS system by a tax preparer, a predictive algorithm is immediately applied to the new data in the IRS system, and a predicted classification is decided by the algorithm. Business rules would then determine what happens with that classification. In the IRS case, the rule might be "if no predicted fraud, continue routine processing; if fraud is predicted, alert an examiner for possible audit."

This flow of the tax return from data entry, into the IRS system, through a predictive algorithm, then back out to a human user is an example of a "data pipeline." The different components of the system communicate with one another via Application Programming Interfaces (APIs) that establish locally valid rules for transmitting data and associated communications. An API for a data mining algorithm would establish the required elements for a predictive algorithm to work—the exact predictor variables, their order, data formats, etc. It would also establish the requirements for communicating the results of the algorithm. Algorithms to be used in an automated data pipeline will need to be compliant with the rules of the APIs where they operate.

Finally, once the computational environment is set and functioning, the data miner's work is not done. The environment in which a model operates is typically dynamic, and predictive models often have a short shelf life—one leading consultant finds they rarely continue to function effectively for more than a year. So, even in a fully deployed state, models must be periodically checked and re-evaluated. Once performance flags, it is time to return to prototype mode and see if a new model can be developed.

In this book, our focus will be on the prototyping phase—all the steps that go into properly defining the model and developing and selecting a model. You should be aware, though, that most of the actual work of implementing a data mining model lies in the automated deployment phase. Much of this work is not in the analytic domain; rather, it lies in the domains of databases and computer science, to assure that detailed nuts and bolts of an automated dataflow all work properly.

2.9 | ETHICAL PRACTICE IN DATA MINING[2]

Prior to the advent of internet-connected devices, the biggest source of big data was public interaction on the internet. Social media users, as well as shoppers and searchers on the internet, have made an implicit deal with the big companies that provide these services: users can take advantage of powerful search, shopping and social interaction

[2]This section copyright ©2019 Datastats, LLC and Galit Shmueli. Used by permission.

tools for free, and, in return, the companies get access to user data. Since the first edition of this book was published in 2007, ethical issues in data mining and data science have received increasing attention, and new rules and laws are emerging. As a data scientist, you must be aware of the rules and follow them, but you must also think about the implications and use of your work once it goes beyond the prototyping phase.

More and more news stories appear concerning illegal, fraudulent, unsavory or just controversial uses of data science. Many people are unaware just how much detailed data on their personal lives is collected, shared, and sold. A writer for *The Guardian* newspaper downloaded his own personal Facebook data and it came to over 600 megabytes—a vivid and detailed portrait of his life.[3] Any one of dozens of apps on your smartphone can collect a flow of your location information and keep tabs on you.

Financial and medical data have long been covered by both industry standards and government regulation to protect privacy and security. While academic research using human subjects' data in most developed countries has been strictly regulated, the collection, storage, and use of personal data in industry has historically faced much less regulatory scrutiny. But concern has reached beyond the basic issues of protecting against theft and unauthorized disclosure of personal information, to the data mining and analytics methods that underlie the harvest and use of such data. In credit scoring, for example, industry regulatory requirements (such as those under Basel II) require that any deployed credit scoring models be highly repeatable, transparent, and auditable (Saddiqi, 2017).

In 2018, the European Union came out, for the first time, with an EU-wide regulation called the General Data Protection Regulation (GDPR). The GDPR limits and restricts the use and storage of personal data by companies and organizations operating in the EU and abroad, insofar as these organizations "monitor the behavior" of or "offer goods or services" to EU-residing data subjects. The GDPR thereby has the potential to affect any organization processing the personal data of EU-based data subjects, regardless of where the processing occurs. "Processing" includes any operation on the data, including pre-processing and the use of data mining algorithms.

The story of Cambridge University Professor Alexander Kogan is a cautionary tale. Kogan helped develop a Facebook app, "This is Your Digital Life," which collected the answers to quiz questions, as well as user data from Facebook. The purported purpose was a research project on online personality. Although fewer than 270,000 people downloaded the app, it was able to access (via friend connections) data on 87 million users. This feature was of great value to the political consulting company Cambridge

---

[3]Dylan Curran, March 30, 2018, *The Guardian* online US edition, accessed Feb 1, 2019, "Are you ready? Here is all the data Facebook and Google have on you". www.theguardian.com/commentisfree/2018/mar/28/all-the-data-facebook-google-has-on-you-privacy.

Analytica, which used data from the app in its political targeting efforts, and ended up doing work for the Trump 2016 campaign, as well as the 2016 Brexit campaign in the UK.

Great controversy ensued: Facebook's CEO, Mark Zuckerberg was called to account before the US Congress, and Cambridge Analytica was eventually forced into bankruptcy. In an interview with Lesley Stahl on the 60 Minutes television program, Kogan contended that he was an innocent researcher who had fallen into deep water, ethically:

> "You know, I was kinda acting, honestly, quite naively. I thought we were doing everything okay.... I ran this lab that studied happiness and kindness."

How did analytics play a role? Facebook's sophisticated algorithms on network relationships (Chapter 19) allowed the Kogan app to reach beyond its user base and get data from millions of users who had never used the app.[4]

In the legal sphere, organizations must be aware of government, contractual, and industry "best-practices" regulations and obligations. But the analytics professional and data scientist must think beyond the codified rules, and think how the predictive technologies they are working on might ultimately be used. Here is just a sampling of some of the concerns that have arisen:

1. *Big brother watching*: Law enforcement and state security analysts can use personal demographic and location information for legitimate purposes, for example, collecting information on associates of a known terrorist. But what is considered "legitimate" may be very different in Germany, the United States, China, and North Korea. At the time of this writing, an active issue in the United States and Europe was fear that the Chinese company Huawei's control of new 5G network standards would compromise Western security. Predictive modeling (Chapters 6–13) and network analysis (Chapter 19) are widely used in surveillance, whether for good or ill. At the same time, companies are also using similar privacy-invading technologies for commercial gains. Google was recently fined 50 million Euro by French regulators for "[depriving] the users of essential guarantees regarding processing operations that can reveal important parts of their private life".[5]
2. *Automated weapon targeting and use*: Armed drones play an increasing role in war, and image recognition is used to facilitate navigation of flight paths, as well

[4]www.cbsnews.com/news/aleksandr-kogan-the-link-between-cambridge-analytica-and-facebook-60-minutes/.

[5]www.washingtonpost.com/world/europe/france-fines-google-nearly-57-million-for-first-major-violation-of-new-european-privacy-regime/2019/01/21/89e7ee08-1d8f-11e9-a759-2b8541bbbe20_story.html.

as help to identify and suggest targets. Should this capability also be allowed to "pull the trigger," say, if a target appears to be a match to an intended target or class of targets? The leading actors in automated targeting may say now that they draw a red line at turning decision-making over to the machine, but the technology has a dynamic of its own. Adversaries and other actors may not draw such a line. Moreover, in an arms race situation, one or more parties are likely to conclude that others will not draw such a line, and seek to proactively develop this capability. Automatic weapon targeting is just an extreme case of automated decision-making made possible by data mining analytics.

3. *Bias and Discrimination*: Automated decision making based on predictive models is now becoming pervasive in many aspects of human life, from credit card transaction alerts and airport security detentions, through college admissions, CV screening for employment, to predictive policing and recidivism scores used by judges. Cathy O'Neil describes multiple cases where such automated decision making becomes "weapons of math destruction," defined by opacity, scale, and damage (O'Neil, 2016). Predictive models in general facilitate these automated decisions; deep learning style neural networks are the standard tool for image and voice recognition. When algorithms are trained on data that already contain human bias, the algorithms learn the bias thereby perpetuating, expanding and magnifying it. The ProPublica group has been publishing articles about various such discrimination cases.[6]

   Governments have already started trying to address this issue: New York City passed the United States' first algorithmic accountability law in 2017, where a task force will monitor the fairness and validity of algorithms used by municipal agencies. In February 2019, legislators in Washington State held a hearing on an algorithmic accountability bill that would establish guidelines for procurement and use of automated decision systems in government "in order to protect consumers, improve transparency, and create more market predictability."[7] As for company use of automated decision-making, in the EU, the GDPR allows EU subjects to opt-out of automated decision-making.

4. *Internet conspiracy theories, rumors and "lynch" mobs*: Before the internet, the growth and dissemination of false rumors and fake conspiracy theories was limited naturally: "broadcast" media had gatekeepers, and one-to-one communications, though unrestricted, were too slow to support much more than local gossip. Social media has not only removed the gatekeepers and expanded the reach of an individual, but also provided interfaces and algorithms that add fuel to the fire. The messaging application WhatsApp, via its message forwarding facility,

[6] www.propublica.org/series/machine-bias.

[7] www.fastcompany.com/90302465/washington-introduces-landmark-algorithmic-accountability-laws.

was instrumental in sparking instant lynch mobs in India in 2018, as false rumors about child abductors spread rapidly. Fake Facebook and Twitter accounts, most notably under Russian control, have helped create and spread divisive and destabilizing messaging in Western democracies with a goal of affecting election outcomes.

A key element in fostering the rapid viral spread of false and damaging messaging is the recommendation algorithms used in social media—these are trained to show you "news" that you are most likely to be interested in (see Chapter 14). And what interests people, and makes them click, "like," and forward, is the car wreck, not the free flow of traffic.

5. *Psychological manipulation and distraction*: A notable aspect of the Cambridge Analytica controversy was the company's claim that it could use "psychographic profiling" based on Facebook data to manipulate behavior. There is some evidence that such psychological manipulation is possible: Matz et al. (in their 2017 PNAS paper "Psychological targeting as an effective approach to digital mass persuasion") found "In three field experiments that reached over 3.5 million individuals with psychologically tailored advertising, we find that matching the content of persuasive appeals to individuals' psychological characteristics significantly altered their behavior as measured by clicks and purchases." But prior psychological profiles are not needed to manipulate behavior. Facebook advisers embedded with the US presidential campaign of Donald Trump guided an extremely complex and continuous system of microtargeted experimentation to determine what display and engagement variables were most effective with specific voters.

   Predictive algorithms, and the statistical principles of experimentation, are central to these automated algorithmic efforts to affect individual behavior. At a more basic level, there is concern that these continuous engagement algorithms can contribute to "digital addiction" and a reduction in ability to concentrate. Paul Lewis, writing in *The Guardian*, says algorithms like these contribute to a state of "'continuous partial attention', severely limiting people's ability to focus."[8] Some of the most powerful critiques have come from those with inside knowledge. An early Facebook investor, Roger McNamee, writes in his book *Zucked*, that Facebook is "terrible for America." Chamath Palihapatiya,[9] formerly Facebook's VP for user growth, now says Facebook is "destroying how society works."

---

[8] *The Guardian* online, posted October 6, 2017 www.theguardian.com/technology/2017/oct/05/smartphone-addiction-silicon-valley-dystopia.

[9] Palihapatiya was quoted by Jared Gilmour in the Sacramento Bee online, posted December 11, 2017 www.sacbee.com/news/nation-world/national/article189213899.html.

6. *Data brokers and unintended uses of personal data*: Reacting to a growing US crisis of opioid addiction, some actuarial firms and data brokers are providing doctors with "opioid addiction risk scores" for their patients, to guide them in offering the patients appropriate medications at appropriate doses and durations, with appropriate instructions. It sounds constructive, but what happens when the data also gets to insurers (which it will), employers, and government agencies? For example, could an individual be denied a security clearance simply due to a high opiod addiction risk score?[10] Individuals themselves contribute to the supply of health data when they use health apps that track personal behavior and medical information. The ability to sell such data is often essential for the app developer—a review of apps that track menstrual cycles "found that most rely on the production and analysis of data for financial sustainability."[11]

Where does this leave the analytics professional and data scientist? Data scientists and analytics professionals must consider not just the powerful benefits that their methods can yield in a specific context, but also the harm they can do in other contexts. A good question to ask is "how might an individual, or a country, with malicious designs make use of this technology?" It is not sufficient just to observe the rules that are currently in place; as a data professional you must also think and judge for yourself. Your judgment must cover not just your current intentions and plans (which may be all to the good), but also future implications and possibilities.

DATA MINING SOFTWARE: THE STATE OF THE MARKET

by Herb Edelstein*

The data mining market has changed in some important ways since the last edition of this book. The most significant trends have been the increasing volume of information available and the growing use of the cloud for data storage and analytics. Data mining and analysis have evolved to meet these new demands.

The term "Big Data" reflects the surge in the amount and types of data collected. There is still an enormous amount of transactional data, data warehousing data, scientific data, and clickstream data. However, adding to the massive storage requirements of traditional data is the influx of information from unstructured sources (e.g., customer service calls and images), social media, and more recently the Internet of Things, which produces a flood of sensor data. The number of organizations collecting such data has greatly increased as virtually every business is expanding in these areas.

Rapid technological change has been an important factor. The price of data storage has dropped precipitously. At this writing, hard disk storage has fallen to under $50 per terabyte and solid state drives are under $200 per terabyte. Concomitant with the decrease in storage costs

[10] www.politico.com/story/2019/02/03/health-risk-scores-opioid-abuse-1139978.

[11] broadly.vice.com/en_us/article/8xe4yz/menstrual-app-period-tracker-data-cyber-security.

has been a dramatic increase in bandwidth at ever lower costs. This has enabled the spread of cloud-based computing. Cloud-based computing refers to using remote platforms for storage, data management, and now analysis. Because scaling up the hardware and software infrastructure for Big Data is so complex, many organizations are entrusting their data to outside vendors. The three largest cloud players (Amazon, IBM, and Microsoft) are each reporting annual revenues in excess of US$20 billion, according to *Forbes* magazine.

Managing this much data is a challenging task. While traditional relational DBMSs—such as Oracle, Microsoft's SQL Server, IBMs DB2, and SAPs Adaptive Server Enterprise (formerly Sybase)—are still among the leading data management tools, open source DBMSs, such as Oracles MySQL are becoming increasingly popular. In addition, nonrelational data storage is making headway in storing extremely large amounts of data. For example, Hadoop, an open source tool for managing large distributed database architectures, has become an important player in the cloud database space. However, Hadoop is a tool for the application developer community rather than end users. Consequently, many of the data mining analytics vendors such as SAS have built interfaces to Hadoop.

All the major database management system vendors offer data mining capabilities, usually integrated into their DBMS. Leading products include Microsoft SQL Server Analysis Services, Oracle Data Mining, and Teradata Warehouse Miner. The target user for embedded data mining is a database professional. Not surprisingly, these products take advantage of database functionality, including using the DBMS to transform variables, storing models in the database, and extending the data access language to include model-building and scoring the database. A few products also supply a separate graphical interface for building data mining models. Where the DBMS has parallel processing capabilities, embedded data mining tools will generally take advantage of it, resulting in greater performance. As with the data mining suites described below, these tools offer an assortment of algorithms. Not only does IBM have embedded analytics in DB2, but following its acquisition of SPSS, IBM has incorporated Clementine and SPSS into IBM Modeler.

There are still a large number of stand-alone data mining tools based on a single algorithm or on a collection of algorithms called a suite. Target users include both statisticians and business intelligence analysts. The leading suites include SAS Enterprise Miner, SAS JMP, IBM Modeler, Salford Systems SPM, Statistica, XLMiner, and RapidMiner. Suites are characterized by providing a wide range of functionality, frequently accessed via a graphical user interface designed to enhance model-building productivity. A popular approach for many of these GUIs is to provide a workflow interface in which the data mining steps and analysis are linked together.

Many suites have outstanding visualization tools and links to statistical packages that extend the range of tasks they can perform. They provide interactive data transformation tools as well as a procedural scripting language for more complex data transformations. The suite vendors are working to link their tools more closely to underlying DBMSs; for example, data transformations might be handled by the DBMS. Data mining models can be exported to be incorporated into the DBMS through generating SQL, procedural language code (e.g., C++ or Java), or a standardized data mining model language called Predictive Model Markup Language (PMML).

In contrast to the general-purpose suites, application-specific tools are intended for particular analytic applications such as credit scoring, customer retention, and product marketing.

Their focus may be further sharpened to address the needs of specialized markets such as mortgage lending or financial services. The target user is an analyst with expertise in the application domain. Therefore the interfaces, the algorithms, and even the terminology are customized for that particular industry, application, or customer. While less flexible than general-purpose tools, they offer the advantage of already incorporating domain knowledge into the product design, and can provide very good solutions with less effort. Data mining companies including SAS, IBM, and RapidMiner offer vertical market tools, as do industry specialists such as Fair Isaac. Other companies, such as Domo, are focusing on creating dashboards with analytics and visualizations for business intelligence.

Another technological shift has occurred with the spread of open source model building tools and open core tools. A somewhat simplified view of open source software is that the source code for the tool is available at no charge to the community of users and can be modified or enhanced by them. These enhancements are submitted to the originator or copyright holder, who can add them to the base package. Open core is a more recent approach in which a core set of functionality remains open and free, but there are proprietary extensions that are not free.

The most important open source statistical analysis software is R. R is descended from a Bell Labs program called S, which was commercialized as S+. Many data mining algorithms have been added to R, along with a plethora of statistics, data management tools, and visualization tools. Because it is essentially a programming language, R has enormous flexibility but a steeper learning curve than many of the GUI-based tools. Although there are some GUIs for R, the overwhelming majority of use is through programming.

Python is rapidly growing in popularity as a data analysis tool and for developing analytical applications. This is due in part because it is faster than R and easier to use than C++ or Java. Scikit-Learn is an open source Python library that provides a comprehensive suite of tools for data analysis that is widely used in the Python community. Orange is a visual interface for Python and Scikit-Learn using wrappers designed to simplify doing analysis. Developed at the University of Ljubljana in Slovenia, Orange is open-source software that uses a workflow interface to provide a greatly improved way to use Python for analysis.

As mentioned above, the cloud-computing vendors have moved into the data mining/predictive analytics business by offering AaaS (Analytics as a Service) and pricing their products on a transaction basis. These products are oriented more toward application developers than business intelligence analysts. A big part of the attraction of mining data in the cloud is the ability to store and manage enormous amounts of data without requiring the expense and complexity of building an in-house capability. This can also enable a more rapid implementation of large distributed multi-user applications. Cloud based data can be used with non-cloud-based analytics if the vendors analytics do not meet the users needs.

Amazon has added Amazon Machine Learning to its Amazon Web Services (AWS), taking advantage of predictive modeling tools developed for Amazon's internal use. AWS supports both relational databases and Hadoop data management. Models cannot be exported, because they are intended to be applied to data stored on the Amazon cloud.

Google is very active in cloud analytics with its BigQuery and Prediction API. BigQuery allows the use of Google infrastructure to access large amounts of data using a SQL-like interface. The Prediction API can be accessed from a variety of languages including R and Python. It uses a variety of machine learning algorithms and automatically selects the best results.

Unfortunately, this is not a transparent process. Furthermore, as with Amazon, models cannot be exported.

Microsoft is an active player in cloud analytics with its Azure Machine Learning Studio and Stream Analytics. Azure works with Hadoop clusters as well as with traditional relational databases. Azure ML offers a broad range of algorithms such as boosted trees and support vector machines as well as supporting R scripts and Python. Azure ML also supports a workflow interface making it more suitable for the nonprogrammer data scientist. The real-time analytics component is designed to allow streaming data from a variety of sources to be analyzed on the fly. Microsoft also acquired Revolution Analytics, a major player in the R analytics business, with a view to integrating Revolution's "R Enterprise" with SQL Server and Azure ML. R Enterprise includes extensions to R that eliminate memory limitations and take advantage of parallel processing.

One drawback of the cloud-based analytics tools is a relative lack of transparency and user control over the algorithms and their parameters. In some cases, the service will simply select a single model that is a black box to the user. Another drawback is that for the most part cloud-based tools are aimed at more sophisticated data scientists who are systems savvy.

Data science is playing a central role in enabling many organizations to optimize everything from production to marketing. New storage options and analytical tools promise even greater capabilities. The key is to select technology that's appropriate for an organization's unique goals and constraints. As always, human judgment is the most important component of a data mining solution.

This book's focus is on a comprehensive understanding of the different techniques and algorithms used in data mining, and less on the data management requirements of real-time deployment of data mining models.

***

*Herb Edelstein is president of Two Crows Consulting (www.twocrows.coml), a leading data mining consulting firm near Washington, DC. He is an internationally recognized expert in data mining and data warehousing, a widely published author on these topics, and a popular speaker.

PROBLEMS

2.1. Assuming that data mining techniques are to be used in the following cases, identify whether the task required is supervised or unsupervised learning.

- **a.** Deciding whether to issue a loan to an applicant based on demographic and financial data (with reference to a database of similar data on prior customers).
- **b.** In an online bookstore, making recommendations to customers concerning additional items to buy based on the buying patterns in prior transactions.
- **c.** Identifying a network data packet as dangerous (virus, hacker attack) based on comparison to other packets whose threat status is known.
- **d.** Identifying segments of similar customers.

e. Predicting whether a company will go bankrupt based on comparing its financial data to those of similar bankrupt and nonbankrupt firms.

f. Estimating the repair time required for an aircraft based on a trouble ticket.

g. Automated sorting of mail by zip code scanning.

h. Printing of custom discount coupons at the conclusion of a grocery store checkout based on what you just bought and what others have bought previously.

2.2. Describe the difference in roles assumed by the validation partition and the test partition.

2.3. Consider the sample from a bank database shown in Table 2.16; it was selected randomly from a larger database to be the training set. *Personal Loan* indicates whether a solicitation for a personal loan was accepted and is the response variable. A campaign is planned for a similar solicitation in the future and the bank is looking for a model that will identify likely responders. Examine the data carefully and indicate what your next step would be.

2.4. Consider the sample from a database of credit applicants in Table 2.17. Comment on the likelihood that it was sampled randomly, and whether it is likely to be a useful sample.

TABLE 2.16 **SAMPLE FROM A BANK DATABASE**

OBS	AGE	EXPERIENCE	INCOME	ZIP CODE	FAMILY	CC AVG	EDUC	MORTGAGE	PERSONAL LOAN	SECURITIES ACCT
1	25	1	49	91107	4	1.6	1	0	0	1
4	35	9	100	94112	1	2.7	2	0	0	0
5	35	8	45	91330	4	1	2	0	0	0
9	35	10	81	90089	3	0.6	2	104	0	0
10	34	9	180	93023	1	8.9	3	0	1	0
12	29	5	45	90277	3	0.1	2	0	0	0
17	38	14	130	95010	4	4.7	3	134	1	0
18	42	18	81	94305	4	2.4	1	0	0	0
21	56	31	25	94015	4	0.9	2	111	0	0
26	43	19	29	94305	3	0.5	1	97	0	0
29	56	30	48	94539	1	2.2	3	0	0	0
30	38	13	119	94104	1	3.3	2	0	1	0
35	31	5	50	94035	4	1.8	3	0	0	0
36	48	24	81	92647	3	0.7	1	0	0	0
37	59	35	121	94720	1	2.9	1	0	0	0
38	51	25	71	95814	1	1.4	3	198	0	0
39	42	18	141	94114	3	5	3	0	1	1
41	57	32	84	92672	3	1.6	3	0	0	1

2.5. Using the concept of overfitting, explain why when a model is fit to training data, zero error with those data is not necessarily good.

TABLE 2.17 SAMPLE FROM A DATABASE OF CREDIT APPLICATIONS

OBS	CHECK ACCT	DURATION	HISTORY	NEW CAR	USED CAR	FURNITURE	RADIO TV	EDUC	RETRAIN	AMOUNT	SAVE ACCT	RESPONSE
1	0	6	4	0	0	0	1	0	0	1169	4	1
8	1	36	2	0	1	0	0	0	0	6948	0	1
16	0	24	2	0	0	0	1	0	0	1282	1	0
24	1	12	4	0	1	0	0	0	0	1804	1	1
32	0	24	2	0	0	1	0	0	0	4020	0	1
40	1	9	2	0	0	0	1	0	0	458	0	1
48	0	6	2	0	1	0	0	0	0	1352	2	1
56	3	6	1	1	0	0	0	0	0	783	4	1
64	1	48	0	0	0	0	0	0	1	14,421	0	0
72	3	7	4	0	0	0	1	0	0	730	4	1
80	1	30	2	0	0	1	0	0	0	3832	0	1
88	1	36	2	0	0	0	0	1	0	12,612	1	0
96	1	54	0	0	0	0	0	0	1	15,945	0	0
104	1	9	4	0	0	1	0	0	0	1919	0	1
112	2	15	2	0	0	0	0	1	0	392	0	1

2.6. In fitting a model to classify prospects as purchasers or nonpurchasers, a certain company drew the training data from internal data that include demographic and purchase information. Future data to be classified will be lists purchased from other sources, with demographic (but not purchase) data included. It was found that "refund issued" was a useful predictor in the training data. Why is this not an appropriate variable to include in the model?

2.7. A dataset has 1000 records and 50 variables with 5% of the values missing, spread randomly throughout the records and variables. An analyst decides to remove records with missing values. About how many records would you expect to be removed?

2.8. Normalize the data in Table 2.18, showing calculations.

TABLE 2.18

Age	Income ($)
25	49,000
56	156,000
65	99,000
32	192,000
41	39,000
49	57,000

2.9. Statistical distance between records can be measured in several ways. Consider Euclidean distance, measured as the square root of the sum of the squared differences. For the first two records in Table 2.18, it is

$$\sqrt{(25-56)^2+(49,000-156,000)^2}.$$

Can normalizing the data change which two records are farthest from each other in terms of Euclidean distance?

2.10. Two models are applied to a dataset that has been partitioned. Model A is considerably more accurate than model B on the training data, but slightly less accurate than model B on the validation data. Which model are you more likely to consider for final deployment?

2.11. The dataset *ToyotaCorolla.csv* contains data on used cars on sale during the late summer of 2004 in the Netherlands. It has 1436 records containing details on 38 attributes, including *Price*, *Age*, *Kilometers*, *HP*, and other specifications.

We plan to analyze the data using various data mining techniques described in future chapters. Prepare the data for use as follows:

a. The dataset has two categorical attributes, *Fuel Type* and *Color*. Describe how you would convert these to binary variables. Confirm this using `pandas` methods to transform categorical data into dummies.

b. Prepare the dataset (as factored into dummies) for data mining techniques of supervised learning by creating partitions in Python. Select all the variables and use default values for the random seed and partitioning percentages for training (50%), validation (30%), and test (20%) sets. Describe the roles that these partitions will play in modeling.

PART

II

Data Exploration and Dimension Reduction

CHAPTER 3

Data Visualization

In this chapter, we describe a set of plots that can be used to explore the multidimensional nature of a data set. We present basic plots (bar charts, line graphs, and scatter plots), distribution plots (boxplots and histograms), and different enhancements that expand the capabilities of these plots to visualize more information. We focus on how the different visualizations and operations can support data mining tasks, from supervised tasks (prediction, classification, and time series forecasting) to unsupervised tasks, and provide a few guidelines on specific visualizations to use with each data mining task. We also describe the advantages of interactive visualization over static plots. The chapter concludes with a presentation of specialized plots suitable for data with special structure (hierarchical, network, and geographical).

3.1 | INTRODUCTION[1]

The popular saying "a picture is worth a thousand words" refers to the ability to condense diffused verbal information into a compact and quickly understood graphical image. In the case of numbers, data visualization and numerical summarization provide us with both a powerful tool to explore data and an effective way to present results (Few, 2012).

Where do visualization techniques fit into the data mining process, as described so far? They are primarily used in the preprocessing portion of the data mining process. Visualization supports data cleaning by finding incorrect values (e.g., patients whose age is 999 or −1), missing values, duplicate rows, columns with all the same value, and the like. Visualization techniques are also useful for variable derivation and selection: they can help determine which variables to include in the analysis and which might be redundant. They can also help with determining appropriate bin sizes, should binning of numerical variables be needed (e.g., a numerical outcome variable might need to be converted to a binary variable if a yes/no decision is required). They can also play a role in combining categories as part of the data reduction process. Finally, if the data have yet to be collected and collection is expensive (as with the Pandora project at its outset, see Chapter 7), visualization methods can help determine, using a sample, which variables and metrics are useful.

In this chapter, we focus on the use of graphical presentations for the purpose of *data exploration*, particularly with relation to predictive analytics. Although our focus is not on visualization for the purpose of data reporting, this chapter offers ideas as to the effectiveness of various graphical displays for the purpose of data presentation. These offer a wealth of useful presentations beyond tabular summaries and basic bar charts, which are currently the most popular form of data presentation in the business environment. For an excellent discussion of using charts to report business data, see Few (2012). In terms of reporting data mining results graphically, we describe common graphical displays elsewhere in the book, some of which are technique-specific [e.g., dendrograms for hierarchical clustering (Chapter 15), network charts for social network analysis (Chapter 19), and tree charts for classification and regression trees (Chapter 9)] while others are more general [e.g., receiver operating characteristic (ROC) curves and lift charts for classification (Chapter 5) and profile plots and heatmaps for clustering (Chapter 15)].

Note: The term "graph" can have two meanings in statistics. It can refer, particularly in popular usage, to any of a number of figures to represent data (e.g., line chart, bar plot, histogram, etc.). In a more technical use, it refers to the data structure and visualization in networks (see Chapter 19). Using the term "plot" for the visualizations we explore in this chapter avoids this confusion.

Data exploration is a mandatory initial step whether or not more formal analysis follows. Graphical exploration can support free-form exploration for the purpose of understanding the data structure, cleaning the data (e.g., identifying unexpected gaps or "illegal" values), identifying outliers, discovering initial patterns (e.g., correlations among variables and surprising clusters), and generating interesting questions. Graphical exploration can also be more focused, geared toward specific questions of interest. In the data mining context, a combination is needed: free-form exploration performed with the purpose of supporting a specific goal.

Graphical exploration can range from generating very basic plots to using operations such as filtering and zooming interactively to explore a set of interconnected visualizations that include advanced features such as color and multiple-panels. This chapter is not meant to be an exhaustive guidebook on visualization techniques, but instead discusses main principles and features that support data exploration in a data mining context. We start by describing varying levels of sophistication in terms of visualization, and show the advantages of different features and operations. Our discussion is from the perspective of how visualization supports the subsequent data mining goal. In particular, we distinguish between supervised and unsupervised learning; within supervised learning, we also further distinguish between classification (categorical outcome variable) and prediction (numerical outcome variable).

Python

There are a variety of Python libraries for data visualizations. The oldest, but also most flexible library is `matplotlib`. It is widely used and there are many resources available to get started and to find help. A number of other libraries are built around it and make the generation of plots often quicker.

`Seaborn` and `pandas` are two of the libraries that are wrappers around `matplotlib`. Both are very useful to create plots quickly. However, even if these are used, a good knowledge of `matplotlib` helps to have more control over the final plot.

The `ggplot` library is modeled after the equally named R package by Hadley Wickham. It is based on the "Grammar of Graphics," a term coined by Leland Wilkinson to define a system of plotting theory and nomenclature. Learning `ggplot` effectively means becoming familiar with this philosophy and technical language of plotting.

`Bokeh` is an interesting new development to create interactive plots, dashboards and data applications for web browers.

In this chapter, we mainly use `pandas` for data visualizations and cover possible customization of the plots using `matplotlib` commands. A few other packages are used for specialized plots: `seaborn` for heatmaps, `gmaps` and `cartopy` for map visualizations.

import required functionality for this chapter

```
import os
import calendar
import numpy as np
import networkx as nx
import pandas as pd
from pandas.plotting import scatter_matrix, parallel_coordinates
import seaborn as sns
from sklearn import preprocessing
import matplotlib.pylab as plt
```

3.2 | DATA EXAMPLES

To illustrate data visualization, we use two datasets used in additional chapters in the book.

Example 1: Service Feedback and Usage Data

The dataset (*Service_Usage.csv*) pertains to a leading service organization. It represents a portion of a larger dataset that captures service outlet-wise service usage data. The field names as well as figures have been adapted to the learning needs of this chapter. A description of each variable is given in Table 3.1 and a sample of the first nine records is shown in Table 3.2. In the original dataset, there were numerous variables available, but 11 variables were selected for this sample dataset. These variables comprise 7 variables pertaining to service usage and feedback behavior, 3 profile variables (State, Place density, and Operational Yrs), and 1 service center identifier code. All the variables of feedback behavior available as counts within a service center for the last six-month period have been transformed into a percentage of total traffic, whereas service usage has been transformed into percentage growth over the previous six months. One more categorical variable showing high or low service usage as 1 or 0 (UL) has been created from a continuous variable service growth variable captured as a percentage increase in service usage transactions over the transaction in the previous six months (UG).

We consider three possible tasks:

1. A supervised predictive task, where the outcome variable of interest is the UG.
2. A supervised classification task, where the outcome variable of interest is the binary variable UL that indicates whether the service usage level is high or low based on a cut-off level of 12%.
3. An unsupervised task, where the goal is to cluster service centers based on available variables.
   (UG and UL are not used together in any of the three cases)

TABLE 3.1 VARIABLE DESCRIPTION OF THE SERVICE_USAGE DATASET

Variable	Description
CentreID	Service Centre Code spread across various states
State	State of India
PD	Population density in the catchment area
OY	Number of years since centre establishment
CMT	No. of customer who made complaint/s as % of total traffic
RP	% complaints resolved

TABLE 3.1 VARIABLE DESCRIPTION OF THE SERVICE_USAGE DATASET (*Continued*)

FBK	No. of customer who gave feedback as % of total traffic
IAS	No. of customer who provided Immediately actionable suggestions as % of total traffic
STAS	No. of customer who provided short term actionable suggestions as % of total traffic
LTAS	No. of customer who provided long term actionable suggestions as % of total traffic
UG	Six monthly service usage growth percentage
UL	Six monthly service usage growth percentage transformed into high (1) and low levels (0) based on a cut off of 12% growth

TABLE 3.2 FIRST SEVEN RECORDS IN THE SERVICE_USAGE DATASET

code for opening the Service_Usage and viewing the first 7 records

```
import pandas as pd
su=pd.read_csv('Service_Usage.csv')
su.head(7)
```

Output

```
In [6]:  Su.head(7)
Out[6]:   CentreID        State    PD OY    CMT     RP    FBK    IAS   STAS   LTAS     UG UL
        0   OD9360       Odisha Medium  8 0.1373 0.5531 0.1215 0.5358 0.1928 0.0126 0.1298  1
        1   AN1392       Andhra Medium  5 0.0786 0.5531 0.0876 0.1212 0.3989 0.0010 0.1386  1
                        Pradesh
        2   PU8465       Punjab    Low  4 0.1945 0.5317 0.0419 0.0119 0.0192 0.0007 0.1413  1
        3   AN3297       Andhra Medium  7 0.0434 0.3888 0.0760 0.3083 0.2505 0.0133 0.1208  1
                        Pradesh
        4   PU8331       Punjab    Low  7 0.0777 0.6287 0.0447 0.6016 0.0125 0.0110 0.1426  1
        5   GU1991      Gujarat    Low  7 0.1729 0.5260 0.1669 0.4384 0.2825 0.0064 0.1051  0
        6   MA2451  Maharashtra   High  2 0.1401 0.3800 0.0191 0.5049 0.1982 0.0148 0.1021  0
```

Example 2: Time Series Indices of Industrial Production of India

The data refers to the Index of Industrial Production at 2-digit industry level indices with weights, annual average indices, and growth over the corresponding period of the previous year. The data has been taken from the open public data site of India data.gov.in. The contributing ministry of this data is the Ministry of Statistics and Program Implementation.

Source: https://data.gov.in/resources/time-series-indices-industrial-production-1980-81-series

3.3 | BASIC CHARTS: BAR CHARTS, LINE GRAPHS, AND SCATTER PLOTS

The three most effective basic plots are bar charts, line graphs, and scatter plots. These plots are easy to create in Python using `pandas` and are the plots most commonly used in the current business world, in both data exploration and presentation (unfortunately, pie charts are also popular, although they are usually ineffective visualizations). Basic charts support data exploration by displaying one or two columns of data (variables) at a time. This is useful in the early stages of getting familiar with the data structure, the amount and types of variables, the volume and type of missing values, etc.

The nature of the data mining task and domain knowledge about the data will affect the use of basic charts in terms of the amount of time and effort allocated to different variables. In supervised learning, there will be more focus on the outcome variable. In scatter plots, the outcome variable is typically associated with the y-axis. In unsupervised learning (for the purpose of data reduction or clustering), basic plots that convey relationships (such as scatter plots) are preferred.

The top-left panel in Figure 3.1a displays a line chart for the time series of yearly-production data of Mining sector in India. Line graphs are used primarily for showing time series. The choice of time frame to plot, as well as the temporal scale, should depend on the horizon of the forecasting task and on the nature of the data.

Bar charts are useful for comparing a single statistic (e.g., average, count, percentage) across groups. The height of the bar (or length in a horizontal display) represents the value of the statistic, and different bars correspond to different groups. Two examples are shown in Figure 3.1c,d. Figure 3.1c shows a bar chart for a numerical variable (UG) and Figure 3.1d shows a bar chart for a categorical variable (UL). In each, separate bars are used to denote service usage growth across three categories of population density (PD). The chart with the numerical output UG (Figure 3.1c) uses the average UG on the y-axis. This supports the predictive task: the numerical outcome is on the y-axis and the x-axis is used for a potential categorical predictor.[2] (Note that the x-axis on a bar chart must be used only for categorical variables, because the order of bars in a bar chart should be interchangeable.) For the classification task (Figure 3.1d), the y-axis indicates the percent of people with value above 12% and the x-axis is a categorical variable with three categories. Figure 3.1b displays a scatter plot of CMT vs. FBK. This is an important plot in the prediction task. (Note that the x-axis on a bar chart must be used only for categorical variables, because the order of bars in a bar chart should be interchangeable.) For the classification task, Figure 3.1d the y-axis indicates the percent of usage level with a mean value above 12% and the x-axis is a categorical variable indicating three categories of place population density mentioned

---

[2]We refer here to a bar chart with vertical bars. The same principles apply if using a bar chart with horizontal lines, except that the x-axis is now associated with the numerical variable and the y-axis with the categorical variable.

as High, Medium, and Low. This graph indicates us that the population density is less likely a direct significant predictor of service usage growth.

For unsupervised learning, the scatter plot helps study the association between two numerical variables in terms of information overlap as well as identifying clusters of observations.

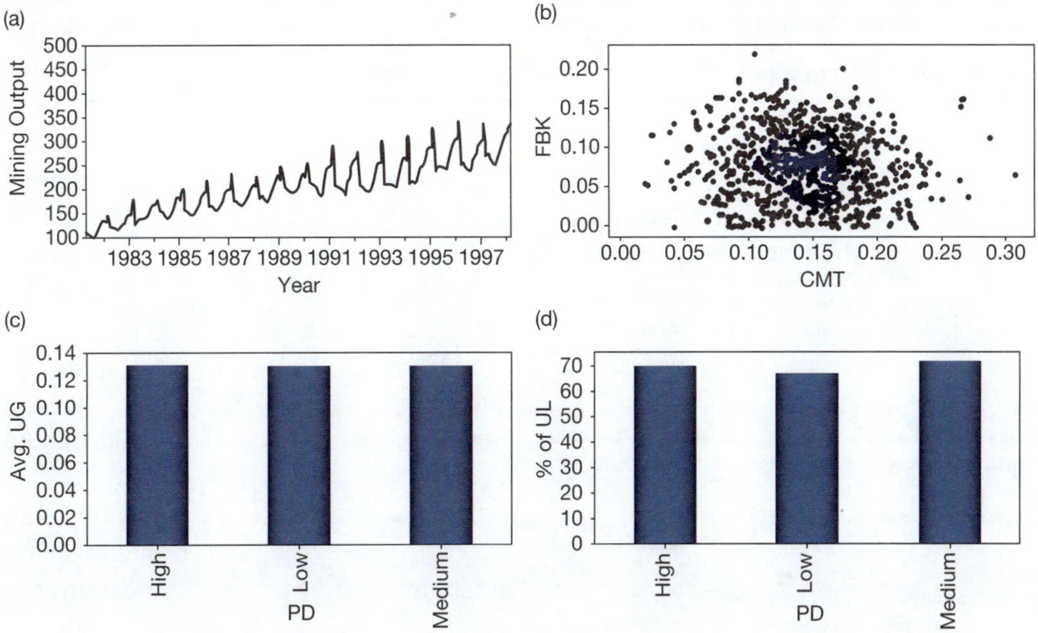

FIGURE 3.1 **BASIC PLOTS: LINE GRAPH (a), SCATTER PLOT (b), BAR CHART FOR NUMERICAL VARIABLE (c), AND BAR CHART FOR CATEGORICAL VARIABLE (d)**

code for creating Figure 3.1

```
## Load the Timeseries data and convert to be suitable for time series analysis
Mining=pd.read_csv("Timeseries Data.csv")
Mining1=Mining.iloc[:,0:2]
Mining1.Months=pd.to_datetime(Mining1.Months)
Mining_s = pd.Series(Mining1.Mining.values, index=Mining1.Months)
```

Panda version

```
## line graph
Mining_s.plot(ylim=[100, 500], legend=False)
plt.xlabel('Year') # set x-axis label
plt.ylabel('Mining Output') # set y-axis label

su=pd.read_csv('Service_Usage.csv')
## scatter plot with axes names
```

```
su.plot.scatter(x='CMT', y='FBK', legend=False)
## barchart of PD vs. mean UG
# compute mean UG per PD = ("Low","Medium","High")
ax = su.groupby('PD').mean().UG.plot(kind='bar')
ax.set_ylabel('Avg. UG')
## barchart of PD vs. UL
dataForPlot = su.groupby('PD').mean()['UL'] * 100
ax = dataForPlot.plot(kind='bar', figsize=[5, 3])
ax.set_ylabel('% of UL')
```

Matplotlib version to adjust all four above plots in a 2 × 2 frame

```
figure, axis = plt.subplots(2, 2)

#line graph
ts['Months']=pd.to_datetime(ts.Months)
ts1=pd.Series(ts.Mining.values,index=ts.Months)
axis[0,0].plot(ts1.index, ts1)
plt.rcParams['figure.figsize'] = [40, 20]
axis[0,0].set_xlabel('Months') # set x-axis label
axis[0,0].set_ylabel('Mining Output') # set y-axis label

# Set the color of the points in the scatterplot and draw as open circles.
axis[1,0].scatter(su.CMT, su.FBK, color='C2', facecolor='red')
plt.rcParams['figure.figsize'] = [40, 20]
axis[1,0].set_xlabel('CMT');
axis[1,0].set_ylabel('FBK')
dataForPlot = su.groupby('PD').mean().UG

## barchart of PD vs. mean UG
# compute mean UG per PD = (Low, Medium, High)
axis[0,1].bar(dataForPlot.index, dataForPlot, color=['C1','C3','C5'])
plt.rcParams['figure.figsize'] = [40, 20]
axis[0,1].set_xlabel('PD')
axis[0,1].set_ylabel('Avg.UG')

## barchart of PD vs. UL
dataForPlot = su.groupby('PD').mean().UL * 100
axis[1,1].bar(dataForPlot.index, dataForPlot, color=['C1','C3','C5'])
plt.rcParams['figure.figsize'] = [40, 20]
axis[1,1].set_xlabel('PD');
axis[1,1].set_ylabel('% of UL')
```

All three basic plots highlight information about service usage of a service firm, as well as changes over time in sector production in India (line chart), relationships between numerical variables of service usage dimensions (scatter plot), and differences between subgroups (bar chart).

Distribution Plots: Boxplots and Histograms

Before moving on to more sophisticated visualizations that enable multidimensional investigation, we note two important plots that are usually not considered "basic charts" but are very useful in statistical and data mining contexts. The *boxplot* and the *histogram* are two plots that display the entire distribution of a numerical variable. Although averages are very popular and useful summary statistics, there is usually much to be gained by looking at additional statistics such as the median and standard deviation of a variable, and even more so by examining the entire distribution. Whereas bar charts can only use a single aggregation, boxplots and histograms display the entire distribution of a numerical variable. Boxplots are also effective for comparing subgroups by generating side-by-side boxplots, or for looking at distributions over time by creating a series of boxplots.

Distribution plots are useful in supervised learning for determining potential data mining methods and variable transformations. For example, skewed numerical variables might warrant transformation (e.g., moving to a logarithmic scale) if used in methods that assume normality (e.g., linear regression, discriminant analysis).

A histogram represents the frequencies of all x values with a series of vertical connected bars. For example, in the left panel of Figure 3.2, there are over 150 centers where the mean value (UG) is between 0.11 to 0.15 and more than 200 cities with UG value between 0.13 to 0.14.

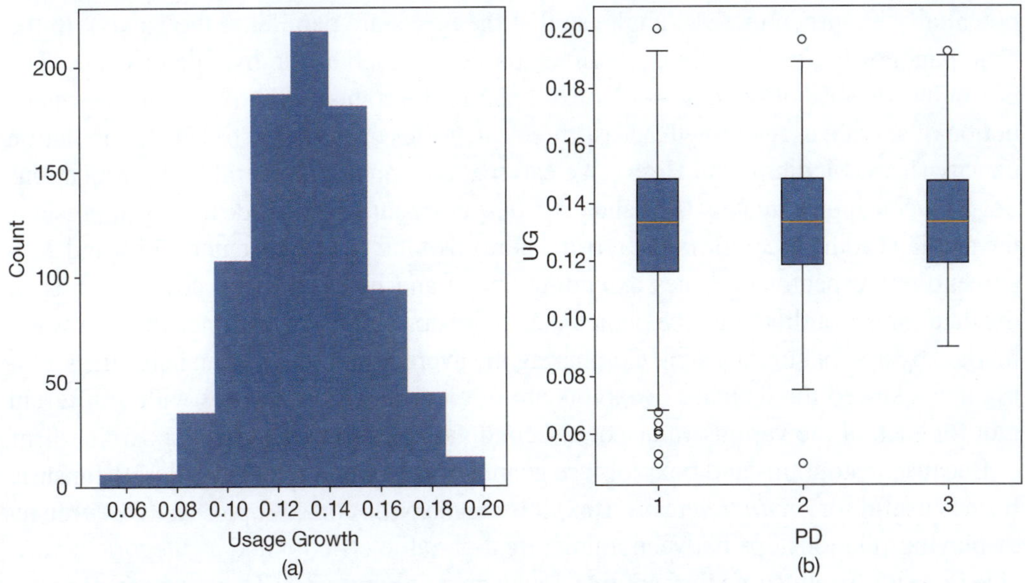

FIGURE 3.2 DISTRIBUTION CHARTS FOR NUMERICAL VARIABLE USAGE GROWTH (UG). (a) HISTOGRAM, (b) BOXPLOT

code for creating Figure 3.2

```
## histogram of Usage Growth(UG)
ax = su.UG.hist()
ax.set_xlabel('Usage Growth');
ax.set_ylabel('count')

## boxplot of UG for different values of PD
ax = su.boxplot(column='UG', by='PD')
ax.set_ylabel('UG')
plt.suptitle('')
# Suppress the titles
plt.title('')

# alternative plot with matplotlib

figure, (axis1,axis2)= plt.subplots(1,2)
axis1.hist(su.UG)
dataForPlot = [list(su[su.PD=="Low"].UG),
list(su[su.PD=="Medium"].UG),
list(su[su.PD=="High"].UG)]
axis2.boxplot(dataForPlot)
plt.show()
```

A boxplot represents the variable being plotted on the *y*-axis (although the plot can potentially be turned in a 90° angle, so that the boxes are parallel to the *x*-axis). In the right panel of Figure 3.2, there are three boxplots (called a side-by-side boxplot). The box encloses 50% of the data — for example, in the right-hand box depicts the distribution of service usage growth across three categories of locations based on population density (Low, Medium, and High). We can see that spread of central 50% of locations lies between approximately 0.11 and 0.15. The horizontal line inside the box represents the median (50th percentile). The top and bottom of the box represent the 75th and 25th percentiles, respectively. Lines extending above and below the box cover the rest of the data range; outliers may be depicted as points or circles. Sometimes the average is marked by a + (or similar) sign. Comparing the average and the median helps in assessing how skewed the data are. Boxplots are often arranged in a series with a different plot for each of the various values of a second variable, shown on the *x*-axis.

Because histograms and boxplots are geared toward numerical variables, their basic form is useful for *prediction* tasks. Boxplots can also support *unsupervised learning* by displaying relationships between a numerical variable (*y*-axis) and a categorical variable (*x*-axis). To illustrate these points, look again at Figure 3.2. The left panel shows a histogram of UG, revealing a normal distribution. In case it would have been skewed, transforming the output variable to log (UG) could be used to improve results of a linear regression predictor.

The right panel in Figure 3.2 shows side-by-side boxplots comparing the distribution of UG for services that are located across three categories of locations similar to Figure 3.1. We see that the average UG for services is almost closer in all categories. This information is useful for identifying the potential importance of any potential predictor for choosing data mining methods that can capture the non-overlapping area between the three distributions (e.g., trees).

Boxplots and histograms applied to numerical variables can also provide directions for deriving new variables, for example, they can indicate how to bin a numerical variable (e.g., binning a numerical outcome in order to use a naive Bayes classifier, or in the Services Feedback and Usage example, choosing the cutoff to convert UG to UL).

Finally, side-by-side boxplots are useful in classification tasks for evaluating the potential of numerical predictors. This is done by using the x-axis for the categorical outcome and the y-axis for a numerical predictor. An example is shown in Figure 3.3, where we can see the effects of four numerical predictors on UL. The pairs that are most separated (e.g., RP) indicate potentially useful predictors.

The main weakness of basic charts and distribution plots, in their basic form (i.e., using position in relation to the axes to encode values), is that they can only display two variables and therefore cannot reveal high-dimensional information. Each of the basic charts has two dimensions, where each dimension is dedicated to a single variable. In data mining, the data are usually multivariate by nature, and the analytics are designed to capture and measure multivariate information. Visual exploration should therefore also incorporate this important aspect. In the next section, we describe how to extend basic charts (and distribution plots) to multidimensional data visualization by adding features, employing manipulations, and incorporating interactivity. We then present several specialized charts that are geared toward displaying special data structures (Section 3.5).

code for creating Figure 3.3

```
## side-by-side boxplots
fig, axes = plt.subplots(nrows=1, ncols=4, figsize=(14, 8))
su.boxplot(column='CMT', by='UL', ax=axes[0])
su.boxplot(column='RP', by='UL', ax=axes[1])
su.boxplot(column='FBK', by='UL', ax=axes[2])
su.boxplot(column='IAS', by='UL', ax=axes[3])
for ax in axes:
    ax.set_xlabel('UL')
plt.suptitle('') # Suppress the overall title
plt.tight_layout() # Increase the separation between the plots
```

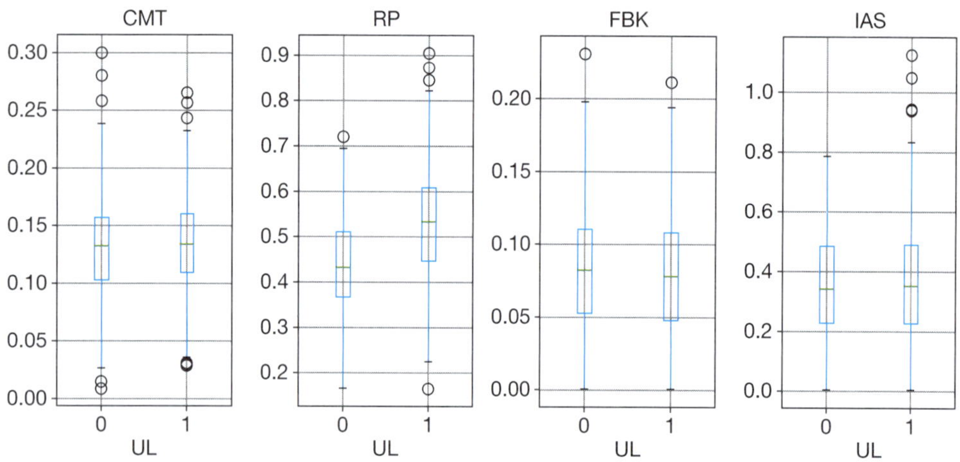

FIGURE 3.3 SIDE-BY-SIDE BOXPLOTS FOR EXPLORING THE UL OUTPUT VARIABLE BY DIFFERENT NUMERICAL PREDICTORS. IN A SIDE-BY-SIDE BOXPLOT, ONE AXIS IS USED FOR A CATEGORICAL VARIABLE, AND THE OTHER FOR A NUMERICAL VARIABLE.

Heatmaps: Visualizing Correlations and Missing Values

A *heatmap* is a graphical display of numerical data where color is used to denote values. In a data mining context, heatmaps are especially useful for two purposes: for visualizing correlation tables and for visualizing missing values in the data. In both cases, the information is conveyed in a two-dimensional table. A correlation table for p variables has p rows and p columns. A data table contains p columns (variables) and n rows (observations). If the number of rows is huge, then a subset can be used. In both cases, it is much easier and faster to scan the color-coding rather than the values. Note that heatmaps are useful when examining a large number of values, but they are not a replacement for more precise graphical display, such as bar charts, because color differences cannot be perceived accurately.

An example of a correlation table heatmap is shown in Figure 3.4, showing all the pairwise correlations between 8 numeric variables (UG and 7 predictors from column 4 to column 10). Darker/dense shades correspond to stronger (positive or negative) correlation. It is easy to quickly spot the high and low correlations.

code for creating Figure 3.4

```
## simple heatmap of correlations (without values)
corr = su.corr()
sns.heatmap(corr, xticklabels=corr.columns, yticklabels=corr.columns)

# Change the colormap to a divergent scale and fix the range of the colormap
sns.heatmap(corr, xticklabels=corr.columns, yticklabels=corr.columns, vmin=-1,
            vmax=1, cmap="RdBu")
# Include information about values (example demonstrate how to control the size of
```

```
# the plot
fig, ax = plt.subplots()
fig.set_size_inches(11, 7)
sns.heatmap(corr, annot=True, fmt=".1f", cmap="RdBu", center=0, ax=ax)
```

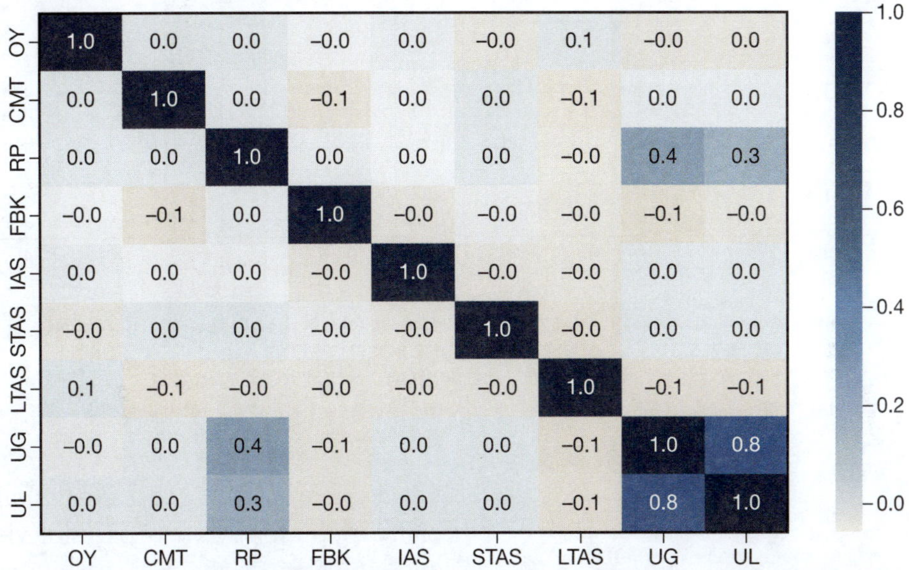

FIGURE 3.4 HEATMAP OF A CORRELATION TABLE. DARKER VALUES DENOTE STRONGER CORRELATION. BLUE/RED REPRESENT POSITIVE/NEGATIVE VALUES, RESPECTIVELY.

code for generating a heatmap of missing values similar to Figure 3.5

```
df = pd.read_csv('NYPD_Motor_Vehicle_Collisions_1000.csv').sort_values(['DATE'])

# given a dataframe df create a copy of the array that is 0 if a field contains a
# value and 1 for NaN
naInfo = np.zeros(df.shape)
naInfo[df.isna().values] = 1
naInfo = pd.DataFrame(naInfo, columns=df.columns)

fig, ax = plt.subplots()
fig.set_size_inches(13, 9)
ax = sns.heatmap(naInfo, vmin=0, vmax=1, cmap=["white", "#666666"], cbar=False, ax=ax)
ax.set_yticks([])

# draw frame around figure
rect = plt.Rectangle((0, 0), naInfo.shape[1], naInfo.shape[0], linewidth=1,
                     edgecolor='lightgrey', facecolor='none')
rect = ax.add_patch(rect)
rect.set_clip_on(False)

plt.xticks(rotation=80)
```

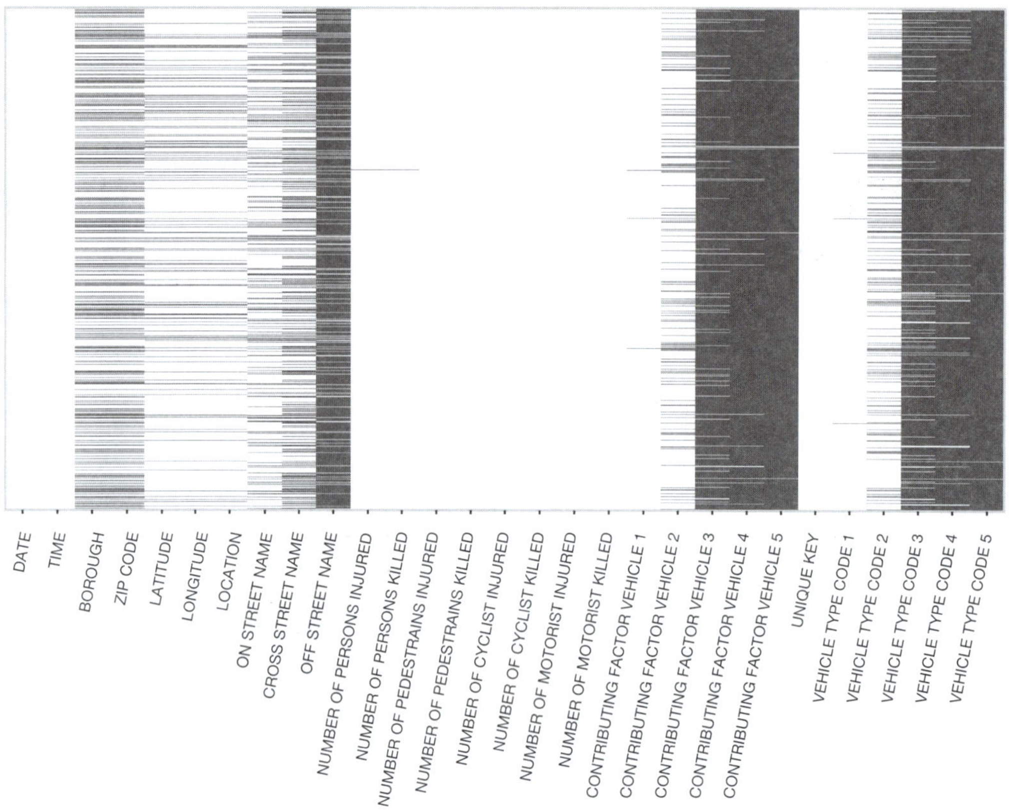

FIGURE 3.5 HEATMAP OF MISSING VALUES IN A DATASET ON MOTOR VEHICLE COLLISIONS. GREY DENOTES MISSING VALUE

In a missing value heatmap, rows correspond to records and columns to variables. We use a binary coding of the original dataset where 1 denotes a missing value and 0 otherwise. This new binary table is then colored such that only missing value cells (with value 1) are colored. Figure 3.5 shows an example of a missing value heatmap for a dataset on motor vehicle collisions.[3] The missing data heatmap helps visualize the level and amount of "missingness" in the dataset. Some patterns of "missingness" easily emerge: variables that are missing for nearly all observations, as well as clusters of rows that are missing many values. Variables with little missingness are also visible. This information can then be used for determining how to handle the missingness (e.g., dropping some variables, dropping some records, imputing, or via other techniques).

[3]The data were obtained from https://data.cityofnewyork.us/Public-Safety/NYPD-Motor-Vehicle-Collisions/h9gi-nx95.

3.4 | MULTIDIMENSIONAL VISUALIZATION

Basic plots can convey richer information with features such as color, size, and multiple panels, and by enabling operations such as rescaling, aggregation, and interactivity. These additions allow looking at more than one or two variables at a time. The beauty of these additions is their effectiveness in displaying complex information in an easily understandable way. Effective features are based on understanding how visual perception works (see Few, 2009 for a discussion). The purpose is to make the information more understandable, not just to represent the data in higher dimensions (such as three-dimensional plots that are usually ineffective visualizations).

Adding Variables: Color, Size, Shape, Multiple Panels, and Animation

In order to include more variables in a plot, we must consider the type of variable to include. To represent additional categorical information, the best way is to use hue, shape, or multiple panels. For additional numerical information, we can use color intensity or size. Temporal information can be added via animation.

Incorporating additional categorical and/or numerical variables into the basic (and distribution) plots means that we can now use all of them for both prediction and classification tasks. For example, we mentioned earlier that a basic scatter plot cannot be used for studying the relationship between a categorical outcome and predictors (in the context of classification). However, a very effective plot for classification is a scatter plot of two numerical predictors color-coded by the categorical outcome variable. An example is shown in the top panel of Figure 3.6, with color denoting UL (Service Usage level).

In the context of prediction, color-coding supports the exploration of the conditional relationship between the numerical outcome (on the *y*-axis) and a numerical predictor. Color-coded scatter plots then help assess the need for creating interaction terms (e.g., is the relationship between usage growth (UG) and % complaints resolved (RP) different for locations based on population density (PD).

Color can also be used to include further categorical variables into a bar chart, as long as the number of categories is small. When the number of categories is large, a better alternative is to use multiple panels. Creating multiple panels (also called "trellising") is done by splitting the observations according to a categorical variable, and creating a separate plot (of the same type) for each category. An example is shown in the bottom panel of Figure 3.6, where a bar chart of average UG by OY is broken down into two panels by UL. All these explorations are useful for prediction and classification.

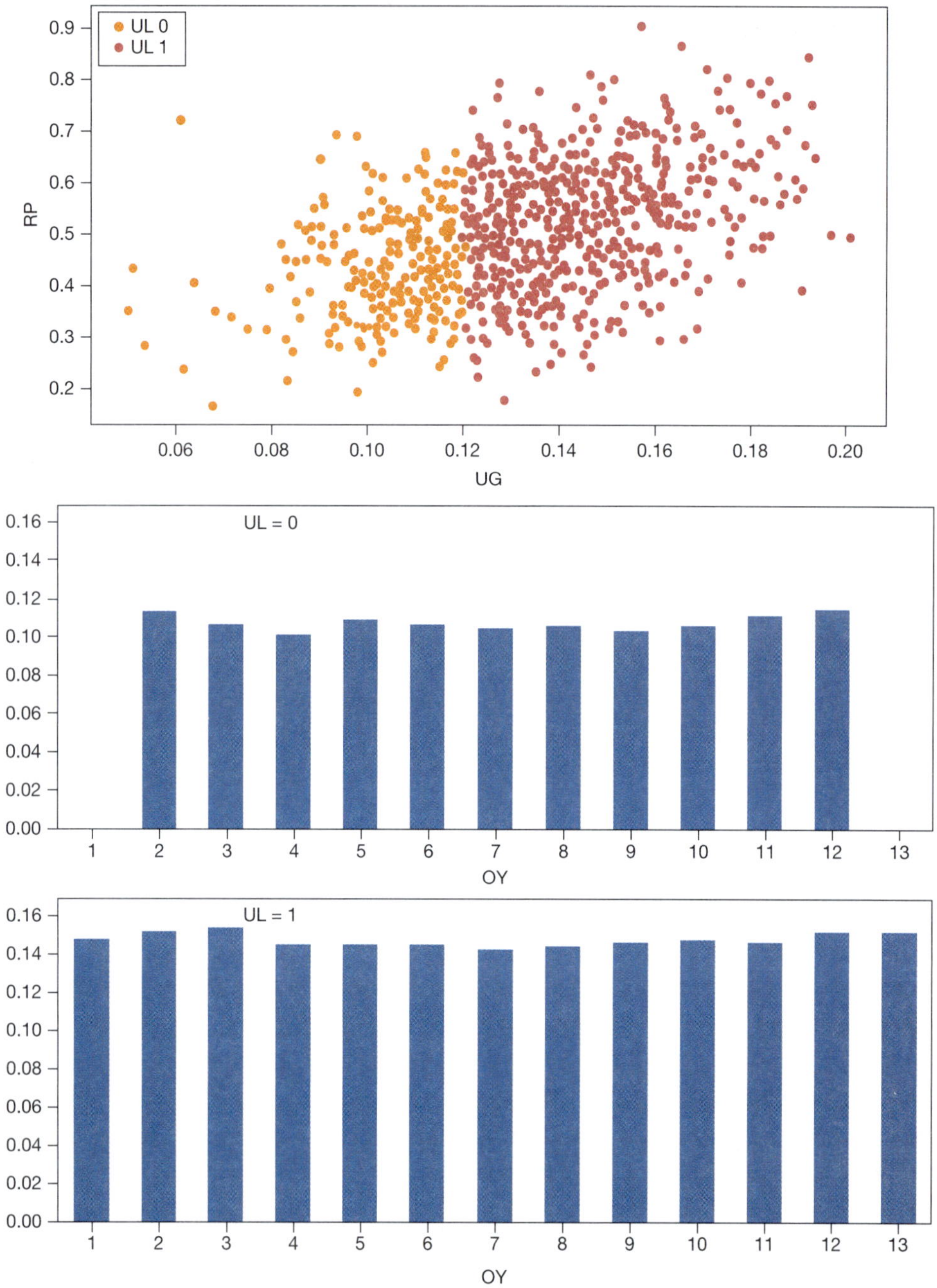

FIGURE 3.6 ADDING CATEGORICAL VARIABLES BY COLOR-CODING AND MULTIPLE PANELS

Code for creating Figure 3.6

```
# Color the scatter points by the value of UL
fig, ax = plt.subplots(figsize= (18,6))
for catValue, color in (0, 'C1'), (1, 'C3'):
        subset_df = su[su.UL == catValue]
        ax.scatter(subset_df.UG, subset_df.RP, s= 100, color=color, edgecolor='b')
ax.set_xlabel('UG')
ax.set_ylabel('RP')
ax.legend(["UL 0", "UL 1"])
plt.show()

## panel plots
# compute mean UG per UL and OY
dataForPlot_df = su.groupby(['UL','OY']).mean()['UG']
# We determine all possible OY values to use as ticks
ticks = set(su.OY)
for i in range(2):
    for t in ticks.difference(dataForPlot_df[i].index):
        dataForPlot_df.loc[(i, t)] = 0
# reorder to rows, so that the index is sorted
dataForPlot_df = dataForPlot_df[sorted(dataForPlot_df.index)]
# Determine a common range for the y axis
yRange = [0, max(dataForPlot_df) * 1.1]
fig, axes = plt.subplots(nrows=2, ncols=1, figsize=(10,8))
dataForPlot_df[0].plot.bar(x='OY', ax=axes[0], ylim=yRange)
dataForPlot_df[1].plot.bar(x='OY', ax=axes[1], ylim=yRange)
axes[0].annotate('UL = 0', xy=(3.5, .15),fontsize=18)
axes[1].annotate('UL = 1', xy=(3.5, .15), fontsize=18)
plt.show()
```

A special plot that uses scatter plots with multiple panels is the *scatter plot matrix*. In it, all pairwise scatter plots are shown in a single display. The panels in a matrix scatter plot are organized in a special way, such that each column and each row correspond to a variable, thereby the intersections create all the possible pairwise scatter plots. The scatter plot matrix is useful in unsupervised learning for studying the associations between numerical variables, detecting outliers and identifying clusters. For supervised learning, it can be used for examining pairwise relationships (and their nature) between predictors to support variable transformations and variable selection (see Correlation Analysis in Chapter 4). For prediction, it can also be used to depict the relationship of the outcome with the numerical predictors.

An example of a scatter plot matrix is shown in Figure 3.7, with UG and three predictors. Below the diagonal are the scatter plots. Variable name indicates the *y*-axis variable. For example, the plots in the bottom row all have UG on the *y*-axis (which allows studying the individual outcome–predictor relations). We can see different types of relationships from the different shapes (e.g., a linear relationship between UG and RP and in case there is a skewed relationship, same may require a transformation).

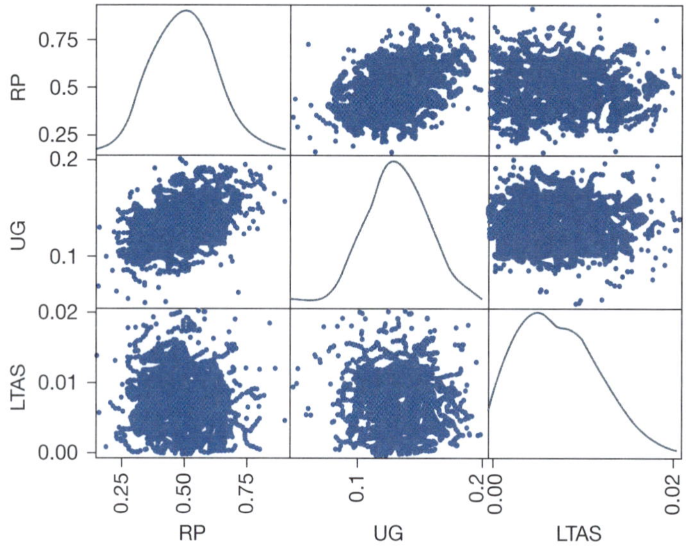

FIGURE 3.7 SCATTER PLOT MATRIX FOR UG AND TWO NUMERICAL PREDICTORS

code for creating Figure 3.7

```
# Display scatterplots between the different variables
# The diagonal shows the distribution for each variable
df = su[['RP', 'UG', 'LTAS']]
axes = scatter_matrix(df, alpha=1, figsize=(4, 4), diagonal='kde')
corr = df.corr().as_matrix()
for i, j in zip(*plt.np.triu_indices_from(axes, k=1)):
    axes[i, j].annotate('%.3f' %corr[i,j], (0.8, 0.8),
                        xycoords='axes fraction', ha='center', va='center')
plt.show()
```

Once hue is used, further categorical variables can be added via shape and multiple panels. However, one must proceed cautiously in adding multiple variables, as the display can become over-cluttered and then visual perception is lost.

Adding a numerical variable via size is useful especially in scatter plots (thereby creating "bubble plots"), because in a scatter plot, points represent individual observations. In plots that aggregate across observations (e.g., boxplots, histograms, bar charts), size and hue are not normally incorporated.

Finally, adding a temporal dimension to a plot to show how the information changes over time can be achieved via animation. A famous example is Rosling's animated scatter plots showing how world demographics changed over the years (www.gapminder.org). However, while animations of this type work for "statistical storytelling," they are not very effective for data exploration.

Manipulations: Rescaling, Aggregation and Hierarchies, Zooming, Filtering

Most of the time spent in data mining projects is spent in preprocessing. Typically, considerable effort is expended getting all the data in a format that can actually be used in the data mining software. Additional time is spent processing the data in ways that improve the performance of the data mining procedures. This preprocessing step in data mining includes variable transformation and derivation of new variables to help models perform more effectively. Transformations include changing the numeric scale of a variable, binning numerical variables, and condensing categories in categorical variables. The following manipulations support the preprocessing step as well the choice of adequate data mining methods. They do so by revealing patterns and their nature.

Rescaling Changing the scale in a display can enhance the plot and illuminate relationships. For example, in Figure 3.8, we have used another select sample of 269 cases and three variables (attached dataset *Transformation_Example.csv*). The variables comprise previous score of a student (Prev_Score), present score (Present_Score), and present score categorized into High, Medium, and Low coded as 3, 2, and 1 respectively. Here we see the effect of changing both axes of the scatter plot (top) and the *y*-axis of a boxplot (bottom) to logarithmic (log) scale. Whereas the original plots (left) are hard to understand, the patterns become visible in log scale (right). In the histograms, the nature of the relationship between Present_Score and Prev_Score is hard to determine in the original scale, because too many of the points are "crowded" near the *y*-axis. The rescaling removes this crowding and allows a better view of the linear relationship between the two log-scaled variables (indicating a log–log relationship). In the boxplot, displaying the crowding toward the *x*-axis in the original units does not allow us to compare the two box sizes, their locations, lower outliers, and most of the distribution information. Rescaling removes the "crowding to the *x*-axis" effect, thereby allowing a comparison of the two boxplots.

Aggregation and Hierarchies Another useful manipulation of scaling is changing the level of aggregation. For a temporal scale, we can aggregate by different granularity (e.g., monthly, daily, hourly) or even by a "seasonal" factor of interest such as month-of-year or day-of-week. A popular aggregation for time series is a moving average, where the average of neighboring values within a given window size is plotted. Moving average plots enhance visualizing a global trend (see Chapter 16).

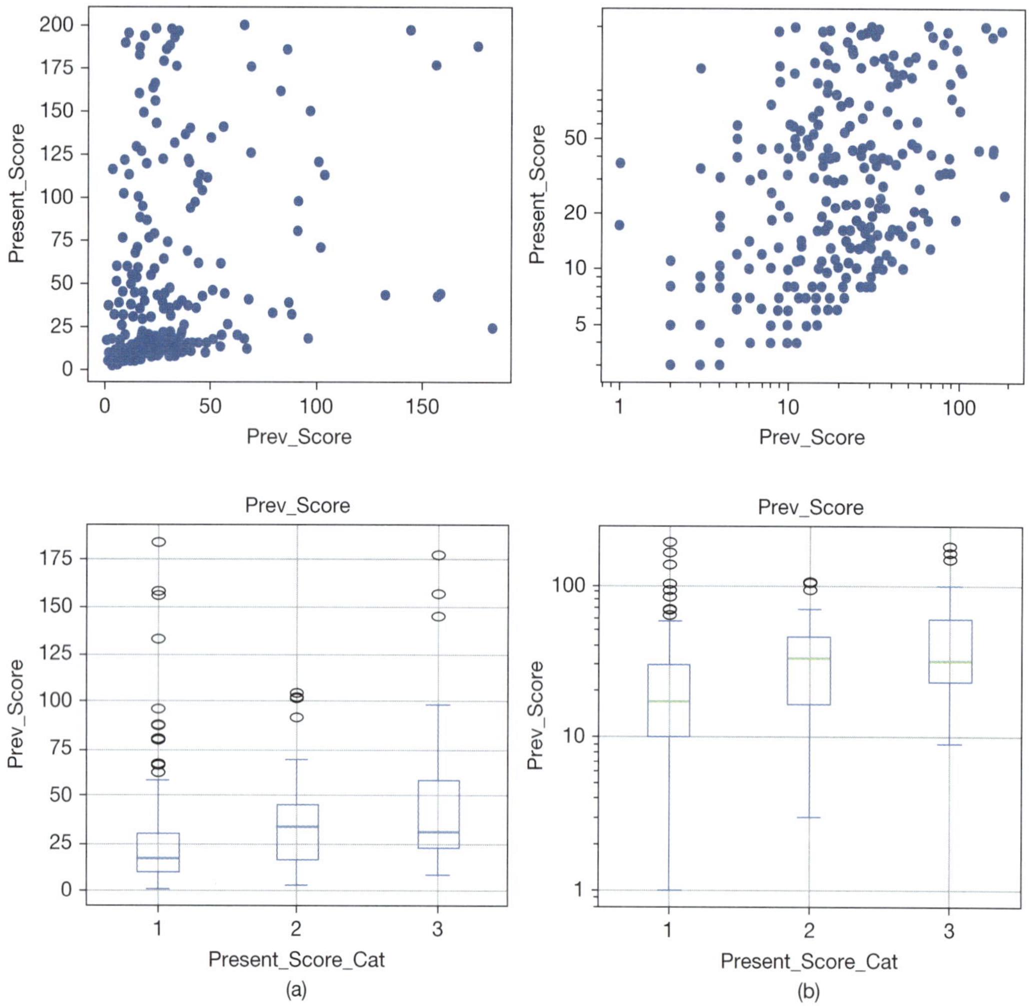

FIGURE 3.8 RESCALING CAN ENHANCE PLOTS AND REVEAL PATTERNS. (a) ORIGINAL SCALE, (b) LOGARITHMIC SCALE

code for creating Figure 3.8

```
# Avoid the use of scientific notation for the log axis
plt.rcParams['axes.formatter.min_exponent'] = 4

## scatter plot: regular and log scale
fig, axes = plt.subplots(nrows=1, ncols=2, figsize=(7, 4))

# regular scale
trans.plot.scatter(x='Prev_Score', y='Present_Score', ax=axes[0])
# log scale
```

```
ax = trans.plot.scatter(x='Prev_Score', y='Present_Score', logx=True, logy=True, ax=axes[1])
ax.set_yticks([5, 10, 20, 50])
ax.set_yticklabels([5, 10, 20, 50])
plt.tight_layout(); plt.show()

## boxplot: regular and log scale
fig, axes = plt.subplots(nrows=1, ncols=2, figsize=(8, 6))

# regular scale
ax = trans.boxplot(column='Prev_Score', by='Present_Score_Cat', ax=axes[0], color='C0')
ax.set_xlabel('Present_Score_Cat');
ax.set_ylabel('Prev_Score')

# log scale
ax = trans.boxplot(column='Prev_Score', by='Present_Score_Cat', ax=axes[1])
ax.set_xlabel('Present_Score_Cat');
ax.set_ylabel('Prev_Score');
ax.set_yscale('log') # suppress the title
axes[0].get_figure().suptitle('');
plt.tight_layout();
plt.show()
```

Non-temporal variables can be aggregated if some meaningful hierarchy exists: geographical (State locations in India in Service Feedback and Usage example), organizational (people within departments within units), etc. Figure 3.9 illustrates two types of aggregation for the sector-wise production indices data. The original monthly series is shown in the top-left panel. Seasonal aggregation (by month-of-year) is shown in the bottom-left panel, where it is easy to see the peak in production in March and the dip in April-September. The bottom-right panel shows temporal aggregation, where the series is now displayed in yearly aggregates. This plot reveals the global long-term trend in minning production and the generally increasing trend from 1981 onwards.

Examining different scales, aggregations, or hierarchies supports both supervised and unsupervised tasks in that it can reveal patterns and relationships at various levels, and can suggest new sets of variables with which to work.

Zooming and Panning The ability to zoom in and out of certain areas of the data on a plot is important for revealing patterns and outliers. We are often interested in more detail on areas of dense information or of special interest. Panning refers to the operation of moving the zoom window to other areas (popular in mapping applications such as Google Maps). An example of zooming is shown in Figure 3.9, where the mining Production Index is zoomed in to the years 1996 and 1997 of the series.

Zooming and panning support supervised and unsupervised methods by detecting areas of different behavior, which may lead to creating new interaction terms, new variables, or even separate models for data subsets. In addition, zooming and panning can help choose between methods that assume global behavior (e.g., regression models) and data-driven methods (e.g., exponential smoothing forecasters and *k*-nearest-neighbors classifiers), and indicate the level of global/local behavior (as manifested by parameters such as *k* in *k*-nearest neighbors, the size of a tree, or the smoothing parameters in exponential smoothing).

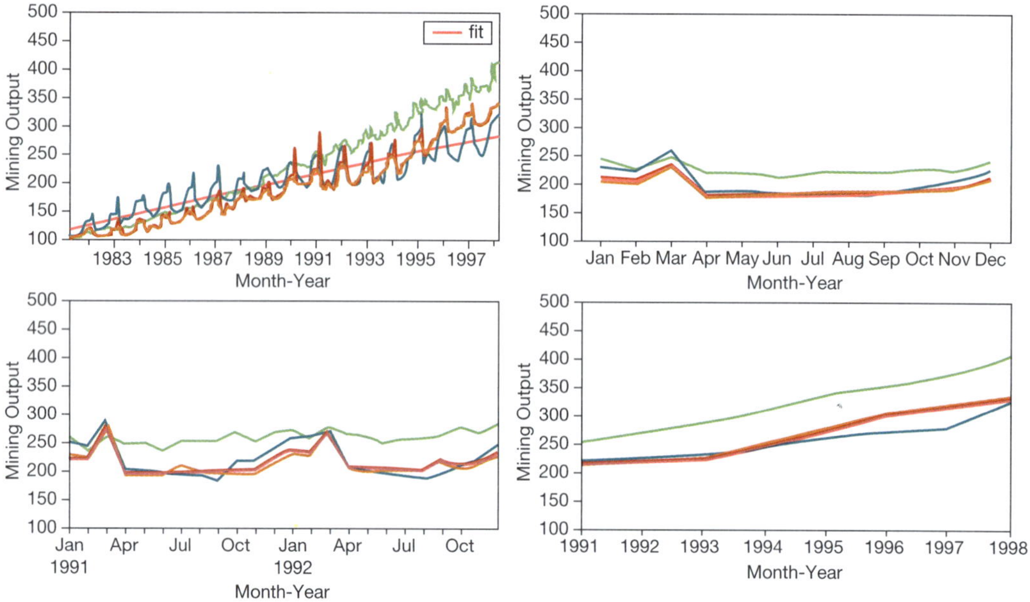

FIGURE 3.9 TIME SERIES LINE GRAPHS USING DIFFERENT AGGREGATIONS, ADDING CURVES, AND ZOOMING IN

code for creating Figure 3.9

```
ts=pd.read_csv('Timeseries Data.csv')
fig, axes = plt.subplots(nrows=2, ncols=2, figsize=(10, 7))
ts.Months=pd.to_datetime(ts.Months)
ts.set_index('Months', inplace=True)
# fit quadratic curve and display
quadraticFit = np.poly1d(np.polyfit(range(len(ts)), ts.Mining, 2))
ts_fit = pd.DataFrame({'fit': [quadraticFit(t) for t in range(len(ts))]})
ts_fit.index = ts.index
ax = ts.plot(ylim=[100, 500], legend=False, ax=axes[0][0])
```

```
ts_fit.plot(ax=ax)
# set x and y-axis label
ax.set_xlabel('Month-Year');
ax.set_ylabel('Mining Output')

# Zoom in 2-year period 1/1/1991 to 12/1/1992
Mining_2yrs =ts.loc['1991-01-01':'1992-12-01']
ax = Mining_2yrs.plot(ylim=[100, 500], legend=False, ax=axes[1][0])
# set x and y-axis label
ax.set_xlabel('Month-Year');
ax.set_ylabel('Mining Output')
# Average by month
byMonth = ts.groupby(by=[ts.index.month]).mean()
ax = byMonth.plot(ylim=[100, 500], legend=False, ax=axes[0][1])
# set x and y-axis label
ax.set_xlabel('Month-Year');
ax.set_ylabel('Mining Output')
yticks = [-2.0,-1.75,-1.5,-1.25,-1.0,-0.75,-0.5,-0.25,0.0]
ax.set_xticks(range(1, 13))
ax.set_xticklabels([calendar.month_abbr[i] for i in range(1, 13)]);
# Average by year (exclude data from 2004)
byYear = ts.loc['1991-01-01':'2003-12-01'].groupby(pd.Grouper(freq='A')).mean()
ax = byYear.plot(ylim=[100, 500], legend=False, ax=axes[1][1])
# set x and y-axis label
ax.set_xlabel('Month-Year');
ax.set_ylabel('Mining Output')
plt.tight_layout()
plt.show()
```

Filtering Filtering means removing some of the observations from the plot. The purpose of filtering is to focus the attention on certain data while eliminating "noise" created by other data. Filtering supports supervised and unsupervised learning in a similar way to zooming and panning: it assists in identifying different or unusual local behavior.

Reference: Trend Lines and Labels

Trend lines and using in-plot labels also help to detect patterns and outliers. Trend lines serve as a reference, and allow us to more easily assess the shape of a pattern. Although linearity is easy to visually perceive, more elaborate relationships such as exponential and polynomial trends are harder to assess by eye. Trend lines are useful in line graphs as well as in scatter plots. An example is shown in Figure 3.9a, where a polynomial curve is overlaid on the original line graph (see also Chapter 16).

In displays that are not overcrowded, the use of in-plot labels can be useful for better exploration of outliers and clusters. An example is shown in Figure 3.10 (a reproduction of Figure 15.1 with the addition of labels). The figure shows different utilities on a scatter plot that compares fuel cost with total sales. We might be interested in clustering the data, and using clustering algorithms to identify clusters that differ markedly with respect to fuel cost and sales. Figure 3.10, with the labels, helps visualize these clusters and their members (e.g., Nevada and Puget are part of a clear cluster with low fuel costs and high sales). For more on clustering and on this example, see Chapter 15.

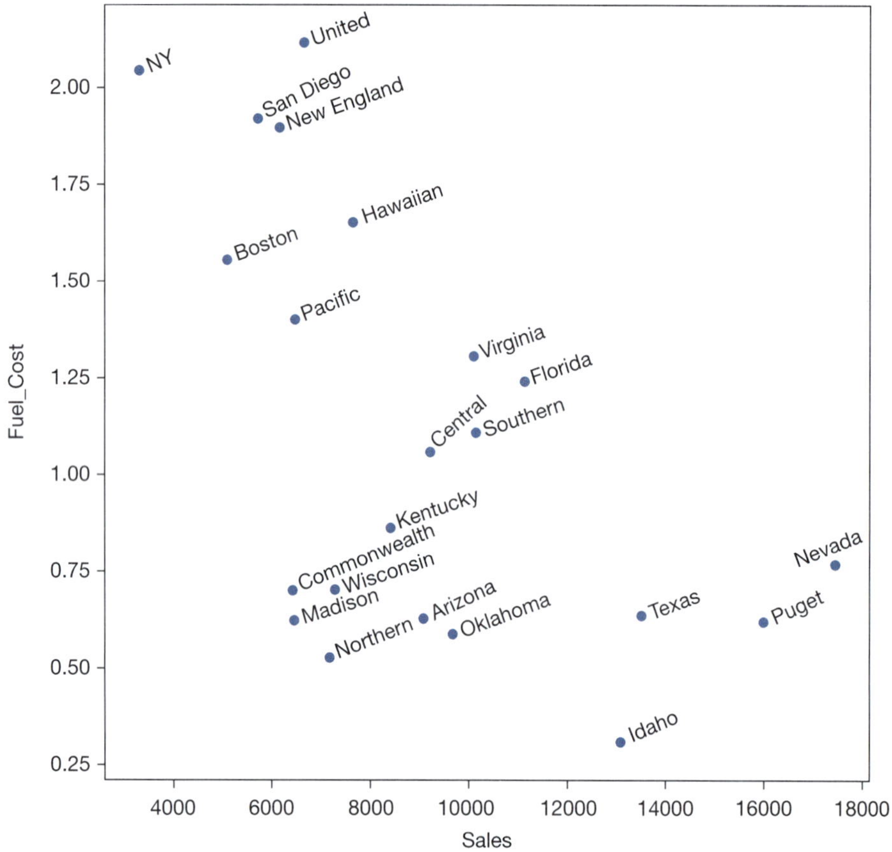

FIGURE 3.10 SCATTER PLOT WITH LABELED POINTS

code for creating Figure 3.10

```
utilities_df = pd.read_csv('Utilities.csv')

ax = utilities_df.plot.scatter(x='Sales', y='Fuel_Cost', figsize=(6, 6))
points = utilities_df[['Sales','Fuel_Cost','Company']]
_ = points.apply(lambda x:
            ax.text(*x, rotation=20, horizontalalignment='left',
                    verticalalignment='bottom', fontsize=8), axis=1)
```

Scaling Up to Large Datasets

When the number of observations (rows) is large, plots that display each individual observation (e.g., scatter plots) can become ineffective. Aside from using aggregated charts such as boxplots, some alternatives are:

1. Sampling—drawing a random sample and using it for plotting
2. Reducing marker size
3. Using more transparent marker colors and removing fill
4. Breaking down the data into subsets (e.g., by creating multiple panels)
5. Using aggregation (e.g., bubble plots where size corresponds to number of observations in a certain range)
6. Using jittering (slightly moving each marker by adding a small amount of noise)

An example of the advantage of plotting a sample over the large dataset is shown in Figure 12.2 in Chapter 12, where a scatter plot of 5000 records is plotted alongside a scatter plot of a sample. Figure 3.11 illustrates an improved plot of the full dataset by using smaller markers, using jittering to uncover overlaid points, and more transparent colors. We can see that larger areas of the plot are dominated by the grey class, the black class is mainly on the right, while there is a lot of overlap in the top-right area.

code for creating Figure 3.11

```
def jitter(x, factor=1):
    """ Add random jitter to x values """
    sx = np.array(sorted(x))
    delta = sx[1:] - sx[:-1]
    minDelta = min(d for d in delta if d > 0)
    a = factor * minDelta / 5
    return x + np.random.uniform(-a, a, len(x))

universal_df = pd.read_csv('UniversalBank.csv')

saIdx = universal_df[universal_df['Securities Account'] == 1].index

plt.figure(figsize=(10,6))
plt.scatter(jitter(universal_df.drop(saIdx).Income),
            jitter(universal_df.drop(saIdx).CCAvg),
            marker='o', color='grey', alpha=0.2)
plt.scatter(jitter(universal_df.loc[saIdx].Income),
            jitter(universal_df.loc[saIdx].CCAvg),
            marker='o', color='red', alpha=0.2)
```

```
plt.xlabel('Income')
plt.ylabel('CCAvg')
plt.ylim((0.05, 20))
axes = plt.gca()
axes.set_xscale("log")
axes.set_yscale("log")
plt.show()
```

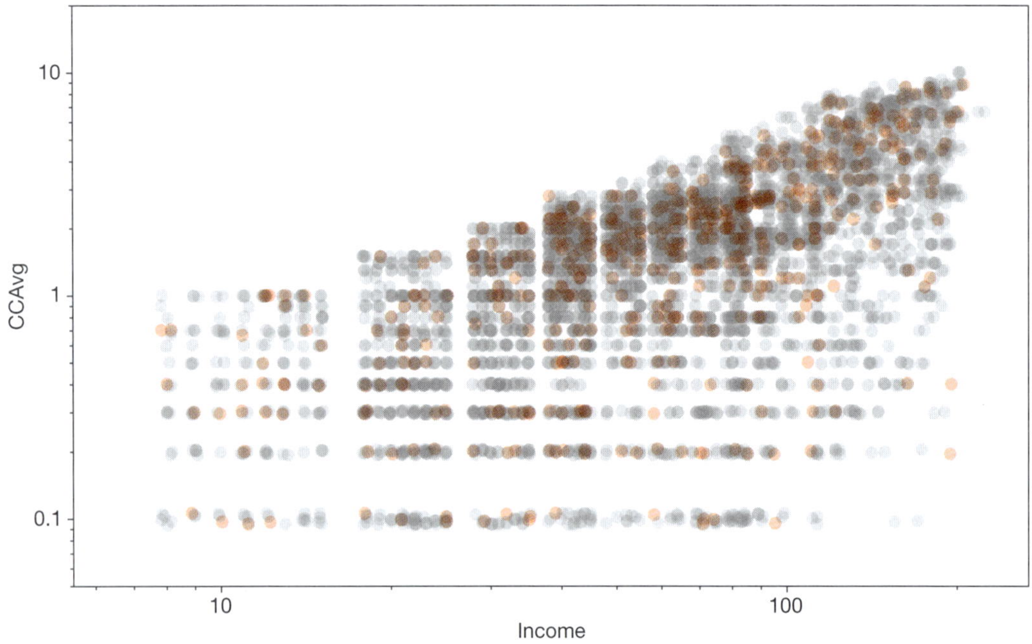

FIGURE 3.11 SCATTER PLOT OF LARGE DATASET WITH REDUCED MARKER SIZE, JITTERING, AND MORE TRANSPARENT COLORING

Multivariate Plot: Parallel Coordinates Plot

Another approach toward presenting multidimensional information in a two-dimensional plot is via specialized plots such as the *parallel coordinates plot*. In this plot, a vertical axis is drawn for each variable. Then each observation is represented by drawing a line that connects its values on the different axes, thereby creating a "multivariate profile." An example is shown in Figure 3.12 for the Service Usage data. In this display, separate panels are used for the two values of Usage Level UL = 0 and UL = 1, in order to compare the profiles of users in the two classes (for a classification task). We can see investigate deeper into differences in various types of feedback and suggestions behavior across both categories of Service Usage coded as UL = 1 or 0. We can use zoom facility to expand the plots (in case using R-Studio) for a magnified graph.

These type of observation gives indication of useful predictors and suggests possible binning for some numerical predictors.

Parallel coordinates plots are also useful in unsupervised tasks. They can reveal clusters, outliers, and information overlap across variables. A useful manipulation is to reorder the columns to better reveal observation clustering.

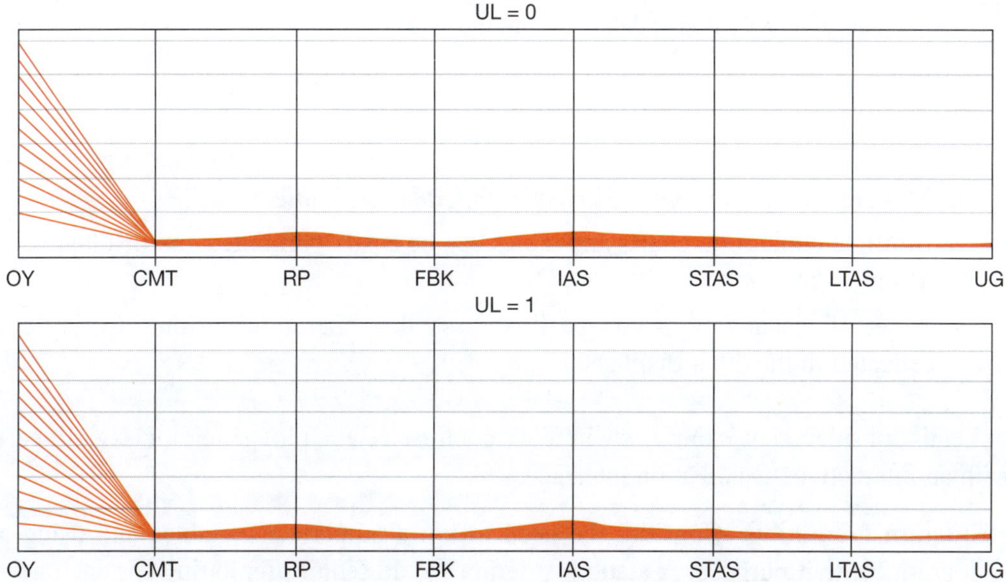

FIGURE 3.12 PARALLEL COORDINATES PLOT FOR SERVICE USAGE DATA. EACH OF THE VARIABLES (SHOWN ON THE HORIZONTAL AXIS) IS SCALED TO 0–100%. PANELS ARE USED TO DISTINGUISH USAGE LEVELS (UL)

code for creating Figure 3.12

```
# Transform the axes, so that they all have the same range
su=pd.read_csv('Service_Usage.csv')
su1=su[su.columns[3:12]]
min_max_scaler = preprocessing.MinMaxScaler()
dataToPlot = pd.DataFrame(min_max_scaler.fit_transform(su1),
columns=su1.columns)

fig, axes = plt.subplots(nrows=2, ncols=1, figsize=(13,8))
for i in (0, 1):
  parallel_coordinates(su1.loc[dataToPlot.UL == i],'UL', ax=axes[i],
linewidth=1, color='r')
    axes[i].set_title('UL = {}'.format(i))
    axes[i].set_yticklabels([])
    axes[i].legend().set_visible(False)

plt.tight_layout()  # Increase the separation between the plots
```

Interactive Visualization

Similar to the interactive nature of the data mining process, interactivity is key to enhancing our ability to gain information from graphical visualization. In the words of Few (2009), an expert in data visualization:

> We can only learn so much when staring at a static visualization such as a printed graph ...If we can't interact with the data ...we hit the wall.

By interactive visualization, we mean an interface that supports the following principles:

1. Making changes to a chart is *easy, rapid, and reversible.*
2. Multiple concurrent charts and tables can be easily combined and displayed on a single screen.
3. A set of visualizations can be linked, so that operations in one display are reflected in the other displays.

Let us consider a few examples where we contrast a static plot generator (e.g., Excel) with an interactive visualization interface.

Histogram Rebinning Consider the need to bin a numerical variables and using a histogram for that purpose. A static histogram would require replotting for each new binning choice. If the user generates multiple plots, then the screen becomes cluttered. If the same plot is recreated, then it is hard to compare different binning choices. In contrast, an interactive visualization would provide an easy way to change bin width interactively (see, e.g., the slider below the histogram in Figure 3.13), and then the histogram would automatically and rapidly replot as the user changes the bin width.

Aggregation and Zooming Consider a time series forecasting task, given a long series of data. Temporal aggregation at multiple levels is needed for determining short- and long-term patterns. Zooming and panning are used to identify unusual periods. A static plotting software requires the user to compute new variables for each temporal aggregation (e.g., aggregate daily data to obtain weekly aggregates). Zooming and panning requires manually changing the min and max values on the axis scale of interest (thereby losing the ability to quickly move between different areas without creating multiple charts). An interactive visualization would provide immediate temporal hierarchies which the user can easily switch between. Zooming would be enabled as a slider near the axis (see, e.g., the sliders on the top-left panel in Figure 3.13), thereby allowing direct manipulation and rapid reaction.

Combining Multiple Linked Plots that Fit in a Single Screen To support a classification task, multiple plots are created of the outcome variable vs. potential categorical and numerical predictors. These can include side-by-side boxplots, color-coded scatter plots, and multipanel bar charts. The user wants to detect possible multidimensional relationships (and identify possible outliers) by selecting a certain subset of the data (e.g., a single category of some variable) and locating the observations on the other plots. In a static interface, the user would have to manually organize the plots of interest and resize them in order to fit within a single screen. A static interface would usually not support inter-plot linkage, and even if it did, the entire set of plots would have to be regenerated each time a selection is made. In contrast, an interactive visualization would provide an easy way to automatically organize and resize the set of plots to fit within a screen. Linking the set of plots would be easy, and in response to the users selection on one plot, the appropriate selection would be automatically highlighted in the other plots (see example in Figure 3.13).

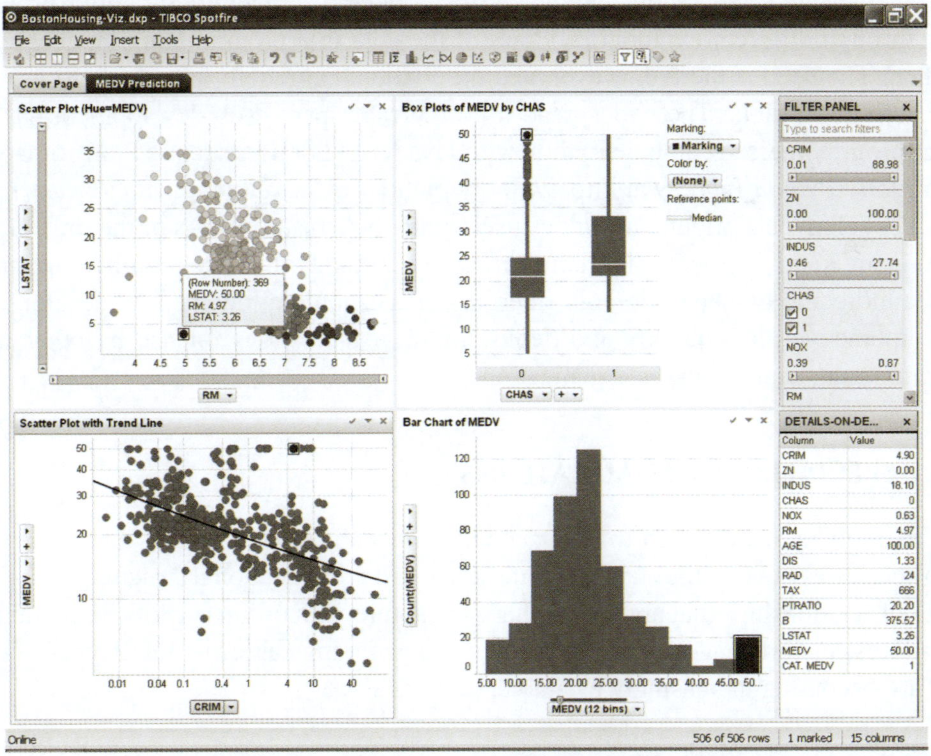

FIGURE 3.13 MULTIPLE INTER-LINKED PLOTS IN A SINGLE VIEW (USING SPOTFIRE). NOTE THE MARKED OBSERVATION IN THE TOP-LEFT PANEL, WHICH IS ALSO HIGHLIGHTED IN ALL OTHER PLOTS

In earlier sections, we used plots to illustrate the advantages of visualizations, because "a picture is worth a thousand words." The advantages of an interactive visualization are even harder to convey in words. As Ben Shneiderman, a well-known researcher in information visualization and interfaces, puts it:

> A picture is worth a thousand words. An interface is worth a thousand pictures.

The ability to interact with plots, and link them together turns plotting into an analytical tool that supports continuous exploration of the data. Several commercial visualization tools provide powerful capabilities along these lines; two very popular ones are Spotfire (http://spotfire.tibco.com) and Tableau (www.tableausoftware.com); Figure 3.13 was generated using Spotfire.

Tableau and Spotfire have spent hundreds of millions of dollars on software R&D and review of interactions with customers to hone interfaces that allow analysts to interact with data via plots smoothly and efficiently. It is difficult to replicate the sophisticated and highly engineered user interface required for rapid progression through different exploratory views of the data in a programming language like Python. The need is there, however, and the Python community is moving to provide interactivity in plots. The widespread use of JavaScript in web development has led some programmers to combine Python with JavaScript libraries such as Plotly or Bokeh (see *Plotly Python Library* at https://plot.ly/python/ or *Developing with JavaScript* at http://bokeh.pydata.org/en/latest/docs/user_guide/bokehjs.html). As of the time of this writing, interactivity tools in Python were evolving, and Python programmers are likely to see more and higher level tools emerging. This should allow them to develop custom interactive plots quickly and deploy these visualizations for use by other non-programming analysts in the organization.

3.5 | SPECIALIZED VISUALIZATIONS

In this section, we mention a few specialized visualizations that are able to capture data structures beyond the standard time series and cross-sectional structures—special types of relationships that are usually hard to capture with ordinary plots. In particular, we address hierarchical data, network data, and geographical data—three types of data that are becoming increasingly available.

Visualizing Networked Data

Network analysis techniques were spawned by the explosion of social and product network data. Examples of social networks are networks of sellers and buyers on eBay and networks of users on Facebook. An example of a product network is the network of products on Amazon (linked through the recommendation system). Network data visualization is available in various network-specialized software, and also in general-purpose software.

A network diagram consists of actors and relations between them. "Nodes" are the actors (e.g., users in a social network or products in a product network), and represented by circles. "Edges" are the relations between nodes, and are represented by lines connecting nodes. For example, in a social network such as Facebook, we can construct a list of users (nodes) and all the pairwise relations (edges) between users who are "Friends." Alternatively, we can define edges as a posting that one user posts on another user's Facebook page. In this setup, we might have more than a single edge between two nodes. Networks can also have nodes of multiple types. A common structure is networks with two types of nodes. An example of a two-type node network is shown in Figure 3.14, where we see a set of transactions between a network of sellers and buyers on the online auction site www.eBay.com [the data are for auctions selling Swarovski beads, and took place during a period of several months; from Jank and Yahav (2010)]. The black circles represent sellers and the grey circles represent buyers. We can see that this marketplace is dominated by a few high-volume sellers. We can also see that many buyers interact with a single seller. The market structures for many individual products could be reviewed quickly in this way. Network providers could use the information, for example, to identify possible partnerships to explore with sellers.

Figure 3.14 was produced using Python's `networkx` package. Another useful package is `python-igraph`. Using these packages, networks can be imported from a variety of sources. The plot's appearance can be customized and various features are available such as filtering nodes and edges, altering the plot's layout, finding clusters of related nodes, calculating network metrics, and performing network analysis (see Chapter 19 for details and examples).

Network plots can be potentially useful in the context of association rules (see Chapter 14). For example, consider a case of mining a dataset of consumers' grocery purchases to learn which items are purchased together ("what goes with what"). A network can be constructed with items as nodes and edges connecting items that were purchased together. After a set of rules is generated by the data mining algorithm (which often contains an excessive number of rules, many of which are unimportant), the network plot can help visualize different rules for the purpose of choosing the interesting ones. For example, a popular "beer and diapers" combination would appear in the network plot as a pair of nodes with very high connectivity. An item which is almost always purchased regardless of other items (e.g., milk) would appear as a very large node with high connectivity to all other nodes.

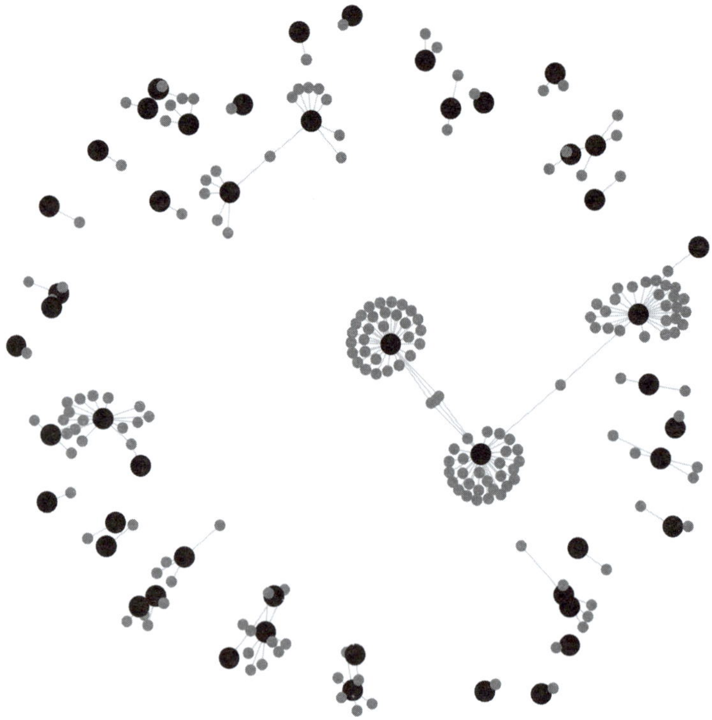

FIGURE 3.14 NETWORK PLOT OF EBAY SELLERS (BLACK CIRCLES) AND BUYERS (GREY CIRCLES) OF SWAROVSKI BEADS

code for creating Figure 3.14

```
ebay_df = pd.read_csv('eBayNetwork.csv')

G = nx.from_pandas_edgelist(ebay_df, source='Seller', target='Bidder')

isBidder = [n in set(ebay_df.Bidder) for n in G.nodes()]
pos = nx.spring_layout(G, k=0.13, iterations=60, scale=0.5)
plt.figure(figsize=(10,10))
nx.draw_networkx(G, pos=pos, with_labels=False,
                 edge_color='lightgray',
                 node_color=['gray' if bidder else 'black' for bidder in isBidder],
                 node_size=[50 if bidder else 200 for bidder in isBidder])
plt.axis('off')
plt.show()
```

Visualizing Hierarchical Data: Treemaps

We discussed hierarchical data and the exploration of data at different hierarchy levels in the context of plot manipulations. *Treemaps* are useful visualizations specialized for exploring large data sets that are hierarchically structured (tree-structured). They allow exploration of various dimensions of the data while maintaining the hierarchical nature of the data. An example is shown in Figure 3.15, which displays a large set of auctions from eBay.com,[4] hierarchically ordered by item category, sub-category, and brand. The levels in the hierarchy of the treemap are visualized as rectangles containing sub-rectangles. Categorical variables can be included in the display by using hue. Numerical variables can be included via rectangle size and color intensity (ordering of the rectangles is sometimes used to reinforce size). In Figure 3.15, size is used to represent the average closing price (which reflects item value) and color intensity represents the percent of sellers with negative feedback (a negative seller feedback indicates buyer dissatisfaction in past transactions and is often indicative of fraudulent seller behavior). Consider the task of classifying ongoing auctions in terms of a fraudulent outcome. From the treemap, we see that the highest proportion of sellers with negative ratings (black) is concentrated in expensive item auctions (Rolex and Cartier wristwatches). Currently, Python offers only simple treemaps with a single hierarchy level and coloring or sizing boxes by additional variables. Figure 3.16 shows a treemap corresponding to Figure 3.15 that was created in R.

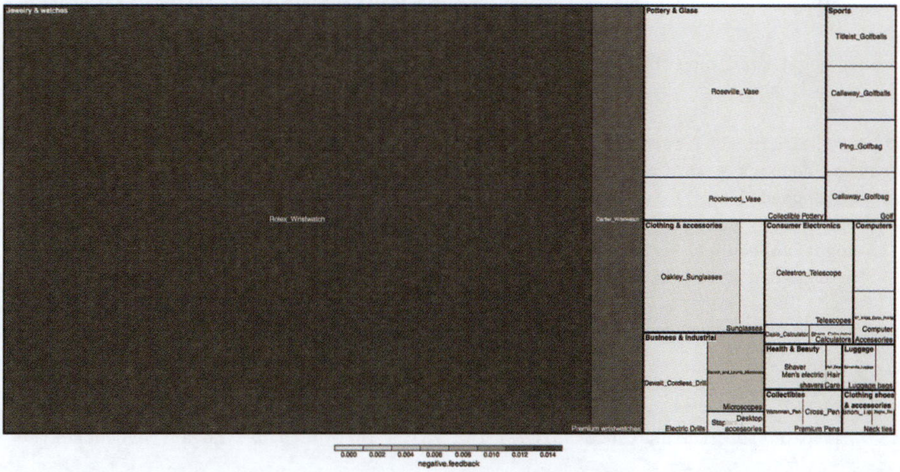

FIGURE 3.15 TREEMAP SHOWING NEARLY 11,000 EBAY AUCTIONS, ORGANIZED BY ITEM CATEGORY, SUBCATEGORY, AND BRAND. RECTANGLE SIZE REPRESENTS AVERAGE CLOSING PRICE (REFLECTING ITEM VALUE). SHADE REPRESENTS PERCENTAGE OF SELLERS WITH NEGATIVE FEEDBACK (DARKER = HIGHER). THIS GRAPH WAS GENERATED USING R; FOR A PYTHON VERSION SEE FIGURE 3.16

---

[4]We thank Sharad Borle for sharing this dataset.

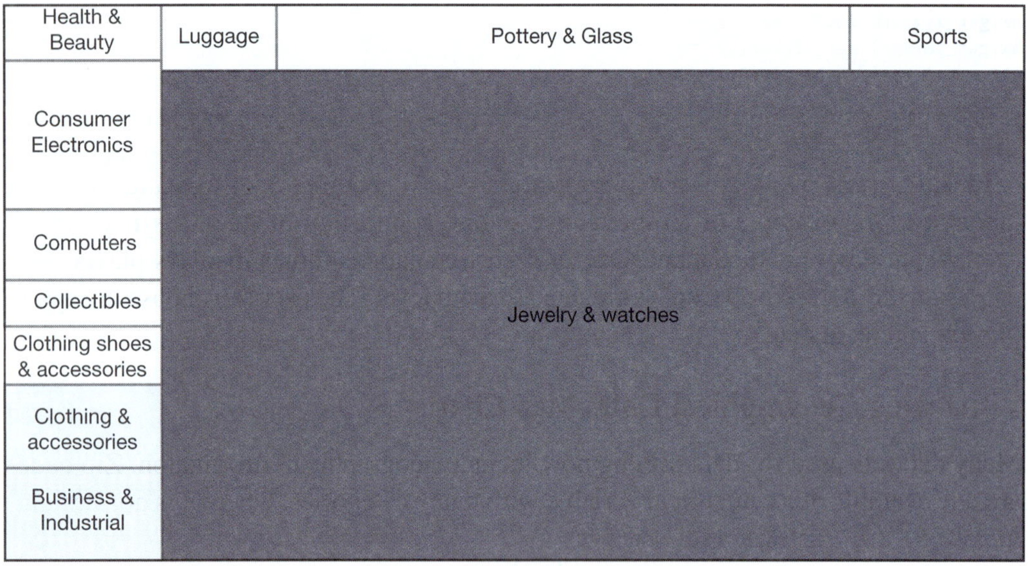

FIGURE 3.16 TREEMAP SHOWING NEARLY 11,000 EBAY AUCTIONS, ORGANIZED BY ITEM CATEGORY. RECTANGLE SIZE REPRESENTS AVERAGE CLOSING PRICE. SHADE REPRESENTS % OF SELLERS WITH NEGATIVE FEEDBACK (DARKER = HIGHER)

code for creating Figure 3.16

```
import squarify

ebayTreemap = pd.read_csv('EbayTreemap.csv')

grouped = []
for category, df in ebayTreemap.groupby(['Category']):
    negativeFeedback = sum(df['Seller Feedback'] < 0) / len(df)
    grouped.append({
        'category': category,
        'negativeFeedback': negativeFeedback,
        'averageBid': df['High Bid'].mean()
    })
byCategory = pd.DataFrame(grouped)

norm = matplotlib.colors.Normalize(vmin=byCategory.negativeFeedback.min(),
                                   vmax=byCategory.negativeFeedback.max())
colors = [matplotlib.cm.Blues(norm(value)) for value in byCategory.negativeFeedback]

fig, ax = plt.subplots()
fig.set_size_inches(9, 5)

squarify.plot(label=byCategory.category, sizes=byCategory.averageBid, color=colors,
              ax=ax, alpha=0.6, edgecolor='grey')
```

```
ax.get_xaxis().set_ticks([])
ax.get_yaxis().set_ticks([])
plt.subplots_adjust(left=0.1)
plt.show()
```

Ideally, treemaps should be explored interactively, zooming to different levels of the hierarchy. One example of an interactive online application of treemaps is currently available at www.drasticdata.nl. One of their treemap examples displays player-level data from the 2014 World Cup, aggregated to team level. The user can choose to explore players and team data.

Visualizing Geographical Data: Map Charts

Many datasets used for data mining now include geographical information. Zip codes are one example of a categorical variable with many categories, where it is not straightforward to create meaningful variables for analysis. Plotting the data on a geographic map can often reveal patterns that are harder to identify otherwise. A map chart uses a geographical map as its background; then color, hue, and other features are used to include categorical or numerical variables. Besides specialized mapping software, maps are now becoming part of general-purpose software, and Google Maps provides APIs (application programming interfaces) that allow organizations to overlay their data on a Google map. While Google Maps is readily available, resulting map charts (such as Figure 3.17) are somewhat inferior in terms of effectiveness compared to map charts in dedicated interactive visualization software.

Figure 3.18 shows two world map charts comparing countries' "well-being" (according to a 2006 Gallup survey) in the top map, to gross domestic product (GDP) in the bottom map. Lighter shade means higher value.

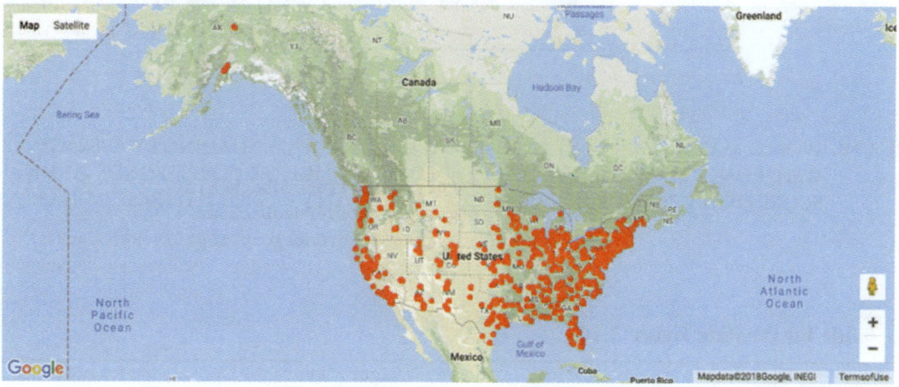

FIGURE 3.17 MAP CHART OF STUDENTS' AND INSTRUCTORS' LOCATIONS ON A GOOGLE MAP. SOURCE: DATA FROM STATISTICS.COM

code for creating Figure 3.17

```
import gmaps
SCstudents = pd.read_csv('SC-US-students-GPS-data-2016.csv')

gmaps.configure(api_key=os.environ['GMAPS_API_KEY'])
fig = gmaps.figure(center=(39.7, -105), zoom_level=3)
fig.add_layer(gmaps.symbol_layer(SCstudents, scale=2,fill_color='red',
                                 stroke_color='red'))
fig
```

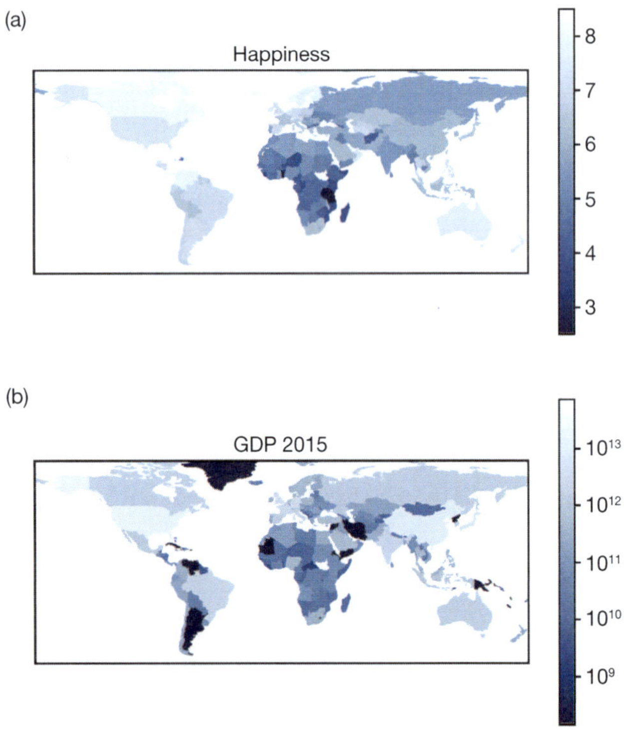

FIGURE 3.18 WORLD MAPS COMPARING "WELL-BEING" (a) TO GDP (b). SHADING BY AVERAGE "GLOBAL WELL-BEING" SCORE (a) OR GDP (b) OF COUNTRY. LIGHTER CORRESPONDS TO HIGHER SCORE OR LEVEL. SOURCE: DATA FROM VEENHOVEN'S WORLD DATABASE OF HAPPINESS

code for creating Figure 3.18

```
import matplotlib
import matplotlib.pyplot as plt
import cartopy
import cartopy.io.shapereader as shpreader
```

```
import cartopy.crs as ccrs

gdp_df = pd.read_csv('gdp.csv', skiprows=4)
gdp_df.rename(columns={'2015': 'GDP2015'}, inplace=True)
gdp_df.set_index('Country Code', inplace=True)  # use three letter country code to
                                                  access rows

# The file contains a column with two letter combinations, use na_filter to avoid
# converting the combination NA into not-a-number
happiness_df = pd.read_csv('Veerhoven.csv', na_filter = False)
happiness_df.set_index('Code', inplace=True)  # use the country name to access rows

fig = plt.figure(figsize=(7, 8))
ax1 = plt.subplot(2, 1, 1, projection=ccrs.PlateCarree())
ax1.set_extent([-150, 60, -25, 60])
ax2 = plt.subplot(2, 1, 2, projection=ccrs.PlateCarree())
ax2.set_extent([-150, 60, -25, 60])

# Create a color mapper
cmap = plt.cm.Blues_r
norm1 = matplotlib.colors.Normalize(vmin=happiness_df.Score.dropna().min(),
                                    vmax=happiness_df.Score.dropna().max())
norm2 = matplotlib.colors.LogNorm(vmin=gdp_df.GDP2015.dropna().min(),
                                  vmax=gdp_df.GDP2015.dropna().max())

shpfilename = shpreader.natural_earth(resolution='110m', category='cultural',
                                      name='admin_0_countries')
reader = shpreader.Reader(shpfilename)
countries = reader.records()
for country in countries:
    countryCode = country.attributes['ADM0_A3']
    if countryCode in gdp_df.index:
        ax2.add_geometries(country.geometry, ccrs.PlateCarree(),
                           facecolor=cmap(norm2(gdp_df.loc[countryCode].GDP2015)))
    # check various attributes to find the matching two-letter combinations
    nation = country.attributes['POSTAL']
    if nation not in happiness_df.index: nation = country.attributes['ISO_A2']
    if nation not in happiness_df.index: nation = country.attributes['WB_A2']
    if nation not in happiness_df.index and country.attributes['NAME'] == 'Norway':
        nation = 'NO'
    if nation in happiness_df.index:
       ax1.add_geometries(country.geometry, ccrs.PlateCarree(),
                          facecolor=cmap(norm1(happiness_df.loc[nation].Score)))

ax2.set_title("GDP 2015")
sm = plt.cm.ScalarMappable(norm=norm2, cmap=cmap)
sm._A = []
cb = plt.colorbar(sm, ax=ax2)
cb.set_ticks([1e8, 1e9, 1e10, 1e11, 1e12, 1e13])

ax1.set_title("Happiness")
sm = plt.cm.ScalarMappable(norm=norm1, cmap=cmap)
sm._A = []
```

```
cb = plt.colorbar(sm, ax=ax1)
cb.set_ticks([3, 4, 5, 6, 7, 8])
plt.show()
```

3.6 SUMMARY: MAJOR VISUALIZATIONS AND OPERATIONS, BY DATA MINING GOAL

Prediction

- Plot outcome on the y-axis of boxplots, bar charts, and scatter plots.
- Study relation of outcome to categorical predictors via side-by-side boxplots, bar charts, and multiple panels.
- Study relation of outcome to numerical predictors via scatter plots.
- Use distribution plots (boxplot, histogram) for determining needed transformations of the outcome variable (and/or numerical predictors).
- Examine scatter plots with added color/panels/size to determine the need for interaction terms.
- Use various aggregation levels and zooming to determine areas of the data with different behavior, and to evaluate the level of global vs. local patterns.

Classification

- Study relation of outcome to categorical predictors using bar charts with the outcome on the y-axis.
- Study relation of outcome to pairs of numerical predictors via color-coded scatter plots (color denotes the outcome).
- Study relation of outcome to numerical predictors via side-by-side boxplots: Plot boxplots of a numerical variable by outcome. Create similar displays for each numerical predictor. The most separable boxes indicate potentially useful predictors.
- Use color to represent the outcome variable on a parallel coordinate plot.
- Use distribution plots (boxplot, histogram) for determining needed transformations of numerical predictor variables.
- Examine scatter plots with added color/panels/size to determine the need for interaction terms.
- Use various aggregation levels and zooming to determine areas of the data with different behavior, and to evaluate the level of global vs. local patterns.

Time Series Forecasting

- Create line graphs at different temporal aggregations to determine types of patterns.
- Use zooming and panning to examine various shorter periods of the series to determine areas of the data with different behavior.
- Use various aggregation levels to identify global and local patterns.
- Identify missing values in the series (that will require handling).
- Overlay trend lines of different types to determine adequate modeling choices.

Unsupervised Learning

- Create scatter plot matrices to identify pairwise relationships and clustering of observations.
- Use heatmaps to examine the correlation table.
- Use various aggregation levels and zooming to determine areas of the data with different behavior.
- Generate a parallel coordinates plot to identify clusters of observations.

PROBLEMS

3.1 Shipments of Household Appliances: Line Graphs. The file *ApplianceShipments.csv* contains the series of quarterly shipments (in millions of dollars) of US household appliances between 1985 and 1989.

a. Create a well-formatted time plot of the data using Python.

b. Does there appear to be a quarterly pattern? For a closer view of the patterns, zoom in to the range of 3500–5000 on the *y*-axis.

c. Using Python, create one chart with four separate lines, one line for each of Q1, Q2, Q3, and Q4. In Python, this can be achieved by add column for quarter and year. Then group the data frame by quarter and then plot shipment versus year for each quarter as a separate series on a line graph. Zoom in to the range of 3500–5000 on the *y*-axis. Does there appear to be a difference between quarters?

d. Using Python, create a line graph of the series at a yearly aggregated level (i.e., the total shipments in each year).

3.2 Sales of Riding Mowers: Scatter Plots. A company that manufactures riding mowers wants to identify the best sales prospects for an intensive sales campaign. In particular, the manufacturer is interested in classifying households as prospective owners or nonowners on the basis of Income (in \$1000s) and Lot Size (in 1000 ft^2). The marketing expert looked at a random sample of 24 households, given in the file *RidingMowers.csv*.

a. Using Python, create a scatter plot of Lot Size vs. Income, color-coded by the outcome variable owner/nonowner. Make sure to obtain a well-formatted plot (create legible labels and a legend, etc.).

3.3 Laptop Sales at a London Computer Chain: Bar Charts and Boxplots. The file *LaptopSalesJanuary2008.csv* contains data for all sales of laptops at a computer chain in London in January 2008. This is a subset of the full dataset that includes data for the entire year.

a. Create a bar chart, showing the average retail price by store. Which store has the highest average? Which has the lowest?

b. To better compare retail prices across stores, create side-by-side boxplots of retail price by store. Now compare the prices in the two stores from (a). Does there seem to be a difference between their price distributions?

3.4 Laptop Sales at a London Computer Chain: Interactive Visualization. *The next exercises are designed for using an interactive visualization tool. The file LaptopSales.csv is a comma-separated file with nearly 300,000 rows. ENBIS (the European Network for Business and Industrial Statistics) provided these data as part of a contest organized in the fall of 2009.*

Scenario: Imagine that you are a new analyst for a company called Acell (a company selling laptops). You have been provided with data about products and sales. You need to help the company with their business goal of planning a product strategy and pricing policies that will maximize Acell's projected revenues in 2009. Using an interactive visualization tool, answer the following questions.

a. Price Questions:

i. At what price are the laptops actually selling?

ii. Does price change with time? (*Hint*: Make sure that the date column is recognized as such. The software should then enable different temporal aggregation choices, e.g., plotting the data by weekly or monthly aggregates, or even by day of week.)

iii. Are prices consistent across retail outlets?

iv. How does price change with configuration?

b. Location Questions:

i. Where are the stores and customers located?

ii. Which stores are selling the most?

iii. How far would customers travel to buy a laptop?

- *Hint 1*: You should be able to aggregate the data, for example, plot the sum or average of the prices.
- *Hint 2*: Use the coordinated highlighting between multiple visualizations in the same page, for example, select a store in one view to see the matching customers in another visualization.

- *Hint 3*: Explore the use of filters to see differences. Make sure to filter in the zoomed out view. For example, try to use a "store location" slider as an alternative way to dynamically compare store locations. This might be more useful to spot outlier patterns if there were 50 store locations to compare.

iv. Try an alternative way of looking at how far customers traveled. Do this by creating a new data column that computes the distance between customer and store.

c. **Revenue Questions:**

  i. How do the sales volume in each store relate to Acell's revenues?

  ii. How does this relationship depend on the configuration?

d. **Configuration Questions:**

  i. What are the details of each configuration? How does this relate to price?

  ii. Do all stores sell all configurations?

CHAPTER 4

Dimension Reduction

In this chapter, we describe the important step of dimension reduction. The dimension of a dataset, which is the number of variables, must be reduced for the data mining algorithms to operate efficiently. This process is part of the pilot/prototype phase of data mining and is done before deploying a model. We present and discuss several dimension reduction approaches: (1) incorporating domain knowledge to remove or combine categories, (2) using data summaries to detect information overlap between variables (and remove or combine redundant variables or categories), (3) using data conversion techniques such as converting categorical variables into numerical variables, and (4) employing automated reduction techniques, such as principal components analysis (PCA), where a new set of variables (which are weighted averages of the original variables) is created. These new variables are uncorrelated and a small subset of them usually contains most of their combined information (hence, we can reduce dimension by using only a subset of the new variables). Finally, we mention data mining methods such as regression models and classification and regression trees, which can be used for removing redundant variables and for combining "similar" categories of categorical variables.

Python

In this chapter, we will use `pandas` for data handling, `scikit-learn` for data transformations, and `matplotlib` for visualization.

import required functionality for this chapter

```
import numpy as np
import pandas as pd
from sklearn.decomposition import PCA
from sklearn import preprocessing
import matplotlib.pylab as plt
```

4.1 | INTRODUCTION

In data mining, one often encounters situations where there is a large number of variables in the database. Even when the initial number of variables is small, this set quickly expands in the data preparation step, where new derived variables are created (e.g., dummies for categorical variables and new forms of existing variables). In such situations, it is likely that subsets of variables are highly correlated with each other. Including highly correlated variables in a classification or prediction model, or including variables that are unrelated to the outcome of interest, can lead to overfitting, and accuracy and reliability can suffer. A large number of variables also poses computational problems for some supervised as well as unsupervised algorithms (aside from questions of correlation). In model deployment, superfluous variables can increase costs due to the collection and processing of these variables.

4.2 | CURSE OF DIMENSIONALITY

The *dimensionality* of a model is the number of predictors or input variables used by the model. The *curse of dimensionality* is the affliction caused by adding variables to multivariate data models. As variables are added, the data space becomes increasingly sparse, and classification and prediction models fail because the available data are insufficient to provide a useful model across so many variables. An important consideration is the fact that the difficulties posed by adding a variable increase exponentially with the addition of each variable. One way to think of this intuitively is to consider the location of an object on a chessboard. It has two dimensions and 64 squares or choices. If you expand the chessboard to a cube, you increase the dimensions by 50%—from two dimensions to three dimensions. However, the location options increase by 800%, to 512 ($8 \times 8 \times 8$). In statistical distance terms, the proliferation of variables means that nothing is close to anything else anymore—too much noise has been added and patterns and structure are no longer discernible. The problem is particularly acute in Big Data applications, including genomics, where, for example, an analysis might have to deal with values for thousands of different genes. One of the key steps in data mining, therefore, is finding ways to reduce dimensionality with minimal sacrifice of accuracy. In the artificial intelligence literature, dimension reduction is often referred to as *factor selection* or *feature extraction*.

4.3 | PRACTICAL CONSIDERATIONS

Although data mining prefers automated methods over domain knowledge, it is important at the first step of data exploration to make sure that the variables measured are reasonable for the task at hand. The integration of expert knowledge through a discussion with the data provider (or user) will probably lead to better results. Practical considerations include: Which variables are most important for the task at hand, and which are most likely to be useless? Which variables are likely to contain much error? Which variables will be available for measurement (and what will it cost to measure them) in the future if the analysis is repeated? Which variables can actually be measured before the outcome occurs? For example, if we want to predict the closing price of an ongoing online auction, we cannot use the number of bids as a predictor because this will not be known until the auction closes.

Example 1: Service Feedback and Usage

We return to the service feed and usage example introduced in Chapter 3. For each service location, a number of variables are given, such as population density, state, etc. A description of all 11 variables is given in Table 4.1 and the first six records are shown in Table 4.2. These variables comprise 7 variables pertaining to service usage and feedback behavior, 3 profile variables (State, Place density, and Operational Yrs.), and service center identifier code. All variables of feedback behavior available as counts within a service center for the last six-month period have been transformed into a percentage of total traffic whereas service usage has been transformed into percentage growth over the previous six months. One more categorical variable showing high or low service usage as 1 or 0 (UL) has been created from a continuous variable service growth variable captured as a percentage increase in service usage transactions over the transaction in the previous six months (UG).

TABLE 4.1 DESCRIPTION OF VARIABLES IN THE SERVICE FEEDBACK AND USAGE EXAMPLE

Variable	Description
CenterID	Service Center Code spread across various states
State	State of India
PD	Population density in the catchment area
OY	Number of years since the center's establishment
CMT	No. of customers who made complaint/s as % of total traffic

(*Continued*)

TABLE 4.1 DESCRIPTION OF VARIABLES IN THE SERVICE FEEDBACK AND USAGE EXAMPLE (*Continued*)

Variable	Description
RP	% complaints resolved
FBK	No. of customers who gave feedback as % of total traffic
IAS	No. of customers who provided Immediately actionable suggestions as % of total traffic
STAS	No. of customers who provided short-term actionable suggestions as % of total traffic
LTAS	No. of customers who provided long-term actionable suggestions as % of total traffic
UG	Six monthly service usage growth percentage
UL	Six monthly service usage growth percentage transformed into high (1) and low levels (0) based on a cut-off of 12% growth

TABLE 4.2 FIRST SIX RECORDS IN THE SERVICE FEEDBACK AND USAGE DATASET

```
import pandas as pd
import numpy as np
su=pd.read_csv('Service_Usage.csv')
su.head(6)
```

	CenterID	State	PD	OY	CMT	RP	FBK	IAS	STAS	LTAS	UG	UL
0	OD9360	Odisha	Medium	8	0.1373	0.5531	0.1215	0.5358	0.1928	0.0126	0.1298	1
1	AN1392	Andhra Pradesh	Medium	5	0.0786	0.5531	0.0876	0.1212	0.3989	0.0010	0.1386	1
2	PU8465	Punjab	Low	4	0.1945	0.5317	0.0419	0.0119	0.0192	0.0007	0.1413	1
3	AN3297	Andhra Pradesh	Medium	7	0.0434	0.3888	0.0760	0.3083	0.2505	0.0133	0.1208	1
4	PU8331	Punjab	Low	7	0.0777	0.6287	0.0447	0.6016	0.0125	0.0110	0.1426	1
5	GU1991	Gujarat	Low	7	0.1729	0.5260	0.1669	0.4384	0.2825	0.0064	0.1051	0

4.4 | DATA SUMMARIES

As we have seen in the chapter on data visualization, an important initial step of data exploration is getting familiar with the data and their characteristics through summaries and graphs. The importance of this step cannot be overstated. The better you understand the data, the better the results from the modeling or mining process.

Numerical summaries and graphs of the data are very helpful for data reduction. The information that they convey can assist in combining categories of a categorical variable, in choosing variables to remove, in assessing the level of information overlap between variables, and more. Before discussing such strategies for reducing the dimension of a data set, let us consider useful summaries and tools.

TABLE 4.3 SUMMARY STATISTICS FOR THE SERVICE USAGE DATA

Table and code for summary statistics

```
In [6]: 1 su.describe()
Out[6]:
```

	OY	CMT	RP	FBK	IAS	STAS	LTAS	UG	UL
count	893.000000	893.000000	893.000000	893.000000	893.000000	893.000000	893.000000	893.000000	893.000000
mean	7.066069	0.134019	0.499777	0.080294	0.357398	0.199428	0.007419	0.132710	0.695409
std	1.988504	0.042180	0.120060	0.042631	0.179275	0.116936	0.004405	0.024316	0.460492
min	1.000000	0.008700	0.163100	0.000100	0.000400	0.000200	0.000000	0.049700	0.000000
25%	6.000000	0.106900	0.411400	0.049400	0.230100	0.110300	0.003900	0.116800	0.000000
50%	7.000000	0.133100	0.498800	0.079900	0.349500	0.191200	0.007000	0.132200	1.000000
75%	8.000000	0.159600	0.583800	0.109200	0.491100	0.278600	0.010500	0.148700	1.000000
max	13.000000	0.300100	0.904200	0.231200	1.128600	0.616500	0.020300	0.200800	1.000000

```
pd.DataFrame({'mean': su.mean(),
'sd': su,std(), 'min': su.min(), 'max': su.max(), 'median': su.median(), 'length': len(su),
'miss.val': su. isnull().sum(),
})
```

	mean	sd	min	max	median	length	miss.val
CMT	0.134019	0.042180	0.0087	0.3001	0.1331	893	0
CenterID	NaN	NaN	AN0023	WE9940	NaN	893	0
FBK	0.080294	0.042631	0.0001	0.2312	0.0799	893	0
IAS	0.357398	0.179275	0.0004	1.1286	0.3495	893	0
LTAS	0.007419	0.004405	0.0	0.0203	0.0070	893	0
OY	7.066069	1.988504	1	13	7.0000	893	0
PD	NaN	NaN	High	Medium	NaN	893	0
RP	0.499777	0.120060	0.1631	0.9042	0.4988	893	0
STAS	0.199428	0.116936	0.0002	0.6165	0.1912	893	0
State	NaN	NaN	Andhra Pradesh	West Bengal	NaN	893	0
UG	0.132710	0.024316	0.0497	0.2008	0.1322	893	0
UL	0.695409	0.460492	0	1	1.0000	893	0

Summary Statistics

The pandas package offers several methods that assist in summarizing data. The DataFrame method *describe()* gives an overview of the entire set of variables in the data. The methods *mean(), std(), min(), max(), median(),* and *len()* are also very helpful for learning about the characteristics of each variable. First, they give us information about the scale and type of values that the variable takes. The min and max statistics can be used to detect extreme values that might be errors. The mean and median give a sense of the central values of that variable, and a large deviation between the two also indicates skew. The standard deviation gives a sense of how dispersed the data are (relative to the mean). Further options, such as the combination of *.isnull().sum(),* which gives the number of null values, can tell us about missing values.

Table 4.3 shows summary statistics (and Python code) for the Service Usage example. We immediately see that the different variables have very different ranges of values. Variation in scale across variables can distort analyses if not treated properly. Another observation that can be made is that the mean of the first variable are closer to median values indicative of very low skewness. None of the variables have missing values. There also do not appear to be indications of extreme values that might result from typing errors. Also CenterID, State, and PD are categorical variables or objects, the summary statistics used for other numeric variables are not relevant.

Next, we summarize relationships between two or more variables. For numerical variables, we can compute a complete matrix of correlations between each pair of variables, using the pandas method *corr()*. Table 4.4 shows the correlation matrix for the Service Usage variables. We see that most correlations are low and that many are negative. Recall also the visual display of a correlation matrix via a heatmap (see Figure 3.4 in Chapter 3 for the heatmap corresponding to this correlation table). We will return to the importance of the correlation matrix, in the context of correlation analysis.

TABLE 4.4 CORRELATION MATRIX OF SERVICE USAGE VARIABLES & CODE

```
In [20]: 1 su.corr().round(4)
Out[20]:
```

	OY	CMT	RP	FBK	IAS	STAS	LTAS	UG	UL
OY	1.0000	0.0295	0.0241	-0.0019	0.0056	-0.0226	0.0537	-0.0054	0.0049
CMT	0.0295	1.0000	0.0103	0.0642	0.0010	0.0491	-0.0554	0.0189	0.0353
RP	0 0241	0.0103	1.0000	0.0047	0.0034	0.0387	-0.0340	0.4349	0.3450
FBK	-0.0019	-0.0642	0.0047	1.0000	-0.0319	-0.0073	-0.0451	-0.0719	-0.0298
IAS	0.0056	0.0010	0.0034	-0.0319	1.0000	-0.0394	-0.0338	0.0170	0.0254
STAS	-0.0226	0.0491	0.0387	-0.0073	-0.0394	1.0000	-0.0485	0.0303	0.0332
LTAS	0.0537	-0.0554	-0.0340	-0.0451	-0.0338	-0.0485	1.0000	-0.0623	-0.0641
UG	-0.0054	0.0189	0.4349	0.0719	0.0170	0.0303	-0.0623	1.0000	0.7524
UL	0.0049	0.0353	0.3450	-0.0298	0.0254	0.0332	-0.0641	0.7524	1.0000

Aggregation and Pivot Tables

Another very useful approach for exploring the data is aggregation by one or more variables. For aggregation by a single variable, we can use the pandas method *value_counts()*. For example, Table 4.5 shows the count of usage levels high and low as 1 and 0. We can see around 70% consumers (621 out of 893) have high usage levels.

TABLE 4.5 GROUPS OF USAGE LEVEL (UL) & NUMBER OF SERVICE CENTERS ACROSS STATES

Python code and output

```
su.UL.value_counts()
su.groupby(['State'])['CenterID'].count()
1    621
0    272
Name: UL, dtype: int64

State
Andhra Pradesh    140
Assam              91
Gujarat            62
Haryana            37
Karnataka         111
Kerala             39
Maharashtra       124
Odisha             44
Punjab             64
Tamil Nadu         56
Uttar Pradesh      69
West Bengal        56
Name: CenterID, dtype: int64
```

The *groupby()* method can be used for aggregating by one or more variables, and computing a range of summary statistics (count, mean, median, etc.). For categorical variables, we obtain a breakdown of the records by the combination of categories. For instance, number of service centers grouped by states (the variable State is chosen as the grouping variable). It appears that the number of service location are disproportionately spread across states as some states like Maharashtra, Andhra Pradesh, and Karnataka have more than 100 centers whereas Uttar Pradesh even a high-population state has only 69 centers. It could be probed further. In Table 4.6, we compute the average Usage Growth (UG) by PD and State. In this case PD or State is a numerical variable like it ranges from 0-10, it should be first grouped into bins of size 1 (0–1, 1–2, etc.). Note the empty values, denoting that there are no values in the dataset with those combinations.

TABLE 4.6 FETCHING AVG OF VARIABLES ACROSS MULTIPLE CATEGORICAL VARIABLES

Python code and output

```
su.groupby(['State', 'PD'])['UG'].mean()
Out[53]:
State           PD
Andhra Pradesh  Low       0.130442
                Medium    0.136454
Assam           Low       0.133603
                Medium    0.130480
Gujarat         Low       0.131213
                Medium    0.133605
Haryana         Low       0.123223
                Medium    0.127279
Karnataka       Low       0.134944
                Medium    0.128629
Kerala          Low       0.123267
                Medium    0.139113
Maharashtra     High      0.133679
                Low       0.138017
Odisha          Low       0.135216
                Medium    0.141469
Punjab          Low       0.130207
                Medium    0.132563
Tamil Nadu      High      0.131616
                Low       0.131789
Uttar Pradesh   High      0.134293
                Low       0.130314
West Bengal     High      0.135035
                Low       0.129433
Name: UG, dtype: float64
```

Another useful method is *pivot_table()* in the pandas package, that allows the creation of pivot tables by reshaping the data by the aggregating variables of our choice. For example, Table 4.7 computes the average of UG by PD and State and presents it as a pivot table.

In classification tasks, where the goal is to find predictor variables that distinguish between two classes, a good exploratory step is to produce summaries for each class. This can assist in detecting useful predictors that display some separation between the two classes. Data summaries are useful for almost any data mining task and are therefore an important preliminary step for cleaning and understanding the data before carrying out further analyses.

TABLE 4.7 USE OF PIVOT FUNCTION TO CREATE TABULAR SUMMARIES

Python code and output

```
In [55]: # use pivot_table() to reshape data and generate pivot table
         pd.pivot_table(su, values='UG', index=['State'], columns=['PD'],
         aggfunc=np.mean, margins=True)

Out[55]:
```

PD	High	Low	Medium	All
State				
Andhra Pradesh	NaN	0.130442	0.136454	0.132890
Assam	NaN	0.133603	0.130480	0.131715
Gujarat	NaN	0.131213	0.133605	0.132061
Haryana	NaN	0.123223	0.127279	0.125854
Kamataka	NaN	0.134944	0.128629	0.132612
Kerala	NaN	0.123267	0.139113	0.133018
Maharashtra	0.133679	0.138017	NaN	0.136198
Odisha	NaN	0.135216	0.141469	0.137064
Punjab	NaN	0.130207	0.132563	0.130906
Tamil Nadu	0.131616	0.131789	NaN	0.131730
Uttar Pradesh	0.134293	0.130314	NaN	0.131871
West Bengal	0.135035	0.129433	NaN	0.132034
All	0.133781	0.132301	0.133014	0.132710

4.5 | CORRELATION ANALYSIS

In datasets with a large number of variables (which are likely to serve as predictors), there is usually much overlap in the information covered by the set of variables. One simple way to find redundancies is to look at a correlation matrix. This shows all the pairwise correlations between variables. Pairs that have a very strong (positive or negative) correlation contain a lot of overlap in information and are good candidates for data reduction by removing one of the variables. Removing variables that are strongly correlated to others is useful for avoiding multicollinearity problems that can arise in various models. (*Multicollinearity* is the presence of two or more predictors sharing the same linear relationship with the outcome variable.)

Correlation analysis is also a good method for detecting duplications of variables in the data. Sometimes, the same variable appears accidentally more than once in the dataset (under a different name) because the dataset was merged from multiple sources, the same phenomenon is measured in different units, and so on. Using correlation table heatmaps, as shown in Chapter 3, can make the task of identifying strong correlations easier.

4.6 REDUCING THE NUMBER OF CATEGORIES IN CATEGORICAL VARIABLES

When a categorical variable has many categories, and this variable is destined to be a predictor, many data mining methods will require converting it into many dummy variables. In particular, a variable with m categories will be transformed into either m or $m - 1$ dummy variables (depending on the method). This means that even if we have very few original categorical variables, they can greatly inflate the dimension of the dataset. One way to handle this is to reduce the number of categories by combining close or similar categories. Combining categories requires incorporating expert knowledge and common sense. Pivot tables are useful for this task: We can examine the sizes of the various categories and how the outcome variable behaves in each category. Generally, categories that contain very few observations are good candidates for combining with other categories. Use only the categories that are most relevant to the analysis and label the rest as "other." In classification tasks (with a categorical outcome variable), a pivot table broken down by the outcome classes can help identify categories that do not separate the classes. Those categories too are candidates for inclusion in the "other" category. An example is shown in Figure 4.1, where the distribution of outcome variable UG is broken down by Resolution Percentage (RP) converted first into RP_BIN. We can see that the distribution of UL is indicative of high Service Usage growth levels at higher levels of complaint resolution percentage. But rather than having nine levels in the next steps of analysis, it may be easier to work with lesser levels of RP which can be achieved through the visualization in Figure 4.1. Nine categories can be divided into three broad groups based on an RP cutoff. In essence, these plots help reduce categories of categorical variables in a predictive analysis project to reduce noise.

code for creating Figure 4.1

```
su['RP_BIN']=pd.cut(x=su['RP'], bins=[0,.1,.2,.3,.4,.5,.6,.7,.8,.9,1])
# use method crosstab to create a cross-tabulation of two variables
tbl = pd.crosstab(su.UL, su.RP_BIN)
# convert numbers to ratios prop
propTbl = tbl / tbl.sum()
propTbl.round(2)
ax = propTbl.transpose().plot(kind='bar', stacked=True)

plt.title('Distribution of UL by RP')
plt.legend(loc='center left', bbox_to_anchor=(1, 0.5))
plt.show()
```

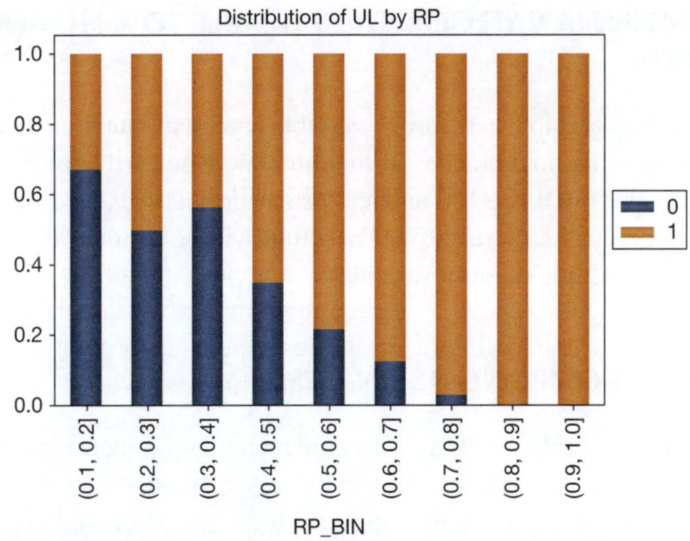

FIGURE 4.1 DISTRIBUTION OF UL BY RP- STRETCHED PROPORTION CHART

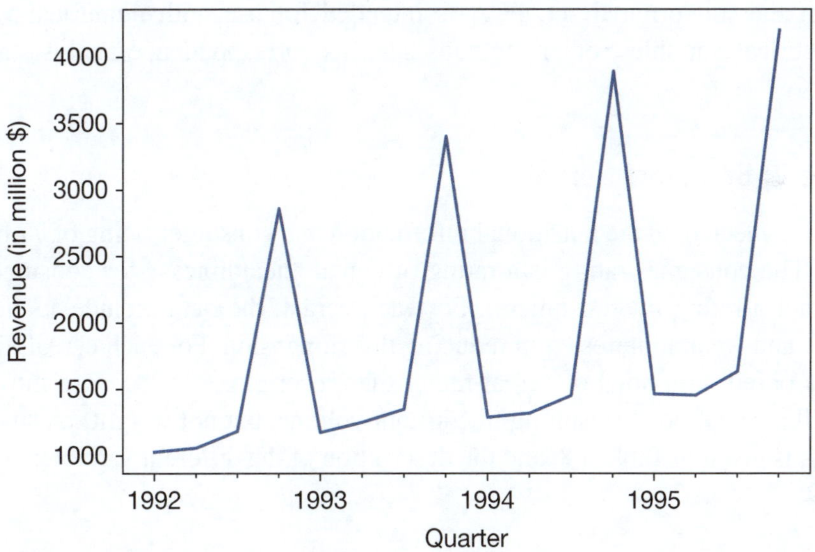

FIGURE 4.2 QUARTERLY REVENUES OF TOYS "R" US, 1992–1995

In a time series context where we might have a categorical variable denoting season (such as month, or hour of day) that will serve as a predictor, reducing categories can be done by examining the time series plot and identifying similar periods. For example, the time plot in Figure 4.2 shows the quarterly revenues of Toys "R" Us between 1992 and 1995. Only quarter 4 periods appear different, and therefore, we can combine quarters 1–3 into a single category.

4.7 | CONVERTING A CATEGORICAL VARIABLE TO A NUMERICAL VARIABLE

Sometimes the categories in a categorical variable represent intervals. Common examples are age group or income bracket. If the interval values are known (e.g., category 2 is the age interval 20–30), we can replace the categorical value ("2" in the example) with the mid-interval value (here "25"). The result will be a numerical variable which no longer requires multiple dummy variables.

4.8 | PRINCIPAL COMPONENTS ANALYSIS

Principal components analysis (PCA) is a useful method for dimension reduction, especially when the number of variables is large. PCA is especially valuable when we have subsets of measurements that are measured on the same scale and are highly correlated. In that case, it provides a few variables (often as few as three) that are weighted linear combinations of the original variables, and that retain the majority of the information of the full original set. PCA is intended for use with numerical variables. For categorical variables, other methods such as correspondence analysis are more suitable.

Example 2: Breakfast Cereals

Data were collected on the nutritional information and consumer rating of 77 breakfast cereals.[1] The consumer rating is a rating of cereal "healthiness" for consumer information (not a rating by consumers). For each cereal, the data include 13 numerical variables, and we are interested in reducing this dimension. For each cereal, the information is based on a bowl of cereal rather than a serving size, because most people simply fill a cereal bowl (resulting in constant volume, but not weight). A snapshot of these data is given in Table 4.8, and the description of the different variables is given in Table 4.9.

---

[1]The data are available at http://lib.stat.cmu.edu/DASL/Stories/HealthyBreakfast.html.

TABLE 4.8 SAMPLE FROM THE 77 BREAKFAST CEREALS DATASET

Cereal name	mfr	Type	Calories	Protein	Fat	Sodium	Fiber	Carbo	Sugars	Potass	Vitamins
100% Bran	N	C	70	4	1	130	10	5	6	280	25
100% Natural Bran	Q	C	120	3	5	15	2	8	8	135	0
All-Bran	K	C	70	4	1	260	9	7	5	320	25
All-Bran with Extra Fiber	K	C	50	4	0	140	14	8	0	330	25
Almond Delight	R	C	110	2	2	200	1	14	8		25
Apple Cinnamon Cheerios	G	C	110	2	2	180	1.5	10.5	10	70	25
Apple Jacks	K	C	110	2	0	125	1	11	14	30	25
Basic 4	G	C	130	3	2	210	2	18	8	100	25
Bran Chex	R	C	90	2	1	200	4	15	6	125	25
Bran Flakes	P	C	90	3	0	210	5	13	5	190	25
Cap'n'Crunch	Q	C	120	1	2	220	0	12	12	35	25
Cheerios	G	C	110	6	2	290	2	17	1	105	25
Cinnamon Toast Crunch	G	C	120	1	3	210	0	13	9	45	25
Clusters	G	C	110	3	2	140	2	13	7	105	25
Cocoa Puffs	G	C	110	1	1	180	0	12	13	55	25
Corn Chex	R	C	110	2	0	280	0	22	3	25	25
Corn Flakes	K	C	100	2	0	290	1	21	2	35	25
Corn Pops	K	C	110	1	0	90	1	13	12	20	25
Count Chocula	G	C	110	1	1	180	0	12	13	65	25
Cracklin' Oat Bran	K	C	110	3	3	140	4	10	7	160	25

TABLE 4.9 DESCRIPTION OF THE VARIABLES IN THE BREAKFAST CEREAL DATASET

Variable	Description
mfr	Manufacturer of cereal (American Home Food Products, General Mills, Kellogg, etc.)
type	Cold or hot
calories	Calories per serving
protein	Grams of protein
fat	Grams of fat
sodium	Milligrams of sodium
fiber	Grams of dietary fiber
carbo	Grams of complex carbohydrates
sugars	Grams of sugars
potass	Milligrams of potassium
vitamins	Vitamins and minerals: 0, 25, or 100, indicating the typical percentage of FDA recommended
shelf	Display shelf (1, 2, or 3, counting from the floor)
weight	Weight in ounces of one serving
cups	Number of cups in one serving
rating	Rating of the cereal calculated by consumer reports

We focus first on two variables: *calories* and *consumer rating*. These are given in Table 4.10. The average calories across the 77 cereals is 106.88 and the average consumer rating is 42.67. The estimated covariance matrix between the two variables is

$$S = \begin{bmatrix} 379.63 & -188.68 \\ -188.68 & 197.32 \end{bmatrix}.$$

TABLE 4.10 CEREAL CALORIES AND RATINGS

Cereal	Calories	Rating	Cereal	Calories	Rating
100% Bran	70	68.40297	Just Right Fruit & Nut	140	36.471512
100% Natural Bran	120	33.98368	Kix	110	39.241114
All-Bran	70	59.42551	Life	100	45.328074
All-Bran with Extra Fiber	50	93.70491	Lucky Charms	110	26.734515
Almond Delight	110	34.38484	Maypo	100	54.850917
Apple Cinnamon Cheerios	110	29.50954	Muesli Raisins, Dates & Almonds	150	37.136863
Apple Jacks	110	33.17409	Muesli Raisins, Peaches & Pecans	150	34.139765

TABLE 4.10 CEREAL CALORIES AND RATINGS (*Continued*)

Cereal	Calories	Rating	Cereal	Calories	Rating
Basic 4	130	37.03856	Mueslix Crispy Blend	160	30.313351
Bran Chex	90	49.12025	Multi-Grain Cheerios	100	40.105965
Bran Flakes	90	53.31381	Nut&Honey Crunch	120	29.924285
Cap'n'Crunch	120	18.04285	Nutri-Grain Almond-Raisin	140	40.69232
Cheerios	110	50.765	Nutri-grain Wheat	90	59.642837
Cinnamon Toast Crunch	120	19.82357	Oatmeal Raisin Crisp	130	30.450843
Clusters	110	40.40021	Post Nat. Raisin Bran	120	37.840594
Cocoa Puffs	110	22.73645	Product 19	100	41.50354
Corn Chex	110	41.44502	Puffed Rice	50	60.756112
Corn Flakes	100	45.86332	Puffed Wheat	50	63.005645
Corn Pops	110	35.78279	Quaker Oat Squares	100	49.511874
Count Chocula	110	22.39651	Quaker Oatmeal	100	50.828392
Cracklin' Oat Bran	110	40.44877	Raisin Bran	120	39.259197
Cream of Wheat (Quick)	100	64.53382	Raisin Nut Bran	100	39.7034
Crispix	110	46.89564	Raisin Squares	90	55.333142
Crispy Wheat & Raisins	100	36.1762	Rice Chex	110	41.998933
Double Chex	100	44.33086	Rice Krispies	110	40.560159
Froot Loops	110	32.20758	Shredded Wheat	80	68.235885
Frosted Flakes	110	31.43597	Shredded Wheat 'n'Bran	90	74.472949
Frosted Mini-Wheats	100	58.34514	Shredded Wheat spoon size	90	72.801787
Fruit & Fibre Dates, Walnuts & Oats	120	40.91705	Smacks	110	31.230054
Fruitful Bran	120	41.01549	Special K	110	53.131324
Fruity Pebbles	110	28.02577	Strawberry Fruit Wheats	90	59.363993
Golden Crisp	100	35.25244	Total Corn Flakes	110	38.839746
Golden Grahams	110	23.80404	Total Raisin Bran	140	28.592785
Grape Nuts Flakes	100	52.0769	Total Whole Grain	100	46.658844
Grape-Nuts	110	53.37101	Triples	110	39.106174
Great Grains Pecan	120	45.81172	Trix	110	27.753301
Honey Graham Ohs	120	21.87129	Wheat Chex	100	49.787445
Honey Nut Cheerios	110	31.07222	Wheaties	100	51.592193
Honey-comb	110	28.74241	Wheaties Honey Gold	110	36.187559
Just Right Crunchy Nuggets	110	36.52368			

It can be seen that the two variables are strongly correlated with a negative correlation of

$$-0.69 = \frac{-188.68}{\sqrt{(379.63)(197.32)}}.$$

Roughly speaking, 69% of the total variation in both variables is actually "co-variation," or variation in one variable that is duplicated by similar variation in the other variable. Can we use this fact to reduce the number of variables, while making maximum use of their unique contributions to the overall variation? Since there is redundancy in the information that the two variables contain, it might be possible to reduce the two variables to a single variable without losing too much information. The idea in PCA is to find a linear combination of the two variables that contains most, even if not all, of the information, so that this new variable can replace the two original variables. Information here is in the sense of variability: What can explain the most variability *among* the 77 cereals? The total variability here is the sum of the variances of the two variables, which in this case is 379.63 + 197.32 = 577. This means that *calories* accounts for 66% = 379.63/577 of the total variability, and *rating* for the remaining 34%. If we drop one of the variables for the sake of dimension reduction, we lose at least 34% of the total variability. Can we redistribute the total variability between two new variables in a more polarized way? If so, it might be possible to keep only the one new variable that (hopefully) accounts for a large portion of the total variation.

Figure 4.3 shows a scatter plot of *rating* vs. *calories*. The line z_1 is the direction in which the variability of the points is largest. It is the line that captures the most variation in the data if we decide to reduce the dimensionality of the data from two to one. Among all possible lines, it is the line for which, if we project the points in the dataset orthogonally to get a set of 77 (one-dimensional) values, the variance of the z_1 values will be maximum. This is called the *first principal component*. It is also the line that minimizes the sum-of-squared perpendicular distances from the line. The z_2-axis is chosen to be perpendicular to the z_1-axis. In the case of two variables, there is only one line that is perpendicular to z_1, and it has the second largest variability, but its information is uncorrelated with z_1. This is called the *second principal component*. In general, when we have more than two variables, once we find the direction z_1 with the largest variability, we search among all the orthogonal directions to z_1 for the one with the next-highest variability. That is z_2. The idea is then to find the coordinates of these lines and to see how they redistribute the variability.

Running PCA in `scikit-learn` is done with the class *sklearn.decomposition.PCA*. Table 4.11 shows the output from running PCA on the two variables *calories* and *rating*. The value *components_* of this function is the rotation matrix, which gives the weights that are used to project the original points onto the two new directions. The weights for z_1 are given by (−0.847, 0.532), and for z_2 they are given by (0.532, 0.847). The *summary* gives the reallocated variance: z_1 accounts for 86% of the total variability and z_2 for the remaining 14%. Therefore, if we drop z_2, we still maintain 86% of the total variability.

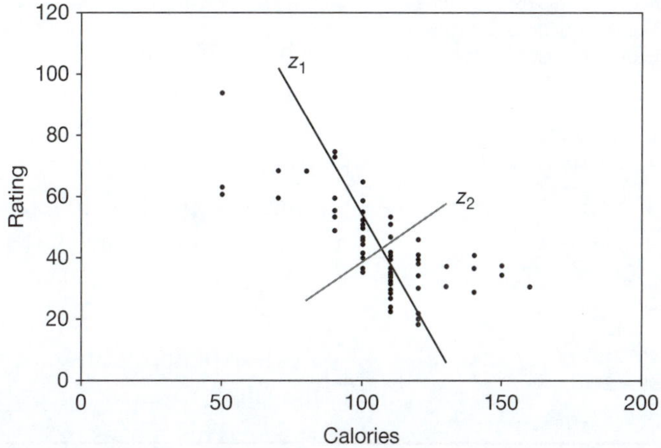

FIGURE 4.3 SCATTER PLOT OF *RATING* VS. *CALORIES* FOR 77 BREAKFAST CEREALS, WITH THE TWO PRINCIPAL COMPONENT DIRECTIONS

TABLE 4.11 PCA ON THE TWO VARIABLES *CALORIES* AND *RATING*

code for running PCA

```
cereals_df = pd.read_csv('Cereals.csv')
pcs = PCA(n_components=2)
pcs.fit(cereals_df[['calories', 'rating']])

pcsSummary = pd.DataFrame({'Standard deviation': np.sqrt(pcs.explained_variance_),
                           'Proportion of variance': pcs.explained_variance_ratio_,
                           'Cumulative proportion': np.cumsum(pcs.explained_
                                                              variance_ratio_)})
pcsSummary = pcsSummary.transpose()
pcsSummary.columns = ['PC1', 'PC2']
pcsSummary.round(4)

pcsComponents_df = pd.DataFrame(pcs.components_.transpose(), columns=['PC1', 'PC2'],
                                index=['calories', 'rating'])
pcsComponents_df

scores = pd.DataFrame(pcs.transform(cereals_df[['calories', 'rating']]),
                      columns=['PC1', 'PC2'])
scores.head()
```

(Continued)

TABLE 4.11 PCA ON THE TWO VARIABLES *CALORIES* AND *RATING* (*Continued*)

Output

```
# pcsSummary
                             PC1     PC2
Standard deviation       22.3165  8.8844
Proportion of variance    0.8632  0.1368
Cumulative proportion     0.8632  1.0000

# Components
               PC1       PC2
calories -0.847053  0.531508
rating    0.531508  0.847053

# Scores
         PC1        PC2
0  44.921528   2.197183
1 -15.725265  -0.382416
2  40.149935  -5.407212
3  75.310772  12.999126
4  -7.041508  -5.357686
```

The weights are used to compute principal component scores, which are the projected values of *calories* and *rating* onto the new axes (after subtracting the means). The *transform* method of the PCS object can be used to determine the score from the original data. The first column is the projection onto z_1 using the weights (0.847, −0.532). The second column is the projection onto z_2 using the weights (0.532, 0.847). For example, the first score for the 100% Bran cereal (with 70 calories and a rating of 68.4) is $(-0.847)(70 - 106.88) + (0.532)(68.4 - 42.67) = 44.92$.

Note that the means of the new variables z_1 and z_2 are zero, because we've subtracted the mean of each variable. The sum of the variances $\text{var}(z_1) + \text{var}(z_2)$ is equal to the sum of the variances of the original variables, var(*calories*) + var(*rating*). Furthermore, the variances of z_1 and z_2 are 498 and 79, respectively, so the first principal component, z_1, accounts for 86% of the total variance. Since it captures most of the variability in the data, it seems reasonable to use one variable, the first principal score, to represent the two variables in the original data. Next, we generalize these ideas to more than two variables.

Principal Components

Let us formalize the procedure described above so that it can easily be generalized to $p > 2$ variables. Denote the original p variables by $X_1, X_2, \ldots, X_p$. In PCA, we are looking for a set of new variables $Z_1, Z_2, \ldots, Z_p$ that are weighted averages of the original variables (after subtracting their mean):

$$Z_i = a_{i,1}(X_1 - \overline{X}_1) + a_{i,2}(X_2 - \overline{X}_2) + \cdots + a_{i,p}(X_p - \overline{X}_p), \quad i = 1, \ldots, p, \tag{4.1}$$

where each pair of Z's has correlation $= 0$. We then order the resulting Z's by their variance, with Z_1 having the largest variance and Z_p having the smallest variance. The software computes the weights $a_{i,j}$, which are then used in computing the principal component scores.

A further advantage of the principal components compared to the original data is that they are uncorrelated (correlation coefficient = 0). If we construct regression models using these principal components as predictors, we will not encounter problems of multicollinearity.

Let us return to the breakfast cereal dataset with all 15 variables, and apply PCA to the 13 numerical variables. The resulting output is shown in Table 4.12. Note that the first three components account for more than 96% of the total variation associated with all 13 of the original variables. This suggests that we can capture most of the variability in the data with less than 25% of the original dimensions in the data. In fact, the first two principal components alone capture 92.6% of the total variation. However, these results are influenced by the scales of the variables, as we describe next.

TABLE 4.12 PCA OUTPUT USING ALL 13 NUMERICAL VARIABLES IN THE BREAKFAST CEREALS DATASET. THE TABLE SHOWS RESULTS FOR THE FIRST FIVE PRINCIPAL COMPONENTS

```
pcs = PCA()
pcs.fit(cereals_df.iloc[:, 3:].dropna(axis=0))
pcsSummary_df = pd.DataFrame({'Standard deviation': np.sqrt(pcs.explained_variance_),
                              'Proportion of variance': pcs.explained_variance_ratio_,
                              'Cumulative proportion': np.cumsum(pcs.explained_variance_ratio_)})
pcsSummary_df = pcsSummary_df.transpose()
pcsSummary_df.columns = ['PC{}'.format(i) for i in range(1, len(pcsSummary_df.columns) + 1)]
pcsSummary_df.round(4)
```

```
                            PC1      PC2      PC3      PC4     PC5     PC6  \
Standard deviation      83.7641  70.9143  22.6437  19.1815  8.4232  2.0917
Proportion of variance   0.5395   0.3867   0.0394   0.0283  0.0055  0.0003
Cumulative proportion    0.5395   0.9262   0.9656   0.9939  0.9993  0.9997

                           PC7     PC8     PC9    PC10    PC11   PC12  PC13
Standard deviation      1.6994  0.7796  0.6578  0.3704  0.1864  0.063   0.0
Proportion of variance  0.0002  0.0000  0.0000  0.0000  0.0000  0.000   0.0
Cumulative proportion   0.9999  1.0000  1.0000  1.0000  1.0000  1.000   1.0
```

(Continued)

TABLE 4.12 PCA OUTPUT USING ALL 13 NUMERICAL VARIABLES IN THE BREAKFAST CEREALS DATASET. THE TABLE SHOWS RESULTS FOR THE FIRST FIVE PRINCIPAL COMPONENTS (*Continued*)

```
pcsComponents_df = pd.DataFrame(pcs.components_.transpose(), columns=pcsSummary_df.columns,
                                index=cereals_df.iloc[:, 3:].columns)
pcsComponents_df.iloc[:,:5]

               PC1       PC2       PC3       PC4       PC5
calories -0.077984 -0.009312  0.629206 -0.601021  0.454959
protein   0.000757  0.008801  0.001026  0.003200  0.056176
fat       0.000102  0.002699  0.016196 -0.025262 -0.016098
sodium   -0.980215  0.140896 -0.135902 -0.000968  0.013948
fiber     0.005413  0.030681 -0.018191  0.020472  0.013605
carbo    -0.017246 -0.016783  0.017370  0.025948  0.349267
sugars   -0.002989 -0.000253  0.097705 -0.115481 -0.299066
potass    0.134900  0.986562  0.036782 -0.042176 -0.047151
vitamins -0.094293  0.016729  0.691978  0.714118 -0.037009
shelf     0.001541  0.004360  0.012489  0.005647 -0.007876
weight   -0.000512  0.000999  0.003806 -0.002546  0.003022
cups     -0.000510 -0.001591  0.000694  0.000985  0.002148
rating    0.075296  0.071742 -0.307947  0.334534  0.757708
```

comments

Use method *dropna(axis=0)* to remove observations that contain missing values. Note the use of the *transpose()* method to get the scores

Normalizing the Data

A further use of PCA is to understand the structure of the data. This is done by examining the weights to see how the original variables contribute to the different principal components. In our example, it is clear that the first principal component is dominated by the sodium content of the cereal: it has the highest (in this case, positive) weight. This means that the first principal component is in fact measuring how much sodium is in the cereal. Similarly, the second principal component seems to be measuring the amount of potassium. Since both these variables are measured in milligrams, whereas the other nutrients are measured in grams, the scale is obviously leading to this result. The variances of potassium and sodium are much larger than the variances of the other variables, and thus the total variance is dominated by these two variances. A solution is to normalize the data before performing the PCA. Normalization (or standardization) means replacing each original variable by a standardized version of the variable that has unit variance. This is easily accomplished by dividing each variable by its standard deviation. The effect of this normalization is to give all variables equal importance in terms of variability.

When should we normalize the data like this? It depends on the nature of the data. When the units of measurement are common for the variables (e.g., dollars), and when their scale reflects their importance (sales of jet fuel, sales of heating oil), it is probably best not to normalize (i.e., not to rescale the data so that they have unit variance). If the variables are measured in different units so that it is unclear how to compare the variability of different variables (e.g., dollars for some, parts per million for others) or if for variables measured in the same units, scale does not reflect importance (earnings per share, gross revenues), it is generally advisable to normalize. In this way, the differences in units of measurement do not affect the principal components' weights. In the rare situations where we can give relative weights to variables, we multiply the normalized variables by these weights before doing the PCA.

Thus far, we have calculated principal components using the covariance matrix. An alternative to normalizing and then performing PCA is to perform PCA on the correlation matrix instead of the covariance matrix. Most software programs allow the user to choose between the two. Remember that using the correlation matrix means that you are operating on the normalized data.

Returning to the breakfast cereal data, we normalize the 13 variables due to the different scales of the variables and then perform PCA (or equivalently, we use PCA applied to the correlation matrix). The output is given in Table 4.13.

TABLE 4.13 PCA OUTPUT USING ALL *NORMALIZED* 13 NUMERICAL VARIABLES IN THE BREAKFAST CEREALS DATASET. THE TABLE SHOWS RESULTS FOR THE FIRST FIVE PRINCIPAL COMPONENTS

```
pcs = PCA()
pcs.fit(preprocessing.scale(cereals_df.iloc[:, 3:].dropna(axis=0)))
pcsSummary_df = pd.DataFrame({'Standard deviation': np.sqrt(pcs.explained_variance_),
                    'Proportion of variance': pcs.explained_variance_ratio_,
                    'Cumulative proportion': np.cumsum(pcs.explained_variance_ratio_)})
pcsSummary_df = pcsSummary_df.transpose()
pcsSummary_df.columns = ['PC{}'.format(i) for i in range(1, len(pcsSummary_df.columns) + 1)]
pcsSummary_df.round(4)

                          PC1     PC2     PC3     PC4     PC5     PC6  \
Standard deviation     1.9192  1.7864  1.3912  1.0166  1.0015  0.8555
Proportion of variance 0.2795  0.2422  0.1469  0.0784  0.0761  0.0555
Cumulative proportion  0.2795  0.5217  0.6685  0.7470  0.8231  0.8786

                          PC7     PC8     PC9    PC10    PC11    PC12  PC13
Standard deviation     0.8251  0.6496  0.5658  0.3051  0.2537  0.1399   0.0
Proportion of variance 0.0517  0.0320  0.0243  0.0071  0.0049  0.0015   0.0
Cumulative proportion  0.9303  0.9623  0.9866  0.9936  0.9985  1.0000   1.0
```

(*Continued*)

TABLE 4.13 PCA OUTPUT USING ALL *NORMALIZED* 13 NUMERICAL VARIABLES IN THE BREAKFAST CEREALS DATASET. THE TABLE SHOWS RESULTS FOR THE FIRST FIVE PRINCIPAL COMPONENTS (*Continued*)

```
pcsComponents_df = pd.DataFrame(pcs.components_.transpose(), columns=pcsSummary_df.columns,
                                index=cereals_df.iloc[:, 3:].columns)
pcsComponents_df.iloc[:,:5]

               PC1       PC2       PC3       PC4       PC5
calories -0.299542 -0.393148  0.114857 -0.204359  0.203899
protein   0.307356 -0.165323  0.277282 -0.300743  0.319749
fat      -0.039915 -0.345724 -0.204890 -0.186833  0.586893
sodium   -0.183397 -0.137221  0.389431 -0.120337 -0.338364
fiber     0.453490 -0.179812  0.069766 -0.039174 -0.255119
carbo    -0.192449  0.149448  0.562452 -0.087835  0.182743
sugars   -0.228068 -0.351434 -0.355405  0.022707 -0.314872
potass    0.401964 -0.300544  0.067620 -0.090878 -0.148360
vitamins -0.115980 -0.172909  0.387859  0.604111 -0.049287
shelf     0.171263 -0.265050 -0.001531  0.638879  0.329101
weight   -0.050299 -0.450309  0.247138 -0.153429 -0.221283
cups     -0.294636  0.212248  0.140000 -0.047489  0.120816
rating    0.438378  0.251539  0.181842 -0.038316  0.057584
```

Use *preprocessing.scale* to normalize data prior to running PCA.

Now we find that we need seven principal components to account for more than 90% of the total variability. The first two principal components account for only 52% of the total variability, and thus reducing the number of variables to two would mean losing a lot of information. Examining the weights, we see that the first principal component measures the balance between two quantities: (1) calories and cups (large negative weights) vs. (2) protein, fiber, potassium, and consumer rating (large positive weights). High scores on principal component 1 mean that the cereal is low in calories and the amount per bowl, and high in protein, and potassium. Unsurprisingly, this type of cereal is associated with a high consumer rating. The second principal component is most affected by the weight of a serving, and the third principal component by the carbohydrate content. We can continue labeling the next principal components in a similar fashion to learn about the structure of the data.

When the data can be reduced to two dimensions, a useful plot is a scatter plot of the first vs. second principal scores with labels for the observations (if the dataset is not too large[2]). To illustrate this, Figure 4.4 displays the first two principal component scores for the breakfast cereals.

[2]Python's labeled scatter plots currently generate too much over-plotting of labels when the number of markers is as large as in this example.

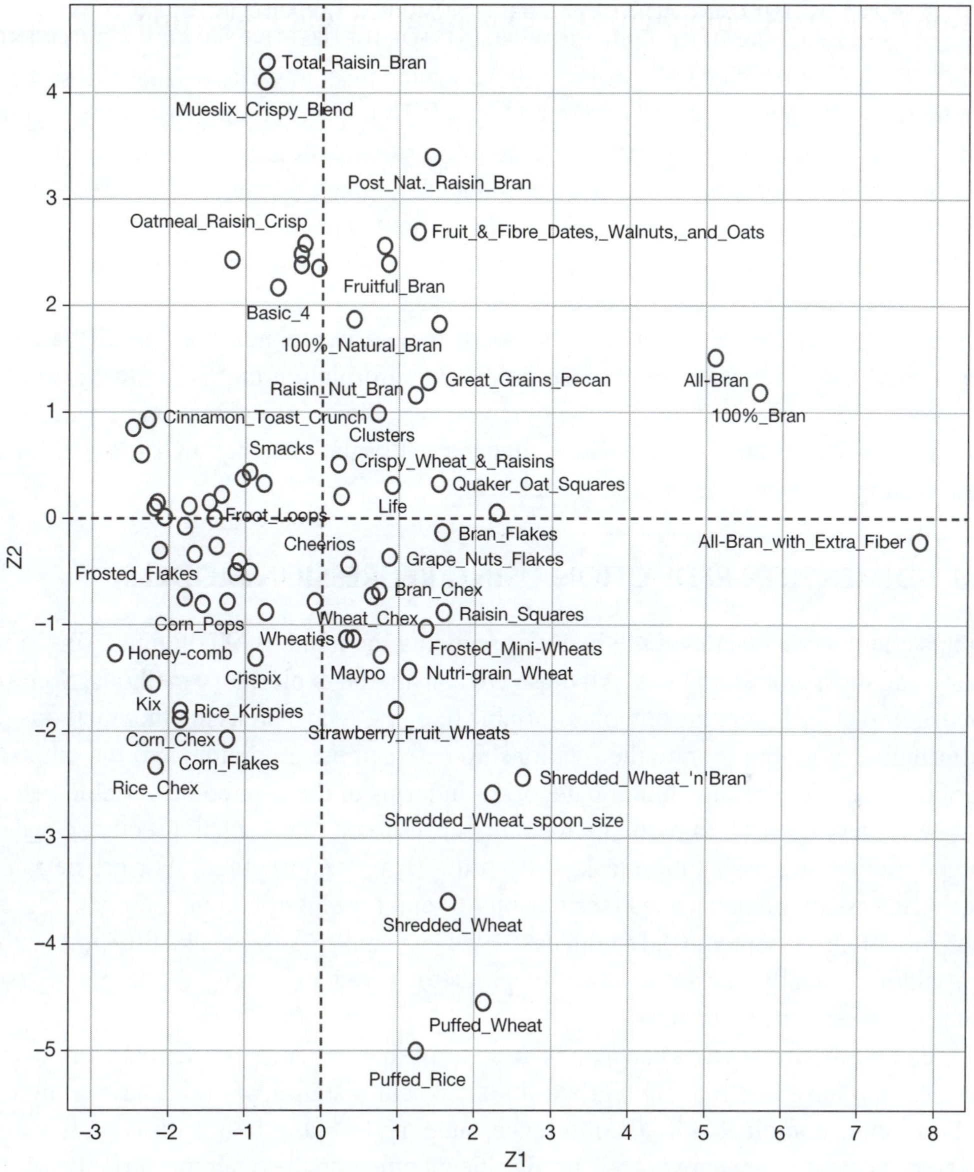

FIGURE 4.4 SCATTER PLOT OF THE SECOND VS. FIRST PRINCIPAL COMPONENTS SCORES FOR THE NORMALIZED BREAKFAST CEREAL OUTPUT (CREATED USING TABLEAU)

We can see that as we move from right (bran cereals) to left, the cereals are less "healthy" in the sense of high calories, low protein and fiber, and so on. Also, moving from bottom to top, we get heavier cereals (moving from puffed rice to raisin bran). These plots are especially useful if interesting clusters of observations can be found. For instance, we see here that children's cereals are close together on the middle-left part of the plot.

Using Principal Components for Classification and Prediction

When the goal of the data reduction is to have a smaller set of variables that will serve as predictors, we can proceed as following: Apply PCA to the predictors using the training data. Use the output to determine the number of principal components to be retained. The predictors in the model now use the (reduced number of) principal scores columns. For the validation set, we can use the weights computed from the training data to obtain a set of principal scores by applying the weights to the variables in the validation set. These new variables are then treated as the predictors.

One disadvantage of using a subset of principal components as predictors in a supervised task, is that we might lose predictive information that is nonlinear (e.g., a quadratic effect of a predictor on the outcome variable or an interaction between predictors). This is because PCA produces linear transformations, thereby capturing linear relationships between the original variables.

4.9 | DIMENSION REDUCTION USING REGRESSION MODELS

In this chapter, we discussed methods for reducing the number of columns using summary statistics, plots, and PCA. All these are considered exploratory methods. Some of them completely ignore the outcome variable (e.g., PCA), whereas in other methods we informally try to incorporate the relationship between the predictors and the outcome variable (e.g., combining similar categories, in terms of their outcome variable behavior). Another approach to reducing the number of predictors, which directly considers the predictive or classification task, is by fitting a regression model. For prediction, a linear regression model is used (see Chapter 6) and for classification, a logistic regression model (see Chapter 10). In both cases, we can employ subset selection procedures that algorithmically choose a subset of predictor variables among the larger set (see details in the relevant chapters).

Fitted regression models can also be used to further combine similar categories: categories that have coefficients that are not statistically significant (i.e., have a high *p*-value) can be combined with the reference category, because their distinction from the reference category appears to have no significant effect on the outcome variable. Moreover, categories that have similar coefficient values (and the same sign) can often be combined, because their effect on the outcome variable is similar. See the example in Chapter 10 on predicting delayed flights for an illustration of how regression models can be used for dimension reduction.

4.10 DIMENSION REDUCTION USING CLASSIFICATION AND REGRESSION TREES

Another method for reducing the number of columns and for combining categories of a categorical variable is by applying classification and regression trees (see Chapter 9). Classification trees are used for classification tasks and regression trees for prediction tasks. In both cases, the algorithm creates binary splits on the predictors that best classify/predict the outcome variable (e.g., above/below age 30). Although we defer the detailed discussion to Chapter 9, we note here that the resulting tree diagram can be used for determining the important predictors. Predictors (numerical or categorical) that do not appear in the tree can be removed. Similarly, categories that do not appear in the tree can be combined.

PROBLEMS

4.1. Breakfast Cereals. Use the data for the breakfast cereals example in Section 4.8 to explore and summarize the data as follows:

a. Which variables are quantitative/numerical? Which are ordinal? Which are nominal?

b. Compute the mean, median, min, max, and standard deviation for each of the quantitative variables. This can be done using pandas as shown in Table 4.3.

c. Plot a histogram for each of the quantitative variables. Based on the histograms and summary statistics, answer the following questions:

i. Which variables have the largest variability?

ii. Which variables seem skewed?

iii. Are there any values that seem extreme?

d. Plot a side-by-side boxplot comparing the calories in hot vs. cold cereals. What does this plot show us?

e. Plot a side-by-side boxplot of consumer rating as a function of the shelf height. If we were to predict consumer rating from shelf height, does it appear that we need to keep all three categories of shelf height?

f. Compute the correlation table for the quantitative variable (method *corr()*). In addition, generate a matrix plot for these variables (see Figure 3.4 on how to do this using the seaborn library).

i. Which pair of variables is most strongly correlated?

ii. How can we reduce the number of variables based on these correlations?

iii. How would the correlations change if we normalized the data first?

g. Consider the first PC of the analysis of the 13 numerical variables in Table 4.12. Describe briefly what this PC represents.

4.2. **University Rankings.** The dataset on American college and university rankings (available from www.dataminingbook.com) contains information on 1302 American colleges and universities offering an undergraduate program. For each university, there are 17 measurements that include continuous measurements (such as tuition and graduation rate) and categorical measurements (such as location by state and whether it is a private or a public school).

a. Remove all categorical variables. Then remove all records with missing numerical measurements from the dataset.

b. Conduct a principal components analysis on the cleaned data and comment on the results. Should the data be normalized? Discuss what characterizes the components you consider key.

4.3. **Sales of Toyota Corolla Cars.** The file *ToyotaCorolla.csv* contains data on used cars (Toyota Corollas) on sale during late summer of 2004 in the Netherlands. It has 1436 records containing details on 38 attributes, including Price, Age, Kilometers, HP, and other specifications. The goal will be to predict the price of a used Toyota Corolla based on its specifications.

a. Identify the categorical variables.

b. Explain the relationship between a categorical variable and the series of binary dummy variables derived from it.

c. How many dummy binary variables are required to capture the information in a categorical variable with N categories?

d. Use Python to convert the categorical variables in this dataset into dummy variables, and explain in words, for one record, the values in the derived binary dummies.

e. Use Python to produce a correlation matrix and matrix plot. Comment on the relationships among variables.

4.4. **Chemical Features of Wine.** Table 4.14 shows the PCA output on data (non-normalized) in which the variables represent chemical characteristics of wine, and each case is a different wine.

a. The data are in the file *Wine.csv*. Consider the rows labeled "Proportion of Variance." Explain why the value for PC1 is so much greater than that of any other column.

b. Comment on the use of normalization (standardization) in part (a).

TABLE 4.14 PRINCIPAL COMPONENTS OF NON-NORMALIZED WINE DATA

code for running PCA on the wine data

```
wine_df = pd.read_csv('Wine.csv')
wine_df = wine_df.drop(columns=['Type'])
pcs = PCA()
pcs.fit(wine_df.dropna(axis=0))
pcsSummary_df = pd.DataFrame({'Standard deviation': np.sqrt(pcs.explained_variance_),
                              'Proportion of variance': pcs.explained_variance_ratio_,
                              'Cumulative proportion': np.cumsum(pcs.explained_variance_ratio_)})
pcsSummary_df = pcsSummary_df.transpose()
pcsSummary_df.columns = ['PC{}'.format(i) for i in range(1, len(pcsSummary_df.columns) + 1)]
pcsSummary_df.round(4)

                              PC1      PC2     PC3     PC4     PC5     PC6  \
Standard deviation       314.9632  13.1353  3.0722  2.2341  1.1085  0.9171
Proportion of variance     0.9981   0.0017  0.0001  0.0001  0.0000  0.0000
Cumulative proportion      0.9981   0.9998  0.9999  1.0000  1.0000  1.0000

                            PC7     PC8     PC9    PC10    PC11    PC12    PC13
Standard deviation       0.5282  0.3891  0.3348  0.2678  0.1938  0.1452  0.0906
Proportion of variance   0.0000  0.0000  0.0000  0.0000  0.0000  0.0000  0.0000
Cumulative proportion    1.0000  1.0000  1.0000  1.0000  1.0000  1.0000  1.0000

pcsComponents_df = pd.DataFrame(pcs.components_.transpose(), columns=pcsSummary_df.columns,
                                index=wine_df.columns)
pcsComponents_df.iloc[:,:5]

                           PC1       PC2       PC3       PC4       PC5
Alcohol               0.001659  0.001203 -0.016874 -0.141447  0.020337
Malic_Acid           -0.000681  0.002155 -0.122003 -0.160390 -0.612883
Ash                   0.000195  0.004594 -0.051987  0.009773  0.020176
Ash_Alcalinity       -0.004671  0.026450 -0.938593  0.330965  0.064352
Magnesium             0.017868  0.999344  0.029780  0.005394 -0.006149
Total_Phenols         0.000990  0.000878  0.040485  0.074585  0.315245
Flavanoids            0.001567 -0.000052  0.085443  0.169087  0.524761
Nonflavanoid_Phenols -0.000123 -0.001354 -0.013511 -0.010806 -0.029648
Proanthocyanins       0.000601  0.005004  0.024659  0.050121  0.251183
Color_Intensity       0.002327  0.015100 -0.291398 -0.878894  0.331747
Hue                   0.000171 -0.000763  0.025978  0.060035  0.051524
OD280_OD315           0.000705 -0.003495  0.070324  0.178200  0.260639
Proline               0.999823 -0.017774 -0.004529  0.003113 -0.002299
```

PART

III

Performance Evaluation

CHAPTER 5

Evaluating Predictive Performance

In this chapter, we discuss how the predictive performance of data mining methods can be assessed. We point out the danger of overfitting to the training data, and the need to test model performance on data that were not used in the training step. We discuss popular performance metrics. For prediction, metrics include Average Error, MAPE, and RMSE (based on the validation data). For classification tasks, metrics based on the confusion matrix include overall accuracy, specificity and sensitivity, and metrics that account for misclassification costs. We also show the relation between the choice of cutoff value and classification performance, and present the ROC (Receiver Operating Characteristic) curve, which is a popular chart for assessing method performance at different cutoff values. When the goal is to accurately classify the most interesting or important records, called *ranking*, rather than accurately classify the entire sample (e.g., the 10% of customers most likely to respond to an offer, or the 5% of claims most likely to be fraudulent), lift charts are used to assess performance. We also discuss the need for oversampling rare classes and how to adjust performance metrics for the oversampling. Finally, we mention the usefulness of comparing metrics based on the validation data to those based on the training data for the purpose of detecting overfitting. While some differences are expected, extreme differences can be indicative of overfitting.

Python

In this chapter, we will use `pandas` for data handling, `statsmodels` for regression models, `scikit-learn` for performance metrics, and `matplotlib` for visualization. We will also make use of the utility functions from the Python Utilities Functions Appendix.

import required functionality for this chapter

```
import math
import pandas as pd
from sklearn.model_selection import train_test_split
from sklearn.linear_model import LinearRegression
from sklearn.metrics import accuracy_score, roc_curve, auc
import matplotlib.pylab as plt

from dmba import regressionSummary, classificationSummary
from dmba import liftChart, gainsChart
```

5.1 | INTRODUCTION

In supervised learning, we are interested in predicting the outcome variable for new records. Three main types of outcomes of interest are:

Predicted numerical value: when the outcome variable is numerical (e.g., house price)

Predicted class membership: when the outcome variable is categorical (e.g., buyer/nonbuyer)

Propensity: the probability of class membership, when the outcome variable is categorical (e.g., the propensity to default)

Prediction methods are used for generating numerical predictions, while classification methods ("classifiers") are used for generating propensities and, using a cutoff value on the propensities, we can generate predicted class memberships.

A subtle distinction to keep in mind is the two distinct predictive uses of classifiers: one use, *classification*, is aimed at predicting class membership for new records. The other, *ranking*, is detecting among a set of new records the ones most likely to belong to a class of interest.

Let's now examine the approach for judging the usefulness of a prediction method used for generating numerical predictions (Section 5.2), a classifier used for classification (Section 5.3), and a classifier used for ranking (Section 5.4). In Section 5.5, we'll look at evaluating performance under the scenario of oversampling.

5.2 | EVALUATING PREDICTIVE PERFORMANCE

First, let us emphasize that predictive accuracy is not the same as goodness-of-fit. Classical statistical measures of performance are aimed at finding a model that fits well to the data on which the model was trained. In data mining, we are interested in models that have high predictive accuracy when applied to *new* records. Measures such as R^2 and standard error of estimate are common metrics in classical regression modeling, and residual analysis is used to gauge goodness-of-fit in that situation. However, these measures do not tell us much about the ability of the model to predict new records.

For assessing prediction performance, several measures are used. In all cases, the measures are based on the validation set, which serves as a more objective ground than the training set to assess predictive accuracy. This is because records in the validation set are more similar to the future records to be predicted, in the sense that they are not used to select predictors or to estimate the model parameters. Models are trained on the training set, applied to the validation set, and measures of accuracy then use the prediction errors on that validation set.

Naive Benchmark: The Average

The benchmark criterion in prediction is using the average outcome value (thereby ignoring all predictor information). In other words, the prediction for a new record is simply the average across the outcome values of the records in the training set ($\bar{y}$). This is sometimes called a naive benchmark. A good predictive model should outperform the benchmark criterion in terms of predictive accuracy.

Prediction Accuracy Measures

The prediction error for record i is defined as the difference between its actual outcome value and its predicted outcome value: $e_i = y_i - \hat{y}_i$. A few popular numerical measures of predictive accuracy are:

MAE (mean absolute error/deviation) = $\frac{1}{n}\sum_{i=1}^{n} |e_i|$. This gives the magnitude of the average absolute error.

Mean Error = $\frac{1}{n}\sum_{i=1}^{n} e_i$. This measure is similar to MAE except that it retains the sign of the errors, so that negative errors cancel out positive errors of the same magnitude. It therefore gives an indication of whether the predictions are on average over- or underpredicting the outcome variable.

MPE (mean percentage error) = $100 \times \frac{1}{n}\sum_{i=1}^{n} e_i / y_i$. This gives the percentage score of how predictions deviate from the actual values (on average), taking into account the direction of the error.

MAPE (mean absolute percentage error) = $100 \times \frac{1}{n} \sum_{i=1}^{n} |e_i / y_i|$. This measure gives a percentage score of how predictions deviate (on average) from the actual values.

RMSE (root mean squared error) = $\sqrt{\frac{1}{n} \sum_{i=1}^{n} e_i^2}$. This is similar to the standard error of estimate in linear regression, except that it is computed on the validation data rather than on the training data. It has the same units as the outcome variable.

Such measures can be used to compare models and to assess their degree of prediction accuracy. Note that all these measures are influenced by outliers. To check outlier influence, we can compute median-based measures (and compare to the above mean-based measures) or simply plot a histogram or boxplot of the errors. Plotting the prediction errors' distribution is in fact very useful and can highlight more information than the metrics alone. We will use the *Ent_Test.csv* dataset to explain the concepts here. This dataset carries 15 variables that pertain to aspirants of B-school admission who appear for various mock tests offered by different coaching institutions before the main test to improve their effectiveness and preparedness. The dataset also included scores of students in one of the major entrance tests as the target variable. There are also two case identifiers, four profile variables, the number of previous attempts for the same main test, and the number of mock tests attempted.

To illustrate the use of predictive accuracy measures and charts of prediction error distribution, consider the error metrics and charts shown in Table 5.1 and Figure 5.1. These are the result of fitting a certain predictive model to performance in the Main Test for students undergoing the coaching. The training set includes 1020 students and the validation set includes 680 students. Results are displayed separately for the training and validation sets. We can see from the histogram and boxplot corresponding to the validation set that most errors are in the [−20, 20] range.

Comparing Training and Validation Performance

Errors that are based on the training set tell us about model fit, whereas those that are based on the validation set (called "prediction errors") measure the model's ability to predict new data (predictive performance). We expect training errors to be smaller than the validation errors (because the model was fitted using the training set), and the more complex the model, the greater the likelihood that it will *overfit* the training data (indicated by a greater difference between the training and validation errors). In an extreme case of overfitting, the training errors would be zero (perfect fit of the model to the training data), and the validation errors would be non-zero and non-negligible. For this reason, it is important to compare the error plots and metrics (RMSE, MAE, etc.) of the training and validation sets. Table 5.1 illustrates this comparison: the training set performance measures appear slightly lower (better) than those for the validation set and the charts in Figure 5.1, which reveal more than the metrics alone, show a similar distribution of errors in the training and validation sets.

TABLE 5.1 PREDICTION ERROR METRICS FROM A MODEL FOR MAIN TEST TRAINING AND VALIDATION

code for accuracy measure

```
et=pd.read_csv('Ent_Test.csv')
# select columns for regression analysis)
# create a list of predictor variables by remvoing output variables and text columns
excludeColumns = ('CaseID', 'Cand_ID', 'Region', 'Degree', 'Gender', 'Coaching',
'Prev_Attempts','Main_Tst')
predictors = [s for s in et if s not in excludeColumns]
outcome = 'Main_Tst'
# partition data
X = et[predictors]
y = et[outcome]
train_X, valid_X, train_y, valid_y = train_test_split(X, y, test_size=0.4,random_state=1)
# train linear regression model
reg = LinearRegression()
reg.fit(train_X, train_y)
# evaluate performance
# training
regressionSummary(train_y, reg.predict(train_X))
# validation
regressionSummary(valid_y, reg.predict(valid_X))
```

Partial output

```
#  Training
Regression statistics

 Mean Error (ME) : -0.0000
 Root Mean Squared Error (RMSE) : 12.2056
 Mean Absolute Error (MAE) : 9.6835
 Mean Percentage Error (MPE) : -1.6237
 Mean Absolute Percentage Error (MAPE) : 10.1517
#  Validation
Regression statistics

 Mean Error (ME) : -1.0999
 Root Mean Squared Error (RMSE) : 11.8633
 Mean Absolute Error (MAE) : 9.4451
 Mean Percentage Error (MPE) : -2.7424
 Mean Absolute Percentage Error (MAPE) : 10.1747
```

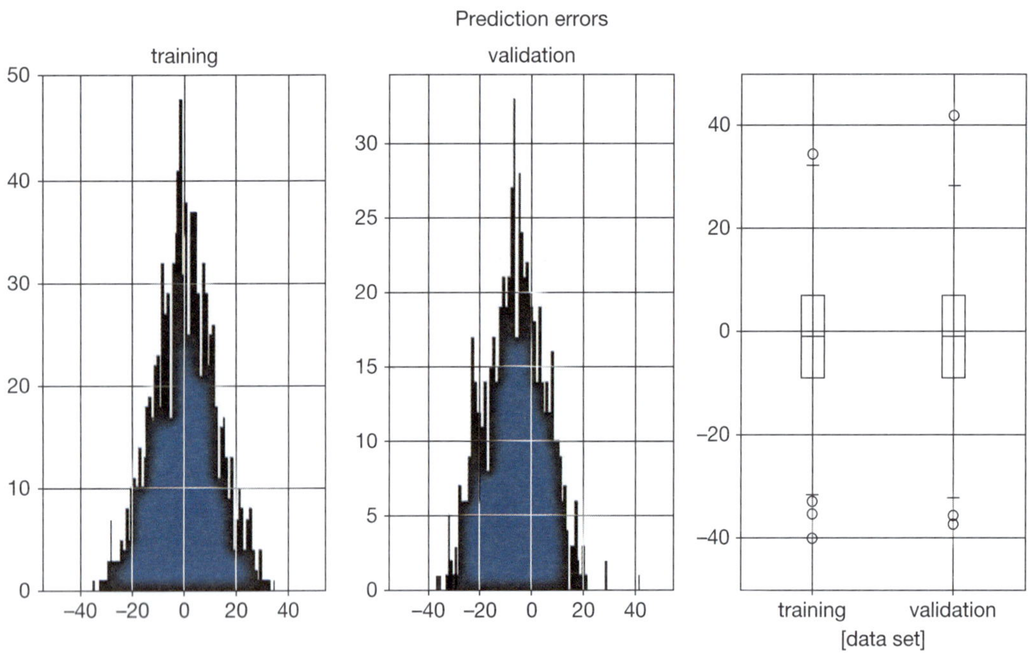

FIGURE 5.1 HISTOGRAMS AND BOXPLOTS OF ENT TEST DATA PREDICTION ERRORS, FOR TRAINING AND VALIDATION SETS

code for creating Figure 5.1

```
pred_error_train = pd.DataFrame({
     'residual': train_y - reg.predict(train_X),
     'data set': 'training'
})
pred_error_valid = pd.DataFrame({
    'residual': valid_y - reg.predict(valid_X),
    'data set': 'validation'
})
boxdata_df = pred_error_train.append(pred_error_valid, ignore_index=True)

fig, axes = plt.subplots(nrows=1, ncols=3)
fig.set_size_inches(14, 6)
common = {'bins': 100, 'range': [-50, 50]}
pred_error_train.hist(ax=axes[0], **common)
pred_error_valid.hist(ax=axes[1], **common)
boxdata_df.boxplot(ax=axes[2], by='data set')

axes[0].set_title('training')
axes[1].set_title('validation')
axes[2].set_title(' ')
axes[2].set_ylim(-50, 50)
plt.suptitle('Prediction errors')
plt.subplots_adjust(bottom=0.1, top=0.85, wspace=0.35)
plt.show()
```

Cumulative Gains and Lift Charts

In some applications, the goal is to search, among a set of new records, for a subset of records that gives the highest cumulative predicted values. In such cases, a graphical way to assess predictive performance is through the *cumulative gains chart* and *lift chart*. This compares the model's predictive performance to a baseline model that has no predictors.[1] Cumulative gains and lift charts for a continuous response are relevant only when we are searching for a set of records that gives the highest cumulative predicted values. Such charts are not relevant if we are interested in predicting the outcome value for *each* new record.

To illustrate this type of goal, called *ranking*, consider a car rental firm that renews its fleet regularly so that customers drive late-model cars. This entails disposing of a large quantity of used vehicles on a continuing basis. Since the firm is not primarily in the used car sales business, it tries to dispose of as much of its fleet as possible through volume sales to used car dealers. However, it is profitable to sell a limited number of cars through its own channels. Its volume deals with the used car dealers allow it flexibility to pick and choose which cars to sell in this fashion, so it would like to have a model for selecting cars for resale through its own channels. Since all cars were purchased some time ago and the deals with the used car dealers are for fixed prices (specifying a given number of cars of a certain make and model class), the cars' costs are now irrelevant and the dealer is interested only in maximizing revenue. This is done by selecting for its own resale, the cars likely to generate the most revenue. The lift chart in this case gives the predicted lift for revenue.

The cumulative gains and lift charts are based on ordering the set of records of interest (typically validation data) by their predicted value, from high to low. Then, we accumulate the actual values and plot their cumulative value (=gains) on the y-axis as a function of the number of records accumulated (the x-axis value). This is the *cumulative gains* curve. This curve is compared to assigning a naive prediction ($\hat{y}_i$) to each record and accumulating these average values, which results in a diagonal line. The further away the cumulative gains curve from the diagonal benchmark line, the better the model is doing in separating records with high value outcomes from those with low value outcomes. The same information can be presented in a decile lift chart, where the ordered records are grouped into 10 deciles, and for each decile, the chart presents the ratio of model gains to naive benchmark gains, which is called *lift*.

Figure 5.2 shows a cumulative gains chart and decile lift chart based on fitting a linear regression model to the Ent_Test data. The charts are based on the validation data of 680 students data. It can be seen that the model's predictive performance in

---

[1] The terms *lift* and *gains* are occasionally used interchangeably; to avoid confusion we use the prevalent definitions in which *cumulative gains* refers to the sum of outcome values for the top cases identified by a model, and *lift* to the ratio of that sum to the sum obtained through random selection.

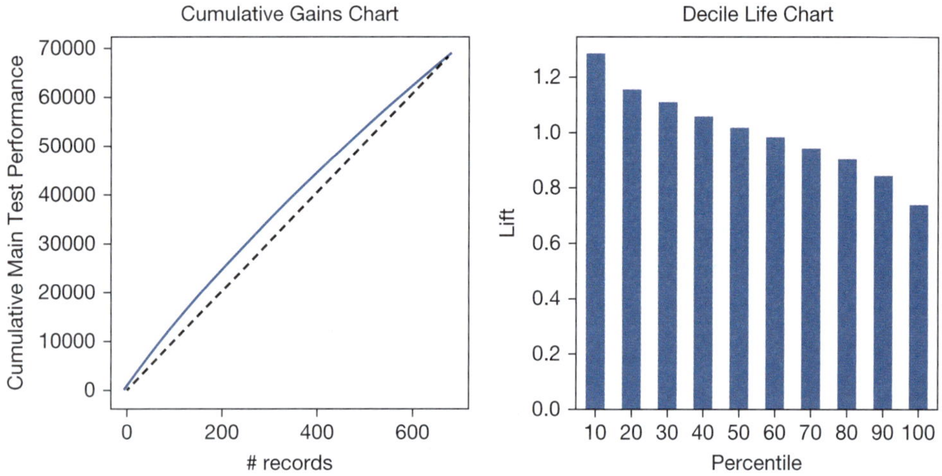

FIGURE 5.2 CUMULATIVE GAINS CHART AND DECILE LIFT CHART

code for generating cumulative gains and decile lift charts in Figure 5.2

```
pred_v = pd.Series(reg.predict(valid_X))
pred_v = pred_v.sort_values(ascending=False)

fig, axes = plt.subplots(nrows=1, ncols=2)
ax = gainsChart(pred_v, ax=axes[0])
ax.set_ylabel('Cumulative Main Test Performance')
ax.set_title('Cumulative Gains Chart')

ax = liftChart(pred_v, ax=axes[1], labelBars=False)
ax.set_ylabel('Lift')

plt.tight_layout()
plt.show()
```

terms of gains is better than the baseline model, since its cumulative gains curve is higher than that of the baseline model. The charts in Figure 5.2 would be useful in the following scenario: choosing the top 10% of the records that gave the highest predicted performing students, for example, we would identify right performing students based on this model 1.25 times more than picking 10% students at random. This lift number can also be computed from the cumulative gains chart by mapping the values.

5.3 | JUDGING CLASSIFIER PERFORMANCE

The need for performance measures arises from the wide choice of classifiers and predictive methods. Not only do we have several different methods, but even within a single method there are usually many options that can lead to completely different results. A simple example is the choice of predictors used within a particular predictive algorithm. Before we study these various algorithms in detail and face decisions on how to set these options, we need to know how we will measure success.

A natural criterion for judging the performance of a classifier is the probability of making a *misclassification error*. Misclassification means that the record belongs to one class but the model classifies it as a member of a different class. A classifier that makes no errors would be perfect, but we do not expect to be able to construct such classifiers in the real world due to "noise" and not having all the information needed to classify records precisely. Is there a minimal probability of misclassification that we should require of a classifier?

Benchmark: The Naive Rule

A very simple rule for classifying a record into one of m classes, ignoring all predictor information $(x_1, x_2, \ldots, x_p)$ that we may have, is to classify the record as a member of the majority class. In other words, "classify as belonging to the most prevalent class." The *naive rule* is used mainly as a baseline or benchmark for evaluating the performance of more complicated classifiers. Clearly, a classifier that uses external predictor information (on top of the class membership allocation) should outperform the naive rule. There are various performance measures based on the naive rule that measure how much better than the naive rule a certain classifier performs.

Similar to using the sample mean $(\hat{y}_i)$ as the naive benchmark in the numerical outcome case, the naive rule for classification relies solely on the y information and excludes any additional predictor information.

Class Separation

If the classes are well separated by the predictor information, even a small dataset will suffice in finding a good classifier, whereas if the classes are not separated at all by the predictors, even a very large dataset will not help. Figure 5.3 illustrates this for a two-class case. Panel (a) includes a small dataset ($n = 24$ records) where two predictors (income and lot size) are used for separating owners from nonowners (we thank Dean Wichern for this example, described in Johnson and Wichern, 2002). Here, the predictor information seems useful in that it separates the two classes (owners/nonowners). Panel (b) shows a much larger dataset ($n = 5000$ records) where the two predictors (income and monthly average credit card spending) do not separate the two classes well in most of the higher ranges (loan acceptors/nonacceptors).

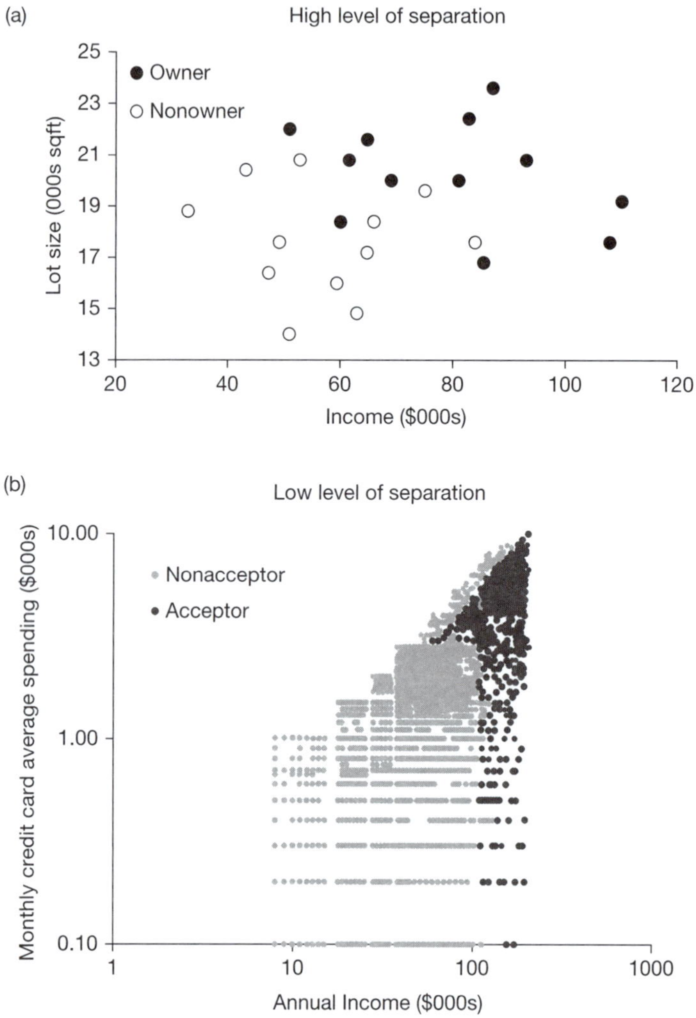

FIGURE 5.3 HIGH (a) AND LOW (b) LEVELS OF SEPARATION BETWEEN TWO CLASSES, USING TWO PREDICTORS

The Confusion (Classification) Matrix

In practice, most accuracy measures are derived from the *confusion matrix*, also called *classification matrix*. This matrix summarizes the correct and incorrect classifications that a classifier produced for a certain dataset. Rows and columns of the confusion matrix correspond to the predicted and true (actual) classes, respectively. Table 5.2 shows an example of a classification (confusion) matrix for a two-class (0/1) problem resulting from applying a certain classifier to 3000 records. The two diagonal cells (upper left, lower right) give the number of correct classifications, where the predicted class coincides with the actual class of the record. The off-diagonal cells give counts of misclassification. The lower left cell gives the number of class 1 members that were

TABLE 5.2 CONFUSION MATRIX BASED ON 3000 RECORDS AND TWO CLASSES

	Predict class 0	Predict class 1
Actual 0	2689	25
Actual 1	85	201

misclassified as 0's (in this example, there were 85 such misclassifications). Similarly, the upper right cell gives the number of class 0 members that were misclassified as 1's (25 such records). In Python, we can obtain a confusion matrix using the function *confusion_matrix()* in the `scikit-learn` package. This function creates the cross-tabulation of actual and predicted classes. The utility *ClassificationSummary* (see Appendix) produces a more readable confusion matrix. We will see an example later in this chapter.

The confusion matrix gives estimates of the true classification and misclassification rates. Of course, these are estimates and they can be incorrect, but if we have a large enough dataset and neither class is very rare, our estimates will be reliable. Sometimes, we may be able to use public data such as US Census data to estimate these proportions. However, in most business settings, we will not know them.

Using the Validation Data

To obtain an honest estimate of future classification error, we use the confusion matrix that is computed from the *validation data*. In other words, we first partition the data into training and validation sets by random selection of records. We then construct a classifier using the training data, and then apply it to the validation data. This will yield the predicted classifications for records in the validation set (see Figure 2.4 in Chapter 2). We then summarize these classifications in a confusion matrix. Although we can summarize our results in a confusion matrix for training data as well, the resulting confusion matrix is not useful for getting an honest estimate of the misclassification rate for new data due to the danger of overfitting.

In addition to examining the validation data confusion matrix to assess the classification performance on new data, we compare the training data confusion matrix to the validation data confusion matrix, in order to detect overfitting: although we expect somewhat inferior results on the validation data, a large discrepancy in training and validation performance might be indicative of overfitting.

Accuracy Measures

Different accuracy measures can be derived from the classification matrix. Consider a two-class case with classes C_1 and C_2 (e.g., buyer/non-buyer). The schematic confusion matrix in Table 5.3 uses the notation $n_{i,j}$ to denote the number of records that are class C_i members and were classified as C_j members. Of course, if $i \neq j$, these are counts of misclassifications. The total number of records is $n = n_{1,1} + n_{1,2} + n_{2,1} + n_{2,2}$.

TABLE 5.3 CONFUSION MATRIX: MEANING OF EACH CELL

		Predicted class	
		C_1	C_2
Actual class	C_1	$n_{1,1}$ = number of C_1 records classified correctly	$n_{1,2}$ = number of C_1 records classified incorrectly as C_2
	C_2	$n_{2,1}$ = number of C_2 records classified incorrectly as C_1	$n_{2,2}$ = number of C_2 records classified correctly

A main accuracy measure is the *estimated misclassification rate*, also called the *overall error rate*. It is given by

$$\text{err} = \frac{n_{1,2} + n_{2,1}}{n},$$

where n is the total number of records in the validation dataset. In the example in Table 5.2, we get err $= (25 + 85)/3000 = 3.67\%$.

We can measure accuracy by looking at the correct classifications—the full half of the cup—instead of the misclassifications. The *overall accuracy* of a classifier is estimated by

$$\text{accuracy} = 1 - \text{err} = \frac{n_{1,1} + n_{2,2}}{n}.$$

In the example, we have $(201 + 2689)/3000 = 96.33\%$.

Propensities and Cutoff for Classification

The first step in most classification algorithms is to estimate the probability that a record belongs to each of the classes. These probabilities are also called *propensities*. Propensities are typically used either as an interim step for generating predicted class membership (classification), or for rank-ordering the records by their probability of belonging to a class of interest. Let us consider their first use in this section. The second use is discussed in Section 5.4.

If overall classification accuracy (involving all the classes) is of interest, the record can be assigned to the class with the highest probability. In many records, a single class is of special interest, so we will focus on that particular class and compare the propensity of belonging to that class to a *cutoff value* set by the analyst. This approach can be used with two classes or more than two classes, though it may make sense in such cases to consolidate classes so that you end up with two: the class of interest and all other classes. If the probability of belonging to the class of interest is above the cutoff, the record is assigned to that class.

CUTOFF VALUES FOR TRIAGE

In some cases, it is useful to have two cutoffs, and allow a "cannot say" option for the classifier. In a two-class situation, this means that for a record, we can make one of three predictions: The record belongs to C_1, or the record belongs to C_2, or we cannot make a prediction because there is not enough information to pick C_1 or C_2 confidently. Records that the classifier cannot classify are subjected to closer scrutiny either by using expert judgment or by enriching the set of predictor variables by gathering additional information that is perhaps more difficult or expensive to obtain. An example is classification of documents found during legal discovery (reciprocal forced document disclosure in a legal proceeding). Under traditional human-review systems, qualified legal personnel are needed to review what might be tens of thousands of documents to determine their relevance to a case. Using a classifier and a triage outcome, documents could be sorted into clearly relevant, clearly not relevant, and the gray area documents requiring human review. This substantially reduces the costs of discovery.

The default cutoff value in two-class classifiers is 0.5. Thus, if the probability of a record being a class C_1 member is greater than 0.5, that record is classified as a C_1. Any record with an estimated probability of less than 0.5 would be classified as a C_2. It is possible, however, to use a cutoff that is either higher or lower than 0.5. A cutoff greater than 0.5 will end up classifying fewer records as C_1's, whereas a cutoff less than 0.5 will end up classifying more records as C_1. Typically, the misclassification rate will rise in either case.

Consider the data in Table 5.4, showing the actual class for 24 records, sorted by the probability that the record is an "owner" (as estimated by a data mining algorithm). If we adopt the standard 0.5 as the cutoff, our misclassification rate is 3/24, whereas if we instead adopt a cutoff of 0.25, we classify more records as owners and the misclassification rate goes up (comprising more nonowners misclassified as owners) to 5/24. Conversely, if we adopt a cutoff of 0.75, we classify fewer records as owners. The misclassification rate goes up (comprising more owners misclassified as nonowners) to 6/24. All this can be seen in the classification tables in Table 5.5.

To see the entire range of cutoff values and how the accuracy or misclassification rates change as a function of the cutoff, we can plot the performance measure of interest vs. the cutoff. The results for the riding mowers example are shown in Figure 5.4. We can see that the accuracy level is pretty stable around 0.8 for cutoff values between 0.2 and 0.8.

TABLE 5.4 24 RECORDS WITH THEIR ACTUAL CLASS AND THE PROBABILITY (PROPENSITY) OF THEM BEING CLASS "OWNER" MEMBERS, AS ESTIMATED BY A CLASSIFIER

Actual class	Probability of class "owner"	Actual class	Probability of class "owner"
Owner	0.9959	Owner	0.5055
Owner	0.9875	Nonowner	0.4713
Owner	0.9844	Nonowner	0.3371
Owner	0.9804	Owner	0.2179
Owner	0.9481	Nonowner	0.1992
Owner	0.8892	Nonowner	0.1494
Owner	0.8476	Nonowner	0.0479
Nonowner	0.7628	Nonowner	0.0383
Owner	0.7069	Nonowner	0.0248
Owner	0.6807	Nonowner	0.0218
Owner	0.6563	Nonowner	0.0161
Nonowner	0.6224	Nonowner	0.0031

TABLE 5.5 CONFUSION MATRICES BASED ON CUTOFFS OF 0.5, 0.25, AND 0.75 (RIDING MOWERS EXAMPLE)

```
owner_df = pd.read_csv('ownerExample.csv')

## cutoff = 0.5
predicted = ['owner' if p > 0.5 else 'nonowner' for p in owner_df.Probability]
classificationSummary(owner_df.Class, predicted, class_names=['nonowner', 'owner'])

Confusion Matrix (Accuracy 0.8750)

       Prediction
 Actual nonowner    owner
nonowner       10       2
 owner          1      11

## cutoff = 0.25
predicted = ['owner' if p > 0.25 else 'nonowner' for p in owner_df.Probability]
classificationSummary(owner_df.Class, predicted, class_names=['nonowner', 'owner'])

Confusion Matrix (Accuracy 0.7917)

       Prediction
 Actual nonowner    owner
nonowner        8       4
 owner          1      11

## cutoff = 0.75
predicted = ['owner' if p > 0.75 else 'nonowner' for p in owner_df.Probability]
classificationSummary(owner_df.Class, predicted, class_names=['nonowner', 'owner'])
```

TABLE 5.5 CONFUSION MATRICES BASED ON CUTOFFS OF 0.5, 0.25, AND 0.75 (RIDING MOWERS EXAMPLE) (*Continued*)

```
Confusion Matrix (Accuracy 0.7500)

        Prediction
 Actual nonowner   owner
nonowner       11       1
 owner          5       7
```

function *classificationSummary* can be found in the Python Utilities Functions Appendix.

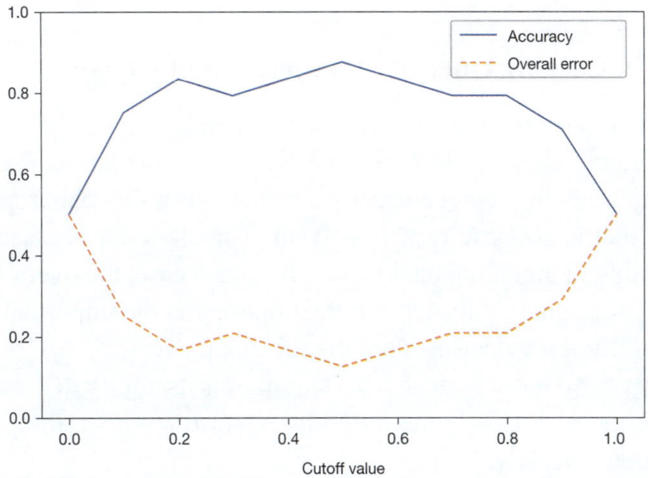

FIGURE 5.4 PLOTTING ACCURACY AND OVERALL ERROR AS A FUNCTION OF THE CUTOFF VALUE (RIDING MOWERS EXAMPLE)

code for creating Figure 5.4

```
df = pd.read_csv('liftExample.csv')

cutoffs = [i * 0.1 for i in range(0, 11)]
accT = []
for cutoff in cutoffs:
    predicted = [1 if p > cutoff else 0 for p in df.prob]
    accT.append(accuracy_score(df.actual, predicted))

line_accuracy = plt.plot(cutoffs, accT, '-', label='Accuracy')[0]
line_error = plt.plot(cutoffs, [1 - acc for acc in accT], '--', label='Overall error')[0]
plt.ylim([0,1])
plt.xlabel('Cutoff Value')
plt.legend(handles=[line_accuracy, line_error])
plt.show()
```

Why would we want to use cutoff values different from 0.5 if they increase the misclassification rate? The answer is that it might be more important to classify owners properly than nonowners, and we would tolerate a greater misclassification of the latter. Or the reverse might be true; in other words, the costs of misclassification might be asymmetric. We can adjust the cutoff value in such a case to classify more records as the high-value class, that is, accept more misclassifications where the misclassification cost is low. Keep in mind that we are doing so after the data mining model has already been selected—we are not changing that model. It is also possible to incorporate costs into the picture before deriving the model. These subjects are discussed in greater detail below.

Performance in Case of Unequal Importance of Classes

Suppose that it is more important to predict membership correctly in class C_1 than in class C_2. An example is predicting the financial status (bankrupt/solvent) of firms. It may be more important to predict correctly a firm that is going bankrupt than to predict correctly a firm that is going to remain solvent. The classifier is essentially used as a system for detecting or signaling bankruptcy. In such a case, the overall accuracy is not a good measure for evaluating the classifier. Suppose that the important class is C_1. The following pair of accuracy measures are the most popular:

The sensitivity (also termed recall) of a classifier is its ability to detect the important class members correctly. This is measured by $n_{1,1} / (n_{1,1} + n_{1,2})$, the percentage of C_1 members classified correctly.

The specificity of a classifier is its ability to rule out C_2 members correctly. This is measured by $n_{2,2} / (n_{2,1} + n_{2,2})$, the percentage of C_2 members classified correctly.

It can be useful to plot these measures against the cutoff value in order to find a cutoff value that balances these measures.

ROC Curve A more popular method for plotting the two measures is through *ROC* (Receiver Operating Characteristic) *curves*. Starting from the lower left, the ROC curve plots the pairs {sensitivity, specificity} as the cutoff value descends from 1 to 0. (A typical alternative presentation is to plot 1-specificity on the x-axis, which allows 0 to be placed on the left end of the axis, and 1 on the right.) Better performance is reflected by curves that are closer to the top-left corner. The comparison curve is the diagonal, which reflects the average performance of a guessing classifier that has no information about the predictors or outcome variable. This guessing classifier guesses that a proportion α of the records is 1's and therefore assigns each record an equal probability $P(Y = 1) = \alpha$. In this case, on average, a proportion α of the 1's will be correctly classified (Sensitivity = α), and a proportion α of the 0s will be correctly classified (1 – Specificity = α). As we increase the cutoff value α from 0 to 1, we get the diagonal line Sensitivity = 1 − Specificity. Note that the naive rule is one point on this diagonal line, where α = proportion of actual 1's.

A common metric to summarize an ROC curve is "area under the curve (AUC)," which ranges from 1 (perfect discrimination between classes) to 0.5 (no better than random guessing). The ROC curve for the owner/nonowner example and its corresponding AUC are shown in Figure 5.5.

COMPUTING RATES: FROM WHOSE POINT OF VIEW?

Sensitivity and specificity measure the performance of a classifier from the point of view of the "classifying agency" (e.g., a company classifying customers or a hospital classifying patients). They answer the question "how well does the classifier segregate the important class members?". It is also possible to measure accuracy from the perspective of the entity being classified (e.g., the customer or the patient), who asks "given my predicted class, what is my chance of actually belonging to that class?", although this question is usually less relevant in a data mining application. The terms "false discovery rate" and "false omission rate" are measures of performance from the perspective of the individual entity. If C_1 is the important (positive) class, then they are defined as

The false discovery rate (FDR) is the proportion of C_1 predictions that are wrong, equal to $n_{2,1}/(n_{1,1}+n_{2,1})$. Note that this is a ratio within the row of C_1 predictions (i.e., it uses only records that were classified as C_1).

The false omission rate (FOR) is the proportion of C_2 predictions that are wrong, equal to $n_{1,2}/(n_{1,2}+n_{2,2})$. Note that this is a ratio within the row of C_2 predictions (i.e., it uses only records that were classified as C_2).

Asymmetric Misclassification Costs

Implicit in our discussion of the lift curve, which measures how effective we are in identifying the members of one particular class, is the assumption that the error of misclassifying a record belonging to one class is more serious than for the other class. For example, misclassifying a household as unlikely to respond to a sales offer when it belongs to the class that would respond incurs a greater cost (the opportunity cost of the foregone sale) than the converse error. In the former case, you are missing out on a sale worth perhaps tens or hundreds of dollars. In the latter, you are incurring the costs of contacting someone who will not purchase. In such a scenario, using the misclassification rate as a criterion can be misleading.

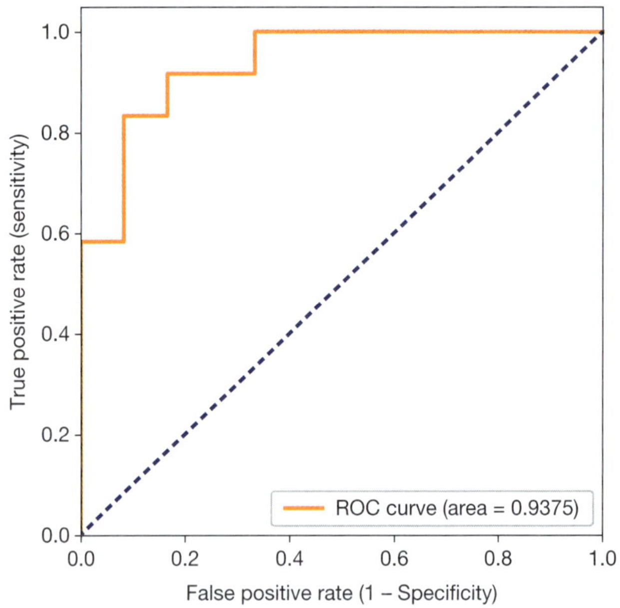

FIGURE 5.5 ROC CURVE FOR RIDING MOWERS EXAMPLE

code for generating ROC curve and computing AUC

```
from sklearn.metrics import roc_curve, auc

# compute ROC curve and AUC
fpr, tpr, _ = roc_curve(df.actual, df.prob)
roc_auc = auc(fpr, tpr)

plt.figure(figsize=[5, 5])
plt.plot(fpr, tpr, color='darkorange',
        lw=2, label='ROC curve (area = %0.4f)' % roc_auc)
plt.plot([0, 1], [0, 1], color='navy', lw=2, linestyle='--')
plt.xlim([0.0, 1.0])
plt.ylim([0.0, 1.05])
plt.xlabel('False Positive Rate (1 - Specificity)')
plt.ylabel('True Positive Rate (Sensitivity)')
plt.legend(loc="lower right")
```

Note that we are assuming that the cost (or benefit) of making correct classifications is zero. At first glance, this may seem incomplete. After all, the benefit (negative cost) of classifying a buyer correctly as a buyer would seem substantial. And in other circumstances (e.g., scoring our classification algorithm to fresh data to implement our decisions), it will be appropriate to consider the actual net dollar impact of each possible classification (or misclassification). Here, however, we are attempting to assess the value of a classifier in terms of classification error, so it greatly simplifies matters if we can capture all cost/benefit information in the misclassification cells. So, instead of recording the benefit of classifying a respondent household correctly, we record the cost of failing to classify it as a respondent household. It amounts to the same thing and our goal becomes the minimization of costs, whether the costs are actual costs or missed benefits (opportunity costs).

Consider the situation where the sales offer is mailed to a random sample of people for the purpose of constructing a good classifier. Suppose that the offer is accepted by 1% of those households. For these data, if a classifier simply classifies every household as a non-responder, it will have an error rate of only 1% but it will be useless in practice. A classifier that misclassifies 2% of buying households as nonbuyers and 20% of the nonbuyers as buyers would have a higher error rate but would be better if the profit from a sale is substantially higher than the cost of sending out an offer. In these situations, if we have estimates of the cost of both types of misclassification, we can use the confusion matrix to compute the expected cost of misclassification for each record in the validation data. This enables us to compare different classifiers using overall expected costs (or profits) as the criterion.

Suppose that we are considering sending an offer to 1000 more people, where on average 1% of whom respond (1). Naively classifying everyone as a 0 has an error rate of only 1%. Using a data mining routine, suppose that we can produce these classifications:

	Predict class 0	Predict class 1
Actual 0	970	20
Actual 1	2	8

These classifications have an error rate of $100 \times (20 + 2)/1000 = 2.2\%$—higher than the naive rate.

Now suppose that the profit from a responder is \$10 and the cost of sending the offer is \$1. Classifying everyone as a 0 still has a misclassification rate of only 1%, but yields a profit of \$0. Using the data mining routine, despite the higher misclassification rate, yields a profit of \$60.

The matrix of profit is as follows (nothing is sent to the predicted 0's so there are no costs or sales in that column):

Profit	Predict class 0	Predict class 1
Actual 0	0	–\$20
Actual 1	0	\$80

Looked at purely in terms of costs, when everyone is classified as a 0, there are no costs of sending the offer; the only costs are the opportunity costs of failing to make sales to the ten 1's = \$100. The cost (actual costs of sending the offer, plus the opportunity costs of missed sales) of using the data mining routine to select people to send the offer to is only \$48, as follows:

Costs	Predict class 0	Predict class 1
Actual 0	0	\$20
Actual 1	\$20	\$8

However, this does not improve the actual classifications themselves. A better method is to change the classification rules (and hence the misclassification rates) as discussed in the preceding section, to reflect the asymmetric costs.

A popular performance measure that includes costs is the *average misclassification cost*, which measures the average cost of misclassification per classified record. Denote by q_1 the cost of misclassifying a class C_1 record (as belonging to class C_2) and by q_2 the cost of misclassifying a class C_2 record (as belonging to class C_1). The average misclassification cost is

$$\frac{q_1 n_{1,2} + q_2 n_{2,1}}{n}.$$

Thus, we are looking for a classifier that minimizes this quantity. This can be computed, for instance, for different cutoff values.

It turns out that the optimal parameters are affected by the misclassification costs only through the ratio of these costs. This can be seen if we write the foregoing measure slightly differently:

$$\frac{q_1 n_{1,2} + q_2 n_{2,1}}{n} = \frac{n_{1,2}}{n_{1,1} + n_{1,2}} \frac{n_{1,1} + n_{1,2}}{n} q_1 + \frac{n_{2,1}}{n_{2,1} + n_{2,2}} \frac{n_{2,1} + n_{2,2}}{n} q_2.$$

Minimizing this expression is equivalent to minimizing the same expression divided by a constant. If we divide by q_1, it can be seen clearly that the minimization depends only on q_2/q_1 and not on their individual values. This is very practical, because in many cases it is difficult to assess the costs associated with misclassifying a C_1 member and a C_2 member, but estimating the ratio is easier.

This expression is a reasonable estimate of future misclassification cost if the proportions of classes C_1 and C_2 in the sample data are similar to the proportions of classes C_1 and C_2 that are expected in the future. If instead of a random sample, we draw a sample such that one class is oversampled (as described in the next section), then the sample proportions of C_1's and C_2's will be distorted compared to the future or population. We can then correct the average misclassification cost measure for the distorted sample proportions by incorporating estimates of the true proportions (from external data or domain knowledge), denoted by $p(C_1)$ and $p(C_2)$, into the formula:

$$\frac{n_{1,2}}{n_{1,1} + n_{1,2}} p(C_1)\, q_1 + \frac{n_{2,1}}{n_{2,1} + n_{2,2}} p(C_2)\, q_2.$$

Using the same logic as above, it can be shown that optimizing this quantity depends on the costs only through their ratio (q_2 / q_1) and on the prior probabilities only through their ratio $[p(C_2) / p(C_1)]$. This is why software packages that incorporate costs and prior probabilities might prompt the user for ratios rather than actual costs and probabilities.

Generalization to More Than Two Classes

All the comments made above about two-class classifiers extend readily to classification into more than two classes. Let us suppose that we have m classes $C_1, C_2, \ldots, C_m$. The confusion matrix has m rows and m columns. The misclassification cost associated with the diagonal cells is, of course, always zero. Incorporating prior probabilities of the various classes (where now we have m such numbers) is still done in the same manner. However, evaluating misclassification costs becomes much more complicated: For an m-class case, we have $m(m - 1)$ types of misclassifications. Constructing a matrix of misclassification costs thus becomes prohibitively complicated.

5.4 | JUDGING RANKING PERFORMANCE

We now turn to the predictive goal of detecting, among a set of new records, the ones most likely to belong to a class of interest. Recall that this differs from the goal of predicting class membership for each new record.

Gains and Lift Charts for Binary Data

We already introduced cumulative gains charts and lift charts in the context of a numerical outcome (Section 5.2). We now describe these charts for a binary outcome. This is a more common usage than for predicted continuous outcomes. The gains and lift help us determine how effectively we can "skim the cream" by selecting a relatively small number of records and getting a relatively large portion of the responders.[2] The input required to construct these charts is a validation dataset that has been "scored" by appending to each record the propensity that it will belong to a given class.

---

[2]The terms *lift* and *gains* are occasionally used interchangeably; to avoid confusion we use the prevalent definitions in which *gains* refers to total numbers or percentages of cases of interest identified by a model, and *lift* to the ratio of such cases to those found through random selection.

Let's continue with the case in which a particular class is relatively rare and of much more interest than the other class: tax cheats, debt defaulters, or responders to a mailing. We would like our classification model to sift through the records and sort them according to which ones are most likely to be tax cheats, responders to the mailing, and so on. We can then make more informed decisions. For example, we can decide how many and which tax returns to examine if looking for tax cheats. The model will give us an estimate of the extent to which we will encounter more and more non-cheaters as we proceed through the sorted data starting with the records most likely to be tax cheats. Or we can use the sorted data to decide to which potential customers a limited-budget mailing should be targeted. In other words, we are describing the case when our goal is to obtain a rank ordering among the records according to their class membership propensities.

Sorting by Propensity To construct a cumulative gains chart, we sort the set of records by propensity, in descending order. This is the propensity to belong to the important class, say C_1. Then, in each row, we compute the cumulative number of C_1 members (Actual Class = C_1). For example, Table 5.6 shows the 24 records ordered in descending class "1" propensity. The right-most column accumulates the number of actual 1's. The cumulative gains chart then plots this cumulative column against the number of records.

It is straightforward to create a cumulative gains chart in Python—see Figure 5.6.

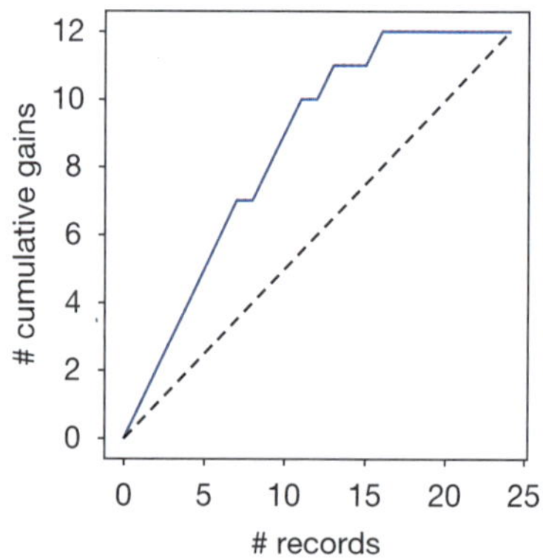

FIGURE 5.6 CUMULATIVE GAINS CHART FOR THE MOWER EXAMPLE

code for creating a cumulative gains chart

```
df = pd.read_csv('liftExample.csv')
df = df.sort_values(by=['prob'], ascending=False)
gainsChart(df.actual, figsize=(4, 4))
```

TABLE 5.6 RECORDS SORTED BY PROPENSITY OF OWNERSHIP (HIGH TO LOW) FOR THE MOWER EXAMPLE

Obs	Propensity of 1	Actual class	Cumulative actual class
1	0.995976726	1	1
2	0.987533139	1	2
3	0.984456382	1	3
4	0.980439587	1	4
5	0.948110638	1	5
6	0.889297203	1	6
7	0.847631864	1	7
8	0.762806287	0	7
9	0.706991915	1	8
10	0.680754087	1	9
11	0.656343749	1	10
12	0.622419543	0	10
13	0.505506928	1	11
14	0.471340450	0	11
15	0.337117362	0	11
16	0.217967810	1	12
17	0.199240432	0	12
18	0.149482655	0	12
19	0.047962588	0	12
20	0.038341401	0	12
21	0.024850999	0	12
22	0.021806029	0	12
23	0.016129906	0	12
24	0.003559986	0	12

Interpreting the Cumulative Gains Chart What is considered good or bad performance? The ideal ranking performance would place all the 1's at the beginning (the actual 1's would have the highest propensities and be at the top of the table), and all the 0's at the end. A curve corresponding to this ideal case would be a diagonal line with slope 1 which turns into a horizontal line (once all the 1's were accumulated). In the example, the curve for the best possible classifier—a classifier that makes no errors—would overlap the existing curve at the start, continue with a slope of 1 until it reached all the twelve 1's, then continue horizontally to the right.

In contrast, a useless model would be one that randomly assigns propensities (shuffling the 1's and 0's randomly in the Actual Class column). Such behavior would increase the cumulative number of 1's, on average, by $\frac{\#1's}{n}$ in each row. And in fact, this is the diagonal dotted line joining the points (0,0) to (24,12) seen in Figure 5.6. This serves as a reference line. For any given number of records (the x-axis value), it represents the expected number of 1 classifications (=gains) if we did not have a model but simply selected records at random. It provides a benchmark against which we can evaluate the ranking performance of the model. In this example, although our model is not perfect, it seems to perform much better than the random benchmark.

How do we read a cumulative gains chart? For a given number of records (x-axis), the gains curve value on the y-axis tells us how much better we gain, and we can compare it to the gains from random assignment. For example, looking at Figure 5.6, if we use our model to choose the top 10 records, the curve tells us that we would be right for about nine of them. If we simply select 10 records at random, we expect to be right for $10 \times 12/24 = 5$ records. In terms of lift, the model gives us a "lift" in detecting class 1 members of $9/5 = 1.8$. The lift will vary with the number of records we choose to act on. A good classifier will give us a high lift when we act on only a few records. As we include more records, the lift will typically decrease.

Decile Lift Charts

The information from the cumulative gains chart can be portrayed as a *decile lift chart*, as shown in Figure 5.7, which is widely used in direct marketing predictive modeling. The decile lift chart aggregates all the lift information into 10 buckets. The bars show, on the y-axis, the factor by which our model outperforms a random assignment of 0's and 1's, taking one decile at a time. Reading the bar on the left, we see that taking 10% of the records that are ranked by the model as "the most probable 1's" (having the highest propensities) yields twice as many 1's as would a random selection of 10% of the records. In this example, the decile lift chart indicates that we can even use the model to select the top 40% records with the highest propensities and still perform almost twice as well as random.

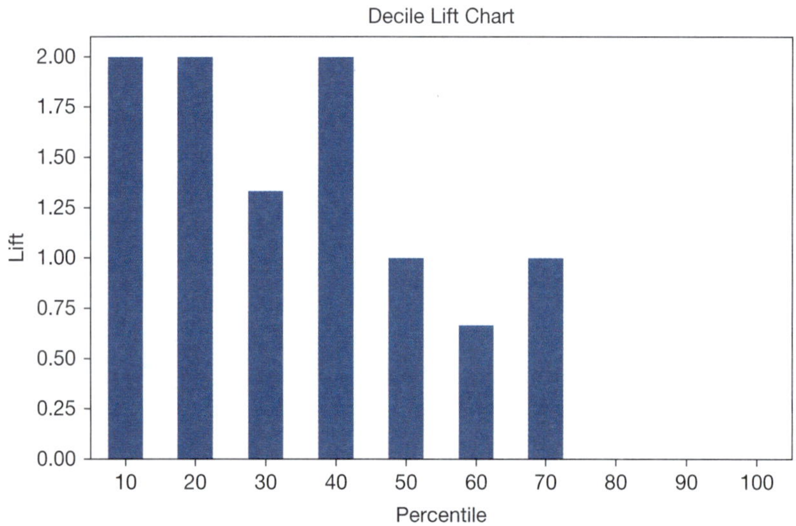

FIGURE 5.7 DECILE LIFT CHART

code for creating a decile lift chart

```
# use liftChart method from utilities
liftChart(df.actual, labelBars=False)
```

Beyond Two Classes

Gains and lift charts cannot be used with a multiclass classifier unless a single "important class" is defined and the classifications are reduced to "important" and "unimportant" classes.

Gains and Lift Charts Incorporating Costs and Benefits

When the benefits and costs of correct and incorrect classification are known or can be estimated, the gains and lift charts are still a useful presentation and decision tool. As before, we need a classifier that assigns to each record a propensity that it belongs to a particular class. The procedure is then as follows:

1. Sort the records in descending order of predicted probability of success (where *success* = belonging to the class of interest).
2. For each record, record the cost (benefit) associated with the actual outcome.
3. For the highest propensity (i.e., first) record, its x-axis value is 1 and its y-axis value is its cost or benefit (computed in Step 2) on the cumulative gains curve.
4. For the next record, again calculate the cost (benefit) associated with the actual outcome. Add this to the cost (benefit) for the previous record. This sum is the y-axis coordinate of the second point on the cumulative gains curve. Its x-axis value is 2.
5. Repeat Step 4 until all records have been examined. Connect all the points, and this is the cumulative gains curve.
6. The reference line is a straight line from the origin to the point y = total net benefit and $x = n (n = \text{number of records})$.

Note: It is entirely possible for a reference line that incorporates costs and benefits to have a negative slope if the net value for the entire dataset is negative. For example, if the cost of mailing to a person is \$0.65, the value of a responder is \$25, and the overall response rate is 2%, the expected net value of mailing to a list of 10,000 is $(0.02 \times \$25 \times 10,000) - (\$0.65 \times 10,000) = \$5000 - \$6500 = -\$1500$. Hence, the y-value at the far right of the lift curve (x = 10,000) is −1500, and the slope of

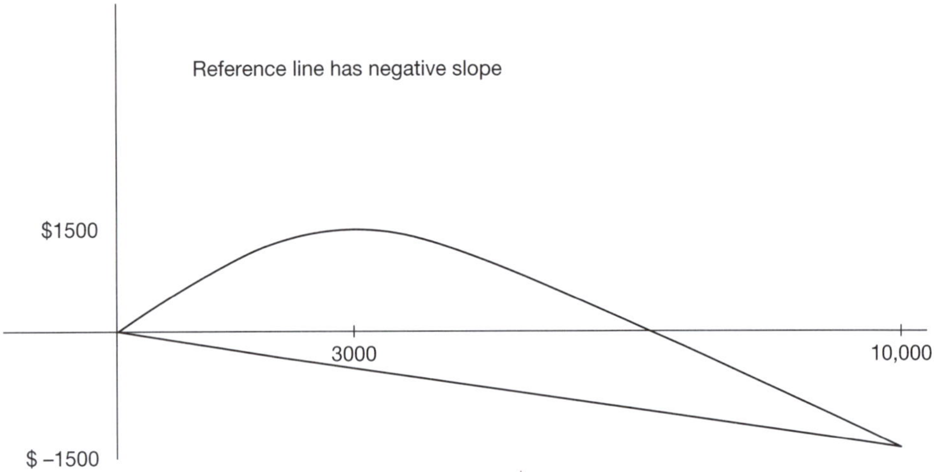

FIGURE 5.8 CUMULATIVE GAINS CURVE INCORPORATING COSTS

the reference line from the origin will be negative. The optimal point will be where the cumulative gains curve is at a maximum (i.e., mailing to about 3000 people) in Figure 5.8.

Cumulative Gains as a Function of Cutoff

We could also plot the cumulative gains as a function of the cutoff value. The only difference is the scale on the x-axis. When the goal is to select the top records based on a certain budget, the cumulative gains vs. number of records is preferable. In contrast, when the goal is to find a cutoff that distinguishes well between the two classes, the cumulative gains vs. cutoff value is more useful.

5.5 | OVERSAMPLING

As we saw briefly in Chapter 2, when classes are present in very unequal proportions, simple random sampling may produce too few of the rare class to yield useful information about what distinguishes them from the dominant class. In such cases, stratified sampling is often used to oversample the records from the rarer class and improve the performance of classifiers. It is often the case that the rarer events are the more interesting or important ones: responders to a mailing, those who commit fraud, defaulters on debt, and the like. This same stratified sampling procedure is sometimes called *weighted sampling* or *undersampling*, the latter referring to the fact that the more plentiful class is undersampled, relative to the rare class. We shall stick to the term *oversampling*.

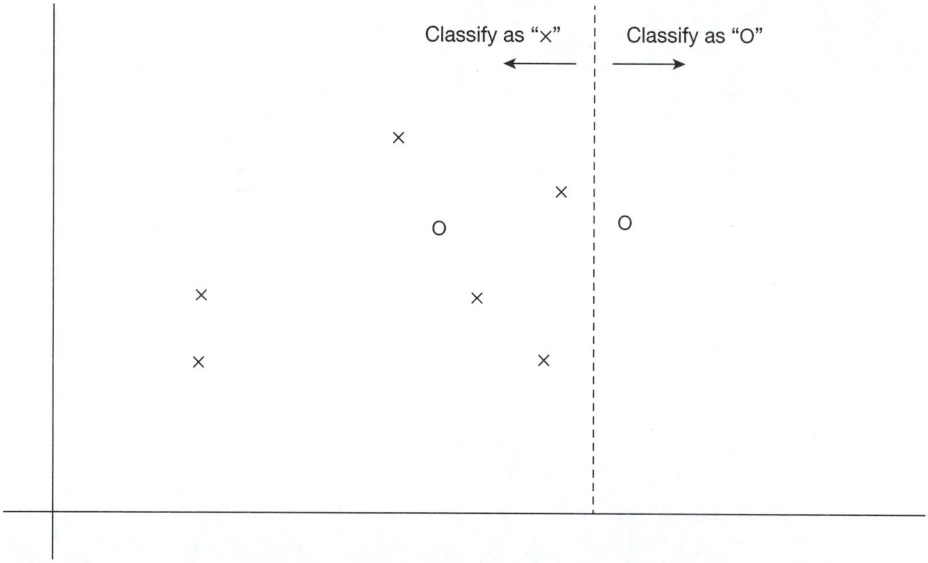

FIGURE 5.9 CLASSIFICATION ASSUMING EQUAL COSTS OF MISCLASSIFICATION

> In all discussions of *oversampling*, we assume the common situation in which there are two classes, one of much greater interest than the other. Data with more than two classes do not lend themselves to this procedure.

Consider the data in Figure 5.9, where × represents non-responders, and ∘, responders. The two axes correspond to two predictors. The dashed vertical line does the best job of classification under the assumption of equal costs: it results in just one misclassification (one ∘ is misclassified as an ×). If we incorporate more realistic misclassification costs—let's say that failing to catch a ∘ is five times as costly as failing to catch an ×—the costs of misclassification jump to 5. In such a case, a horizontal line as shown in Figure 5.10, does a better job: it results in misclassification costs of just 2.

Oversampling is one way of incorporating these costs into the training process. In Figure 5.11, we can see that classification algorithms would automatically determine the appropriate classification line if four additional ∘'s were present at each existing ∘. We can achieve appropriate results either by taking five times as many ∘'s as we would get from simple random sampling (by sampling with replacement if necessary), or by replicating the existing ∘'s fourfold.

Oversampling without replacement in accord with the ratio of costs (the first option above) is the optimal solution, but may not always be practical. There may not be an adequate number of responders to assure that there will be enough of them to fit

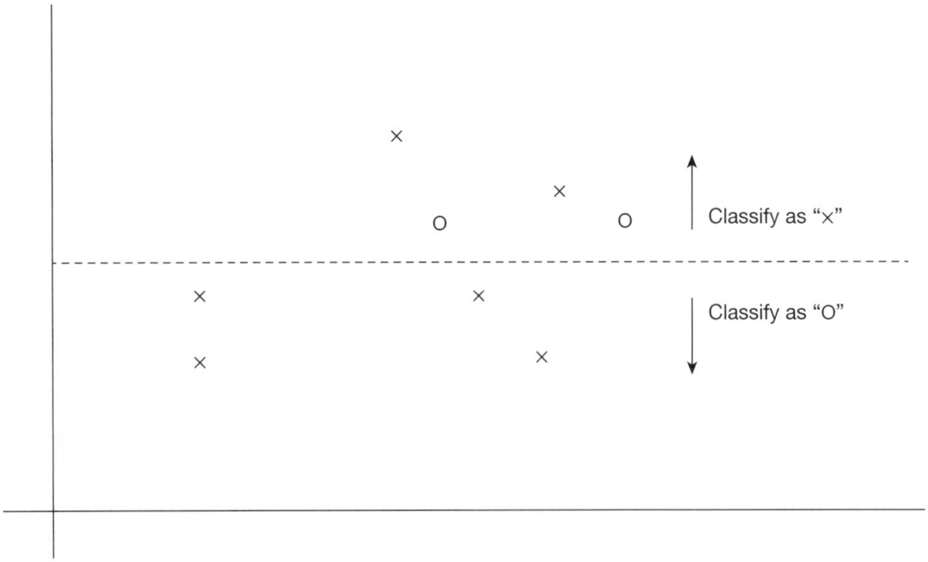

FIGUR 5.10 CLASSIFICATION ASSUMING UNEQUAL COSTS OF MISCLASSIFICATION

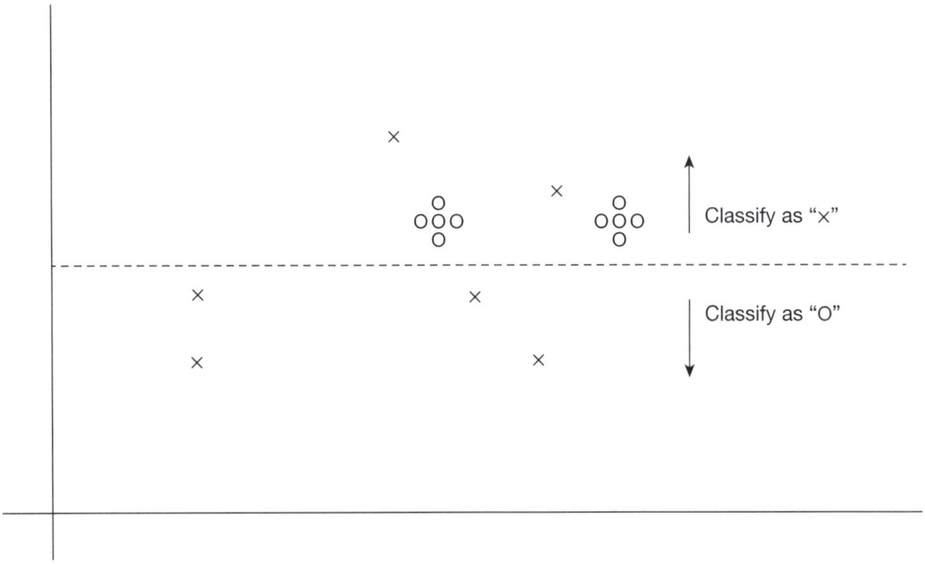

FIGURE 5.11 CLASSIFICATION USING OVERSAMPLING TO ACCOUNT FOR UNEQUAL COSTS

a model if they constitute only a small proportion of the total. Also, it is often the case that our interest in discovering responders is known to be much greater than our interest in discovering non-responders, but the exact ratio of costs is difficult to determine. When faced with very low response rates in a classification problem, practitioners often sample equal numbers of responders and non-responders as a relatively effective and convenient approach. Whatever approach is used, when it comes time to assess and predict model performance, we will need to adjust for the oversampling in one of two ways:

1. score the model to a validation set that has been selected without oversampling (i.e., via simple random sampling), or
2. score the model to an oversampled validation set, and reweight the results to remove the effects of oversampling.

The first method is more straightforward and easier to implement. We describe how to oversample and how to evaluate performance for each of the two methods.

> When classifying data with very low response rates, practitioners typically:
>
> - train models on data that are 50% responder, 50% non-responder
> - validate the models with an unweighted (simple random) sample from the original data

Oversampling the Training Set

How is weighted sampling done? When responders are sufficiently scarce that you will want to use all of them, one common procedure is as follows:

1. First, the response and non-response data are separated into two distinct sets, or *strata*.
2. Records are then randomly selected for the training set from each stratum. Typically, one might select half the (scarce) responders for the training set, then an equal number of non-responders.
3. The remaining responders are put in the validation set.
4. Non-responders are randomly selected for the validation set in sufficient numbers to maintain the original ratio of responders to non-responders.
5. If a test set is required, it can be taken randomly from the validation set.

Evaluating Model Performance Using a Non-oversampled Validation Set

Although the oversampled data can be used to train models, they are often not suitable for evaluating model performance, because the number of responders will (of course) be exaggerated. The most straightforward way of gaining an unbiased estimate of model performance is to apply the model to regular data (i.e., data not oversampled). In short, train the model on oversampled data, but validate it with regular data.

Evaluating Model Performance if Only Oversampled Validation Set Exists

In some cases, very low response rates may make it more practical to use oversampled data not only for the training data, but also for the validation data. This might happen, for example, if an analyst is given a dataset for exploration and prototyping that is already oversampled to boost the proportion with the rare response of interest (perhaps because it is more convenient to transfer and work with a smaller dataset). In such cases, it is still possible to assess how well the model will do with real data, but this requires the oversampled validation set to be reweighted, in order to restore the class of records that were underrepresented in the sampling process. This adjustment should be made to the confusion matrix and to the lift chart in order to derive good accuracy measures. These adjustments are described next.

I. Adjusting the Confusion Matrix for Oversampling Suppose the response rate in the data as a whole is 2%, and that the data were oversampled, yielding a sample in which the response rate is 25 times higher (50% responders). The relationship is as follows:

Responders: 2% of the whole data; 50% of the sample

Non-Responders: 98% of the whole data, 50% of the sample

Each responder in the whole data is worth 25 responders in the sample (50/2). Each non-responder in the whole data is worth 0.5102 non-responders in the sample (50/98). We call these values *oversampling weights*.

Assume that the validation confusion matrix looks like this:

CONFUSION MATRIX, OVERSAMPLED DATA (VALIDATION)

	Predicted 0	Predicted 1	Total
Actual 0	390	110	500
Actual 1	80	420	500
Total	470	530	1000

At this point, the misclassification rate appears to be $(80 + 110) / 1000 = 19\%$, and the model ends up classifying 53% of the records as 1's. However, this reflects the performance on a sample where 50% are responders.

To estimate predictive performance when this model is used to score the original population (with 2% responders), we need to undo the effects of the oversampling. The actual number of responders must be divided by 25, and the actual number of non-responders divided by 0.5102.

The revised confusion matrix is as follows:

CONFUSION MATRIX, REWEIGHTED

	Predicted 0	Predicted 1	Total
Actual 0	390/0.5102 = 764.4	110/0.5102 = 215.6	980
Actual 1	80/25 = 3.2	420/25 = 16.8	20
Total			1000

The adjusted misclassification rate is $(3.2 + 215.6)/1000 = 21.9\%$. The model ends up classifying $(215.6 + 16.8)/1000 = 23.24\%$ of the records as 1's, when we assume 2% responders.

II. Adjusting the Cumulative Gains Curve for Oversampling Lift and the cumulative gains curve are likely to be more useful measures in low-response situations, where our interest lies not so much in classifying all the records correctly as in finding a model that guides us toward those records most likely to contain the response of interest (under the assumption that scarce resources preclude examining or contacting all the records). Typically, our interest in such a case is in maximizing value or minimizing cost, so we will show the adjustment process incorporating the benefit/cost element. The following procedure can be used:

1. Sort the validation records in order of the predicted probability of success (where success = belonging to the class of interest).
2. For each record, record the cost (benefit) associated with the actual outcome.
3. Divide that value by the oversampling rate. For example, if responders are overweighted by a factor of 25, divide by 25.
4. For the highest probability (i.e., first) record, the value above is the y-coordinate of the first point on the cumulative gains curve. The x-coordinate is index number 1.
5. For the next record, again calculate the adjusted value associated with the actual outcome. Add this to the adjusted cost (benefit) for the previous record. This sum is the y-coordinate of the second point on the cumulative gains curve. The x-coordinate is index number 2.
6. Repeat Step 5 until all records have been examined. Connect all the points, and this is the cumulative gains curve.
7. The reference line is a straight line from the origin to the point y = total net benefit and $x = n$ (n = number of records).

PROBLEMS

5.1 A data mining routine has been applied to a transaction dataset and has classified 88 records as fraudulent (30 correctly so) and 952 as non-fraudulent (920 correctly so). Construct the confusion matrix and calculate the overall error rate.

5.2 Suppose that this routine has an adjustable cutoff (threshold) mechanism by which you can alter the proportion of records classified as fraudulent. Describe how moving the cutoff up or down would affect

a. the classification error rate for records that are truly fraudulent

b. the classification error rate for records that are truly nonfraudulent

5.3 FiscalNote is a startup founded by a Washington, DC entrepreneur and funded by a Singapore sovereign wealth fund, the Winklevoss twins of Facebook fame, and others. It uses machine learning and data mining techniques to predict for its clients whether legislation in the US Congress and in US state legislatures will pass or not. The company reports 94% accuracy. (*Washington Post*, November 21, 2014, "Capital Business")

Considering just bills introduced in the US Congress, do a bit of internet research to learn about numbers of bills introduced and passage rates. Identify the possible types of misclassifications, and comment on the use of overall accuracy as a metric. Include a discussion of other possible metrics and the potential role of propensities.

5.4 Consider Figure 5.12, the decile lift chart for the transaction data model, applied to new data.

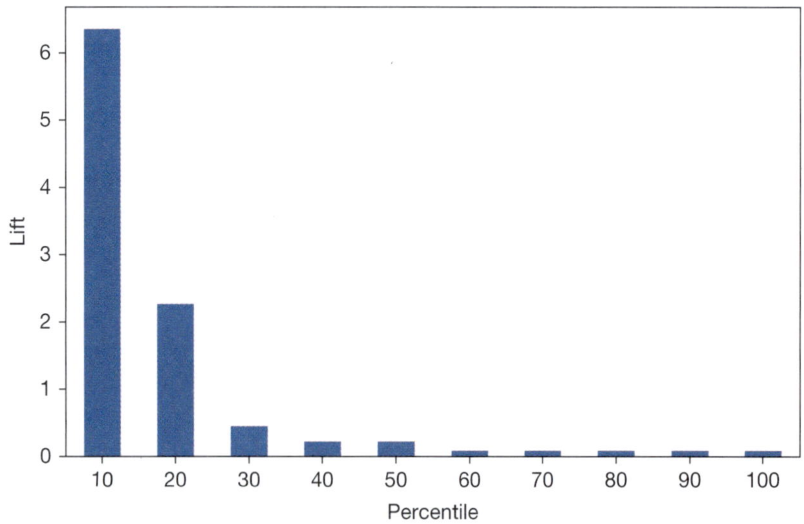

FIGURE 5.12 DECILE LIFT CHART FOR TRANSACTION DATA

a. Interpret the meaning of the first and second bars from the left.

b. Explain how you might use this information in practice.

c. Another analyst comments that you could improve the accuracy of the model by classifying everything as nonfraudulent. If you do that, what is the error rate?

d. Comment on the usefulness, in this situation, of these two metrics of model performance (error rate and lift).

5.5 A large number of insurance records are to be examined to develop a model for predicting fraudulent claims. Of the claims in the historical database, 1% were judged to be fraudulent. A sample is taken to develop a model, and oversampling is used to provide a balanced sample in light of the very low response rate. When applied to this sample ($n = 800$), the model ends up correctly classifying 310 frauds, and 270 nonfrauds. It missed 90 frauds, and classified 130 records incorrectly as frauds when they were not.

a. Produce the confusion matrix for the sample as it stands.

b. Find the adjusted misclassification rate (adjusting for the oversampling).

c. What percentage of new records would you expect to be classified as fraudulent?

5.6 A firm that sells software services has been piloting a new product and has records of 500 customers who have either bought the services or decided not to. The target value is the estimated profit from each sale (excluding sales costs). The global mean is about \$2500. However, the cost of the sales effort is not cheap—the company figures it comes to \$2500 for each of the 500 customers (whether they buy or not). The firm developed a predictive model in hopes of being able to identify the top spenders in the future. The cumulative gains and decile lift charts for the validation set are shown in Figure 5.13.

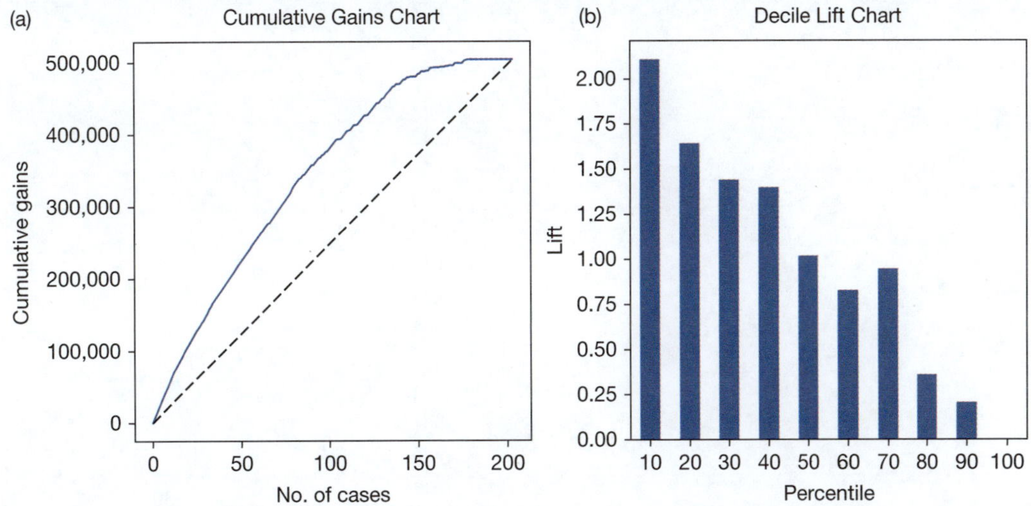

FIGURE 5.13 CUMULATIVE GAINS (a) AND DECILE LIFT CHARTS (b) FOR SOFTWARE SERVICES PRODUCT SALES (VALIDATION SET)

a. If the company begins working with a new set of 1000 leads to sell the same services, similar to the 500 in the pilot study, without any use of predictive modeling to target sales efforts, what is the estimated profit?

b. If the firm wants the average profit on each sale to roughly double the sales effort cost, and applies an appropriate cutoff with this predictive model to a new set of 1000 leads, how far down the new list of 1000 should it proceed (how many deciles)?

c. Still considering the new list of 1000 leads, if the company applies this predictive model with a lower cutoff of $2500, how far should it proceed down the ranked leads, in terms of deciles?

d. Why use this two-stage process for predicting sales—why not simply develop a model for predicting profit for the 1000 new leads?

e. Table 5.7 shows a small set of predictive model validation results for a classification model, with both actual values and propensities.

f. Calculate error rates, sensitivity, and specificity using cutoffs of 0.25, 0.5, and 0.75.

g. Create a decile lift chart.

TABLE 5.7 PROPENSITIES AND ACTUAL CLASS MEMBERSHIP FOR VALIDATION DATA

Propensity of 1	Actual
0.03	0
0.52	0
0.38	0
0.82	1
0.33	0
0.42	0
0.55	1
0.59	0
0.09	0
0.21	0
0.43	0
0.04	0
0.08	0
0.13	0
0.01	0
0.79	1
0.42	0
0.29	0
0.08	0
0.02	0

PART

IV

Prediction and Classification Methods

CHAPTER 6

Multiple Linear Regression

In this chapter, we introduce linear regression models for the purpose of prediction. We discuss the differences between fitting and using regression models for the purpose of inference (as in classical statistics) and for prediction. A predictive goal calls for evaluating model performance on a validation set, and for using predictive metrics. We then raise the challenges of using many predictors and describe variable selection algorithms that are often implemented in linear regression procedures.

Python

In this chapter, we will use `pandas` for data handling, and `scikit-learn` for building the models, and variable (feature) selection. We will also make use of the utility functions from the Python Utilities Functions Appendix. We could also use `statsmodels` for the linear regression models, however, `statsmodels` provides more information than needed for predictive modeling. Use the following import statements for the Python code in this chapter.

import required functionality for this chapter

```
import pandas as pd
from sklearn.model_selection import train_test_split
from sklearn.linear_model import LinearRegression, Lasso, Ridge, LassoCV,
    BayesianRidge
import statsmodels.formula.api as sm
import matplotlib.pylab as plt
```

```
from dmba import regressionSummary, exhaustive_search
from dmba import backward_elimination, forward_selection, stepwise_selection
from dmba import adjusted_r2_score, AIC_score, BIC_score
```

6.1 | INTRODUCTION

The most popular model for making predictions is the *multiple linear regression model* encountered in most introductory statistics courses and textbooks. This model is used to fit a relationship between a numerical *outcome variable* Y (also called the *response*, *target*, or *dependent variable*) and a set of *predictors* $X_1, X_2, \ldots, X_p$ (also referred to as *independent variables*, *input variables*, *regressors*, or *covariates*). The assumption is that the following function approximates the relationship between the predictors and outcome variable:

$$Y = \beta_0 + \beta_1 x_1 + \beta_2 x_2 + \cdots + \beta_p x_p + \epsilon, \tag{6.1}$$

where $\beta_0, \ldots, \beta_p$ are *coefficients* and ϵ is the *noise* or *unexplained* part. Data are then used to estimate the coefficients and to quantify the noise. In predictive modeling, the data are also used to evaluate model performance.

Regression modeling means not only estimating the coefficients but also choosing which predictors to include and in what form. For example, a numerical predictor can be included as is, or in logarithmic form [log(X)], or in a binned form (e.g., age group). Choosing the right form depends on domain knowledge, data availability, and needed predictive power.

Multiple linear regression is applicable to numerous predictive modeling situations. Examples are predicting customer activity on credit cards from their demographics and historical activity patterns, predicting expenditures on vacation travel based on historical frequent flyer data, predicting staffing requirements at help desks based on historical data and product and sales information, predicting sales from cross-selling of products from historical information, and predicting the impact of discounts on sales in retail outlets.

6.2 | EXPLANATORY VS. PREDICTIVE MODELING

Before introducing the use of linear regression for prediction, we must clarify an important distinction that often escapes those with earlier familiarity with linear regression from courses in statistics. In particular, the two popular but different objectives behind fitting a regression model are:

1. Explaining or quantifying the average effect of inputs on an outcome (explanatory or descriptive task, respectively)
2. Predicting the outcome value for new records, given their input values (predictive task)

The classical statistical approach is focused on the first objective. In that scenario, the data are treated as a random sample from a larger population of interest. The regression model estimated from this sample is an attempt to capture the *average* relationship in the larger population. This model is then used in decision-making to generate statements such as "a unit increase in service speed (X_1) is associated with an average increase of 5 points in customer satisfaction (Y), all other factors ($X_2, X_3, \ldots, X_p$) being equal." If X_1 is known to *cause* Y, then such a statement indicates actionable policy changes—this is called explanatory modeling. When the causal structure is unknown, then this model quantifies the degree of *association* between the inputs and outcome variable, and the approach is called descriptive modeling.

In predictive analytics, however, the focus is typically on the second goal: predicting new individual records. Here we are not interested in the coefficients themselves, nor in the "average record," but rather in the predictions that this model can generate for new records. In this scenario, the model is used for micro-decision-making at the record level. In our previous example, we would use the regression model to predict customer satisfaction for each new customer of interest.

Both explanatory and predictive modeling involve using a dataset to fit a model (i.e., to estimate coefficients), checking model validity, assessing its performance, and comparing to other models. However, the modeling steps and performance assessment differ in the two cases, usually leading to different final models. Therefore, the choice of model is closely tied to whether the goal is explanatory or predictive.

In explanatory and descriptive modeling, where the focus is on modeling the average record, we try to fit the best model to the data in an attempt to learn about the underlying relationship in the population. In contrast, in predictive modeling (data mining), the goal is to find a regression model that best predicts new individual records. A regression model that fits the existing data too well is not likely to perform well with new data. Hence, we look for a model that has the highest predictive power by evaluating it on a holdout set and using predictive metrics (see Chapter 5).

Let us summarize the main differences in using a linear regression in the two scenarios:

1. A good explanatory model is one that fits the data closely, whereas a good predictive model is one that predicts new records accurately. Choices of input variables and their form can therefore differ.

2. In explanatory models, the entire dataset is used for estimating the best-fit model, to maximize the amount of information that we have about the hypothesized relationship in the population. When the goal is to predict outcomes of new individual records, the data are typically split into a training set and a validation set. The training set is used to estimate the model, and the validation or *holdout set* is used to assess this model's predictive performance on new, unobserved data.
3. Performance measures for explanatory models measure how close the data fit the model (how well the model approximates the data) and how strong the average relationship is, whereas in predictive models performance is measured by predictive accuracy (how well the model predicts new individual records).
4. In explanatory models the focus is on the coefficients (β), whereas in predictive models the focus is on the predictions ($\hat{y}$).

For these reasons, it is extremely important to know the goal of the analysis before beginning the modeling process. A good predictive model can have a looser fit to the data on which it is based, and a good explanatory model can have low prediction accuracy. In the remainder of this chapter, we focus on predictive models because these are more popular in data mining and because most statistics textbooks focus on explanatory modeling.

6.3 | ESTIMATING THE REGRESSION EQUATION AND PREDICTION

Once we determine the predictors to include and their form, we estimate the coefficients of the regression formula from the data using a method called *ordinary least squares* (OLS). This method finds values $\hat{\beta}_0, \hat{\beta}_1, \hat{\beta}_2, \ldots, \hat{\beta}_p$ that minimize the sum of squared deviations between the actual outcome values (Y) and their predicted values based on that model ($\hat{Y}$).

To predict the value of the outcome variable for a record with predictor values $x_1, x_2, \ldots, x_p$, we use the equation

$$\hat{Y} = \hat{\beta}_0 + \hat{\beta}_1 x_1 + \hat{\beta}_2 x_2 + \cdots + \hat{\beta}_p x_p. \tag{6.2}$$

Predictions based on this equation are the best predictions possible in the sense that they will be unbiased (equal to the true values on average) and will have the smallest mean squared error compared to any unbiased estimates *if* we make the following assumptions:

1. The noise ϵ (or equivalently, Y) follows a normal distribution.
2. The choice of predictors and their form is correct (*linearity*).

3. The records are independent of each other.
4. The variability in the outcome values for a given set of predictors is the same regardless of the values of the predictors (*homoskedasticity*).

An important and interesting fact for the predictive goal is that *even if we drop the first assumption and allow the noise to follow an arbitrary distribution, these estimates are very good for prediction,* in the sense that among all linear models, as defined by equation (6.1), the model using the least squares estimates, $\hat{\beta}_0, \hat{\beta}_1, \hat{\beta}_2, \ldots, \hat{\beta}_p$, will have the smallest mean squared errors. The assumption of a normal distribution is required in explanatory modeling, where it is used for constructing confidence intervals and statistical tests for the model parameters.

Even if the other assumptions are violated, it is still possible that the resulting predictions are sufficiently accurate and precise for the purpose they are intended for. The key is to evaluate predictive performance of the model, which is the main priority. Satisfying assumptions is of secondary interest and residual analysis can give clues to potential improved models to examine.

Example: Predicting the Price of Used Toyota Corolla Cars

A large Toyota car dealership offers purchasers of new Toyota cars the option to buy their used car as part of a trade-in. In particular, a new promotion promises to pay high prices for used Toyota Corolla cars for purchasers of a new car. The dealer then sells the used cars for a small profit. To ensure a reasonable profit, the dealer needs to be able to predict the price that the dealership will get for the used cars. For that reason, data were collected on all previous sales of used Toyota Corollas at the dealership. The data include the sales price and other information on the car, such as its age, mileage, fuel type, and engine size. A description of each of these variables is given in Table 6.1. A sample of this dataset is shown in Table 6.2. The total number of records in the dataset is 1000 cars (we use the first 1000 cars from the dataset *ToyotoCorolla.csv*). After partitioning the data into training (60%) and validation (40%) sets, we fit a multiple linear regression model between price (the outcome variable) and the other variables (as predictors) using only the training set. Table 6.3 shows the estimated coefficients. Notice that the Fuel Type predictor has three categories (*Petrol*, *Diesel*, and *CNG*). We therefore have two dummy variables in the model: Fuel_Type_Petrol (0/1) and Fuel_Type_Diesel (0/1); the third, for CNG (0/1), is redundant given the information on the first two dummies. Including the redundant dummy would cause the regression to fail, since the redundant dummy will be a perfect linear combination of the other two.

TABLE 6.1 VARIABLES IN THE TOYOTA COROLLA EXAMPLE

Variable	Description
Price	Offer price in Euros
Age	Age in months as of August 2004
Kilometers	Accumulated kilometers on odometer
Fuel type	Fuel type (*Petrol, Diesel, CNG*)
HP	Horsepower
Metallic	Metallic color? (Yes = 1, No = 0)
Automatic	Automatic (Yes = 1, No = 0)
CC	Cylinder volume in cubic centimeters
Doors	Number of doors
QuartTax	Quarterly road tax in Euros
Weight	Weight in kilograms

TABLE 6.2 PRICES AND ATTRIBUTES FOR USED TOYOTA COROLLA CARS (SELECTED ROWS AND COLUMNS ONLY)

Price	Age	Kilometers	Fuel type	HP	Metallic	Auto-matic	CC	Doors	Quart tax	Weight
13,500	23	46,986	Diesel	90	1	0	2000	3	210	1165
13,750	23	72,937	Diesel	90	1	0	2000	3	210	1165
13,950	24	41,711	Diesel	90	1	0	2000	3	210	1165
14,950	26	48,000	Diesel	90	0	0	2000	3	210	1165
13,750	30	38,500	Diesel	90	0	0	2000	3	210	1170
12,950	32	61,000	Diesel	90	0	0	2000	3	210	1170
16,900	27	94,612	Diesel	90	1	0	2000	3	210	1245
18,600	30	75,889	Diesel	90	1	0	2000	3	210	1245
21,500	27	19,700	Petrol	192	0	0	1800	3	100	1185
12,950	23	71,138	Diesel	69	0	0	1900	3	185	1105
20,950	25	31,461	Petrol	192	0	0	1800	3	100	1185
19,950	22	43,610	Petrol	192	0	0	1800	3	100	1185
19,600	25	32,189	Petrol	192	0	0	1800	3	100	1185
21,500	31	23,000	Petrol	192	1	0	1800	3	100	1185
22,500	32	34,131	Petrol	192	1	0	1800	3	100	1185
22,000	28	18,739	Petrol	192	0	0	1800	3	100	1185
22,750	30	34,000	Petrol	192	1	0	1800	3	100	1185
17,950	24	21,716	Petrol	110	1	0	1600	3	85	1105
16,750	24	25,563	Petrol	110	0	0	1600	3	19	1065
16,950	30	64,359	Petrol	110	1	0	1600	3	85	1105
15,950	30	67,660	Petrol	110	1	0	1600	3	85	1105
16,950	29	43,905	Petrol	110	0	1	1600	3	100	1170
15,950	28	56,349	Petrol	110	1	0	1600	3	85	1120
16,950	28	32,220	Petrol	110	1	0	1600	3	85	1120

TABLE 6.2 PRICES AND ATTRIBUTES FOR USED TOYOTA COROLLA CARS (SELECTED ROWS AND COLUMNS ONLY) (*Continued*)

Price	Age	Kilometers	Fuel type	HP	Metallic	Auto-matic	CC	Doors	Quart tax	Weight
16,250	29	25,813	Petrol	110	1	0	1600	3	85	1120
15,950	25	28,450	Petrol	110	1	0	1600	3	85	1120
17,495	27	34,545	Petrol	110	1	0	1600	3	85	1120
15,750	29	41,415	Petrol	110	1	0	1600	3	85	1120
11,950	39	98,823	CNG	110	1	0	1600	5	197	1119

TABLE 6.3 LINEAR REGRESSION MODEL OF PRICE VS. CAR ATTRIBUTES

code for fitting a regression model

```
# reduce data frame to the top 1000 rows and select columns for regression analysis
car_df = pd.read_csv('ToyotaCorolla.csv')
car_df = car_df.iloc[0:1000]

predictors = ['Age_08_04', 'KM', 'Fuel_Type', 'HP', 'Met_Color', 'Automatic', 'CC',
              'Doors', 'Quarterly_Tax', 'Weight']
outcome = 'Price'

# partition data
X = pd.get_dummies(car_df[predictors], drop_first=True)
y = car_df[outcome]
train_X, valid_X, train_y, valid_y = train_test_split(X, y, test_size=0.4,
                                                      random_state=1)

car_lm = LinearRegression()
car_lm.fit(train_X, train_y)

# print coefficients
print(pd.DataFrame({'Predictor': X.columns, 'coefficient': car_lm.coef_}))

# print performance measures (training data)
regressionSummary(train_y, car_lm.predict(train_X))
```

Partial Output

```
           Predictor  coefficient
0          Age_08_04  -140.748761
1                 KM    -0.017840
2                 HP    36.103419
3          Met_Color    84.281830
4          Automatic   416.781954
5                 CC     0.017737
```

(*Continued*)

TABLE 6.3 LINEAR REGRESSION MODEL OF PRICE VS. CAR ATTRIBUTES (*Continued*)

```
6             Doors    -50.657863
7     Quarterly_Tax     13.625325
8            Weight     13.038711
9  Fuel_Type_Diesel   1066.464681
10 Fuel_Type_Petrol   2310.249543

Regression statistics

                      Mean Error (ME) : 0.0000
       Root Mean Squared Error (RMSE) : 1400.5823
            Mean Absolute Error (MAE) : 1046.9072
          Mean Percentage Error (MPE) : -1.0223
Mean Absolute Percentage Error (MAPE) : 9.2994
```

The regression coefficients are then used to predict prices of individual used Toyota Corolla cars based on their age, mileage, and so on. Table 6.4 shows a sample of predicted prices for 20 cars in the validation set, using the estimated model. It gives the predictions and their errors (relative to the actual prices) for these 20 cars. Below the predictions, we have overall measures of predictive accuracy. Note that the mean error (ME) is \$104 and RMSE = \$1313. A histogram of the residuals (Figure 6.1) shows that most of the errors are between ±\$2000. This error magnitude might be small relative to the car price, but should be taken into account when considering the profit. Another observation of interest is the large positive residuals (under-predictions), which may or may not be a concern, depending on the application. Measures such as the mean error, and error percentiles are used to assess the predictive performance of a model and to compare models.

TABLE 6.4 PREDICTED PRICES (AND ERRORS) FOR 20 CARS IN VALIDATION SET AND SUMMARY PREDICTIVE MEASURES FOR ENTIRE VALIDATION SET (CALLED TEST SET IN R)

code for fitting a regression model to training set and predicting prices in validation set

```
# Use predict() to make predictions on a new set
car_lm_pred = car_lm.predict(valid_X)

result = pd.DataFrame({'Predicted': car_lm_pred, 'Actual': valid_y,
                       'Residual': valid_y - car_lm_pred})
print(result.head(20))

# print performance measures (validation data)
regressionSummary(valid_y, car_lm_pred)
```

TABLE 6.4 PREDICTED PRICES (AND ERRORS) FOR 20 CARS IN VALIDATION SET AND SUMMARY PREDICTIVE MEASURES FOR ENTIRE VALIDATION SET (CALLED TEST SET IN R) (*Continued*)

Output

```
        Predicted  Actual     Residual
507  10607.333940   11500   892.666060
818   9272.705792    8950  -322.705792
452  10617.947808   11450   832.052192
368  13600.396275   11450 -2150.396275
242  12396.694660   11950  -446.694660
929   9496.498212    9995   498.501788
262  12480.063217   13500  1019.936783
810   8834.146068    7950  -884.146068
318  12183.361282    9900 -2283.361282
49   19206.965683   21950  2743.034317
446  10987.498309   11950   962.501691
142  18501.527375   19950  1448.472625
968   9914.690947    9950    35.309053
345  13827.299932   14950  1122.700068
971   7966.732543   10495  2528.267457
133  17185.242041   15950 -1235.242041
104  19952.658062   19450  -502.658062
6    16570.609280   16900   329.390720
600  13739.409113   11250 -2489.409113
496  11267.513740   11750   482.486260

Regression statistics

                      Mean Error (ME) : 103.6803
       Root Mean Squared Error (RMSE) : 1312.8523
            Mean Absolute Error (MAE) : 1017.5972
          Mean Percentage Error (MPE) : -0.2633
Mean Absolute Percentage Error (MAPE) : 9.0111
```

code for plotting histogram of validation errors

```
car_lm_pred = car_lm.predict(valid_X)
all_residuals = valid_y - car_lm_pred

# Determine the percentage of datapoints with a residual in [-1406, 1406] = approx.
# 75\%
print(len(all_residuals[(all_residuals > -1406) & (all_residuals < 1406)]) /
len(all_residuals))

pd.DataFrame({'Residuals': all_residuals}).hist(bins=25)
plt.show()
```

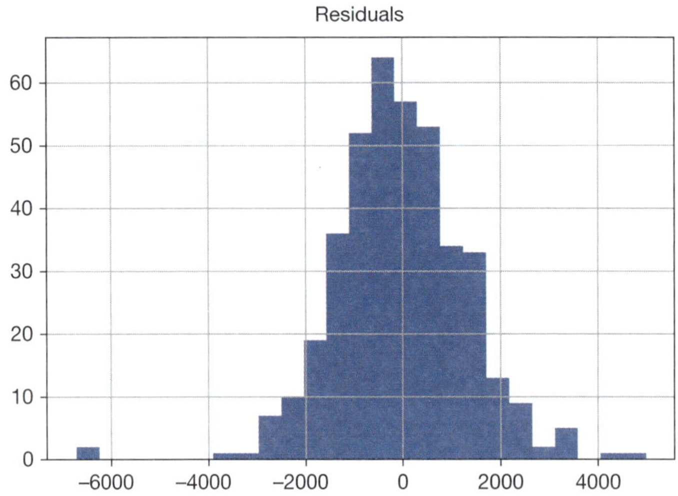

FIGURE 6.1 HISTOGRAM OF MODEL ERRORS (BASED ON VALIDATION SET)

6.4 | VARIABLE SELECTION IN LINEAR REGRESSION

Reducing the Number of Predictors

A frequent problem in data mining is that of using a regression equation to predict the value of a dependent variable when we have many variables available to choose as predictors in our model. Given the high speed of modern algorithms for multiple linear regression calculations, it is tempting in such a situation to take a kitchen-sink approach: Why bother to select a subset? Just use all the variables in the model.

Another consideration favoring the inclusions of numerous variables is the hope that a previously hidden relationship will emerge. For example, a company found that customers who had purchased anti-scuff protectors for chair and table legs had lower credit risks. However, there are several reasons for exercising caution before throwing all possible variables into a model.

- It may be expensive or not feasible to collect a full complement of predictors for future predictions.
- We may be able to measure fewer predictors more accurately (e.g., in surveys).
- The more predictors, the higher the chance of missing values in the data. If we delete or impute records with missing values, multiple predictors will lead to a higher rate of record deletion or imputation.
- *Parsimony* is an important property of good models. We obtain more insight into the influence of predictors in models with few parameters.

- Estimates of regression coefficients are likely to be unstable, due to *multicollinearity* in models with many variables. (Multicollinearity is the presence of two or more predictors sharing the same linear relationship with the outcome variable.) Regression coefficients are more stable for parsimonious models. One very rough rule of thumb is to have a number of records n larger than $5(p + 2)$, where p is the number of predictors.
- It can be shown that using predictors that are uncorrelated with the outcome variable increases the variance of predictions.
- It can be shown that dropping predictors that are actually correlated with the outcome variable can increase the average error (bias) of predictions.

The last two points mean that there is a trade-off between too few and too many predictors. In general, accepting some bias can reduce the variance in predictions. This *bias–variance trade-off* is particularly important for large numbers of predictors, because in that case, it is very likely that there are variables in the model that have small coefficients relative to the standard deviation of the noise and also exhibit at least moderate correlation with other variables. Dropping such variables will improve the predictions, as it reduces the prediction variance. This type of bias–variance trade-off is a basic aspect of most data mining procedures for prediction and classification. In light of this, methods for reducing the number of predictors p to a smaller set are often used.

How to Reduce the Number of Predictors

The first step in trying to reduce the number of predictors should always be to use domain knowledge. It is important to understand what the various predictors are measuring and why they are relevant for predicting the outcome variable. With this knowledge, the set of predictors should be reduced to a sensible set that reflects the problem at hand. Some practical reasons for predictor elimination are the expense of collecting this information in the future; inaccuracy; high correlation with another predictor; many missing values; or simply irrelevance. Also helpful in examining potential predictors are summary statistics and graphs, such as frequency and correlation tables, predictor-specific summary statistics and plots, and missing value counts.

The next step makes use of computational power and statistical performance metrics. In general, there are two types of methods for reducing the number of predictors in a model. The first is an *exhaustive search* for the "best" subset of predictors by fitting regression models with all the possible combinations of predictors. The exhaustive search approach is not practical in many applications due to the large number of possible models. The second approach is to search through a partial set of models. We describe these two approaches next.

Exhaustive Search The idea here is to evaluate all subsets of predictors. Since the number of subsets for even moderate values of p is very large, after the algorithm creates the subsets and runs all the models, we need some way to examine the most promising subsets and to select from them. The challenge is to select a model that is not too simplistic in terms of excluding important parameters (the model is *under-fit*), nor overly complex thereby modeling random noise (the model is *over-fit*). Several criteria for evaluating and comparing models are based on metrics computed from the training data:

One popular criterion is the *adjusted* R^2, which is defined as

$$R^2_{\text{adj}} = 1 - \frac{n-1}{n-p-1}(1 - R^2),$$

where R^2 is the proportion of explained variability in the model (in a model with a single predictor, this is the squared correlation). Like R^2, higher values of R^2_{adj} indicate better fit. Unlike R^2, which does not account for the number of predictors used, R^2_{adj} uses a penalty on the number of predictors. This avoids the artificial increase in R^2 that can result from simply increasing the number of predictors but not the amount of information. It can be shown that using R^2_{adj} to choose a subset is equivalent to choosing the subset that minimizes the training RMSE.

A second popular set of criteria for balancing under-fitting and over-fitting are the *Akaike Information Criterion* (*AIC*) and Schwartz's *Bayesian Information Criterion* (*BIC*). AIC and BIC measure the goodness of fit of a model, but also include a penalty that is a function of the number of parameters in the model. As such, they can be used to compare various models for the same data set. *AIC* and *BIC* are estimates of prediction error based in information theory. For linear regression, AIC and BIC can be computed from the formulas:

$$\text{AIC} = n \ln(\text{SSE}/n) + n(1 + \ln(2\pi)) + 2(p + 1), \quad (6.3)$$

$$\text{BIC} = n \ln(\text{SSE}/n) + n(1 + \ln(2\pi)) + \ln(n)(p + 1), \quad (6.4)$$

where SSE is the model's sum of squared errors. In general, models with smaller AIC and BIC values are considered better.

Finally, a useful point to note is that for a fixed size of subset, R^2, R^2_{adj}, AIC, and BIC all select the same subset. In fact, there is no difference between them in the order of merit they ascribe to subsets of a fixed size. This is good to know if comparing models with the same number of predictors, but often we want to compare models with different numbers of predictors.

Table 6.5 gives the results of applying an exhaustive search on the Toyota Corolla price data (with the 11 predictors). Because Python does not have an exhaustive search routine, we created a loop that iterates through all predictor combinations and within models with the same number of predictors, selects the models with the highest R^2_{adj} (which is equivalent to choosing one of the other measures mentioned above). The code reports the best model with a single predictor, two predictors, and so on. It can be seen that the R^2_{adj} increases until eight predictors are used and then slowly decreases. The AIC also indicates that a model with eight predictors is good. The dominant predictor in all models is the age of the car, with horsepower, weight and mileage playing important roles as well.

TABLE 6.5 EXHAUSTIVE SEARCH FOR REDUCING PREDICTORS IN TOYOTA COROLLA EXAMPLE

code for exhaustive search

We make use of the utility function *exhaustive_search()*; the source code of this function is included in the appendix. The function takes three arguments: a list of all features, a function that creates a model for a given set of features, and a function that scores the model.

```
def train_model(variables):
    model = LinearRegression()
    model.fit(train_X[list(variables)], train_y)
    return model

def score_model(model, variables):
    pred_y = model.predict(train_X[list(variables)])
    # we negate as score is optimized to be as low as possible
    return -adjusted_r2_score(train_y, pred_y, model)

allVariables = train_X.columns
results = exhaustive_search(allVariables, train_model, score_model)

data = []
for result in results:
    model = result['model']
    variables = list(result['variables'])
    AIC = AIC_score(train_y, model.predict(train_X[variables]), model)

    d = {'n': result['n'], 'r2adj': -result['score'], 'AIC': AIC}
    d.update({var: var in result['variables'] for var in allVariables})
    data.append(d)
pd.DataFrame(data, columns=('n', 'r2adj', 'AIC') + tuple(sorted(allVariables)))
```

Output

```
   n     r2adj           AIC  Age_08_04  Automatic     CC  Doors  Fuel_Type_Diesel  \
0  1  0.767901  10689.712094       True      False  False  False             False
1  2  0.801160  10597.910645       True      False  False  False             False
```

(Continued)

TABLE 6.5 EXHAUSTIVE SEARCH FOR REDUCING PREDICTORS IN TOYOTA COROLLA EXAMPLE (*Continued*)

```
2    3  0.829659  10506.084235       True       False  False  False             False
3    4  0.846357  10445.174820       True       False  False  False             False
4    5  0.849044  10435.578836       True       False  False  False             False
5    6  0.853172  10419.932278       True       False  False  False             False
6    7  0.853860  10418.104025       True       False  False  False              True
7    8  0.854297  10417.290103       True        True  False  False              True
8    9  0.854172  10418.789079       True        True  False   True              True
9   10  0.854036  10420.330800       True        True  False   True              True
10  11  0.853796  10422.298278       True        True   True   True              True

    Fuel_Type_Petrol     HP     KM  Met_Color  Quarterly_Tax  Weight
0              False  False  False      False          False   False
1              False   True  False      False          False   False
2              False   True  False      False          False    True
3              False   True   True      False          False    True
4              False   True   True      False           True    True
5               True   True   True      False           True    True
6               True   True   True      False           True    True
7               True   True   True      False           True    True
8               True   True   True      False           True    True
9               True   True   True       True           True    True
10              True   True   True       True           True    True
```

Popular Subset Selection Algorithms The second method of finding the best subset of predictors relies on a partial, iterative search through the space of all possible regression models. The end product is one best subset of predictors (although there do exist variations of these methods that identify several close-to-best choices for different sizes of predictor subsets). This approach is computationally cheaper, but it has the potential of missing "good" combinations of predictors. None of the methods guarantee that they yield the best subset for any criterion, such as R^2_{adj}. They are reasonable methods for situations with a large number of predictors, but for a moderate number of predictors, the exhaustive search is preferable.

Three popular iterative search algorithms are *forward selection*, *backward elimination*, and *stepwise regression*. In *forward selection*, we start with no predictors and then add predictors one by one. Each predictor added is the one (among all predictors) that has the largest contribution to R^2 on top of the predictors that are already in it. The algorithm stops when the contribution of additional predictors is not statistically significant. The main disadvantage of this method is that the algorithm will miss pairs or groups of predictors that perform very well together but perform poorly as single predictors. This is similar to interviewing job candidates for a team project one by one, thereby missing groups of candidates who perform superiorly together ("colleagues"), but poorly on their own or with non-colleagues.

In *backward elimination*, we start with all predictors and then at each step, eliminate the least useful predictor (according to statistical significance). The algorithm stops when all the remaining predictors have significant contributions. The weakness of this algorithm is that computing the initial model with all predictors can be time-consuming and unstable. *Stepwise regression* is like forward selection except that at each step, we consider dropping predictors that are not statistically significant, as in backward elimination.

There is currently no support in `scikit-learn` or `statsmodels` for stepwise regression. It is however straightforward to implement such an approach in a few lines of code. Table 6.6 shows the result of backward elimination for the Toyota Corolla example. The chosen eight-predictor model is identical to the best eight-predictor model chosen by the exhaustive search. In this example, forward selection (Table 6.7) as well as stepwise regression (Table 6.8) also end up with this same eight-predictor model. This need not be the case with other datasets.

TABLE 6.6 BACKWARD ELIMINATION FOR REDUCING PREDICTORS IN TOYOTA COROLLA EXAMPLE

code for backward elimination

```
def train_model(variables):
    model = LinearRegression()
    model.fit(train_X[variables], train_y)
    return model

def score_model(model, variables):
    return AIC_score(train_y, model.predict(train_X[variables]), model)

allVariables = train_X.columns
best_model, best_variables = backward_elimination(allVariables, train_model,
                                 score_model, verbose=True)

print(best_variables)

regressionSummary(valid_y, best_model.predict(valid_X[best_variables]))
```

Output

```
Variables: Age_08_04, KM, HP, Met_Color, Automatic, CC, Doors, Quarterly_Tax,
           Weight, Fuel_Type_Diesel, Fuel_Type_Petrol
Start: score=10422.30
Step: score=10420.33, remove CC
Step: score=10418.79, remove Met_Color
Step: score=10417.29, remove Doors
Step: score=10417.29, remove None
```

(Continued)

TABLE 6.6 BACKWARD ELIMINATION FOR REDUCING PREDICTORS IN TOYOTA COROLLA EXAMPLE (*Continued*)

```
['Age_08_04', 'KM', 'HP', 'Automatic', 'Quarterly_Tax', 'Weight',
 'Fuel_Type_Diesel', 'Fuel_Type_Petrol']

Regression statistics

                      Mean Error (ME) : 103.3045
       Root Mean Squared Error (RMSE) : 1314.4844
            Mean Absolute Error (MAE) : 1016.8875
          Mean Percentage Error (MPE) : -0.2700
Mean Absolute Percentage Error (MAPE) : 8.9984
```

TABLE 6.7 FORWARD SELECTION FOR REDUCING PREDICTORS IN TOYOTA COROLLA EXAMPLE

```
# The initial model is the constant model - this requires special handling
# in train_model and score_model
def train_model(variables):
    if len(variables) == 0:
        return None
    model = LinearRegression()
    model.fit(train_X[variables], train_y)
    return model

def score_model(model, variables):
    if len(variables) == 0:
        return AIC_score(train_y, [train_y.mean()] * len(train_y), model, df=1)
    return AIC_score(train_y, model.predict(train_X[variables]), model)

best_model, best_variables = forward_selection(train_X.columns, train_model, score_model,
                                 verbose=True)
print(best_variables)
```

Output

```
Start: score=11565.07, constant
Step: score=10689.71, add Age_08_04
Step: score=10597.91, add HP
Step: score=10506.08, add Weight
Step: score=10445.17, add KM
Step: score=10435.58, add Quarterly_Tax
Step: score=10419.93, add Fuel_Type_Petrol
Step: score=10418.10, add Fuel_Type_Diesel
Step: score=10417.29, add Automatic
Step: score=10417.29, add None
['Age_08_04', 'HP', 'Weight', 'KM', 'Quarterly_Tax', 'Fuel_Type_Petrol',
 'Fuel_Type_Diesel', 'Automatic']
```

TABLE 6.8 STEPWISE REGRESSION FOR REDUCING PREDICTORS IN TOYOTA COROLLA EXAMPLE

```
best_model, best_variables = stepwise_selection(train_X.columns, train_model, score_model,
                                                verbose=True)
print(best_variables)
```

Output

```
Start: score=11565.07, constant
Step: score=10689.71, add Age_08_04
Step: score=10597.91, add HP
Step: score=10506.08, add Weight
Step: score=10445.17, add KM
Step: score=10435.58, add Quarterly_Tax
Step: score=10419.93, add Fuel_Type_Petrol
Step: score=10418.10, add Fuel_Type_Diesel
Step: score=10417.29, add Automatic
Step: score=10417.29, unchanged None
['Age_08_04', 'HP', 'Weight', 'KM', 'Quarterly_Tax', 'Fuel_Type_Petrol',
 'Fuel_Type_Diesel', 'Automatic']
```

Once one or more promising models are selected, we run them to evaluate their validation predictive performance. For example, Table 6.6 shows the validation performance of the 8-predictor model, which turns out to be only very slightly better than the 10-predictor model (Table 6.4) in terms of validation metrics. It is possible there may an even smaller model, performing only slightly worse, that is preferable from a parsimony standpoint.

Finally, additional ways to reduce the dimension of the data are by using principal components (Chapter 4) and regression trees (Chapter 9).

Regularization (Shrinkage Models)

Selecting a subset of predictors is equivalent to setting some of the model coefficients to zero. This approach creates an interpretable result—we know which predictors were dropped and which are retained. A more flexible alternative, called regularization or shrinkage, "shrinks" the coefficients toward zero. Recall that adjusted R^2 incorporates a penalty according to the number of predictors p. Shrinkage methods also impose a penalty on the model fit, except that the penalty is not based on the *number* of predictors but rather on some aggregation of the coefficient values (typically predictors are first standardized to have the same scale).

The reasoning behind constraining the magnitude of the $\hat{\beta}$ coefficients is that highly correlated predictors will tend to exhibit coefficients with high standard errors, since small changes in the training data might radically shift which of the correlated predictors gets emphasized. This instability (high standard errors) leads to poor predictive power. By constraining the combined magnitude of the coefficients, this variance is reduced.

The two most popular shrinkage methods are *ridge regression* and *lasso*. They differ in terms of the penalty used: In ridge regression, the penalty is based on the sum of squared coefficients $\sum_{j=1}^{p} \beta_j^2$ (called L2 penalty), whereas lasso uses the sum of absolute values $\sum_{j=1}^{p} |\beta_j|$ (called L1 penalty), for p predictors (excluding an intercept). It turns out that the lasso penalty effectively shrinks some of the coefficients to zero, thereby resulting in a subset of predictors.

Whereas in linear regression coefficients are estimated by minimizing the training data sum of squared errors (SSE), in ridge regression and lasso the coefficients are estimated by minimizing the training data SSE, subject to the penalty term being below some threshold t. This threshold can be set by the user, or chosen by cross-validation.

In Python, regularized linear regression can be run using methods *Lasso* and *Ridge* in `sklearn.linear_model`. The penalty parameter α determines the threshold (a typical default value is $\alpha = 1$; note that $\alpha = 0$ means no penalty and yields ordinary linear regression). The methods *LassoCV*, *RidgeCV*, and *BayesianRidge* offer the added benefit of automatically selecting the penalty parameter. *LassoCV* and *RidgeCV* use cross-validation to determine optimal values for the penalty parameter. A different approach is used in *BayesianRidge* which uses an iterative approach to derive the penalty parameter from the whole training set. Remember to set argument normalize = True or otherwise normalize the data before applying regularized regression models.

Table 6.9 applies ridge and lasso regression to the Toyota Corolla example. We see that in this case the model performance of the optimized Lasso regression is slightly worse than for normal linear regression. Looking at the coefficients, we see that the lasso approach lead to a model with 6 predictors (Age_08_04, KM, HP, Automatic, Quarterly_Tax, Weight). The regularization parameter derived in BayesianRidge regression is very small, which indicates that this dataset does not benefit from regularization. The real strength of these methods becomes more evident when the dataset contains a large number of predictors with high correlation.

APPENDIX: USING STATMODELS

An alternative to `scikit`'s LinearRegression is method *sm.ols* in `statmodels`. The latter produces a more extensive output of the statistical properties of the model, suitable for non-predictive tasks such as statistical inference. Table 6.10 shows the same model for price vs. car attributes from Table 6.3 run using *sm.ols*. For regularization, use `statmodels` method *OLS.fit_regularized*. Set argument L1_wt=0 for ridge regression and L1_wt=1 for lasso.

TABLE 6.9 LASSO AND RIDGE REGRESSION APPLIED TO THE TOYOTA COROLLA DATA

code for regularized linear regression

Code and output (edited)

```
lasso = Lasso(normalize=True, alpha=1)
lasso.fit(train_X, train_y)
regressionSummary(valid_y, lasso.predict(valid_X))

    Regression statistics
                          Mean Error (ME) : 120.6311
           Root Mean Squared Error (RMSE) : 1332.2752
                Mean Absolute Error (MAE) : 1021.5286
              Mean Percentage Error (MPE) : -0.2364
    Mean Absolute Percentage Error (MAPE) : 9.0115

lasso_cv = LassoCV(normalize=True, cv=5)
lasso_cv.fit(train_X, train_y)
regressionSummary(valid_y, lasso_cv.predict(valid_X))
print('Lasso-CV chosen regularization: ', lasso_cv.alpha_)
print(lasso_cv.coef_)

    Regression statistics
                          Mean Error (ME) : 145.1571
           Root Mean Squared Error (RMSE) : 1397.9428
                Mean Absolute Error (MAE) : 1052.4649
              Mean Percentage Error (MPE) : -0.2966
    Mean Absolute Percentage Error (MAPE) : 9.2918
    Lasso-CV chosen regularization:  3.5138
    [-140 -0.018 33.9 0.0 69.4 0.0 0.0 2.71 12.4 0.0 0.0]

ridge = Ridge(normalize=True, alpha=1)
ridge.fit(train_X, train_y)
regressionSummary(valid_y, ridge.predict(valid_X))

    Regression statistics
                          Mean Error (ME) : 154.3286
           Root Mean Squared Error (RMSE) : 1879.7426
                Mean Absolute Error (MAE) : 1353.2735
              Mean Percentage Error (MPE) : -2.3897
    Mean Absolute Percentage Error (MAPE) : 11.1309

bayesianRidge = BayesianRidge(normalize=True)
bayesianRidge.fit(train_X, train_y)
regressionSummary(valid_y, bayesianRidge.predict(valid_X))
alpha = bayesianRidge.lambda_ / bayesianRidge.alpha_
print('Bayesian ridge chosen regularization: ', alpha)

    Regression statistics
                          Mean Error (ME) : 105.5382
           Root Mean Squared Error (RMSE) : 1313.0217
                Mean Absolute Error (MAE) : 1017.2356
```

(Continued)

TABLE 6.9 LASSO AND RIDGE REGRESSION APPLIED TO THE TOYOTA COROLLA DATA (*Continued*)

```
          Mean Percentage Error (MPE) : -0.2703
Mean Absolute Percentage Error (MAPE) : 9.0012
Bayesian ridge chosen regularization: 0.004623
```

TABLE 6.10 LINEAR REGRESSION MODEL OF PRICE VS. CAR ATTRIBUTES USING STATMODELS (COMPARE WITH TABLE 6.3)

code for fitting a regression model

```
# run a linear regression of Price on the remaining 11 predictors in the training set
train_df = train_X.join(train_y)

predictors = train_X.columns
formula = 'Price ~ ' + ' + '.join(predictors)

car_lm = sm.ols(formula=formula, data=train_df).fit()
car_lm.summary()
```

Partial Output

```
                            OLS Regression Results
==============================================================================
Dep. Variable:                  Price   R-squared:                       0.856
Model:                            OLS   Adj. R-squared:                  0.854
Method:                 Least Squares   F-statistic:                     319.0
Date:                Mon, 18 Feb 2019   Prob (F-statistic):          1.73e-239
Time:                        18:38:04   Log-Likelihood:                -5198.1
No. Observations:                 600   AIC:                         1.042e+04
Df Residuals:                     588   BIC:                         1.047e+04
Df Model:                          11
Covariance Type:            nonrobust
====================================================================================
                       coef    std err          t      P>|t|      [0.025      0.975]
------------------------------------------------------------------------------------
Intercept        -1319.3544   1728.427     -0.763      0.446   -4713.997    2075.288
Age_08_04         -140.7488      5.142    -27.374      0.000    -150.847    -130.650
KM                  -0.0178      0.002     -7.286      0.000      -0.023      -0.013
HP                  36.1034      5.321      6.785      0.000      25.653      46.554
Met_Color           84.2818    127.005      0.664      0.507    -165.158     333.721
Automatic          416.7820    259.794      1.604      0.109     -93.454     927.018
CC                   0.0177      0.099      0.179      0.858      -0.177       0.213
Doors              -50.6579     65.187     -0.777      0.437    -178.686      77.371
Quarterly_Tax       13.6253      2.518      5.411      0.000       8.680      18.571
Weight              13.0387      1.602      8.140      0.000       9.893      16.185
```

TABLE 6.10 LINEAR REGRESSION MODEL OF PRICE VS. CAR ATTRIBUTES USING STATMODELS (COMPARE WITH TABLE 6.3) *(Continued)*

```
Fuel_Type_Diesel  1066.4647     527.285       2.023       0.044      30.872    2102.057
Fuel_Type_Petrol  2310.2495     521.045       4.434       0.000    1286.914    3333.585
==============================================================================
Omnibus:                       62.422   Durbin-Watson:                   1.899
Prob(Omnibus):                  0.000   Jarque-Bera (JB):              366.046
Skew:                           0.186   Prob(JB):                     3.27e-80
Kurtosis:                       6.808   Cond. No.                     2.20e+06
```

PROBLEMS

6.1 Predicting Main Entrance Test Performance: The file *Ent_Test.csv* carries 15 variables that pertain to aspirants seeking admission in the top league B-schools of India. Many of these join coaching institutes and improve their preparedness. The coaching institutes, apart from coursework, offer mock tests at regular intervals, which are also open to aspirants not enrolled with the coaching institute. The main tests are conducted mostly once a year by most of the B-schools. Also, candidates make several attempts to get a better percentile to improve their admission chances or selection in the desired B-school in case multiple schools or institutes are organizing a joint entrance test.

The dataset *Ent_Test.csv* includes scores of students in one of the major entrance tests as the target variable. There are also two case identifiers, twelve predictor variables (four profile variables, number of previous attempts for the same main test, total mock tests administered, and scores in six mock tests attempted from three different coaching institutes). The details of the variables are shown in Table 6.11.

TABLE 6.11 DESCRIPTION OF VARIABLES FOR ENTRANCE TEST DATASET

```
CaseID            : dtype int64
Cand_ID           : dtype int64
Region            : dtype object levels "Central India",  "South India" , etc
Degree            : dtype object levels "Engineering" or  "Non-Engineering"
Gender            : dtype object levels "Female","Male"
Coaching          : dtype object "No","Yes"
Prev_Attempts     : dtype int64 Number of previous attempts for Main Test
Tot_Mocks         : dtype int64 number of  mock tests taken
Inst1_Tst1        : dtype int64 Score in Institute1 and Mock Test1
Inst1_Tst2        : dtype int64 Score in Institute1 and Mock Test2
Inst2_Tst1        : dtype int64 Score in Institute2 and Mock Test1
Inst2_Tst2        : dtype int64 Score in Institute2 and Mock Test2
Inst3_Tst1        : dtype int64 Score in Institute3 and Mock Test1
Inst3_Tst2        : dtype int64 Score in Institute3 and Mock Test2
Main_Tst          : dtype int64 Score in the main entrance test
```

a. Why should the data be partitioned into training and validation sets? What will the training set be used for? What will the validation set be used for?

b. Fit a multiple linear regression model to the main test score (Main_Tst) as a function of total mock test attempts (Tot_Mocks) and mock test score (Inst1_Tst1 to Inst3_Tst2-6 variables). Write the equation for predicting the Main_Tst Score from the predictors in the model.

c. Using the estimated regression model, what main test score is predicted for an aspirant who has got following scores in various mock tests? Tot_Mocks : 6, Inst1_Tst1 : 109, Inst1_Tst2 : 112, Inst2_Tst1 : 99, Inst2_Tst2 : 106, Inst3_Tst1 : 78, and Inst3_Tst2 : 94. What is the prediction error?

6.2 Predicting Software Reselling Profits. Tayko Software is a software catalog firm that sells games and educational software. It started out as a software manufacturer and then added third-party titles to its offerings. It recently revised its collection of items in a new catalog, which it mailed out to its customers. This mailing yielded 2000 purchases. Based on these data, Tayko wants to devise a model for predicting the spending amount that a purchasing customer will yield. The file *Tayko.csv* contains information on 2000 purchases. Table 6.12 describes the variables to be used in the problem (the Excel file contains additional variables).

TABLE 6.12 DESCRIPTION OF VARIABLES FOR TAYKO SOFTWARE EXAMPLE

FREQ	Number of transactions in the preceding year
LAST_UPDATE	Number of days since last update to customer record
WEB	Whether customer purchased by Web order at least once
GENDER	Male or female
ADDRESS_RES	Whether it is a residential address
ADDRESS_US	Whether it is a US address
SPENDING (outcome)	Amount spent by customer in test mailing ($)

a. Explore the spending amount by creating a pivot table for the categorical variables and computing the average and standard deviation of spending in each category.

b. Explore the relationship between spending and each of the two continuous predictors by creating two scatterplots (Spending vs. Freq, and Spending vs. last_update_days_ago). Does there seem to be a linear relationship?

c. To fit a predictive model for Spending:

   i. Partition the 2000 records into training and validation sets.

   ii. Run a multiple linear regression model for Spending vs. all six predictors. Give the estimated predictive equation.

   iii. Based on this model, what type of purchaser is most likely to spend a large amount of money?

iv. If we used backward elimination to reduce the number of predictors, which predictor would be dropped first from the model?

v. Show how the prediction and the prediction error are computed for the first purchase in the validation set.

vi. Evaluate the predictive accuracy of the model by examining its performance on the validation set.

vii. Create a histogram of the model residuals. Do they appear to follow a normal distribution? How does this affect the predictive performance of the model?

6.3 Predicting Airfare on New Routes.

The following problem takes place in the United States in the late 1990s, when many major US cities were facing issues with airport congestion, partly as a result of the 1978 deregulation of airlines. Both fares and routes were freed from regulation, and low-fare carriers such as Southwest (SW) began competing on existing routes and starting nonstop service on routes that previously lacked it. Building completely new airports is generally not feasible, but sometimes decommissioned military bases or smaller municipal airports can be reconfigured as regional or larger commercial airports. There are numerous players and interests involved in the issue (airlines, city, state and federal authorities, civic groups, the military, airport operators), and an aviation consulting firm is seeking advisory contracts with these players. The firm needs predictive models to support its consulting service. One thing the firm might want to be able to predict is fares, in the event a new airport is brought into service. The firm starts with the file *Airfares.csv*, which contains real data that were collected between Q3—1996 and Q2—1997. The variables in these data are listed in Table 6.13, and are believed to be important in predicting FARE. Some airport-to-airport data are available, but most data are at the city-to-city level. One question that will be of interest in the analysis is the effect that the presence or absence of Southwest has on FARE.

TABLE 6.13 DESCRIPTION OF VARIABLES FOR AIRFARE EXAMPLE

S_CODE	Starting airport's code
S_CITY	Starting city
E_CODE	Ending airport's code
E_CITY	Ending city
COUPON	Average number of coupons (a one-coupon flight is a nonstop flight, a two-coupon flight is a one-stop flight, etc.) for that route
NEW	Number of new carriers entering that route between Q3—1996 and Q2—1997
VACATION	Whether (Yes) or not (No) a vacation route
SW	Whether (Yes) or not (No) Southwest Airlines serves that route
HI	Herfindahl index: measure of market concentration
S_INCOME	Starting city's average personal income
E_INCOME	Ending city's average personal income

(Continued)

TABLE 6.13 **DESCRIPTION OF VARIABLES FOR AIRFARE EXAMPLE (*Continued*)**

S_POP	Starting city's population
E_POP	Ending city's population
SLOT	Whether or not either endpoint airport is slot-controlled (this is a measure of airport congestion)
GATE	Whether or not either endpoint airport has gate constraints (this is another measure of airport congestion)
DISTANCE	Distance between two endpoint airports in miles
PAX	Number of passengers on that route during period of data collection
FARE	Average fare on that route

a. Explore the numerical predictors and outcome (FARE) by creating a correlation table and examining some scatterplots between FARE and those predictors. What seems to be the best single predictor of FARE?

b. Explore the categorical predictors (excluding the first four) by computing the percentage of flights in each category. Create a pivot table with the average fare in each category. Which categorical predictor seems best for predicting FARE?

c. Find a model for predicting the average fare on a new route:

i. Convert categorical variables into dummy variables. Then, partition the data into training and validation sets. The model will be fit to the training data and evaluated on the validation set.

ii. Use stepwise regression to reduce the number of predictors. You can ignore the first four predictors (S_CODE, S_CITY, E_CODE, E_CITY). Report the estimated model selected.

iii. Repeat (ii) using exhaustive search instead of stepwise regression. Compare the resulting best model to the one you obtained in (ii) in terms of the predictors that are in the model.

iv. Compare the predictive accuracy of both models (ii) and (iii) using measures such as RMSE and average error and lift charts.

v. Using model (iii), predict the average fare on a route with the following characteristics: COUPON = 1.202, NEW = 3, VACATION = No, SW = No, HI = 4442.141, S_INCOME = $28,760, E_INCOME = $27,664, S_POP = 4,557,004, E_POP = 3,195,503, SLOT = Free, GATE = Free, PAX = 12,782, DISTANCE = 1976 miles.

vi. Predict the reduction in average fare on the route in (v) if Southwest decides to cover this route [using model (iii)].

vii. In reality, which of the factors will not be available for predicting the average fare from a new airport (i.e., before flights start operating on those routes)? Which ones can be estimated? How?

viii. Select a model that includes only factors that are available before flights begin to operate on the new route. Use an exhaustive search to find such a model.

ix. Use the model in (viii) to predict the average fare on a route with characteristics COUPON = 1.202, NEW = 3, VACATION = No, SW = No, HI = 4442.141, S_INCOME = $28,760, E_INCOME = $27,664, S_POP = 4,557,004, E_POP = 3,195,503, SLOT = Free, GATE = Free, PAX = 12,782, DISTANCE = 1976 miles.

x. Compare the predictive accuracy of this model with model (iii). Is this model good enough, or is it worthwhile reevaluating the model once flights begin on the new route?

d. In competitive industries, a new entrant with a novel business plan can have a disruptive effect on existing firms. If a new entrant's business model is sustainable, other players are forced to respond by changing their business practices. If the goal of the analysis was to evaluate the effect of Southwest Airlines' presence on the airline industry rather than predicting fares on new routes, how would the analysis be different? Describe technical and conceptual aspects.

6.4 Predicting Prices of Used Cars. The file *ToyotaCorolla.csv* contains data on used cars (Toyota Corolla) on sale during late summer of 2004 in the Netherlands. It has 1436 records containing details on 38 attributes, including Price, Age, Kilometers, HP, and other specifications. The goal is to predict the price of a used Toyota Corolla based on its specifications. (The example in Section 6.3 is a subset of this dataset.)

Split the data into training (50%), validation (30%), and test (20%) datasets.
Run a multiple linear regression with the outcome variable Price and predictor variables Age_08_04, KM, Fuel_Type, HP, Automatic, Doors, Quarterly_Tax, Mfr_Guarantee, Guarantee_Period, Airco, Automatic_airco, CD_Player, Powered_Windows, Sport_Model, and Tow_Bar.

a. What appear to be the three or four most important car specifications for predicting the car's price?

b. Using metrics you consider useful, assess the performance of the model in predicting prices.

CHAPTER 7

k-Nearest Neighbors (*k*-NN)

In this chapter, we describe the *k*-nearest-neighbors algorithm that can be used for classification (of a categorical outcome) or prediction (of a numerical outcome). To classify or predict a new record, the method relies on finding "similar" records in the training data. These "neighbors" are then used to derive a classification or prediction for the new record by voting (for classification) or averaging (for prediction). We explain how similarity is determined, how the number of neighbors is chosen, and how a classification or prediction is computed. *k*-NN is a highly automated data-driven method. We discuss the advantages and weaknesses of the *k*-NN method in terms of performance and practical considerations such as computational time.

Python

In this chapter, we will use `pandas` for data handling, `scikit-learn` for *k*-nearest neighbors models, and `matplotlib` for visualization.

import required functionality for this chapter

```
import pandas as pd
from sklearn import preprocessing
from sklearn.model_selection import train_test_split
from sklearn.metrics import accuracy_score
from sklearn.neighbors import NearestNeighbors, KNeighborsClassifier
import matplotlib.pylab as plt
```

7.1 | THE *k*-NN CLASSIFIER (CATEGORICAL OUTCOME)

The idea in *k*-nearest-neighbors methods is to identify *k* records in the training dataset that are similar to a new record that we wish to classify. We then use these similar (neighboring) records to classify the new record into a class, assigning the new record to the predominant class among these neighbors. Denote the values of the predictors for this new record by $x_1, x_2, \dots, x_p$. We look for records in our training data that are similar or "near" the record to be classified in the predictor space (i.e., records that have values close to $x_1, x_2, \dots, x_p$). Then, based on the classes to which those proximate records belong, we assign a class to the record that we want to classify.

Determining Neighbors

The *k*-nearest-neighbors algorithm is a classification method that does not make assumptions about the form of the relationship between the class membership (Y) and the predictors $X_1, X_2, \dots, X_p$. This is a nonparametric method because it does not involve estimation of parameters in an assumed function form, such as the linear form assumed in linear regression (Chapter 6). Instead, this method draws information from similarities between the predictor values of the records in the dataset.

A central question is how to measure the distance between records based on their predictor values. The most popular measure of distance is the Euclidean distance. The Euclidean distance between two records $(x_1, x_2, \dots, x_p)$ and $(u_1, u_2, \dots, u_p)$ is

$$\sqrt{(x_1 - u_1)^2 + (x_2 - u_2)^2 + \cdots + (x_p - u_p)^2}. \tag{7.1}$$

You will find a host of other distance metrics in Chapters 12 and 15 for both numerical and categorical variables. However, the *k*-NN algorithm relies on many distance computations (between each record to be predicted and every record in the training set), and therefore the Euclidean distance, which is computationally cheap, is the most popular in *k*-NN.

To equalize the scales that the various predictors may have, note that in most cases, predictors should first be standardized before computing a Euclidean distance. Also note that the means and standard deviations used to standardize new records are those of the *training* data, and the new record is not included in calculating them. The validation data, like new data, are also not included in this calculation.

Classification Rule

After computing the distances between the record to be classified and existing records, we need a rule to assign a class to the record to be classified, based on the classes of its neighbors. The simplest case is $k = 1$, where we look for the record that is closest (the nearest neighbor) and classify the new record as belonging to the same class as its closest neighbor. It is a remarkable fact that this simple, intuitive idea of using a single nearest neighbor to classify records can be very powerful when we have a large number of records in our training set. It turns out that the misclassification error of the 1-nearest neighbor scheme has a misclassification rate that is no more than twice the error when we know exactly the probability density functions for each class.

The idea of the *1-nearest neighbor* can be extended to $k > 1$ neighbors as follows:

1. Find the nearest k neighbors to the record to be classified.
2. Use a majority decision rule to classify the record, where the record is classified as a member of the majority class of the k neighbors.

Example: Fruit Variety Classification

In fresh produce retail, retailers buy mixed varieties of some items in one lot, like tomato, mango, potato, apple, etc. For example, mango has several varieties, and sometimes it gets difficult to differentiate. However, customer satisfaction is dependent on how well these varieties are displayed separately and appropriate price signage is displayed. Produce sorters are trained to use relevant dimensions to sort varieties but fresh recruits in the operations function need to be trained on item specifications for effective item sorting and deliver quality output as per acceptable customer specifications. In large-scale sorting processes, automated systems can use similar logic to sort items in terms of grade, variety, level of quality, etc. We have a dataset *Fruit_Variety.csv* (583 cases) with three variables Length (mm), Weight (g), and Variety. Each case represents one unit of apple, and its variety is either "local" or "non-Local". For explanation purposes, we will use a random portion of this dataset with 28 cases in a separate file *Fruit_Variety_Sample.csv* which has 14 units of "local" variety and the rest of "non-Local". Fifteen cases from this sample set are shown in Table 7.1. We first partitioned the data into training data (14 cases) and validation data (14 cases). Obviously, this dataset is too small for partitioning, which can result in unstable results, but we will continue with this partitioning for illustration purposes. A scatter plot of the training data is shown in Figure 7.1.

Now consider a new case with a length of 80 mm and a weight of 120 gm (also shown as "★" in Figure 7.1). Among the cases in the training set, the one closest to the new case (in Euclidean distance after normalizing income and lot size) is case 6, with a length of 82.382 mm and weight of 121.17 g, which is a "local" variety. If we use a 1-NN classifier, we will classify the new household as a local variety, like in case 6. If we use $k = 3$, the three nearest cases are 6, 22, and 20 as can be seen visually in the scatter plot and as computed by the software (see the output in Table 7.2). In this scenario, only one fruit variety of three samples is "Local" but the rest both are "non-Local." The majority vote is therefore "non-Local," and the new case would be classified as "non-Local."

TABLE 7.1 ALL CASES (FRUIT_VARIETY_SAMPLE.CSV) AND VARIABLES

Case_No	Length (mm)	Weight (gms)	Variety
1	67.201	133.91	Local
2	56.202	109.75	Local
3	101.779	169.08	Local
4	55.930	129.50	Local
5	58.905	133.62	Local
6	82.382	121.17	Local
7	42.092	117.17	Local
8	41.480	86.33	Local
9	41.344	82.18	Local
10	35.326	77.96	Local
11	58.157	90.17	Local
12	118.082	95.18	Non-Local
13	90.406	93.88	Non-Local
14	97.461	84.96	Local
15	142.715	181.94	Non-Local

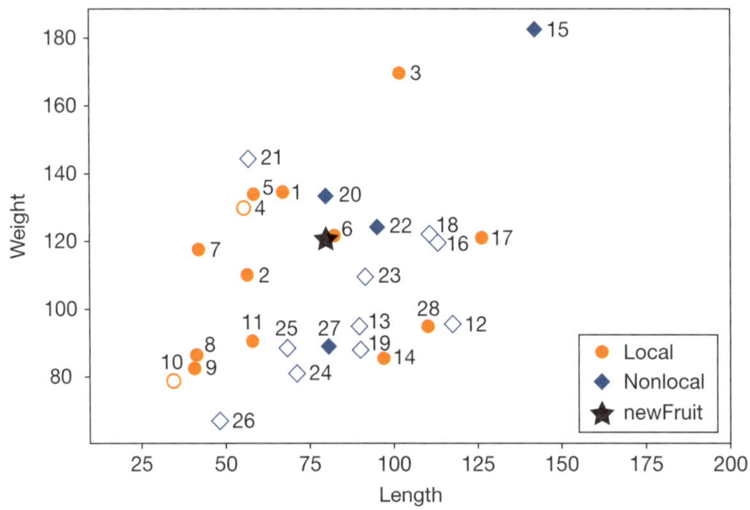

FIGURE 7.1 SCATTER PLOT OF LENGTH VS WEIGHT FOR SAMPLE CASES

code for loading and partitioning the riding mower data, and plotting scatter plot

```
fv=pd.read_csv('Fruit_Variety.csv')
fvs=pd.read_csv("Fruit_Variety_Sample.csv")
trainData, validData = train_test_split(fvs, test_size=0.5, random_state=42)
## new fruit
newFruit = pd.DataFrame([{'Length': 80, 'Weight': 120}])
## scatter plot
```

```
def plotDataset(ax, data, showLabel=True, **kwargs):
    subset = data.loc[data['Variety']=='Local']
    ax.scatter(subset.Length, subset.Weight, marker='o',
        label='Local' if showLabel else None, color='C1', **kwargs)
    subset = data.loc[data['Variety']=='NonLocal']
    ax.scatter(subset.Length, subset.Weight, marker='D',
        label='Nonlocal' if showLabel else None, color='C0', **kwargs)
    plt.xlabel('Length')      # set x-axis label
    plt.ylabel('Weight')      # set y-axis label
    for _, row in data.iterrows():
        ax.annotate(row.Case_No, (row.Length + 2, row.Weight))
    fig, ax = plt.subplots()
plotDataset(ax, trainData)
plotDataset(ax, validData, showLabel=False, facecolors='none')
ax.scatter(newFruit.Length, newFruit.Weight, marker='*',
  label='newFruit', color='black', s=250)
plt.xlabel('Length');
plt.ylabel('Weight')
ax.set_xlim(10, 200)
handles, labels = ax.get_legend_handles_labels()
ax.legend(handles, labels, loc=4)
plt.show()
```

Choosing *k*

The advantage of choosing $k > 1$ is that higher values of k provide smoothing that reduces the risk of overfitting due to noise in the training data. Usually, if k is too low, we may be fitting to the noise in the data. However, if k is too high, we will miss out on the method's ability to capture the local structure in the data, one of its main advantages. In the extreme, $k = n =$ the number of records in the training dataset. In that case, we simply assign all records to the majority class in the training data, irrespective of the values of $(x_1, x_2, \dots, x_p)$, which coincides with the naive rule! This is clearly a case of over smoothing in the absence of useful information in the predictors about the class membership. In other words, we want to balance between overfitting to the predictor information and ignoring this information completely. A balanced choice greatly depends on the nature of the data. The more complex and irregular the structure of the data, the lower the optimum value of k. Typically, values of k fall in the range of 1 to 20. We will use odd numbers to avoid ties.

So how is k chosen? Answer: We choose the k with the best classification performance. We use the training data to classify the records in the validation data, then compute error rates for various choices of k. For our example, if we choose $k = 1$, we will classify in a way that is very sensitive to the local characteristics of the training data. On the other hand, if we choose a large value of k, such as $k = 10$ or 12, we would simply predict the most frequent class in the dataset in all cases. This is a very stable prediction but it completely ignores the information in the predictors. To find a balance, we examine the accuracy (of predictions in the validation set) that results from different choices of k between 1 and 14. For an even number k, if there is a tie in classifying a household, the tie is broken randomly.[1] This is shown in Table 7.3. We would choose $k = 5$, which maximizes our accuracy in the validation set.[2] Note, however, that now the validation set is used as part of the training process (to set k) and does not reflect a true holdout set as before. Ideally, we would want a third test set to evaluate the performance of the method on data that it did not see.

TABLE 7.2 RUNNING k = NN

code for normalizing data and finding nearest neighbors

```
# initialize normalized training, validation, and complete data frames
newFruit = pd.DataFrame([{'Length': 80, 'Weight': 120}])
# use the training data to learn the transformation.
Scaler = preprocessing.StandardScaler()
scaler.fit(trainData[['Length', 'Weight']])
# Note use of array of column names
# Transform the full dataset
fvNorm= pd.concat([pd.DataFrame(scaler.transform(fvs[['Length', 'Weight']]),
                                   columns=['zLength', 'zWeight']),
                        fvs[['Variety', 'Case_No']]], axis=1)
trainNorm = fvNorm.iloc[trainData.index]
validNorm = fvNorm.iloc[validData.index]
newFVSnorm = pd.DataFrame(scaler.transform(newFruit), columns=['zLength', 'zWeight'])

# use NearestNeighbors from scikit-learn to compute knn
from sklearn.neighbors import NearestNeighbors
knn = NearestNeighbors(n_neighbors=3)
knn.fit(trainNorm.iloc[:, 0:2])
distances, indices = knn.kneighbors(newFVSnorm)

# indices is a list of lists, we are only interested in the first element
trainNorm.iloc[indices[0], :]
```

Output

```
     zLength   zWeight   Variety  Case_No
5  -0.073394  0.005732     Local        6
19 -0.144116  0.424654  NonLocal       20
21  0.377239  0.089517  NonLocal       22
```

Once k is chosen, we rerun the algorithm on the combined training and testing sets in order to generate classifications of new records.

[1] If you are interested in reproducibility of results, check the accuracy only for each odd k.

[2] Partitioning such a small dataset is unwise in practice, as results will heavily rely on the particular partition. For instance, if you use a different partitioning, you might obtain a different "optimal" k. We use this example for illustration only.

TABLE 7.3 ACCURACY (OR CORRECT RATE) OF *k*-NN PREDICTIONS IN VALIDATION SET FOR VARIOUS CHOICES OF *k*

code for measuring the accuracy of different *k* values on validation set

```
from sklearn.metrics import accuracy_score
Tx = trainNorm[['zLength', 'zWeight']]
ty = trainNorm['Variety']
Vx = validNorm[['zLength', 'zWeight']]
vy = validNorm['Variety']
# Train a classifier for different values of k
results = []
for k in range(1, 15):
            knn = KneighborsClassifier(n_neighbors=k).fit(Tx, ty)
            results.append({
                        'k': k,
                        'accuracy': accuracy_score(vy, knn.predict(Vx))
            })
# Convert results to a pandas data frame
results = pd.DataFrame(results)
print(results)
```

Output

```
     k  accuracy
0    1  0.571429
1    2  0.642857
2    3  0.357143
3    4  0.500000
4    5  0.857143
5    6  0.642857
6    7  0.714286
7    8  0.785714
8    9  0.428571
9   10  0.357143
10  11  0.500000
11  12  0.642857
12  13  0.642857
13  14  0.500000
```

Setting the Cutoff Value

k-NN uses a majority decision rule to classify a new record, where the record is classified as a member of the majority class of the *k* neighbors. The definition of "majority" is directly linked to the notion of a cutoff value applied to the class membership probabilities. Let us consider a binary outcome case. For a new record, the proportion of class 1 members among its neighbors is an estimate of its propensity (probability) of belonging to class 1. In the Fruit Variety example with $k = 5$, we found that the five nearest neighbors to the new case (with length = 80 and weight = 120) are units with Case_Nos 1, 6, 20, 22, and 23. Since two of these are local variety and the other three are non-local variety, we can estimate for the new case a probability of 0.6 of being a non-local (and 0.4 for being a local variety). Using a simple majority rule is equivalent to setting the cutoff value to 0.5.

As mentioned in Chapter 5, changing the cutoff value affects the confusion matrix (i.e., the error rates). Hence, in some cases we might want to choose a cutoff other than the default 0.5 for the purpose of maximizing accuracy or for incorporating misclassification costs.

TABLE 7.4 CLASSIFYING A NEW FRUIT USING THE "BEST *K*" = 5

code for measuring the accuracy of different *k* values on validation set

```
# Retrain with full dataset
fv_X = fvNorm[['zLength', 'zWeight']]
fv_y = fvNorm['Variety']
knn = KneighborsClassifier(n_neighbors=4).fit(fv_X, fv_y)
distances, indices = knn.kneighbors(newFVSnorm)
print(knn.predict(newFVSnorm))
print('Distances', distances)
print('Indices', indices)
print(fvNorm.iloc[indices[0], :])
```

Output

```
['NonLocal']
Distances [[0.09174816 0.46041965 0.54703609 0.57682701]]
Indices [[ 5 19 21 22 0]]
        zLength   zWeight    Variety  Case_No
5     -0.073394  0.005732      Local        6
19    -0.144116  0.424654  Non-Local       20
21     0.377239  0.089517  Non-Local       22
22     0.263850 -0.431927  Non-Local       23
0     -0.595333  0.456118      Local        1
```

k-NN with More Than Two Classes

The *k*-NN classifier can easily be applied to an outcome with *m* classes, where $m > 2$. The "majority rule" means that a new record is classified as a member of the majority class of its *k* neighbors. An alternative, when there is a specific class that we are interested in identifying (and are willing to "overidentify" records as belonging to this class), is to calculate the proportion of the *k* neighbors that belong to this class of interest, use that as an estimate of the probability (propensity) that the new record belongs to that class, and then refer to a user-specified cutoff value to decide whether to assign the new record to that class. For more on the use of cutoff value in classification where there is a single class of interest, see Chapter 5.

Converting Categorical Variables to Binary Dummies

It usually does not make sense to calculate Euclidean distance between two non-numeric categories (e.g., cookbooks and maps, in a bookstore). Therefore, before *k*-NN can be applied, categorical variables must be converted to binary dummies. In contrast to the situation with statistical models such as regression, all *m* binaries should be created and used with *k*-NN. While mathematically this is redundant, since $m - 1$ dummies contain the same information as *m* dummies, this redundant information does not create the multicollinearity problems that it does for linear models. Moreover, in *k*-NN the use of $m - 1$ dummies can yield different classifications than the use of *m* dummies, and lead to an imbalance in the contribution of the different categories to the model.

7.2 | *k*-NN FOR A NUMERICAL OUTCOME

The idea of *k*-NN can readily be extended to predicting a continuous value (as is our aim with multiple linear regression models). The first step of determining neighbors by computing distances remains unchanged. The second step, where a majority vote of the neighbors is used to determine class, is modified such that we take the average outcome value of the *k*-nearest neighbors to determine the prediction. Often, this average is a weighted average, with the weight decreasing with increasing distance from the point at which the prediction is required. In `scikit-learn`, we can use `KNeighborsRegressor` to compute *k*-NN numerical predictions for the validation set.

Another modification is in the error metric used for determining the "best *k*." Rather than the overall error rate used in classification, RMSE (root-mean-squared error) or another prediction error metric should be used in prediction (see Chapter 5).

PANDORA

Pandora is an Internet music radio service that allows users to build customized "stations" that play music similar to a song or artist that they have specified. Pandora uses a *k*-NN style clustering/classification process called the Music Genome Project to locate new songs or artists that are close to the user-specified song or artist.

Pandora was the brainchild of Tim Westergren, who worked as a musician and a nanny when he graduated from Stanford in the 1980s. Together with Nolan Gasser, who was studying medieval music, he developed a "matching engine" by entering data about a song's characteristics into a spreadsheet. The first result was surprising—a Beatles song matched to a Bee Gees song, but they built a company around the concept. The early days were hard—Westergren racked up over $300,000 in personal debt, maxed out 11 credit cards, and ended up in the hospital once due to stress-induced heart palpitations. A venture capitalist finally invested funds in 2004 to rescue the firm, and as of 2013, it is listed on the NY Stock Exchange.

In simplified terms, the process works roughly as follows for songs:

1. Pandora has established hundreds of variables on which a song can be measured on a scale from 0 to 5. Four such variables from the beginning of the list are
   - Acid Rock Qualities
   - Accordion Playing
   - Acousti-Lectric Sonority
   - Acousti-Synthetic Sonority
2. Pandora pays musicians to analyze tens of thousands of songs, and rate each song on each of these attributes. Each song will then be represented by a row vector of values between 0 and 5, for example, for Led Zeppelin's Kashmir:

   Kashmir 4 0 3 3 ... (high on acid rock attributes, no accordion, etc.)

   This step represents a costly investment, and lies at the heart of Pandora's value because these variables have been tested and selected because they accurately reflect the essence of a song, and provide a basis for defining highly individualized preferences.
3. The online user specifies a song that s/he likes (the song must be in Pandora's database).
4. Pandora then calculates the statistical distance[1] between the user's song and the songs in its database. It selects a song that is close to the user-specified song and plays it.
5. The user then has the option of saying "I like this song," "I don't like this song," or saying nothing.
6. If "like" is chosen, the original song, plus the new song are merged into a 2-song cluster[2] that is represented by a single vector comprising means of the variables in the original two song vectors.
7. If "dislike" is chosen, the vector of the song that is not liked is stored for future reference. (If the user does not express an opinion about the song, in our simplified example here, the new song is not used for further comparisons.)
8. Pandora looks in its database for a new song, one whose statistical distance is close to the "like" song cluster,[3] and not too close to the "dislike" song. Depending on the user's reaction, this new song might be added to the "like" cluster or "dislike" cluster.

Over time, Pandora develops the ability to deliver songs that match a particular taste of a particular user. A single user might build up multiple stations around different song clusters. Clearly, this is a less limiting approach than selecting music in terms of which "genre" it belongs to.

While the process described above is a bit more complex than the basic "classification of new data" process described in this chapter, the fundamental process—classifying a record according to its proximity to other records—is the same at its core. Note the role of domain knowledge in this machine learning process—the variables have been tested and selected by the project leaders, and the measurements have been made by human experts.

Further reading: See www.pandora.com, Wikipedia's article on the Music Genome Project, and Joyce John's article "Pandora and the Music Genome Project," *Scientific Computing*, vol. 23, no. 10: 14, p. 40–41, Sep. 2006.

[1] See Section 12.5 in Chapter 12 for an explanation of statistical distance.

[2] See Chapter 15 for more on clusters.

[3] See Case 21.6 "Segmenting Consumers of Bath Soap" for an exercise involving the identification of clusters, which are then used for classification purposes.

7.3 | ADVANTAGES AND SHORTCOMINGS OF *k*-NN ALGORITHMS

The main advantage of *k*-NN methods is their simplicity and lack of parametric assumptions. In the presence of a large enough training set, these methods perform surprisingly well, especially when each class is characterized by multiple combinations of predictor values. For instance, in real-estate databases, there are likely to be multiple combinations of {home type, number of rooms, neighborhood, asking price, etc.} that characterize homes that sell quickly vs. those that remain for a long period on the market.

There are three difficulties with the practical exploitation of the power of the *k*-NN approach. First, although no time is required to estimate parameters from the training data (as would be the case for parametric models such as regression), the time to find the nearest neighbors in a large training set can be prohibitive. A number of ideas have been implemented to overcome this difficulty. The main ideas are:

- Reduce the time taken to compute distances by working in a reduced dimension using dimension reduction techniques such as principal components analysis (Chapter 4).
- Use sophisticated data structures such as search trees to speed up identification of the nearest neighbor. This approach often settles for an "almost nearest" neighbor to improve speed. An example is using *bucketing*, where the records are grouped into buckets so that records within each bucket are close to each other. For a to-be-predicted record, buckets are ordered by their distance to the record. Starting from the nearest bucket, the distance to each of the records within the bucket is measured. The algorithm stops when the distance to a bucket is larger than the distance to the closest record thus far.

Second, the number of records required in the training set to qualify as large increases exponentially with the number of predictors p. This is because the expected distance to the nearest neighbor goes up dramatically with p unless the size of the training set increases exponentially with p. This phenomenon is known as the *curse of dimensionality*, a fundamental issue pertinent to all classification, prediction, and clustering techniques. This is why we often seek to reduce the number of predictors through methods such as selecting subsets of the predictors for our model or by combining them using methods such as principal components analysis, singular value decomposition, and factor analysis (see Chapter 4).

Third, k-NN is a "lazy learner": the time-consuming computation is deferred to the time of prediction. For every record to be predicted, we compute its distances from the entire set of training records only at the time of prediction. This behavior prohibits using this algorithm for real-time prediction of a large number of records simultaneously.

PROBLEMS

7.1 Calculating Distance with Categorical Predictors. This exercise with a tiny dataset illustrates the calculation of Euclidean distance, and the creation of binary dummies. The online education company Statistics.com segments its customers and prospects into three main categories: IT professionals (IT), statisticians (Stat), and other (Other). It also tracks, for each customer, the number of years since first contact (years). Consider the following customers; information about whether they have taken a course or not (the outcome to be predicted) is included:

Customer 1: Stat, 1 year, did not take course
Customer 2: Other, 1.1 year, took course

a. Consider now the following new prospect:

Prospect 1: IT, 1 year

Using the above information on the two customers and one prospect, create one dataset for all three with the categorical predictor variable transformed into 2 binaries, and a similar dataset with the categorical predictor variable transformed into 3 binaries.

b. For each derived dataset, calculate the Euclidean distance between the prospect and each of the other two customers. (*Note*: While it is typical to normalize data for k-NN, this is not an iron-clad rule and you may proceed here without normalization.)

c. Using k-NN with $k = 1$, classify the prospect as taking or not taking a course using each of the two derived datasets. Does it make a difference whether you use two or three dummies?

7.2 Personal Loan Acceptance. Universal Bank is a relatively young bank growing rapidly in terms of overall customer acquisition. The majority of these customers are liability customers (depositors) with varying sizes of relationship with the bank. The customer base of asset customers (borrowers) is quite small, and the bank is interested in expanding this base rapidly to bring in more loan business. In particular, it wants to explore ways of converting its liability customers to personal loan customers (while retaining them as depositors).

A campaign that the bank ran last year for liability customers showed a healthy conversion rate of over 9% success. This has encouraged the retail marketing department to devise smarter campaigns with better target marketing. The goal is to use k-NN to predict whether a new customer will accept a loan offer. This will serve as the basis for the design of a new campaign.

The file *UniversalBank.csv* contains data on 5000 customers. The data include customer demographic information (age, income, etc.), the customer's relationship with the bank (mortgage, securities account, etc.), and the customer response to the last personal loan campaign (Personal Loan). Among these 5000 customers, only 480 (=9.6%) accepted the personal loan that was offered to them in the earlier campaign.

Partition the data into training (60%) and validation (40%) sets.

a. Consider the following customer: Age = 40, Experience = 10, Income = 84, Family = 2, CCAvg = 2, Education_1 = 0, Education_2 = 1, Education_3 = 0, Mortgage = 0, Securities Account = 0, CD Account = 0, Online = 1, and Credit Card = 1. Perform a k-NN classification with all predictors except ID and ZIP code using $k = 1$. Remember to transform categorical predictors with more than two categories into dummy variables first. Specify the *success* class as 1 (loan acceptance), and use the default cutoff value of 0.5. How would this customer be classified?

b. What is a choice of k that balances between overfitting and ignoring the predictor information?

c. Show the confusion matrix for the validation data that results from using the best k.

d. Consider the following customer: Age = 40, Experience = 10, Income = 84, Family = 2, CCAvg = 2, Education_1 = 0, Education_2 = 1, Education_3 = 0, Mortgage = 0, Securities Account = 0, CD Account = 0, Online = 1 and Credit Card = 1. Classify the customer using the best k.

e. Repartition the data, this time into training, validation, and test sets (50%:30%:20%). Apply the k-NN method with the k chosen above. Compare the confusion matrix of the test set with that of the training and validation sets. Comment on the differences and their reason.

7.3 Predicting Housing Median Prices. The file *BostonHousing.csv* contains information on over 500 census tracts in Boston, where for each tract multiple variables are recorded. The last column (CAT.MEDV) was derived from MEDV, such that it obtains the value 1 if MEDV > 30 and 0 otherwise. Consider the goal of predicting the median value (MEDV) of a tract, given the information in the first 12 columns.

Partition the data into training (60%) and validation (40%) sets.

a. Perform a k-NN prediction with all 12 predictors (ignore the CAT.MEDV column), trying values of k from 1 to 5. Make sure to normalize the data. What is the best k? What does it mean?

b. Predict the MEDV for a tract with the following information, using the best k:

CRIM	ZN	INDUS	CHAS	NOX	RM	AGE	DIS	RAD	TAX	PTRATIO	LSTAT
0.2	0	7	0	0.538	6	62	4.7	4	307	21	10

c. If we used the above *k*-NN algorithm to score the training data, what would be the error of the training set?

d. Why is the validation data error overly optimistic compared to the error rate when applying this *k*-NN predictor to new data?

e. If the purpose is to predict MEDV for several thousands of new tracts, what would be the disadvantage of using *k*-NN prediction? List the operations that the algorithm goes through in order to produce each prediction.

CHAPTER 8

The Naive Bayes Classifier

In this chapter, we introduce the naive Bayes classifier, which can be applied to data with categorical predictors. We review the concept of conditional probabilities, then present the complete, or exact, Bayesian classifier. We next see how it is impractical in most cases, and learn how to modify it and use instead the *naive Bayes* classifier, which is more generally applicable.

Python

In this chapter, we will use pandas for data handling, `scikit-learn` for naive Bayes models, and `matplotlib` for visualization. We will also make use of the utility functions from the Python Utilities Functions Appendix.

import required functionality for this chapter

```
import pandas as pd
from sklearn.model_selection import train_test_split
from sklearn.naive_bayes import MultinomialNB
import matplotlib.pylab as plt
from dmba import classificationSummary, gainsChart
```

8.1 | INTRODUCTION

The naive Bayes method (and, indeed, an entire branch of statistics) is named after the Reverend Thomas Bayes (1702–1761). To understand the naive Bayes classifier, we first look at the complete, or exact, Bayesian classifier. The basic principle is simple. For each record to be classified:

1. Find all the other records with the same predictor profile (i.e., where the predictor values are the same).
2. Determine what classes the records belong to and which class is most prevalent.
3. Assign that class to the new record.

Alternatively (or in addition), it may be desirable to tweak the method so that it answers the question: "What is the propensity of belonging to the class of interest?" instead of "Which class is the most probable?" Obtaining class probabilities allows using a sliding cutoff to classify a record as belonging to class C_i, even if C_i is not the most probable class for that record. This approach is useful when there is a specific class of interest that we are interested in identifying, and we are willing to "overidentify" records as belonging to this class (see Chapter 5 for more details on the use of cutoffs for classification and on asymmetric misclassification costs).

Cutoff Probability Method

1. Establish a cutoff probability for the class of interest above which we consider that a record belongs to that class.
2. Find all the training records with the same predictor profile as the new record (i.e., where the predictor values are the same).
3. Determine the probability that those records belong to the class of interest.
4. If that probability is above the cutoff probability, assign the new record to the class of interest.

Conditional Probability

Both procedures incorporate the concept of *conditional probability*, or the probability of event A given that event B has occurred [denoted $P(A|B)$]. In this case, we will be looking at the probability of the record belonging to class C_i given that its predictor values are $x_1, x_2, \ldots, x_p$. In general, for a response with m classes $C_1, C_2, \ldots, C_m$, and the predictor values $x_1, x_2, \ldots, x_p$, we want to compute

$$P(C_i \mid x_1, \ldots, x_p). \tag{8.1}$$

To classify a record, we compute its probability of belonging to each of the classes in this way, then classify the record to the class that has the highest probability or use the cutoff probability to decide whether it should be assigned to the class of interest.

From this definition, we see that the Bayesian classifier works only with categorical predictors. If we use a set of numerical predictors, then it is highly unlikely that multiple records will have identical values on these numerical predictors. Therefore, numerical predictors must be binned and converted to categorical predictors. *The Bayesian classifier is the only classification or prediction method presented in this book that is especially suited for (and limited to) categorical predictor variables.*

Example 1: Predicting Fraudulent Financial Reporting

An accounting firm has many large companies as customers. Each customer submits an annual financial report to the firm, which is then audited by the accounting firm. For simplicity, we will designate the outcome of the audit as "fraudulent" or "truthful," referring to the accounting firm's assessment of the customer's financial report. The accounting firm has a strong incentive to be accurate in identifying fraudulent reports—if it passes a fraudulent report as truthful, it would be in legal trouble.

The accounting firm notes that, in addition to all the financial records, it also has information on whether or not the customer has had prior legal trouble (criminal or civil charges of any nature filed against it). This information has not been used in previous audits, but the accounting firm is wondering whether it could be used in the future to identify reports that merit more intensive review. Specifically, it wants to know whether having had prior legal trouble is predictive of fraudulent reporting.

In this case, each customer is a record, and the outcome variable of interest, $Y = \{\text{fraudulent, truthful}\}$, has two classes into which a company can be classified: C_1 = fraudulent and C_2 = truthful. The predictor variable—"prior legal trouble"—has two values: 0 (no prior legal trouble) and 1 (prior legal trouble).

The accounting firm has data on 1500 companies that it has investigated in the past. For each company, it has information on whether the financial report was judged fraudulent or truthful and whether the company had prior legal trouble. The data were partitioned into a training set (1000 firms) and a validation set (500 firms). Counts in the training set are shown in Table 8.1.

TABLE 8.1 PIVOT TABLE FOR FINANCIAL REPORTING EXAMPLE

	Prior legal ($X = 1$)	No prior legal ($X = 0$)	Total
Fraudulent (C_1)	50	50	100
Truthful (C_2)	180	720	900
Total	230	770	1000

8.2 | APPLYING THE FULL (EXACT) BAYESIAN CLASSIFIER

Now consider the financial report from a new company, which we wish to classify as either fraudulent or truthful by using these data. To do this, we compute the probabilities, as above, of belonging to each of the two classes.

If the new company had had prior legal trouble, the probability of belonging to the fraudulent class would be *P*(fraudulent | prior legal) = 50/230 (of the 230 companies with prior legal trouble in the training set, 50 had fraudulent financial reports). The probability of belonging to the other class, "truthful," is, of course, the remainder = 180/230.

Using the "Assign to the Most Probable Class" Method

If a company had prior legal trouble, we assign it to the "truthful" class. Similar calculations for the case of no prior legal trouble are left as an exercise to the reader. In this example, using the rule "assign to the most probable class," all records are assigned to the "truthful" class. This is the same result as the naive rule of "assign all records to the majority class."

Using the Cutoff Probability Method

In this example, we are more interested in identifying the fraudulent reports—those are the ones that can land the auditor in jail. We recognize that, in order to identify the fraudulent reports, some truthful reports will be misidentified as fraudulent, and the overall classification accuracy may decline. Our approach is, therefore, to establish a cutoff value for the probability of being fraudulent, and classify all records above that value as fraudulent. The Bayesian formula for the calculation of this probability that a record belongs to class C_i is as follows:

$$P(C_i|x_1, \dots, x_p) = \frac{P(x_1, \dots, x_p|C_i)P(C_i)}{P(x_1, \dots, x_p|C_1)P(C_1) + \cdots + P(x_1, \dots, x_p|C_m)P(C_m)}. \tag{8.2}$$

In this example (where frauds are rarer), if the cutoff were established at 0.20, we would classify a prior legal trouble record as fraudulent because *P*(fraudulent | prior legal) = 50/230 = 0.22. The user can treat this cutoff as a "slider" to be adjusted to optimize performance, like other parameters in any classification model.

Practical Difficulty with the Complete (Exact) Bayes Procedure

The approach outlined above amounts to finding all the records in the sample that are exactly like the new record to be classified in the sense that all the predictor values are all identical. This was easy in the small example presented above, where there was just one predictor.

When the number of predictors gets larger (even to a modest number like 20), many of the records to be classified will be without exact matches. This can be understood in the context of a model to predict voting on the basis of demographic variables. Even a sizable sample may not contain even a single match for a new record who is a male Hispanic with high income from the US Midwest who voted in the last election, did not vote in the prior election, has three daughters and one son, and is divorced. And this is just eight variables, a small number for most data mining exercises. The addition of just a single new variable with five equally frequent categories reduces the probability of a match by a factor of 5.

Solution: Naive Bayes

In the naive Bayes solution, we no longer restrict the probability calculation to those records that match the record to be classified. Instead we use the entire dataset.

Returning to our original basic classification procedure outlined at the beginning of the chapter, recall that the procedure for classifying a new record was:

1. Find all the other records with the same predictor profile (i.e., where the predictor values are the same).
2. Determine what classes the records belong to and which class is most prevalent.
3. Assign that class to the new record.

The naive Bayes modification (for the basic classification procedure) is as follows:

1. For class C_1, estimate the individual conditional probabilities for each predictor $P(x_j|C_1)$—these are the probabilities that the predictor value in the record to be classified occurs in class C_1. For example, for X_1 this probability is estimated by the proportion of x_1 values among the C_1 records in the training set.
2. Multiply these probabilities by each other, then by the proportion of records belonging to class C_1.
3. Repeat Steps 1 and 2 for all the classes.
4. Estimate a probability for class C_i by taking the value calculated in Step 2 for class C_i and dividing it by the sum of such values for all classes.
5. Assign the record to the class with the highest probability for this set of predictor values.

The above steps lead to the naive Bayes formula for calculating the probability that a record with a given set of predictor values $x_1, \dots, x_p$ belongs to class C_1 among m classes. The formula can be written as follows:

$$P_{nb}(C_1|x_1,\dots x_p) = \frac{P(C_1)[P(x_1|C_1)P(x_2|C_1)\cdots P(x_p|C_1)]}{P(C_1)[P(x_1|C_1)P(x_2|C_1)\cdots P(x_p|C_1)]+\cdots+P(C_m)[P(x_1|C_m)P(x_2|C_m)\cdots P(x_p|C_m)]}. \tag{8.3}$$

This is a somewhat formidable formula; see Example 2 for a simpler numerical version. Note that all the needed quantities can be obtained from pivot tables of Y vs. each of the categorical predictors.

The Naive Bayes Assumption of Conditional Independence

In probability terms, we have made a simplifying assumption that the exact *conditional probability* of seeing a record with predictor profile $x_1, x_2, \dots, x_p$ within a certain class, $P(x_1, x_2, \dots, x_p|C_i)$, is well approximated by the product of the individual conditional probabilities $P(x_1|C_i) \times P(x_2|C_i) \times \cdots \times P(x_p|C_i)$. These two quantities are identical when the predictors are independent within each class.

For example, suppose that "lost money last year" is an additional variable in the accounting fraud example. The simplifying assumption we make with naive Bayes is that, within a given class, we no longer need to look for the records characterized both by "prior legal trouble" and "lost money last year." Rather, assuming that the two are independent, we can simply multiply the probability of "prior legal trouble" by the probability of "lost money last year." Of course, complete independence is unlikely in practice, where some correlation between predictors is expected.

In practice, despite the assumption violation, the procedure works quite well—primarily because what is usually needed is not a propensity for each record that is accurate in absolute terms but just a reasonably accurate *rank ordering* of propensities. Even when the assumption is violated, the rank ordering of the records' propensities is typically preserved.

Note that if all we are interested in is a rank ordering, and the denominator remains the same for all classes, it is sufficient to concentrate only on the numerator. The disadvantage of this approach is that the probability values it yields (the propensities), while ordered correctly, are not on the same scale as the exact values that the user would anticipate.

Using the Cutoff Probability Method

The above procedure is for the basic case where we seek maximum classification accuracy for all classes. In the case of the *relatively rare class of special interest*, the procedure is:

1. Establish a cutoff probability for the class of interest above which we consider that a record belongs to that class.
2. For the class of interest, compute the probability that each individual predictor value in the record to be classified occurs in the training data.
3. Multiply these probabilities times each other, then times the proportion of records belonging to the class of interest.
4. Estimate the probability for the class of interest by taking the value calculated in Step 3 for the class of interest and dividing it by the sum of the similar values for all classes.
5. If this value falls above the cutoff, assign the new record to the class of interest, otherwise not.
6. Adjust the cutoff value as needed, as a parameter of the model.

Example 2: Predicting Fraudulent Financial Reports, Two Predictors

Let us expand the financial reports example to two predictors, and, using a small subset of data, compare the complete (exact) Bayes calculations to the naive Bayes calculations.

Consider the 10 customers of the accounting firm listed in Table 8.2. For each customer, we have information on whether it had prior legal trouble, whether it is a small or large company, and whether the financial report was found to be fraudulent or truthful. Using this information, we will calculate the conditional probability of fraud, given each of the four possible combinations {y, small}, {y, large}, {n, small}, {n, large}.

TABLE 8.2 INFORMATION ON 10 COMPANIES

Company	Prior legal trouble	Company size	Status
1	Yes	Small	Truthful
2	No	Small	Truthful
3	No	Large	Truthful
4	No	Large	Truthful
5	No	Small	Truthful
6	No	Small	Truthful
7	Yes	Small	Fraudulent
8	Yes	Large	Fraudulent
9	No	Large	Fraudulent
10	Yes	Large	Fraudulent

Complete (Exact) Bayes Calculations: The probabilities are computed as

$$P(\text{fraudulent}|\text{PriorLegal} = \text{y}, \text{Size} = \text{small}) = 1/2 = 0.5$$

$$P(\text{fraudulent}|\text{PriorLegal} = \text{y}, \text{Size} = \text{large}) = 2/2 = 1$$

$$P(\text{fraudulent}|\text{PriorLegal} = \text{n}, \text{Size} = \text{small}) = 0/3 = 0$$

$$P(\text{fraudulent}|\text{PriorLegal} = \text{n}, \text{Size} = \text{large}) = 1/3 = 0.33$$

Naive Bayes Calculations: Now we compute the naive Bayes probabilities. For the conditional probability of fraudulent behaviors given {PriorLegal = y, Size = small}, the numerator is a multiplication of the proportion of {PriorLegal = y} instances among the fraudulent companies, times the proportion of {Size = small} instances among the fraudulent companies, times the proportion of fraudulent companies: (3/4)(1/4)(4/10) = 0.075. To get the actual probabilities, we must also compute the numerator for the conditional probability of truthful behaviors given {PriorLegal = y, Size = small}: (1/6)(4/6)(6/10) = 0.067. The denominator is then the sum of these two conditional probabilities (0.075 + 0.067 = 0.14). The conditional probability of fraudulent behaviors given {PriorLegal = y, Size = small} is therefore 0.075/0.14 = 0.53. In a similar fashion, we compute all four conditional probabilities:

$$P_{\text{nb}}(\text{fraudulent}|\text{PriorLegal} = \text{y}, \text{Size} = \text{small}) = \frac{(3/4)(1/4)(4/10)}{(3/4)(1/4)(4/10) + (1/6)(4/6)(6/10)} = 0.53$$

$$P_{\text{nb}}(\text{fraudulent}|\text{PriorLegal} = \text{y}, \text{Size} = \text{large}) = 0.87$$

$$P_{\text{nb}}(\text{fraudulent}|\text{PriorLegal} = \text{n}, \text{Size} = \text{small}) = 0.07$$

$$P_{\text{nb}}(\text{fraudulent}|\text{PriorLegal} = \text{n}, \text{Size} = \text{large}) = 0.31$$

Note how close these naive Bayes probabilities are to the exact Bayes probabilities. Although they are not equal, both would lead to exactly the same classification for a cutoff of 0.5 (and many other values). It is often the case that the rank ordering of probabilities is even closer to the exact Bayes method than the probabilities themselves, and for classification purposes it is the rank orderings that matter.

We now consider an example where various product attributes are used to predict customer rating behavior.

Example 3: Predicting Online Buying Behavior

E-commerce platform companies like Amazon, Flipkart, Bookmyshow, Myntra, Yatra, etc., that provide an online platform for sellers to sell their products or services facilitate their sellers as well as buyers and increase their effectiveness through various support instruments. One of the support systems that many of these platforms provide in product selling is facility of the logistics, including inventory handling for sellers by a third party. Sellers in many such cases are asked to pay a fee towards this facilitation, which has many advantages. Through this service, sellers can avail best-in-class fulfillment services and smooth operations with the customers, which translates into higher customer satisfaction.

In our example, we will be using a curated dataset obtained from a larger set to explain the concepts in this chapter. The details of the curated dataset *ecommerce_sample.csv* (1605 cases) are shown in Table 8.3. There is one transaction identifier and four predictor variables (product category, retail price, discounted price, and fulfilment provision opted by the seller). Three more predictor variables have been created from the original predictors (price category, percent discount, and discount level). Price categories vary from 1 to 7, with 1 representing the lowest price and 7 the highest price usually for items like jewelry or computers. Similarly, discount levels have been categorized from no discount to huge discounts where zero discount is coded as 1, whereas 7 indicates discounts of 90% and above. The response or target variable here is rating where customers express their satisfaction with the product and service and give a rating from 1 to 5. There were several cases of "No Rating," which have been filtered out in this curated data set for the purpose of our exercise to focus only on cases where a rating has been given by the buyer.

TABLE 8.3 VARIABLES FOR EXAMPLE E-COMMERCE SERVICES EFFECTIVENESS

Variable	Description
TransID	Transaction identifier
MainPdtCat	Main category of the product sold in the transaction
Retail_Price	Retail price of the product
Discounted_Price	Discounted offered price for the product
Price_Category	Retail price transformed into bins and categorised from 1 (Lowest) to 7 (Highest)
Percent_Discount	Percentage discount on retail price (calculated based on retail and discount price)
Discount_Level	Percent_Discount transformed into categories from 1 (Lowest) and 7 (Highest)
Fulfilment_Item	Fulfilment facility opted by the seller 1 = "Yes" or 0 = "No"
Product_Rating	Rating given by the customer as indicator of satisfaction
Product_Rating_N	Transformed Product_Rating based on values = >3 as "Satisfactory" otherwise "Dissatisfactory".

We have created one more dependent variable in the curated set, which is Product_Rating_N based on our dependent/target variable values – "Satisfactory" in case the rating is equal to or greater than 3, otherwise "Dissatisfactory" assuming 3 as the threshold of customer satisfaction.

The data were first partitioned into training (60%) and validation (40%) sets, and then a naive Bayes classifier was applied to the training set.

The first part of the output in Table 8.4 shows the ratios of satisfactory ratings (where Product_Rating_N = "Satisfactory") and dissatisfactory ratings (Product_Rating_N = "Dissatisfactory") in the training set (called a priori probabilities), followed by the conditional probabilities for each class, as a function of the predictor values. Note that the conditional probabilities in the naive Bayes output can be replicated simply by using pivot tables on the training data, looking at the proportion of records for each value relative to the entire class. This is illustrated in Table 8.5, which displays the proportion of satisfactory (or dissatisfactory) ratings by the customers (each row adds up to 1). Note that in this example, there are no predictor values that were not represented in the training data.

TABLE 8.4 NAIVE BAYES CLASSIFIER APPLIED TO CUSTOMER RATING (TRAINING) DATA

code for running naive Bayes

```
#read dataset
ee=pd.read_csv("Ecommerce_Example1.csv")
# convert to categorical
ee.MainPdtCat = ee.MainPdtCat.astype('category')
ee.Price_Category = ee.Price_Category.astype('category')
ee.Discount_Level = ee.Discount_Level.astype('category')
ee.Fulfilment_Item = ee.Fulfilment_Item.astype('category')
ee.Product_Rating_N = ee.Product_Rating_N.astype('category')
for dtype in ee.dtypes.iteritems():
print(dtype)
predictors=['MainPdtCat','Price_Category', 'Discount_Level','Fulfilment_Item']
X = pd.get_dummies(ee[predictors])
y=ee.Product_Rating_N
classes = list(y.cat.categories)
X_train, X_valid, y_train, y_valid = train_test_split(X, y, test_size=0.40,
random_state=1)
# run naive Bayes
rating_nb = MultinomialNB(alpha=0.01)
rating_nb.fit(X_train, y_train)
# predict probabilities
predProb_train = rating_nb.predict_proba(X_train)
predProb_valid = rating_nb.predict_proba(X_valid)
# predict class membership
y_valid_pred = rating_nb.predict(X_valid)
```

TABLE 8.5 PIVOT TABLE OF PRODUCT RATING BY VARIOUS PREDICTORS (TRAINING DATA)

```
# probability of Product Rating
print(train_df['Flight Status'].value_counts() / len(train_df))
print()

for predictor in predictors:
        # construct the frequency table
        df = train_df[['Product_Rating_N, predictor]]
        freqTable = df.pivot_table(index= Product_Rating_N, columns=predictor, aggfunc=len)
        # divide each value by the sum of the row to get conditional probabilities
        propTable = freqTable.apply(lambda x: x / sum(x), axis=1)
        print(propTable)
        print()
```

To classify a new transaction, we compute the probability indicative of dissatisfaction or satisfaction. Recall that since both will have the same denominator, we can just compare the numerators. Each numerator is computed by multiplying all the conditional probabilities of the relevant predictor values and, finally, multiplying by the proportion of that class (in this case $\hat{P}$(dissatisfied) = 0.5919). Let us use an example: to classify a transaction with product category "Watches", Price Category "1", Discount Level = "4", and Item Fulfilment "0", we first compute the numerators using the values from the pivot tables:

$$\hat{P}(\text{Satisfaction}|\text{Product Category “Watches”, Price Category “1”, Discount Level} = \text{“4” and Item Fulfilment “0”}) \propto (0.0432)(0.0941)(0.2111)(0.9007) = 0.0007,$$

$$\hat{P}(\text{Dissatisfaction}|\text{Product Category “Watches”, Price Category “1”, Discount Level} = \text{“4” and Item Fulfilment “0”}) \propto (0.1807)(0.1807)(0.2526)(0.7719) = 0.0063.$$

The symbol $\propto$ means "is proportional to," reflecting the fact that this calculation deals only with the numerator in the naive Bayes formula (8.3). Comparing the numerators, it is therefore, more likely response from the customer i.e., dissatisfactory rating (less than 3). Note that a record with such a combination of predictor values does not exist in the training set and therefore we use the naive Bayes rather than the exact Bayes. To compute the actual probability, we divide each of the numerators by their sum:

$$\hat{P}(\text{Satisfaction}|\text{Product Category “Watches”, Price Category “1”, Discount Level} = \text{“4” and Item Fulfilment “0”}) = \frac{0.0007}{0.0007 + 0.0063} = 0.1,$$

$$\hat{P}(\text{Dissatisfaction}|\text{Product Category “Watches”, Price Category “1”, Discount Level} = \text{“4” and Item Fulfilment “0”}) = \frac{0.0063}{0.0007 + 0.0063} = 0.9.$$

Of course, we rely on software to compute these probabilities for any records of interest (in the training set, the validation set, or for scoring new data). Table 8.6 shows the estimated probability and class for the example case.

Finally, to evaluate the performance of the naive Bayes classifier for our data, we use the confusion matrix, lift charts, and all the measures that were described in Chapter 5. For our example, the confusion matrices for the training and validation sets are shown in Table 8.7. We see that the overall accuracy level is around 76% for the training data and 71% for the validation data. In comparison, a naive rule that would classify all 642 cases as transactions with a dissatisfactory rating in the validation set would have missed cases with satisfactory ratings. Examining the lift chart (Figure 8.1) shows the strength of the naive Bayes model in capturing the dissatisfactory rating cases effectively when the goal is ranking.

TABLE 8.6 SCORING THE EXAMPLE CUSTOMER TRANSACTION (PROBABILITY AND CLASS)

code for scoring data using naive Bayes

```
# classify a specific customer transaction by searching in the dataset
# for a case  with the specific  predictor values
df = pd.concat([pd.DataFrame({'actual': y_valid, 'predicted': y_valid_pred}),
pd.DataFrame(predProb_valid, index=y_valid.index)], axis=1)
mask= ((X_valid.MainPdtCat_Clothing == 1) & (X_valid.Price_Category_3 == 1) &
      (X_valid.Discount_Level_5==1) & (X_valid.Fulfilment_Item_1 == 0))
df[mask]
```

Output

```
                 actual    predicted         0         1
1383    Dissatisfactory  Satisfactory  0.273092  0.726908
801        Satisfactory  Satisfactory  0.273092  0.726908
1560       Satisfactory  Satisfactory  0.273092  0.726908
120        Satisfactory  Satisfactory  0.273092  0.726908
189        Satisfactory  Satisfactory  0.273092  0.726908
```

TABLE 8.7 CONFUSION MATRICES FOR RATING PREDICTION WITH NAIVE BAYES CLASSIFIER

code for confusion matrices

```
# training
classificationSummary(y_train, y_train_pred, class_names=classes)
# validation
classificationSummary(y_valid, y_valid_pred, class_names=classes)
```

TABLE 8.7 CONFUSION MATRICES FOR RATING PREDICTION WITH NAIVE BAYES CLASSIFIER (*Continued*)

Output

```
Confusion Matrix (Accuracy 0.7435)

                        Prediction
         Actual    Dissatisfactory    Satisfactory
Dissatisfactory                454             126
   Satisfactory                121             262

Confusion Matrix (Accuracy 0.7461)

                        Prediction
         Actual    Dissatisfactory    Satisfactory
Dissatisfactory                287              91
   Satisfactory                 72             192
```

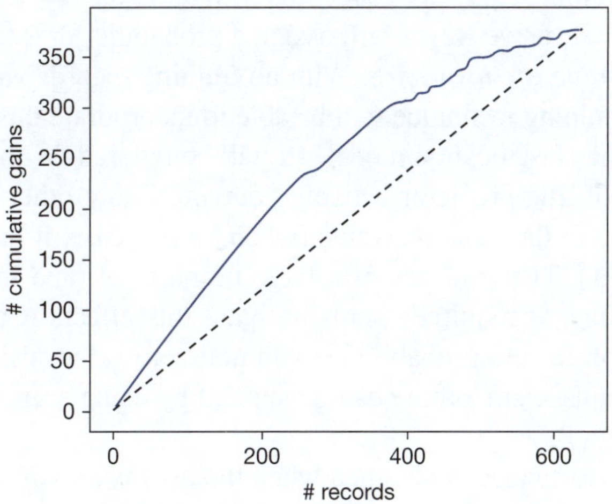

FIGURE 8.1 CUMULATIVE GAINS CHART OF NAIVE BAYES CLASSIFIER APPLIED TO CUSTOMER RATING IN ECOMMERCE EXAMPLE DATA

code for creating Figure 8.1

```
df = pd.DataFrame({'actual': 1 - y_valid.cat.codes, 'prob': predProb_valid[:, 0]})
df = df.sort_values(by=['prob'], ascending=False).reset_index(drop=True)

fig, ax = plt.subplots()
fig.set_size_inches(4, 4)
gainsChart(df.actual, ax=ax)
```

8.3 ADVANTAGES AND SHORTCOMINGS OF THE NAIVE BAYES CLASSIFIER

The naive Bayes classifier's beauty is in its simplicity, computational efficiency, good classification performance, and ability to handle categorical variables directly. In fact, it often outperforms more sophisticated classifiers even when the underlying assumption of independent predictors is far from true. This advantage is especially pronounced when the number of predictors is very large.

Three main issues should be kept in mind, however. First, the naive Bayes classifier requires a very large number of records to obtain good results.

Second, where a predictor category is not present in the training data, naive Bayes assumes that a new record with that category of the predictor has zero probability. This can be a problem if this rare predictor value is important. Consider an example, where the outcome variable is *bought high-value life insurance* and a predictor category is *owns yacht*. If the training data have no records with *owns yacht* = 1, for any new records where *owns yacht* = 1, naive Bayes will assign a probability of 0 to the outcome variable *bought high-value life insurance*. With no training records with *owns yacht* = 1, of course, no data mining technique will be able to incorporate this potentially important variable into the classification model—it will be ignored. With naive Bayes, however, the absence of this predictor actively "outvotes" any other information in the record to assign a 0 to the outcome value (when, in this case, it has a relatively good chance of being a 1). The presence of a large training set (and judicious binning of continuous predictors, if required) helps mitigate this effect. A popular solution in such cases is to replace zero probabilities with non-zero values using a method called *smoothing* (e.g., Laplace smoothing can be applied by using argument Laplace = 0 in function *naiveBayes()*).

Finally, good performance is obtained when the goal is *classification* or *ranking* of records according to their probability of belonging to a certain class. However, when the goal is to *estimate the probability of class membership (propensity)*, this method provides very biased results. For this reason, the naive Bayes method is rarely used in credit scoring (Larsen, 2005).

SPAM FILTERING

Filtering spam in e-mail has long been a widely familiar application of data mining. Spam filtering, which is based in large part on natural language vocabulary, is a natural fit for a naive Bayesian classifier, which uses exclusively categorical variables. Most spam filters are based on this method, which works as follows:

1. Humans review a large number of e-mails, classify them as "spam" or "not spam," and from these select an equal (also large) number of spam e-mails and non-spam e-mails. This is the training data.
2. These e-mails will contain thousands of words; for each word, compute the frequency with which it occurs in the spam dataset, and the frequency with which it occurs in the non-spam dataset. Convert these frequencies into estimated probabilities (i.e., if the word "free" occurs in 500 out of 1000 spam e-mails, and only 100 out of 1000 non-spam e-mails, the probability that a spam e-mail will contain the word "free" is 0.5, and the probability that a non-spam e-mail will contain the word "free" is 0.1).
3. If the only word in a new message that needs to be classified as spam or not spam is "free," we would classify the message as spam, since the Bayesian posterior probability is 0.5/(0.5 + 01) or 5/6 that, given the appearance of "free," the message is spam.
4. Of course, we will have many more words to consider. For each such word, the probabilities described in Step 2 are calculated, and multiplied together, and formula (8.3) is applied to determine the naive Bayes probability of belonging to the classes. In the simple version, class membership (spam or not spam) is determined by the higher probability.
5. In a more flexible interpretation, the ratio between the "spam" and "not spam" probabilities is treated as a score for which the operator can establish (and change) a cutoff threshold—anything above that level is classified as spam.
6. Users have the option of building a personalized training database by classifying incoming messages as spam or not spam, and adding them to the training database. One person's spam may be another person's substance.

It is clear that, even with the "Naive" simplification, this is an enormous computational burden. Spam filters now typically operate at two levels—at servers (intercepting some spam that never makes it to your computer) and on individual computers (where you have the option of reviewing it). Spammers have also found ways to "poison" the vocabulary-based Bayesian approach, by including sequences of randomly selected irrelevant words. Since these words are randomly selected, they are unlikely to be systematically more prevalent in spam than in non-spam, and they dilute the effect of key spam terms such as "Viagra" and "free." For this reason, sophisticated spam classifiers also include variables based on elements other than vocabulary, such as the number of links in the message, the vocabulary in the subject line, determination of whether the "From:" e-mail address is the real originator (anti-spoofing), use of HTML and images, and origination at a dynamic or static IP address (the latter are more expensive and cannot be set up quickly).

PROBLEMS

8.1 Personal Loan Acceptance. The file *UniversalBank.csv* contains data on 5000 customers of Universal Bank. The data include customer demographic information (age, income, etc.), the customer's relationship with the bank (mortgage, securities account, etc.), and the customer response to the last personal loan campaign (Personal Loan). Among these 5000 customers, only 480 (=9.6%) accepted the personal loan that was offered to them in the earlier campaign. In this exercise, we focus on two predictors: Online (whether or not the customer is an active user of online banking services) and Credit Card (abbreviated CC below) (does the customer hold a credit card issued by the bank), and the outcome Personal Loan (abbreviated Loan below).

Partition the data into training (60%) and validation (40%) sets.

a. Create a pivot table for the training data with Online as a column variable, CC as a row variable, and Loan as a secondary row variable. The values inside the table should convey the count. Use the pandas dataframe methods *melt()* and *pivot()*.

b. Consider the task of classifying a customer who owns a bank credit card and is actively using online banking services. Looking at the pivot table, what is the probability that this customer will accept the loan offer? [This is the probability of loan acceptance (Loan = 1) conditional on having a bank credit card (CC = 1) and being an active user of online banking services (Online = 1).]

c. Create two separate pivot tables for the training data. One will have Loan (rows) as a function of Online (columns) and the other will have Loan (rows) as a function of CC.

d. Compute the following quantities [*P*(A | B) means "the probability of A given B"]:

  i. *P*(CC = 1 | Loan = 1) (the proportion of credit card holders among the loan acceptors)

  ii. *P*(Online = 1 | Loan = 1)

  iii. *P*(Loan = 1) (the proportion of loan acceptors)

  iv. *P*(CC = 1 | Loan = 0)

  v. *P*(Online = 1 | Loan = 0)

  vi. *P*(Loan = 0)

e. Use the quantities computed above to compute the naive Bayes probability *P*(Loan = 1 | CC = 1, Online = 1).

f. Compare this value with the one obtained from the pivot table in (b). Which is a more accurate estimate?

g. Which of the entries in this table are needed for computing *P*(Loan = 1 | CC = 1, Online = 1)? In Python, run naive Bayes on the data. Examine the model output on training data, and find the entry that corresponds to *P*(Loan = 1 | CC = 1, Online = 1). Compare this to the number you obtained in (e).

8.2 **Automobile Accidents.** The file *accidentsFull.csv* contains information on 42,183 actual automobile accidents in 2001 in the United States that involved one of three levels of injury: NO INJURY, INJURY, or FATALITY. For each accident, additional information is recorded, such as day of week, weather conditions, and road type. A firm might be interested in developing a system for quickly classifying the severity of an accident based on initial reports and associated data in the system (some of which rely on GPS-assisted reporting).

Our goal here is to predict whether an accident just reported will involve an injury (MAX_SEV_IR = 1 or 2) or will not (MAX_SEV_IR = 0). For this purpose, create a dummy variable called INJURY that takes the value "yes" if MAX_SEV_IR = 1 or 2, and otherwise "no."

a. Using the information in this dataset, if an accident has just been reported and no further information is available, what should the prediction be? (INJURY = Yes or No?) Why?

b. Select the first 12 records in the dataset and look only at the response (INJURY) and the two predictors WEATHER_R and TRAF_CON_R.

  i. Create a pivot table that examines INJURY as a function of the two predictors for these 12 records. Use all three variables in the pivot table as rows/columns.

  ii. Compute the exact Bayes conditional probabilities of an injury (INJURY = Yes) given the six possible combinations of the predictors.

  iii. Classify the 12 accidents using these probabilities and a cutoff of 0.5.

  iv. Compute manually the naive Bayes conditional probability of an injury given WEATHER_R = 1 and TRAF_CON_R = 1.

  v. Run a naive Bayes classifier on the 12 records and 2 predictors using scikit-learn. Check the model output to obtain probabilities and classifications for all 12 records. Compare this to the exact Bayes classification. Are the resulting classifications equivalent? Is the ranking (=ordering) of observations equivalent?

c. Let us now return to the entire dataset. Partition the data into training (60%) and validation (40%).

  i. Assuming that no information or initial reports about the accident itself are available at the time of prediction (only location characteristics, weather conditions, etc.), which predictors can we include in the analysis? (Use the data descriptions page from www.dataminingbook.com.)

  ii. Run a naive Bayes classifier on the complete training set with the relevant predictors (and INJURY as the response). Note that all predictors are categorical. Show the confusion matrix.

  iii. What is the overall error for the validation set?

  iv. What is the percent improvement relative to the naive rule (using the validation set)?

  v. Examine the conditional probabilities in the pivot tables. Why do we get a probability of zero for $P(\text{INJURY} = \text{No} \mid \text{SPD\_LIM} = 5)$?

CHAPTER 9

Classification and Regression Trees

This chapter describes a flexible data-driven method that can be used for both classification (called *classification tree*) and prediction (called *regression tree*). Among the data-driven methods, trees are the most transparent and easy to interpret. Trees are based on separating records into subgroups by creating splits on predictors. These splits create logical rules that are transparent and easily understandable, for example, "IF Age < 55 AND Education > 12 THEN class = 1." The resulting subgroups should be more homogeneous in terms of the outcome variable, thereby creating useful prediction or classification rules. We discuss the two key ideas underlying trees: *recursive partitioning* (for constructing the tree) and *pruning* (for cutting the tree back). In the context of tree construction, we also describe a few metrics of homogeneity that are popular in tree algorithms, for determining the homogeneity of the resulting subgroups of records. We explain that limiting tree size is a useful strategy for avoiding overfitting and show how it is done. We also describe alternative strategies for avoiding overfitting. As with other data-driven methods, trees require large amounts of data. However, once constructed, they are computationally cheap to deploy even on large samples. They also have other advantages such as being highly automated, robust to outliers, and able to handle missing values. In addition to prediction and classification, we describe how trees can be used for dimension reduction. Finally, we introduce *random forests* and *boosted trees*, which combine results from multiple trees to improve predictive power.

Python

In this chapter, we will use pandas for data handling, `scikit-learn` for the models, and `matplotlib` and `pydotplus` for visualization. We will also make use of the utility functions from the Python Utilities Functions Appendix. Use the following import statements for the Python code in this chapter.

import required functionality for this chapter

```
import matplotlib.pyplot as plt
from sklearn.datasets import load_iris
from sklearn.datasets import load_breast_cancer
from sklearn.tree import DecisionTreeClassifier
from sklearn.ensemble import RandomForestClassifier
from sklearn.model_selection import train_test_split
import pandas as pd
import numpy as np
from sklearn import tree
```

9.1 | INTRODUCTION

If one had to choose a classification technique that performs well across a wide range of situations without requiring much effort from the analyst while being readily understandable by the consumer of the analysis, a strong contender would be the tree methodology developed by Breiman et al. (1984). We discuss this classification procedure first, then in later sections we show how the procedure can be extended to prediction of a numerical outcome. The program that Breiman et al. created to implement these procedures was called CART (Classification And Regression Trees). A related procedure is called C4.5.

What is a classification tree? Figure 9.1 shows a tree for classifying bank customers who receive a loan offer as either acceptors or nonacceptors, based on information such as their income, education level, and average credit card expenditure.

Tree Structure

We have two types of nodes in a tree: decision (=splitting) nodes and terminal nodes. Nodes that have successors are called *decision nodes* because if we were to use a tree to classify a new record for which we knew only the values of the predictor variables, we would "drop" the record down the tree so that at each decision node, the appropriate branch is taken until we get to a node that has no successors. Such nodes are called the *terminal nodes* (or *leaves* of the tree), and represent the partitioning of the data by predictors.

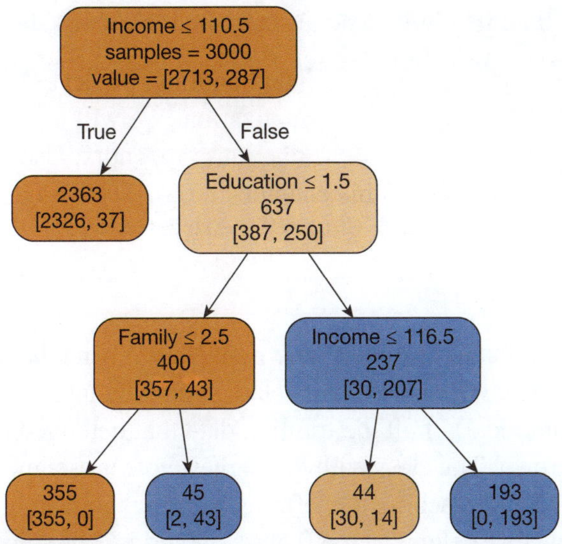

FIGURE 9.1 EXAMPLE OF A TREE FOR CLASSIFYING BANK CUSTOMERS AS LOAN ACCEPTORS OR NONACCEPTORS

It is useful to note that the type of trees grown by Python's *DecisionTreeClassifier()* method, also known as CART or *binary trees*, have the property that the number of terminal nodes is exactly one more than the number of decision nodes.

When using the *export_graphviz()* function from scikit-learn, nodes are represented as boxes. The function has a large number of arguments that allow controlling the final graph. We use the utility function *plotDecisionTree* from the appendix for plotting the graphs in this chapter. With the chosen settings, all nodes contain information about the number of records in that node (samples), the distribution of the classes, and the majority class of that node. In addition, we color the nodes by the average value of the node for regression or purity of node for classification.

For decision nodes, the name of the predictor variable chosen for splitting and its splitting value appear at the top. Of the two child nodes connected below a decision node, the left box is for records that meet the splitting condition ("True"), while the right box is for records that do not meet it ("False").

Decision Rules

One of the reasons that tree classifiers are very popular is that they provide easily understandable decision rules (at least if the trees are not too large). Consider the tree in the example. The *terminal nodes* are colored orange or blue corresponding to a nonacceptor (0) or acceptor (1) classification. The condition at the top of each splitting node gives the predictor and its splitting value for the split (e.g, *Income* ≤110.5 in the top node). *samples=* shows the number of records in that node, and *values=* shows the counts of the two classes (0 and 1) in that node; the labels are only shown in the top node. This tree can easily be translated into a set of rules for classifying a bank customer. For example, the bottom-left node under the "Family" decision node in this tree gives us the following rule:

$$\text{IF}(\textit{Income} > 110.5) \text{ AND } (\textit{Education} \leq 1.5) \text{ AND } (\textit{Family} \leq 2.5)$$
$$\text{THEN } \textit{Class} = 0 \text{ (nonacceptor).}$$

Classifying a New Record

To classify a new record, it is "dropped" down the tree. When it has dropped all the way down to a terminal node, we can assign its class simply by taking a "vote" (or average, if the outcome is numerical) of all the training data that belonged to the terminal node when the tree was grown. The class with the highest vote is assigned to the new record. For instance, a new record reaching the leftmost terminal node in Figure 9.1, which has a majority of records that belong to the 0 class, would be classified as "nonacceptor." Alternatively, we can convert the number of class 0 records in the node to a proportion (propensity) and then compare the proportion to a user-specified cutoff value. In a binary classification situation (typically, with a success class that is relatively rare and of particular interest), we can also establish a lower cutoff to better capture those rare successes (at the cost of lumping in more failures as successes). With a lower cutoff, the votes for the *success* class only need attain that lower cutoff level for the entire terminal node to be classified as a *success*. The cutoff therefore determines the proportion of votes needed for determining the terminal node class. See Chapter 5 for further discussion of the use of a cutoff value in classification, for cases where a single class is of interest.

In the following sections, we show how trees are constructed and evaluated.

9.2 | CLASSIFICATION TREES

The key idea underlying tree construction is *recursive partitioning* of the space of the predictor variables. A second important issue is avoiding over-fitting. We start by explaining recursive partitioning (Section 9.2) and then describe approaches for evaluating and fine-tuning trees while avoiding overfitting (Section 9.3).

Recursive Partitioning

Let us denote the outcome variable by Y and the input (predictor) variables by $X_1, X_2, X_3, \ldots, X_p$. In classification, the outcome variable will be a categorical variable. Recursive partitioning divides up the p-dimensional space of the X predictor variables into nonoverlapping multidimensional rectangles. The predictor variables here are considered to be continuous, binary, or ordinal. This division is accomplished recursively (i.e., operating on the results of prior divisions). First, one of the predictor variables is selected, say X_i, and a value of X_i, say s_i, is chosen to split the p-dimensional space into two parts: one part that contains all the points with $X_i < s_i$ and the other with all the points with $X_i \geq s_i$. Then, one of these two parts is divided in a similar manner by again choosing a predictor variable (it could be X_i or another variable) and a split value for that variable. This results in three (multidimensional) rectangular regions. This process is continued so that we get smaller and smaller rectangular regions. The idea is to divide the entire X-space up into rectangles such that each rectangle is as homogeneous or "pure" as possible. By *pure*, we mean containing records that belong to just one class. (Of course, this is not always possible, as there may be records that belong to different classes but have exactly the same values for every one of the predictor variables.)

Let us illustrate recursive partitioning with an example.

Example 1: Fruit Variety

We again use the fruit variety example (*Dataset Fruit Variety Classification Example.csv*). The operations department would like the produce segregation based on variety to supply these varieties in separate packaging for its buyers in the retail shops. There is a need for an efficient sorting procedure based on appropriate features like size, weight, etc., which can help differentiate varieties like local and non-local in this example. A pilot sample of 14 local and 14 non-local variety units is taken for explanation. The data are shown and plotted in Table 9.1 and Figure 9.2.

TABLE 9.1 LENGTH, WEIGHT, AND VARIETY OF FRUITS FOR 28 UNITS

Unit No	Length (mm)	Weight (gms)	Variety L = Local and NL = Non-Local
1	67.201	161	L
2	56.202	109.75	L
3	101.779	169.08	L
4	55.93	129.5	L
5	58.905	133.62	L
6	82.382	162	L
7	42.092	117.17	L
8	41.48	86.33	L
9	41.344	160	L
10	35.326	77.96	L
11	58.157	90.17	L
12	118.082	95.18	NL
13	90.406	93.88	NL
14	97.461	180.5	L
15	110	80	NL

(*Continued*)

TABLE 9.1 LENGTH, WEIGHT, AND VARIETY OF FRUITS FOR 28 UNITS (*Continued*)

Unit No	Length (mm)	Weight (gms)	Variety L = Local and NL = Non-Local
16	113.288	119.67	NL
17	126.208	120.69	L
18	111.078	142	NL
19	90.729	87.15	NL
20	80.325	133.02	NL
21	80	140.2	NL
22	95.489	123.54	NL
23	92.194	108.79	NL
24	65.5	80	NL
25	68.782	87.69	NL
26	90.5	66.37	NL
27	80.648	88.64	NL
28	130.2	100.5	L

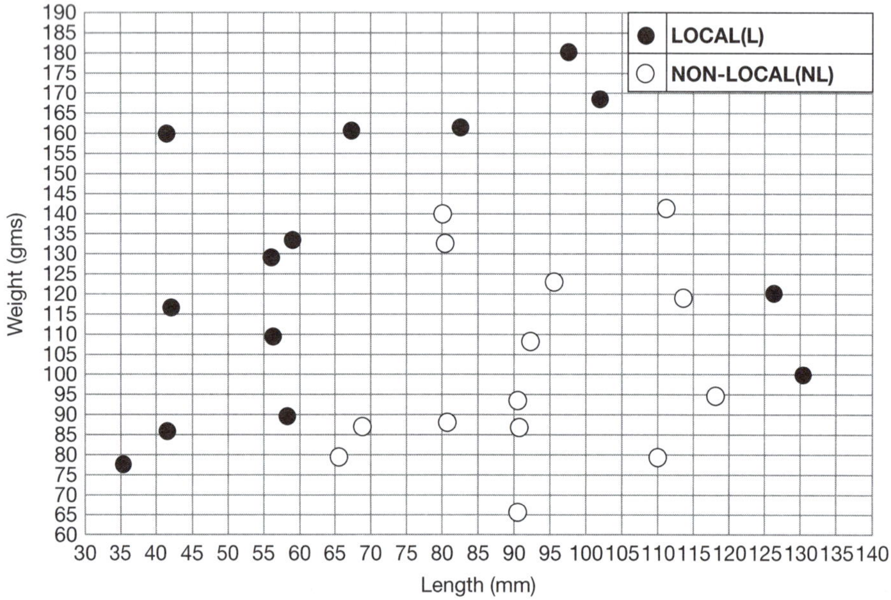

FIGURE 9.2 SCATTER PLOT OF LEGNTH VS. WEIGHT FOR 28 UNITS WHICH COMPRISE LOCAL AND NON LOCAL VARIETIES

If we apply the classification tree procedure to these data, the procedure will choose length for the first split with a splitting value of 62. The scatter chart space is now divided into two rectangles, one with length < 62 and the other with length 62 and above. This is illustrated in Figure 9.3.

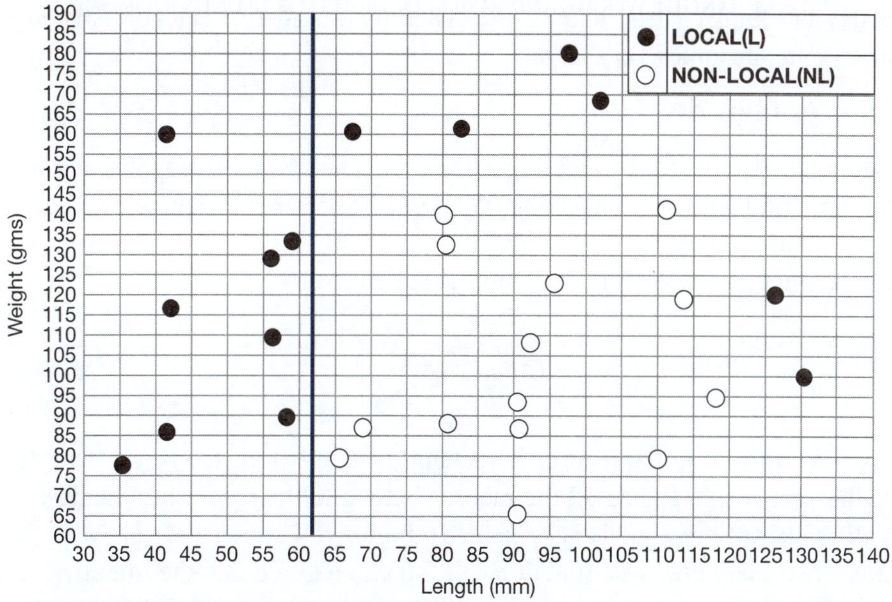

FIGURE 9.3 SPLITTING THE 28 RECORDS BY LENGTH SIZE OF 62

Notice how the split has created two rectangles, each of which is much more homogeneous than the rectangle before the split. The left rectangle contains dots that are only local variety (filled dots) and the right rectangle contains 6 local and 14 non-local variety units.

How was this particular split selected? The algorithm examined each predictor variable (in this case, length and weight) and all possible split values for each variable to find the best split. What are the possible split values for a variable? They are simply the values for each predictor. The splitting rule assesses various cutoff points for all the features used and picks the split point which can partition target points into more homogeneous classes but maximize target points into that homogeneous portion. These split points are ranked according to how much they reduce impurity (heterogeneity) in the resulting rectangle. A pure rectangle is one that is composed of a single class (e.g., Local variety only). The reduction in impurity is defined as overall impurity before the split minus the sum of the impurities for the two rectangles that result from a split.

Categorical Predictors The previous description used numerical predictors; however, categorical predictors can also be used in the recursive partitioning context. To handle categorical predictors, the split choices for a categorical predictor are all ways in which the set of categories can be divided into two subsets. For example, a categorical variable with four categories, say {a, b, c, d}, can be split in seven ways into two subsets: {a} and {b, c, d}; {b} and {a, c, d}; {c} and {a, b, d}; {d} and {a, b, c}; {a, b} and {c, d}; {a, c} and {b, d}; and finally {a, d} and {b, c}. When the number of categories is large, the number of splits becomes very large.

Measures of Impurity

There are a number of ways to measure impurity. The two most popular measures are the *Gini index* and an *entropy measure*. We describe both next. Denote the m classes of the response variable by $k = 1, 2, \ldots, m$.

The Gini impurity index for a rectangle A is defined by

$$I(A) = 1 - \sum_{k=1}^{m} p_k^2,$$

where p_k is the proportion of records in rectangle A that belong to class k. This measure takes values between 0 (when all the records belong to the same class) and $(m - 1)/m$ (when all m classes are equally represented). Figure 9.4 shows the values of the Gini index for a two-class case as a function of p_k. It can be seen that the impurity measure is at its peak when $p_k = 0.5$ (i.e., when the rectangle contains 50% of each of the two classes).

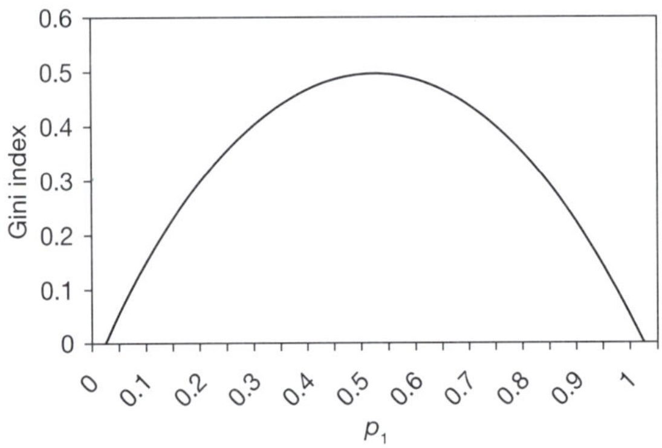

FIGURE 9.4 VALUES OF THE GINI INDEX FOR A TWO-CLASS CASE AS A FUNCTION OF THE PROPORTION OF RECORDS IN CLASS 1 (p_1)

A second impurity measure is the entropy measure. The entropy for a rectangle A is defined by

$$\text{entropy}(A) = -\sum_{k=1}^{m} p_k \log_2(p_k)$$

(to compute $\log_2(x)$ in Python, use function *math.log2(x)*). This measure ranges between 0 (most pure, all records belong to the same class) and $\log_2(m)$ (when all m classes are represented equally). In the two-class case, the entropy measure is maximized (like the Gini index) at $p_k = 0.5$.

Let us compute the impurity in the fruit variety example before and after the first split (using length with the value of 62). The dataset contains 14 local and 14 non local variety cases. This is a two-class case with an equal number of records from each class. Both impurity measures are therefore at their maximum value: Gini = 0.5 and entropy = $\log_2(2) = 1$. After the split, the left rectangle contains eight local cases. The impurity measures for this rectangle are:

$$\text{gini\_left} = 1 - (8/8)^2 = 0$$

$$\text{entropy left} = -(8/8)\log_2(8/8) = 0$$

The right rectangle contains 14 local and six non-local verity units. The impurity measures of the right rectangle are therefore

$$\text{gini\_right} = 1 - (14/20)^2 - (6/20)^2 = 0.42$$

$$\text{entropy right} = -(14/20)\log_2(14/20) - (6/20)\log_2(6/20) = 0.88$$

The combined impurity of the two rectangles that were created by the split is a weighted average of the two impurity measures, weighted by the number of records in each:

$$\text{gini} = (8/28)(0) + (20/28)(0.42) = 0.3$$

$$\text{entropy} = (8/28)(0) + (20/28)(0.88) = 0.628$$

Thus, the Gini impurity index decreased from 0.5 before the split to 0.3 after the split. Similarly, the entropy impurity measure decreased from 1 before the split to 0.62 after the split.

By comparing the reduction in impurity across all possible splits in all possible predictors, the next split is chosen. If we continue splitting the data, the next split is on the weight dimension at the value 152. Figure 9.5 shows that once again the tree procedure has astutely chosen to split a rectangle to increase the purity of the resulting rectangles. The lower-left rectangle, which contains data points with Length $\leq$ 62 and Weight $\leq$ 152, has all points that are local variety; whereas the upper-left rectangle, which contains data points with Length $\leq$ 62 and Weight $\geq$ 152, consists exclusively of a single local variety case. In other words, the two left rectangles are now "pure."

We can see how the recursive partitioning is refining the set of constituent rectangles to become purer as the algorithm proceeds. The final stage of the recursive partitioning is shown in Figure 9.6.

Notice that each rectangle is now pure: it contains data points from just one of the two classes.

The reason the method is called a *classification tree algorithm* is that each split can be depicted as a split of a node into two successor nodes. The first split is shown as a branching of the root node of a tree in Figure 9.7. The tree showing the first two splits is shown in Figure 9.8. The full-grown tree with three splits is shown in Figure 9.9.

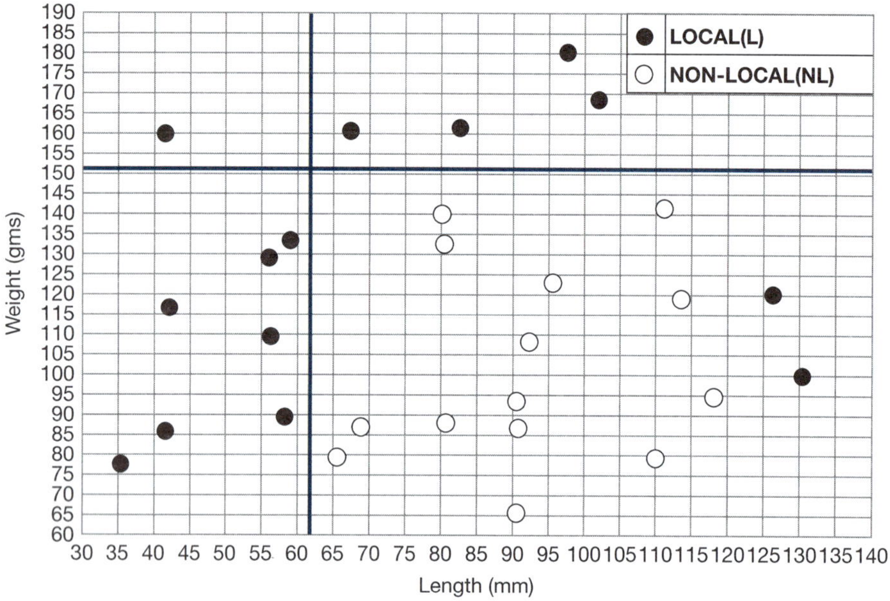

FIGURE 9.5 SPLITTING THE 28 RECORDS FIRST BY LENGTH OF 62 AND THEN WEIGHT VALUE OF 152

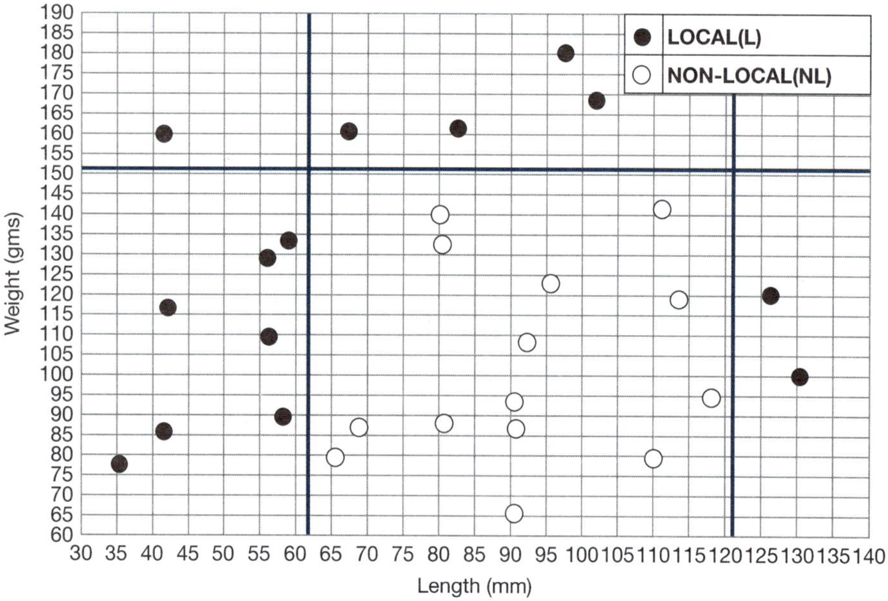

FIGURE 9.6 FINAL STAGE OF RECURSIVE PARTITIONING; EACH RECTANGLE CONSISTING OF A SINGLE CLASS (LOCAL OR NON-LOCAL VARIETY)

code for running and plotting classification tree

```
fv=pd.read_csv('Fruit Variety Classification Example.csv')
fv.featurenames=fv[['Length(mm)', 'Weight(gms)']]
fv.target=fv['Variety']
clf=DecisionTreeClassifier(max_depth = 5,
                          random_state = 0)
clf.fit(fv.featurenames, fv.target)
fn=['Length(mm)', 'Weight(gms)']
cn=['L', 'NL']
fig, axes = plt.subplots(nrows = 1,ncols = 1,figsize = (12,4), dpi=100)
tree.plot_tree(clf, feature_names = fn, class_names=cn, filled = True, proportion= True,
    label='all', rounded= True,);
fig.savefig('imagename.png')
```

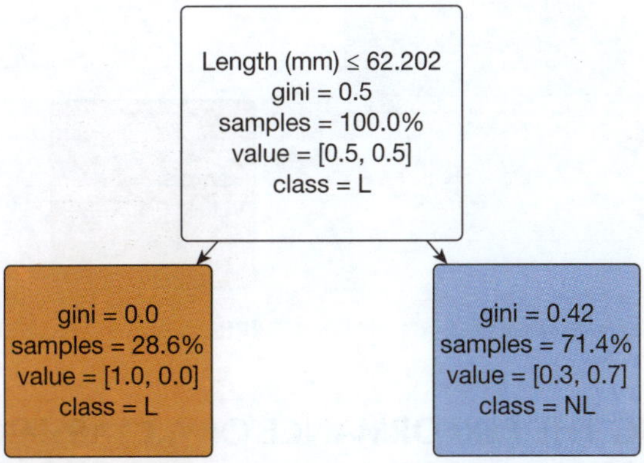

FIGURE 9.7 TREE REPRESENTATION OF FIRST SPLIT (CORRESPONDS TO FIGURE 9.3)

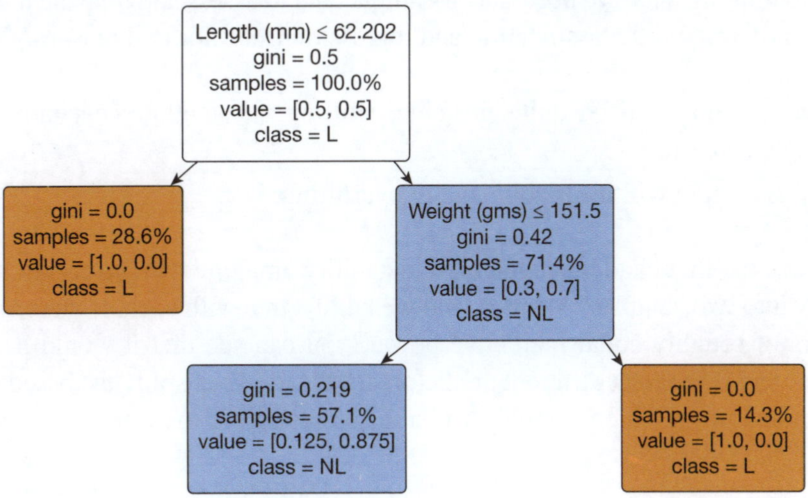

FIGURE 9.8 TREE REPRESENTATION OF FIRST TWO SPLITS

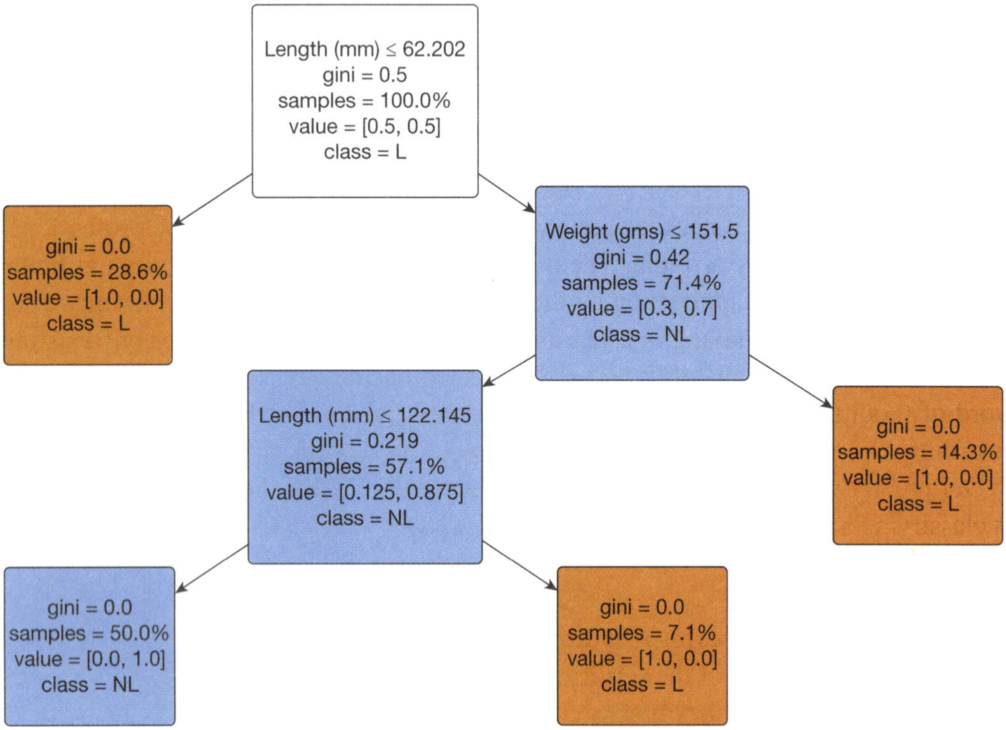

FIGURE 9.9 TREE REPRESENTATION AFTER ALL SPLITS (CORRESPONDS TO FIGURE 9.6)

9.3 | EVALUATING THE PERFORMANCE OF A CLASSIFICATION TREE

We have seen with previous methods that the modeling job is not completed by fitting a model to training data; we need out-of-sample data to assess and tune the model. This is particularly true with classification and regression trees, for two reasons:

- Tree structure can be quite unstable, shifting substantially depending on the sample chosen.
- A fully-fit tree will invariably lead to overfitting.

To visualize the first challenge, potential instability, imagine that we partition the data randomly into two samples, A and B, and we build a tree with each. If there are several predictors of roughly equal predictive power, you can see that it would be easy for samples A and B to select different predictors for the top level split, just based on which records ended up in which sample. And a different split at the top level would likely cascade down and yield completely different sets of rules. So we should view the results of a single tree with some caution.

To illustrate the second challenge, overfitting, let's examine another example.

Example 2: Customer Recommendation Behavior

A leading online service platform, established in 2015, provides in home professional services in major cities of India. The buyers can avail professional services at home by simply opening the application on their device, selecting service, and fixing a convenient time. Service buying is often influenced by the recommendations of existing users. Hence, the sustainability and scale of such businesses is highly influenced by word-of-mouth, ratings, reviews, etc., by customers, which may happen online as well as offline.

Our predictive model will be a classification tree. To assess the accuracy of the tree in classifying new records, we start with the tools and criteria discussed in Chapter 5—partitioning the data into training and validation sets, and later introduce the idea of cross-validation.

This dataset (6000 cases) is a portion of an independent study wherein respondents who had already availed of the service were surveyed to assess their perception of service quality and whether they had recently recommended the service platform to others after availing the last service from the platform. The dataset also includes previous purchase behavior like consumption frequency, spend levels, earlier word-of-mouth actions, and level of participation in social networks. One of the predictor variables is reciprocity once current or past experiences are shared by the respondent with other people, they can expect reciprocal transparency and sharing of service experiences by others. Other predictor variables are perceptions about various service quality dimensions like security, ease of use and access, competence of service technicians, etc. The platform can fine-tune its expansion strategy if it understands the key determinants of customer recommendation behavior.

The goal of an analytical exercise is to find predictors that can help classify customers to identify targets who are more likely to spread word-of-mouth or recommend platform services to others based on their previous engagement profile and preference for various service aspects. Table 9.2 shows a sample of 10 platform customers to illustrate the structure of the data. Among these 6000 customers, 3656 (61%) customers mentioned that they have recommended platform services to others. After randomly partitioning the data into training (3600 records) and validation (2400 records), we use the training data to construct a tree.

TABLE 9.2 SAMPLE OF 10 CUSTOMERS OF RECOMMENDATION BEHAVIOR DATASET

ID	SpendLevel	Service_use	EarlierWoM	SocialActive	Reciprocity	Responsive	Portfolio	Security	Ease	Access	Competence	Relaible	Recommend
100652	1	2	No	High	High	4	5	5	5	7	5	1	Yes
100699	2	1	Yes	High	High	3	5	4	4	4	4	5	Yes
100709	2	2	No	Low	High	5	3	4	4	5	3	5	Yes
100744	1	2	Yes	Low	High	5	5	3	5	5	5	2	Yes
100972	2	1	Yes	High	High	2	5	5	4	6	4	6	Yes
101246	2	2	No	High	High	5	2	3	4	4	3	2	Yes
101355	2	1	No	Low	High	2	5	4	4	5	4	4	Yes
101390	2	1	Yes	High	High	3	4	4	4	2	4	4	Yes
101458	2	1	No	High	High	3	4	3	4	7	3	4	Yes
101666	1	1	No	High	High	3	6	5	5	1	5	4	Yes

A full-grown tree is shown in Figure 9.10. Although it is difficult to see the exact splits, let us assess the performance of this tree with the validation data and compare it to the smaller default tree. Each record in the validation data is "dropped down" the tree and classified according to the terminal node it reaches. These predicted classes can then be compared to the actual memberships via a confusion matrix. When a particular class is of interest, a lift chart is useful for assessing the model's ability to capture those members.

The top node refers to all the records in the training set, of which 2205 customers did recommend and 1395 customers did not recommend. The "Yes" in the top node's rectangle or value greater than 0.5 represents the "did recommend" on the right side. The first split, which is on the social engagement (SocialActive) variable, generates left and right child nodes. To the left is the child node with customers who are "Low" on SocialActive. Customers with SocialActive status of "High" go to the right. The splitting process continues; where it stops depends on the parameter settings of the algorithm. The eventual classification of customers appears in the terminal nodes. Of the eight terminal nodes, three lead to the classification of "Yes," and rest lead to the classification of "No."

FIGURE 9.10 FULL TREE FOR SERVICE RECOMMENDATION EXAMPLE

Python code for Tree generation

```
sr=pd.read_csv('Service_Rcommend.csv')
sr['EarlierWoM']=sr['EarlierWoM'].astype('category')
sr['SocialActive']=sr['SocialActive'].astype('category')
sr['Reciprocity']=sr['Reciprocity'].astype('category')
```

```
sr['EarlierWoM']=sr['EarlierWoM'].cat.codes
sr['SocialActive']=sr['SocialActive'].cat.codes
sr['Reciprocity']=sr['Reciprocity'].cat.codes
sr.featurenames=sr[['SpendLevel', 'Service_use ', 'EarlierWoM', 'SocialActive',
         'Reciprocity', 'Responsive', 'Portfolio', 'Security', 'Ease', 'Access',
         'Competence', 'Relaible']]
sr.target=sr['Recommend']
X_train, X_test, Y_train, Y_test = train_test_split(sr.featurenames, sr.target,test_size=.4,
random_state=0)
clf = DecisionTreeClassifier(max_depth = 50,
                  random_state = 1)
### Train the model on the data
clf.fit(X_train, Y_train)
fn=['SpendLevel', 'Service_use ', 'EarlierWoM', 'SocialActive',
         'Reciprocity', 'Responsive', 'Portfolio', 'Security', 'Ease', 'Access',
         'Competence', 'Relaible']
cn=['Yes', 'No']
fig, axes = plt.subplots(nrows = 1,ncols = 1,figsize = (12,4), dpi=200)
tree.plot_tree(clf,
             feature_names = fn,
             class_names=cn,
             filled = True);
fig.savefig('imagename.png')
```

Tables 9.3 and 9.4 displays the confusion matrices for the training and test sets for the full tree and small tree with four splits. Comparing the two training and test matrices, we see that the full tree has higher accuracy: it is around 96% accurate in classifying the training data, which means it has almost many terminal nodes have high purity. In contrast, the confusion matrices for the smaller tree has relatively less accuracy i.e., 84.6%. This is due to overfitting issues in case of the larger tree.

TABLE 9.3 CONFUSION MATRICES AND ACCURACY FOR THE CLASSIFICATION TREE OF FULL TREE

code for classifying the TEST data using a full tree computing the confusion matrices and accuracy for the training and test data

```
from dmba import plotDecisionTree, classificationSummary, regressionSummary
print("Training Data")
classificationSummary(Y_train, clf.predict(X_train))
print("Testing Data")
classificationSummary(Y_test, clf.predict(X_test))
```

Output

```
Full Tree
Training Data
Confusion Matrix (Accuracy 0.9647)
```

TABLE 9.3 CONFUSION MATRICES AND ACCURACY FOR THE CLASSIFICATION TREE OF FULL TREE *(Continued)*

```
        Prediction
Actual     0    1
     0  1361   34
     1    93 2112

Testing Data
Confusion Matrix (Accuracy 0.7937)

        Prediction
Actual     0    1
     0   719  220
     1   275 1186
```

TABLE 9.4 CONFUSION MATRICES AND ACCURACY FOR THE CLASSIFICATION TREE OF SMALLER TREE

```
clf = DecisionTreeClassifier(max_depth = 4,
random_state = 1)
### Train the model on the data
clf.fit(X_train, Y_train)

from dmba import plotDecisionTree, classificationSummary, regressionSummary
print("Training Data")
classificationSummary(Y_train, clf.predict(X_train))
print("Testing Data")
classificationSummary(Y_test, clf.predict(X_test))
Small Tree (4 Splits)

Training Data
Confusion Matrix (Accuracy 0.8464)

       Prediction
Actual    0    1
     0 1128  267
     1  286 1919

Testing Data
Confusion Matrix (Accuracy 0.8342)

       Prediction
Actual    0    1
     0  750  189
     1  209 1252
```

Sensitivity Analysis Using Cross Validation

Due to the issue of tree instability, it is possible that the performance results will differ markedly when using a different partitioning into training and validation data. It is therefore useful to use cross-validation to evaluate the variability in performance on different data partitioning (see Section 2.5). Table 9.5 shows code and the result

TABLE 9.5 ACCURACY OF THE DEFAULT (FULL) CLASSIFICATION TREE, ON FIVE VALIDATION FOLDS USING 5-FOLD CROSS-VALIDATION

code for computing validation accuracy using 5-fold cross-validation

```
from sklearn.model_selection import cross_val_score
treeClassifier1 = DecisionTreeClassifier(random_state=1)
scores = cross_val_score(treeClassifier1, X_train, Y_train, cv=5)
print('Accuracy scores of each fold: ', [f'{acc:.3f}' for acc in scores])
```

Output

```
Accuracy scores of each fold:  ['0.797', '0.800', '0.803', '0.797', '0.787']
```

of applying Python's *cross_val_score* method to perform 5-fold cross-validation on the full grown (default) tree. We see that the validation accuracy changes significantly across different folds from 0.787 to 0.803.

9.4 | AVOIDING OVERFITTING

One danger in growing deep trees on the training data is overfitting. As discussed in Chapter 5, overfitting will lead to poor performance on new data. If we look at the overall error at the various sizes of the tree, it is expected to decrease as the number of terminal nodes grows until the point of overfitting. Of course, for the training data, the overall error decreases more and more until it is zero at the maximum level of the tree. However, for new data, the overall error is expected to decrease until the point where the tree fully models the relationship between class and the predictors. After that, the tree starts to model the noise in the training set, and we expect the overall error for the test set to start increasing. This is depicted in Figure 9.11. One intuitive reason a large tree may overfit is that its final splits are based on very small numbers of records. In such cases, the class difference is likely to be attributed to noise rather than predictor information.

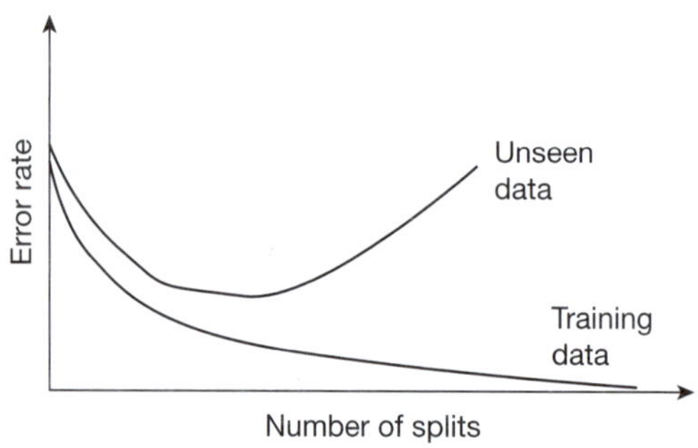

FIGURE 9.11 ERROR RATE AS A FUNCTION OF THE NUMBER OF SPLITS FOR TRAINING VS. VALIDATION DATA: OVERFITTING

Stopping Tree Growth

One can think of different criteria for stopping the tree growth before it starts overfitting the data. Examples are tree depth (i.e., number of splits), minimum number of records in a terminal node, and minimum reduction in impurity. In Python's *DecisionTreeClassifier()*, we can control the depth of the tree, the minimum number of records in a node needed in order to split, the mimimum number of records in a terminal node, etc. The problem is that it is not simple to determine what is a good stopping point using such rules.

Let us return to the Service Recommendation example, this time restricting tree depth, the minimum number of records in a node required for splitting, and the minimum impurity decrease required. The resulting tree are shown in Figure 9.12. The resulting tree has eight terminal nodes, where four are pure but four are not. The smallest terminal node has 33 records.

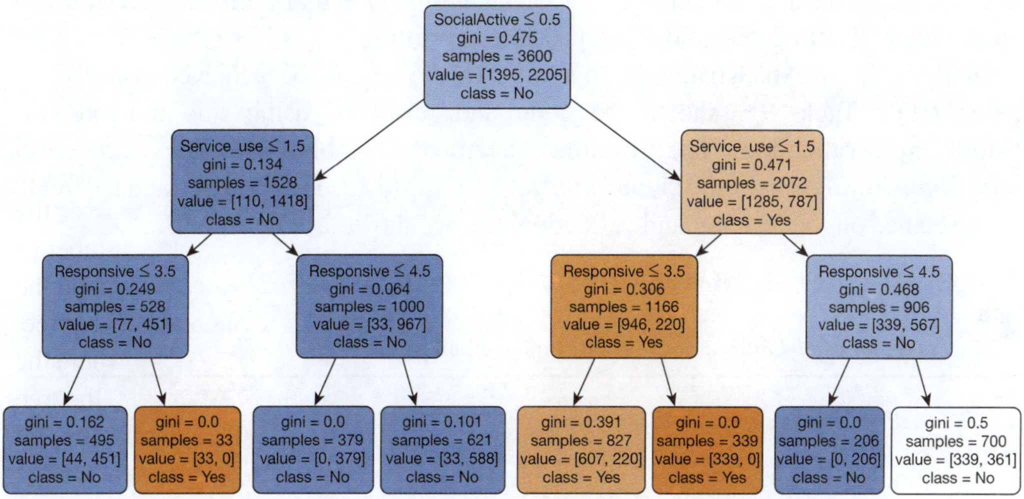

FIGURE 9.12 TREE WITH THREE SPLITS FOR SERVICE RECOMMENDATION EXAMPLE

code for creating a smaller classification tree

```
smallClassTree = DecisionTreeClassifier(max_depth=30, min_samples_split=20,
                        min_impurity_decrease=0.01, random_state=1)
smallClassTree.fit(train_X, train_y)

plotDecisionTree(smallClassTree, feature_names=train_X.columns)
```

Fine-tuning Tree Parameters

As mentioned earlier, the challenge with using tree growth stopping rules such as maximum tree depth is that it is not simple to determine what is a good stopping point using such rules. A solution is to use grid search over combinations of different parameter values. For example, we might want to search for trees with {maximum depths in the range of [5, 30], minimum number of records in terminal nodes between [20, 100], impurity criterion decrease in the range [0.001, 0.01]}. We can use an exhaustive grid search to find the combination that leads to the tree with smallest error (highest accuracy).

If we use the training set to find the tree with the lowest error among all the trees in the searched range, measuring accuracy on that same training data, then we will be overfitting the training data. If we use the validation set to measure accuracy, then, with the numerous grid search trials, we will be overfitting the validation data! A solution is therefore to use cross-validation on the training set, and, after settling on the best tree, use that tree with the validation data to evaluate likely actual performance with new data. This will help detect and avoid possible overfitting.

In Python, an exhaustive grid search of this type can be achieved using *GridSearchCV()*. Table 9.6 shows the code and result of using this method with 5-fold cross-validation. The resulting parameter combination is *max_depth* 5, *min_impurity_decrease* 0.0011, and *min_samples_split* 13. The final tree and the model performance on the training and validation sets are shown in Figure 9.13.

TABLE 9.6 EXHAUSTIVE GRID SEARCH TO FINE TUNE METHOD PARAMETERS

code for using GridSearchCV to fine tune method parameters

```
# Start with an initial guess for parameters
param_grid = {
    'max_depth': [10, 20, 30, 40],
    'min_samples_split': [20, 40, 60, 80, 100],
    'min_impurity_decrease': [0, 0.0005, 0.001, 0.005, 0.01],
}
gridSearch = GridSearchCV(DecisionTreeClassifier(random_state=1), param_grid, cv=5,
                          n_jobs=-1)  # n_jobs=-1 will utilize all available CPUs
gridSearch.fit(X_train, Y_train)
print('Initial score: ', gridSearch.best_score_)
print('Initial parameters: ', gridSearch.best_params_)

# Adapt grid based on result from initial grid search
param_grid = {
    'max_depth': list(range(2, 16)),  # 14 values
    'min_samples_split': list(range(10, 22)), # 11 values
    'min_impurity_decrease': [0.0009, 0.001, 0.0011], # 3 values
}
```

TABLE 9.6 EXHAUSTIVE GRID SEARCH TO FINE TUNE METHOD PARAMETERS (*Continued*)

```
gridSearch = GridSearchCV(DecisionTreeClassifier(random_state=1), param_grid, cv=5,
                          n_jobs=-1)
gridSearch.fit(X_train, Y_train)
print('Improved score: ', gridSearch.best_score_)
print('Improved parameters: ', gridSearch.best_params_)

bestClassTree = gridSearch.best_estimator_
```

Output

```
Initial score:  0.8530555555555555
Initial parameters:  {'max_depth': 10, 'min_impurity_decrease': 0.001,
                      'min_samples_split': 60}
Improved score:  0.8527777777777779
Improved parameters:  {'max_depth': 7, 'min_impurity_decrease': 0.001,
                       'min_samples_split': 10}
```

The exhaustive grid search can quickly become very time consuming. In our example, the first grid search assessed $4 \times 5 \times 5 = 100$ combinations and the second $14 \times 11 \times 3 = 462$ combinations. With even more tune-able parameters the number of possible combinations can become very large. In this case it is better to use *RandomizedSearchCV()* which will randomly sample all possible combinations while limiting the total number of tries (parameter *n_iter*). With *RandomizedSearchCV()*, it is also possible to sample parameter from distributions (e.g., any number between 0 and 1) without listing them individually.

code for plotting and evaluating fine tuned tree

```
# Finetuned Tree Training
clf = DecisionTreeClassifier(max_depth=7, min_impurity_decrease=0.001, min_samples_split= 101)
clf.fit(X_train, Y_train)

# Fine tuned Tree with improved parameters
fn=['SpendLevel', 'Service_use ', 'EarlierWoM', 'SocialActive',
          'Reciprocity', 'Responsive', 'Portfolio', 'Security', 'Ease', 'Access',
          'Competence', 'Relaible']
cn=['Yes', 'No']
fig, axes = plt.subplots(nrows = 1,ncols = 1,figsize = (12,4), dpi=200)
tree.plot_tree(clf,
            feature_names = fn,
            class_names=cn,
            filled = True);
fig.savefig('imagename.png')

# create confusion matrix
print("Training Data")
classificationSummary(Y_train, clf.predict(X_train))
print("Testing Data")
classificationSummary(Y_test, clf.predict(X_test))
```

Output

```
Training Data
Confusion Matrix (Accuracy 0.8575)

       Prediction
Actual     0    1
     0 1117  298
     1  215 1970
Testing Data
Confusion Matrix (Accuracy 0.8488)

       Prediction
Actual     0    1
     0  720  199
     1  164 1317
```

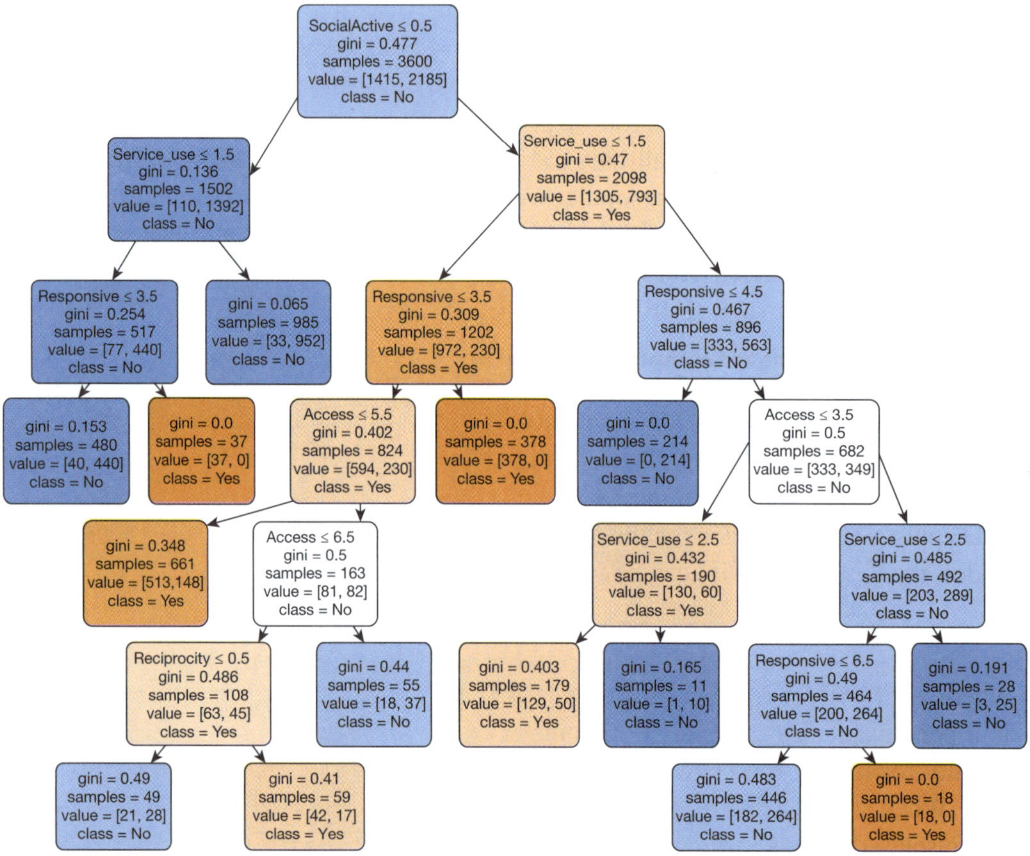

FIGURE 9.13 FINE TUNED CLASSIFICATION TREE FOR SERVICE RECOMMENDATION EXAMPLE

Other Methods for Limiting Tree Size

Several other methods for limiting tree size have been used widely. They are not implemented in Python at this writing, but we note them here for completeness.

CHAID CHAID stands for chi-squared automatic interaction detection, a recursive partitioning method that predates classification and regression tree (CART) procedures by several years and is widely used in database marketing applications to this day. It uses a well-known statistical test (the chi-square test for independence) to assess whether splitting a node improves the purity by a statistically significant amount. In particular, at each node, we split on the predictor with the strongest association with the outcome variable. The strength of association is measured by the p-value of a chi-squared test of independence. If for the best predictor the test does not show a significant improvement, the split is not carried out, and the tree is terminated. A more general class of trees based on this idea is called *conditional inference trees* (see Hothorn et al., 2006).

Pruning The idea behind pruning is to recognize that a very large tree is likely to overfit the training data, and that the smallest branches, which are the last to be grown and are furthest from the trunk, are likely fitting noise in the training data. They may actually contribute to error in fitting new data, so they are lopped off. Pruning the full-grown tree is the basis of the popular CART method (developed by Breiman et al., implemented in multiple data mining software packages such as R's `rpart` package, SAS Enterprise Miner, CART, and MARS) and C4.5 (developed by Quinlan and implemented in packages such as IBM SPSS Modeler). In C4.5, the training data are used both for growing and pruning the tree. In CART, the innovation is to use the validation data to prune back the tree that is grown from training data.

More specifically, the CART algorithm uses a cost-complexity function that balances tree size (complexity) and misclassification error (cost) in order to choose tree size. The cost complexity of a tree is equal to its misclassification error (based on the training data) plus a penalty factor for the size of the tree. For a tree T that has $L(T)$ terminal nodes, the cost complexity can be written as

$$\text{CC}(T) = \text{err}(T) + \alpha L(T),$$

where $\text{err}(T)$ is the fraction of training records that are misclassified by tree T and α is a penalty factor ("complexity parameter") for tree size. When $\alpha = 0$, there is no penalty for having too many nodes in a tree, and this yields the full-grown unpruned tree. When we increase α to a very large value the penalty cost component swamps the misclassification error component of the cost complexity criterion, and the result is simply the tree with the fewest terminal nodes: namely, the tree with one node. So there is a range of trees, from tiny to large, corresponding to a range of α, from large to small. From this sequence of trees it seems natural to choose the one that gave the lowest misclassification error on the validation dataset. Alternatively, rather than relying on a single validation partition, we can use k-fold cross-validation for choosing α.

9.5 | CLASSIFICATION RULES FROM TREES

As described in Section 9.1, classification trees provide easily understandable *classification rules* (if the trees are not too large). Each terminal node is equivalent to a classification rule. Returning to the example, the left-most terminal node in the fine-tuned tree (Figure 9.13) gives us the rule

IF (*Income* ≤ 110.5) AND (*CCAvg* ≤ 2.95)
THEN *Class* = 0.

However, in many cases, the number of rules can be reduced by removing redundancies. For example, consider the rule from the second-from-bottom-left-most terminal node in Figure 9.13:

IF (*Income* ≤ 110.5) AND (*CCAvg* > 2.95) AND (*CD.Account* ≤ *0.5*)
AND (*Income* ≤ 92.5)
THEN *Class* = 0

This rule can be simplified to

IF (*Income* ≤ 92.5) AND (*CCAvg* > 2.95) AND (*CD.Account* ≤ *0.5*)
THEN *Class* = 0

This transparency in the process and understandability of the algorithm that leads to classifying a record as belonging to a certain class is very advantageous in settings where the final classification is not the only thing of interest. Berry and Linoff (2000) give the example of health insurance underwriting, where the insurer is required to show that coverage denial is not based on discrimination. By showing rules that led to denial (e.g., income < $20K AND low credit history), the company can avoid law suits. Compared to the output of other classifiers, such as discriminant functions, tree-based classification rules are easily explained to managers and operating staff. Their logic is certainly far more transparent than that of weights in neural networks!

9.6 | CLASSIFICATION TREES FOR MORE THAN TWO CLASSES

Classification trees can be used with an outcome variable that has more than two classes. In terms of measuring impurity, the two measures presented earlier (the Gini impurity index and the entropy measure) were defined for m classes and hence can be used for any number of classes. The tree itself would have the same structure, except that its terminal nodes would take one of the m-class labels.

9.7 | REGRESSION TREES

The tree method can also be used for a numerical outcome variable. Regression trees for prediction operate in much the same fashion as classification trees. The outcome variable (Y) is a numerical variable in this case, but both the principle and the procedure are the same: Many splits are attempted, and for each, we measure "impurity" in each branch of the resulting tree. The tree procedure then selects the split that minimizes the sum of such measures. To illustrate a regression tree, consider the example of predicting prices of Toyota Corolla automobiles (from Chapter 6). The dataset includes information on 1000 sold Toyota Corolla cars. (We use the first 1000 cars from the dataset *ToyotoCorolla.csv*). The goal is to find a predictive model of price as a function of 10 predictors (including mileage, horsepower, number of doors, etc.). A regression tree for these data was built using a training set of 600 records. The fine-tuned tree is shown in Figure 9.14. Code for training and evaluating the regression tree is given in Table 9.7.

TABLE 9.7 TRAIN AND EVALUATE A FINE-TUNED REGRESSION TREE

code for building a regression tree

```
from sklearn.tree import DecisionTreeRegressor
toyotaCorolla_df = pd.read_csv('ToyotaCorolla.csv').iloc[:1000,:]
toyotaCorolla_df = toyotaCorolla_df.rename(columns={'Age_08_04': 'Age', 'Quarterly_Tax': 'Tax'})

predictors = ['Age', 'KM', 'Fuel_Type', 'HP', 'Met_Color', 'Automatic', 'CC',
              'Doors', 'Tax', 'Weight']
outcome = 'Price'

X = pd.get_dummies(toyotaCorolla_df[predictors], drop_first=True)
y = toyotaCorolla_df[outcome]
train_X, valid_X, train_y, valid_y = train_test_split(X, y, test_size=0.4, random_state=1)

# user grid search to find optimized tree
param_grid = {
    'max_depth': [5, 10, 15, 20, 25],
    'min_impurity_decrease': [0, 0.001, 0.005, 0.01],
    'min_samples_split': [10, 20, 30, 40, 50],
}
gridSearch = GridSearchCV(DecisionTreeRegressor(), param_grid, cv=5, n_jobs=-1)
gridSearch.fit(train_X, train_y)
print('Initial parameters: ', gridSearch.best_params_)

param_grid = {
    'max_depth': [3, 4, 5, 6, 7, 8, 9, 10, 11, 12],
    'min_impurity_decrease': [0, 0.001, 0.002, 0.003, 0.005, 0.006, 0.007, 0.008],
    'min_samples_split': [14, 15, 16, 18, 20, ],
}
```

TABLE 9.7 TRAIN AND EVALUATE A FINE-TUNED REGRESSION TREE (*Continued*)

```
gridSearch = GridSearchCV(DecisionTreeRegressor(), param_grid, cv=5, n_jobs=-1)
gridSearch.fit(train_X, train_y)
print('Improved parameters: ', gridSearch.best_params_)

regTree = gridSearch.best_estimator_

regressionSummary(train_y, regTree.predict(train_X))
regressionSummary(valid_y, regTree.predict(valid_X))
```

Output

```
Initial parameters:  {'max_depth': 10,'min_impurity_decrease': 0.001,'min_samples_split': 20}
Improved parameters: {'max_depth': 6,'min_impurity_decrease': 0.01,'min_samples_split': 12}

Regression statistics

                      Mean Error (ME) : 0.0000
       Root Mean Squared Error (RMSE) : 1058.8202
            Mean Absolute Error (MAE) : 767.7203
          Mean Percentage Error (MPE) : -0.8074
Mean Absolute Percentage Error (MAPE) : 6.8325

Regression statistics

                      Mean Error (ME) : 60.5241
       Root Mean Squared Error (RMSE) : 1554.9146
            Mean Absolute Error (MAE) : 1026.3487
          Mean Percentage Error (MPE) : -1.3082
Mean Absolute Percentage Error (MAPE) : 9.2311
```

We see that the top three levels of the regression tree are dominated by age of the car, its weight, and mileage. In the lower levels we can see that individual details of a car, like powered windows, lead to smaller adjustments of the price.

Three details differ between regression trees and classification trees: prediction, impurity measures, and evaluating performance. We describe these next.

Prediction

Predicting the outcome value for a record is performed in a fashion similar to the classification case: We will use the truncated tree from Figure 9.14 to demonstrate how it works. The predictor information is used for "dropping" the record down the tree until reaching a terminal node. For instance, to predict the price of a Toyota Corolla with Age = 60, Mileage (KM) = 160,000, and Horse_Power (HP) = 100, we drop it down the tree and reach the node that has the value $8392.857 (the lowest node). This is the price prediction for this car according to the tree. In classification trees, the value of the terminal node (which is one of the categories) is determined by the "voting" of the

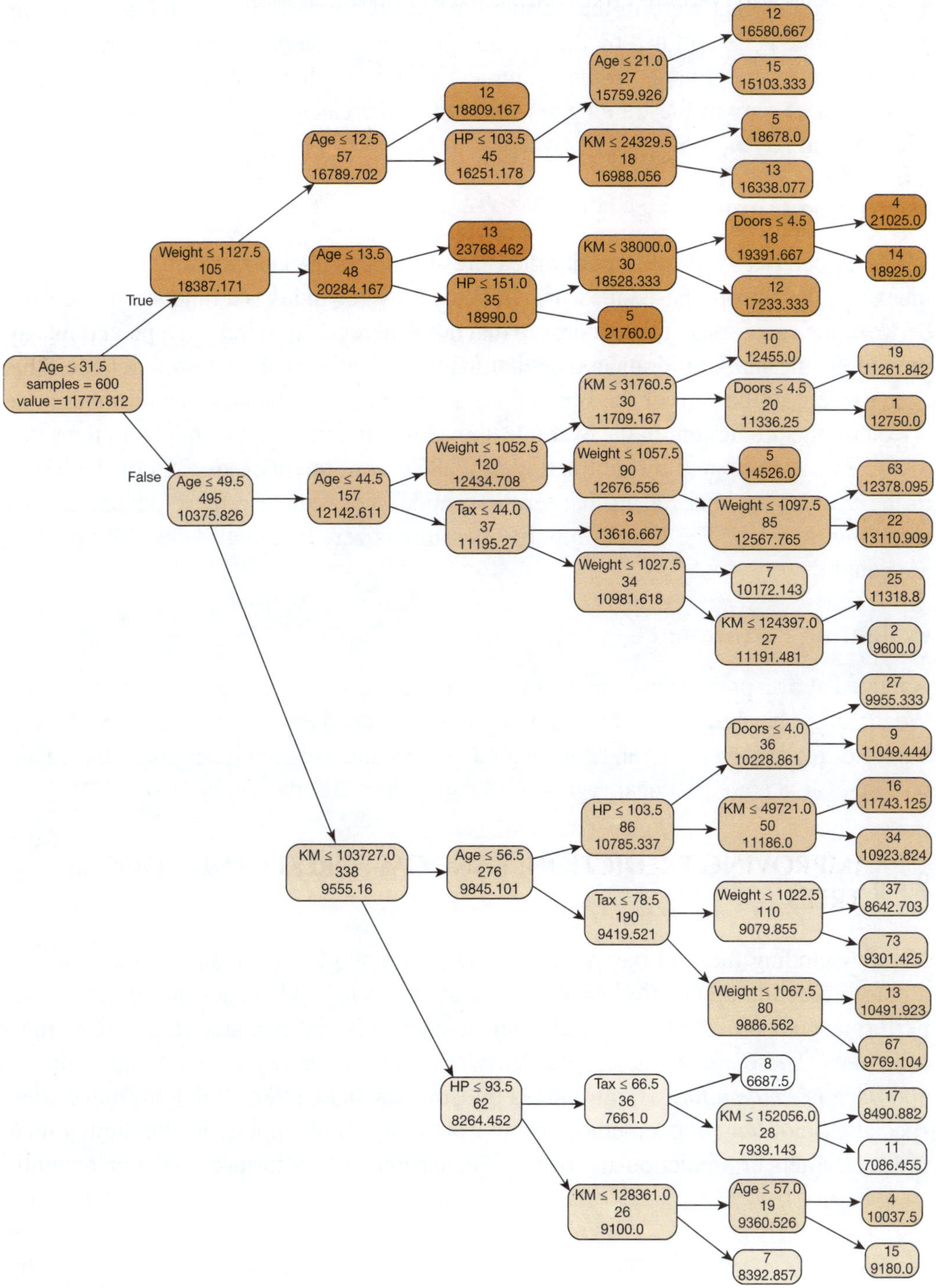

FIGURE 9.14 FINE-TUNED REGRESSION TREE FOR TOYOTA COROLLA PRICES

training records that were in that terminal node. In regression trees, the value of the terminal node is determined by the average outcome value of the training records that were in that terminal node. In the example above, the value $8392.857 is the average price of the 7 cars in the training set that fall in the category of Age > 49.5, KM > 128361, and HP > 93.5.

Measuring Impurity

We described two types of impurity measures for nodes in classification trees: the Gini index and the entropy-based measure. In both cases, the index is a function of the *ratio* between the categories of the records in that node. In regression trees, a typical impurity measure is the sum of the squared deviations from the mean of the terminal node. This is equivalent to the sum of the squared errors, because the mean of the terminal node is exactly the prediction. In the example above, the impurity of the node with the value $8392.857 is computed by subtracting 8392.857 from the price of each of the 7 cars in the training set that fell in that terminal node, then squaring these deviations and summing them up. The lowest impurity possible is zero, when all values in the node are equal.

Evaluating Performance

As stated above, predictions are obtained by averaging the outcome values in the nodes. We therefore have the usual definition of predictions and errors. The predictive performance of regression trees can be measured in the same way that other predictive methods are evaluated (e.g., linear regression), using summary measures such as RMSE.

9.8 IMPROVING PREDICTION: RANDOM FORESTS AND BOOSTED TREES

Notwithstanding the transparency advantages of a single tree as described above, in a pure prediction application, where visualizing a set of rules does not matter, better performance is provided by several extensions to trees that combine results from multiple trees. These are examples of *ensembles* (see Chapter 13). One popular multitree approach is *random forests*, introduced by Breiman and Cutler.[1] Random forests are a special case of *bagging*, a method for improving predictive power by combining multiple classifiers or prediction algorithms. See Chapter 13 for further details on bagging.

[1] For further details on random forests, see https://www.stat.berkeley.edu/~breiman/RandomForests/cc_home.htm.

Random Forests

The basic idea in random forests is to:

1. Draw multiple random samples, with replacement, from the data (this sampling approach is called the *bootstrap*).
2. Using a random subset of predictors at each stage, fit a classification (or regression) tree to each sample (and thus obtain a "forest").
3. Combine the predictions/classifications from the individual trees to obtain improved predictions. Use voting for classification and averaging for prediction.

The code and output in Table 9.8 illustrates applying a random forest in Python to the personal loan example. The validation accuracy of the random forest in this example (0.982) is similar to the single fine-tuned tree, and slightly higher than the single small tree that we fit earlier.

Unlike a single tree, results from a random forest cannot be displayed in a tree-like diagram, thereby losing the interpretability that a single tree provides. However, random forests can produce "variable importance" scores, which measure the relative contribution of the different predictors. The importance score for a particular predictor is computed by summing up the decrease in the Gini index for that predictor over all the trees in the forest. Figure 9.15 shows the variable importance plot generated from the random forest model for the personal loan example. We see that Income and Education have the highest scores, with CCAvg being third. Importance scores for the other predictors are considerably lower.

TABLE 9.8 RANDOM FOREST (PERSONAL LOAN EXAMPLE)

code for running a random forest, plotting variable importance plot, and computing accuracy

```
bank_df = pd.read_csv('UniversalBank.csv')
bank_df.drop(columns=['ID', 'ZIP Code'], inplace=True)

X = bank_df.drop(columns=['Personal Loan'])
y = bank_df['Personal Loan']
train_X, valid_X, train_y, valid_y = train_test_split(X, y, test_size=0.4, random_state=1)

rf = RandomForestClassifier(n_estimators=500, random_state=1)
rf.fit(train_X, train_y)

# variable (feature) importance plot
importances = rf.feature_importances_
std = np.std([tree.feature_importances_ for tree in rf.estimators_], axis=0)
```

TABLE 9.8 RANDOM FOREST (PERSONAL LOAN EXAMPLE) (*Continued*)

```
df = pd.DataFrame({'feature': train_X.columns, 'importance': importances, 'std': std})
df = df.sort_values('importance')
print(df)

ax = df.plot(kind='barh', xerr='std', x='feature', legend=False)
ax.set_ylabel('')
plt.show()

# confusion matrix for validation set
classificationSummary(valid_y, rf.predict(valid_X))
```

Output

```
               feature  importance       std
7   Securities Account    0.003964  0.004998
9               Online    0.006394  0.005350
10          CreditCard    0.007678  0.007053
6             Mortgage    0.034243  0.023469
1           Experience    0.035539  0.016061
0                  Age    0.036258  0.015858
8           CD Account    0.057917  0.043185
3               Family    0.111375  0.053146
4                CCAvg    0.172105  0.103011
5            Education    0.200772  0.101002
2               Income    0.333756  0.129227

Confusion Matrix (Accuracy 0.9820)

       Prediction
Actual    0    1
     0 1803    4
     1   32  161
```

Boosted Trees

The second type of multitree improvement is *boosted trees*. Here a sequence of trees is fitted, so that each tree concentrates on misclassified records from the previous tree.

1. Fit a single tree.
2. Draw a sample that gives higher selection probabilities to misclassified records.
3. Fit a tree to the new sample.
4. Repeat Steps 2 and 3 multiple times.
5. Use weighted voting to classify records, with heavier weight for later trees.

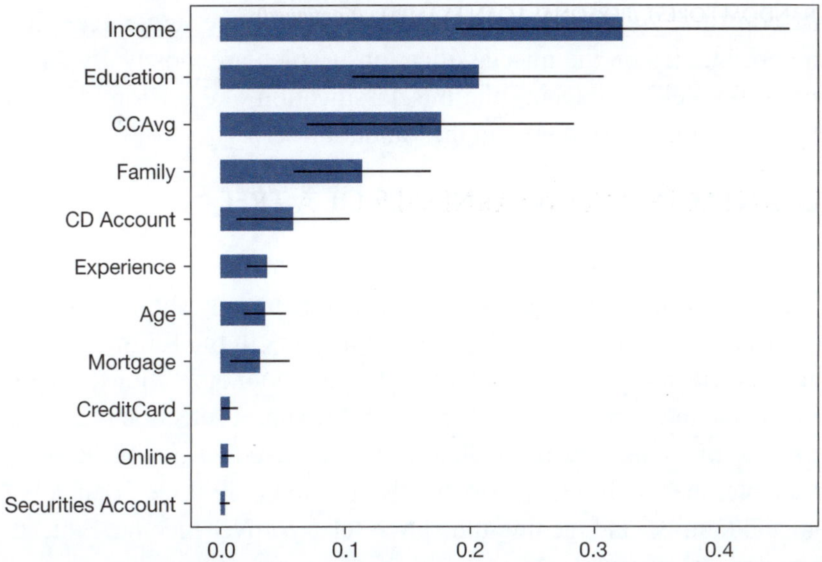

FIGURE 9.15 VARIABLE IMPORTANCE PLOT FROM RANDOM FOREST (PERSONAL LOAN EXAMPLE, FOR CODE SEE TABLE 9.8)

TABLE 9.9 BOOSTED TREE: CONFUSION MATRIX FOR THE VALIDATION SET (LOAN DATA)

code for running boosted trees

```
boost = GradientBoostingClassifier()
boost.fit(train_X, train_y)
classificationSummary(valid_y, boost.predict(valid_X))
```

Output

```
Confusion Matrix (Accuracy 0.9835)

       Prediction
Actual    0    1
     0 1799    8
     1   25  168
```

Table 9.9 shows the result of running a boosted tree on the loan acceptance example that we saw earlier. We can see that compared to the performance of the single small tree, the boosted tree has better performance on the validation data in terms of overall accuracy (0.9835) and especially in terms of correct classification of 1's—the rare class of special interest. Where does boosting's special talent for finding 1's come from? When one class is dominant (0's constitute over 90% of the data here), basic classifiers are tempted to classify cases as belonging to the dominant class, and the 1's in this case constitute most of the misclassifications with the single tree. The boosting algorithm concentrates on the misclassifications (which are mostly 1's), so it is naturally going to do well in reducing the misclassification of 1's (from 43 in the single small tree to 25 in the boosted tree, in the validation set).

9.9 | ADVANTAGES AND WEAKNESSES OF A TREE

Tree methods are good off-the-shelf classifiers and predictors. They are also useful for variable selection, with the most important predictors usually showing up at the top of the tree. Trees require relatively little effort from users in the following senses: First, there is no need for transformation of variables (any monotone transformation of the variables will give the same trees). Second, variable subset selection is automatic since it is part of the split selection. In the loan example, note that out of the set of 14 predictors available, the small tree automatically selected only three predictors (Income, Education, and Family) and the fine-tuned tree selected five (Income, Education, Family, CCAvg, and CD Account).

Trees are also intrinsically robust to outliers, since the choice of a split depends on the *ordering* of values and not on the absolute *magnitudes* of these values. However, they are sensitive to changes in the data, and even a slight change can cause very different splits!

Unlike models that assume a particular relationship between the outcome and predictors (e.g., a linear relationship such as in linear regression and linear discriminant analysis), classification and regression trees are nonlinear and nonparametric. This allows for a wide range of relationships between the predictors and the outcome variable. However, this can also be a weakness: Since the splits are done on one predictor at a time, rather than on combinations of predictors, the tree is likely to miss relationships between predictors, in particular linear structures like those in linear or logistic regression models. Classification trees are useful classifiers in cases where horizontal and vertical splitting of the predictor space adequately divides the classes. But consider, for instance, a dataset with two predictors and two classes, where separation between the two classes is most obviously achieved by using a diagonal line (as shown in Figure 9.16). In such cases, a classification tree is expected to have lower performance than methods such as discriminant analysis. One way to improve performance is to create new predictors that are derived from existing predictors, which can capture hypothesized relationships between predictors (similar to interactions in regression models). Random forests are another solution in such situations.

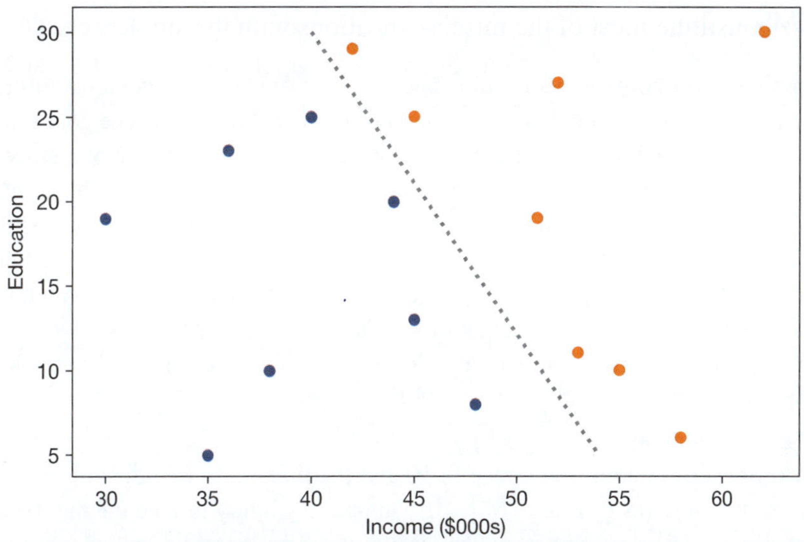

FIGURE 9.16 A TWO-PREDICTOR CASE WITH TWO CLASSES. THE BEST SEPARATION IS ACHIEVED WITH A DIAGONAL LINE, WHICH CLASSIFICATION TREES CANNOT DO

Another performance issue with classification trees is that they require a large dataset in order to construct a good classifier. From a computational aspect, trees can be relatively expensive to grow, because of the multiple sorting involved in computing all possible splits on every variable. Methods for avoiding overfitting, such as cross-validation or pruning the data using the validation set, add further computation time.

Although trees are useful for variable selection, one challenge is that they "favor" predictors with many potential split points. This includes categorical predictors with many categories and numerical predictors with many different values. Such predictors have a higher chance of appearing in a tree. One simplistic solution is to combine multiple categories into a smaller set and bin numerical predictors with many values. Alternatively, some special algorithms avoid this problem by using a different splitting criterion [e.g., conditional inference trees in the R package `party`—see Hothorn et al. (2006)—and QUEST classification trees—see Loh and Shih (1997)].

An appealing feature of trees is that they handle missing data without having to impute values or delete records with missing values. Finally, a very important practical advantage of trees is the transparent rules that they generate. Such transparency is often useful in managerial applications, though this advantage is lost in the ensemble versions of trees (random forests, boosted trees).

PROBLEMS

9.1 Competitive Auctions on eBay.com. The file *eBayAuctions.csv* contains information on 1972 auctions that transacted on eBay.com during May–June 2004. The goal is to use these data to build a model that will classify auctions as competitive or noncompetitive. A *competitive auction* is defined as an auction with at least two bids placed on the item auctioned. The data include variables that describe the item (auction category), the seller (his/her eBay rating), and the auction terms that the seller selected (auction duration, opening price, currency, day-of-week of auction close). In addition, we have the price at which the auction closed. The task is to predict whether or not the auction will be competitive.

Data Preprocessing. Convert variable *Duration* into a categorical variable. Split the data into training (60%) and validation (40%) datasets.

- **a.** Fit a classification tree using all predictors. To avoid overfitting, set the minimum number of records in a terminal node to 50 and the maximum tree depth to 7. Write down the results in terms of rules. (*Note*: If you had to slightly reduce the number of predictors due to software limitations, or for clarity of presentation, which would be a good variable to choose?)
- **b.** Is this model practical for predicting the outcome of a new auction?
- **c.** Describe the interesting and uninteresting information that these rules provide.
- **d.** Fit another classification tree (using a tree with a minimum number of records per terminal node = 50 and maximum depth = 7), this time only with predictors that can be used for predicting the outcome of a new auction. Describe the resulting tree in terms of rules. Make sure to report the smallest set of rules required for classification.
- **e.** Plot the resulting tree on a scatter plot: Use the two axes for the two best (quantitative) predictors. Each auction will appear as a point, with coordinates corresponding to its values on those two predictors. Use different colors or symbols to separate competitive and noncompetitive auctions. Draw lines (you can sketch these by hand or use Python) at the values that create splits. Does this splitting seem reasonable with respect to the meaning of the two predictors? Does it seem to do a good job of separating the two classes?
- **f.** Examine the lift chart and the confusion matrix for the tree. What can you say about the predictive performance of this model?
- **g.** Based on this last tree, what can you conclude from these data about the chances of an auction obtaining at least two bids and its relationship to the auction settings set by the seller (duration, opening price, ending day, currency)? What would you recommend for a seller as the strategy that will most likely lead to a competitive auction?

9.2 Predicting Delayed Flights. The file *FlightDelays.csv* contains information on all commercial flights departing the Washington, DC area and arriving at New York during January 2004. For each flight, there is information on the departure and arrival airports, the distance of the route, the scheduled time and date of the flight, and so on. The variable that we are trying to predict is whether or not a flight is delayed. A delay is defined as an arrival that is at least 15 minutes later than scheduled.

Data Preprocessing. Transform variable day of week (DAY_WEEK) info a categorical variable. Bin the scheduled departure time into eight bins. Use these and all other columns as predictors (excluding DAY_OF_MONTH). Partition the data into training (60%) and validation (40%) sets.

a. Fit a classification tree to the flight delay variable using all the relevant predictors. Do not include DEP_TIME (actual departure time) in the model because it is unknown at the time of prediction (unless we are generating our predictions of delays after the plane takes off, which is unlikely). Use a tree with maximum depth 8 and minimum impurity decrease = 0.01. Express the resulting tree as a set of rules.

b. If you needed to fly between DCA and EWR on a Monday at 7:00 AM, would you be able to use this tree? What other information would you need? Is it available in practice? What information is redundant?

c. Fit the same tree as in (a), this time excluding the Weather predictor. Display both the resulting (small) tree and the full-grown tree. You will find that the small tree contains a single terminal node.

  i. How is the small tree used for classification? (What is the rule for classifying?)

  ii. To what is this rule equivalent?

  iii. Examine the full-grown tree. What are the top three predictors according to this tree?

  iv. Why, technically, does the small tree result in a single node?

  v. What is the disadvantage of using the top levels of the full-grown tree as opposed to the small tree?

  vi. Compare this general result to that from logistic regression in the example in Chapter 10. What are possible reasons for the classification tree's failure to find a good predictive model?

9.3 Predicting Prices of Used Cars (Regression Trees). The file *ToyotaCorolla.csv* contains the data on used cars (Toyota Corolla) on sale during late summer of 2004 in the Netherlands. It has 1436 records containing details on 38 attributes, including Price, Age, Kilometers, HP, and other specifications. The goal is to predict the price of a used Toyota Corolla based on its specifications. (The example in Section 9.7 is a subset of this dataset.)

Data Preprocessing. Split the data into training (60%), and validation (40%) datasets.

a. Run a full-grown regression tree (RT) with outcome variable Price and predictors Age_08_04, KM, Fuel_Type (first convert to dummies), HP, Automatic, Doors, Quarterly_Tax, Mfr_Guarantee, Guarantee_Period, Airco, Automatic_airco, CD_Player, Powered_Windows, Sport_Model, and Tow_Bar. Set random_state=1.

  i. Which appear to be the three or four most important car specifications for predicting the car's price?

ii. Compare the prediction errors of the training and validation sets by examining their RMS error and by plotting the two boxplots. How does the predictive performance of the validation set compare to the training set? Why does this occur?

iii. How might we achieve better validation predictive performance at the expense of training performance?

iv. Create a smaller tree by using GridSearchCV() with cv = 5 to find a fine-tuned tree. Compared to the full-grown tree, what is the predictive performance on the validation set?

b. Let us see the effect of turning the price variable into a categorical variable. First, create a new variable that categorizes price into 20 bins. Now repartition the data keeping Binned_Price instead of Price. Run a classification tree with the same set of input variables as in the RT, and with Binned_Price as the output variable. As in the less deep regression tree, create a smaller tree by using GridSearchCV() with cv = 5 to find a fine-tuned tree.

i. Compare the smaller tree generated by the CT with the smaller tree generated by RT. Are they different? (Look at structure, the top predictors, size of tree, etc.) Why?

ii. Predict the price, using the smaller RT and CT, of a used Toyota Corolla with the specifications listed in Table 9.10.

TABLE 9.10 SPECIFICATIONS FOR A PARTICULAR TOYOTA COROLLA

Variable	Value
Age_-08_-04	77
KM	117,000
Fuel_Type	Petrol
HP	110
Automatic	No
Doors	5
Quarterly_Tax	100
Mfg_Guarantee	No
Guarantee_Period	3
Airco	Yes
Automatic_airco	No
CD_Player	No
Powered_Windows	No
Sport_Model	No
Tow_Bar	Yes

iii. Compare the predictions in terms of the predictors that were used, the magnitude of the difference between the two predictions, and the advantages and disadvantages of the two methods.

CHAPTER 10

Logistic Regression

In this chapter, we describe the highly popular and powerful classification method called logistic regression. Like linear regression, it relies on a specific model relating the predictors with the outcome. The user must specify the predictors to include as well as their form (e.g., including any interaction terms). This means that even small datasets can be used for building logistic regression classifiers, and that once the model is estimated, it is computationally fast and cheap to classify even large samples of new records. We describe the logistic regression model formulation and its estimation from data. We also explain the concepts of "logit," "odds," and "probability" of an event that arise in the logistic model context and the relations among the three. We discuss variable importance and coefficient interpretation, as well as variable selection for dimension reduction, and extensions to multi-class classification.

Python

In this chapter, we will use `pandas` for data handling, `scikit-learn` and `statsmodels` for the models, and `matplotlib` for visualization. We will also make use of the utility functions from the Python Utilities Functions Appendix. Use the following import statements for the Python code in this chapter.

import required functionality for this chapter

```
import numpy as np
import pandas as pd
from sklearn.linear_model import LogisticRegression, LogisticRegressionCV
from sklearn.model_selection import train_test_split
import statsmodels.api as sm
```

```
from mord import LogisticIT
import matplotlib.pylab as plt
import seaborn as sns
from dmba import classificationSummary, gainsChart, liftChart
from dmba.metric import AIC_score
```

10.1 | INTRODUCTION

Logistic regression extends the ideas of linear regression to the situation where the outcome variable, *Y*, is categorical. We can think of a categorical variable as dividing the records into classes. For example, if *Y* denotes a recommendation on holding/selling/buying a stock, we have a categorical variable with three categories. We can think of each of the stocks in the dataset (the records) as belonging to one of three classes: the *hold* class, the *sell* class, and the *buy* class. Logistic regression can be used for classifying a new record, where its class is unknown, into one of the classes, based on the values of its predictor variables (called *classification*). It can also be used in data where the class is known, to find factors distinguishing between records in different classes in terms of their predictor variables, or "predictor profile" (called *profiling*). Logistic regression is used in applications such as

1. Classifying customers as returning or nonreturning (classification)
2. Finding factors that differentiate between male and female top executives (profiling)
3. Predicting the approval or disapproval of a loan based on information such as credit scores (classification)

The logistic regression model is used in a variety of fields: whenever a structured model is needed to explain or predict categorical (in particular, binary) outcomes. One such application is in describing choice behavior in econometrics.

In this chapter, we focus on the use of logistic regression for classification. We deal mostly with a binary outcome variable having two possible classes. In Section 10.5, we show how the results can be extended to the case where *Y* assumes more than two possible classes. Popular examples of binary outcomes are success/failure, yes/no, buy/don't buy, default/don't default, and survive/die. For convenience, we often code the values of the binary outcome variable *Y* as 0 and 1.

Note that in some cases we may choose to convert a continuous outcome variable or an outcome variables with multiple classes into a binary outcome variable for purposes of simplification, reflecting the fact that decision-making may be binary (approve the loan/don't approve, make an offer/don't make an offer). As with multiple linear regression, the predictor variables $X_1, X_2, \ldots, X_k$ may be categorical variables, continuous variables, or a mixture of these two types. While in multiple linear regression the aim is to predict the value of the continuous Y for a new record, in logistic regression the goal is to predict which class a new record will belong to, or simply to *classify* the record into one of the classes. In the stock example, we would want to classify a new stock into one of the three recommendation classes: sell, hold, or buy. Or, we might want to compute for a new record its *propensity* (=the probability) to belong to each class, and then possibly rank a set of new records from highest to lowest propensity in order to act on those with the highest propensity.[1]

In logistic regression, we take two steps: the first step yields estimates of the *propensities* or *probabilities* of belonging to each class. In the binary case, we get an estimate of $p = P(Y = 1)$, the probability of belonging to class 1 (which also tells us the probability of belonging to class 0). In the next step, we use a cutoff value on these probabilities in order to classify each case into one of the classes. For example, in a binary case, a cutoff of 0.5 means that cases with an estimated probability of $P(Y = 1) \geq 0.5$ are classified as belonging to class 1, whereas cases with $P(Y = 1) < 0.5$ are classified as belonging to class 0. This cutoff does not need to be set at 0.5. When the event in question is a low probability but notable or important event (say, 1 = fraudulent transaction), a lower cutoff may be used to classify more cases as belonging to class 1.

10.2 | THE LOGISTIC REGRESSION MODEL

The idea behind logistic regression is straightforward: Instead of using Y directly as the outcome variable, we use a function of it, which is called the *logit*. The logit, it turns out, can be modeled as a linear function of the predictors. Once the logit has been predicted, it can be mapped back to a probability.

To understand the logit, we take several intermediate steps: First, we look at $p = P(Y = 1)$, the probability of belonging to class 1 (as opposed to class 0). In contrast to the binary variable Y, which only takes the values 0 and 1, p can take any value in the interval [0, 1]. However, if we express p as a linear function of the q predictors[2] in the form

$$p = \beta_0 + \beta_1 x_1 + \beta_2 x_2 + \cdots + \beta_q x_q, \qquad (10.1)$$

[1] Potentially, one could use linear regression for classification, by training a linear regression on a 0/1 outcome variable (called a Linear Probability Model). The model is then used to generate numerical predictions which are converted into binary classifications using a threshold. However, linear probability models, despite their name, do not produce proper predicted probabilities. The numerical predictions they produce are useful for comparison to the classification threshold, but are otherwise meaningless.

[2] Unlike elsewhere in the book, where p denotes the number of predictors, in this chapter we use q, to avoid confusion with the probability p.

it is not guaranteed that the right-hand side will lead to values within the interval [0, 1]. The solution is to use a nonlinear function of the predictors in the form

$$p = \frac{1}{1 + e^{-(\beta_0+\beta_1 x_1+\beta_2 x_2+\cdots+\beta_q x_q)}}. \tag{10.2}$$

This is called the *logistic response function*. For any values $x_1, \ldots, x_q$, the right-hand side will always lead to values in the interval [0, 1]. Next, we look at a different measure of belonging to a certain class, known as *odds*. The odds of belonging to class 1 are defined as *the ratio of the probability of belonging to class 1 to the probability of belonging to class 0*:

$$\text{Odds}(Y = 1) = \frac{p}{1-p}. \tag{10.3}$$

This metric is very popular in horse races, sports, gambling, epidemiology, and other areas. Instead of talking about the *probability* of winning or contacting a disease, people talk about the *odds* of winning or contacting a disease. How are these two different? If, for example, the probability of winning is 0.5, the odds of winning are $0.5/0.5 = 1$. We can also perform the reverse calculation: Given the odds of an event, we can compute its probability by manipulating equation (10.3):

$$p = \frac{\text{odds}}{1 + \text{odds}}. \tag{10.4}$$

Substituting equation (10.2) into equation (10.4), we can write the relationship between the odds and the predictors as

$$\text{Odds}(Y = 1) = e^{\beta_0+\beta_1 x_1+\beta_2 x_2+\cdots+\beta_q x_q}. \tag{10.5}$$

This last equation describes a multiplicative (proportional) relationship between the predictors and the odds. Such a relationship is interpretable in terms of percentages, for example, a unit increase in predictor X_j is associated with an average increase of $\beta_j \times 100\%$ in the odds (holding all other predictors constant).

Now, if we take a natural logarithm[3] on both sides, we get the standard formulation of a logistic model:

$$\log(\text{odds}) = \beta_0 + \beta_1 x_1 + \beta_2 x_2 + \cdots + \beta_q x_q. \tag{10.6}$$

The log(odds), called the *logit*, takes values from $-\infty$ (very low odds) to ∞ (very high odds).[4] A logit of 0 corresponds to even odds of 1 (probability = 0.5). Thus, our final

[3]The natural logarithm function is typically denoted ln() or log(). In this book, we use log().

[4]We use the terms *odds* and *odds(Y = 1)* interchangeably.

formulation of the relation between the outcome and the predictors uses the logit as the outcome variable and models it as a *linear function* of the q predictors.

To see the relationship between the probability, odds, and logit of belonging to class 1, look at Figure 10.1, which shows the odds (a) and logit (b) as a function of p. Notice that the odds can take any non-negative value, and that the logit can take any real value.

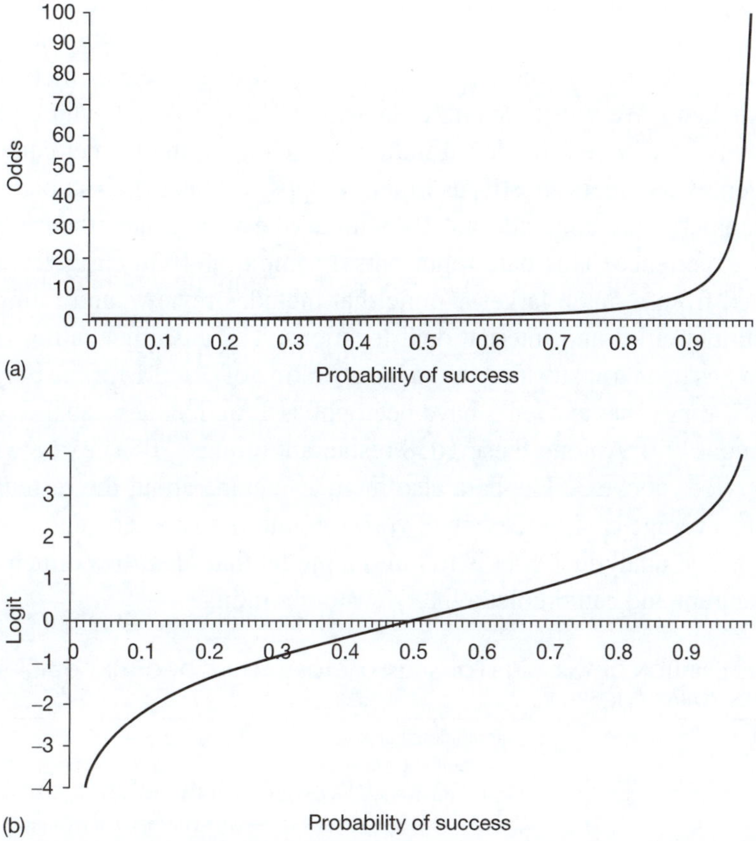

FIGURE 10.1 **(a) ODDS AND (b) LOGIT AS A FUNCTION OF *p***

10.3 | EXAMPLE: RATING INDIAN QUICK FOOD SERVICES

The market size of the Indian restaurant and food services industry stands closer to Rs 3.5 trillion as of 2018 and expected to grow at a yearly rate of 10%. The organized segment accounts for about 30-35% of the industry. Quick services restaurants (QSRs), casual and fine dining restaurants account for about 75-80% of the organized segment, followed by cafes and bakeries, pubs, bars, clubs, and lounges (PBCL) accounting for about 8-10% and institutional catering and kiosks with 13-15% share in the organized market. The QSRs have both fast-food cuisines as well as minimal table services and majorly cater to the millennial and working professionals usually in the age bracket 15-40 years. The USP of QSRs is quick deliveries and competitive pricing that attract consumers. Online QSR have evolved over time in India. Some of the prominent names are Swiggy, Zomato, Uber Eats, Foodpanda, Domino's, Pizza Hut, JustEat, etc. Among these, some provide an online platform for customers to order quick food service from restaurants located in the serviceable area like Zomato, Swiggy, and Uber Eats, whereas Pizza Hut and Domino's provide services through their own chain of outlets or owned kitchens. We will be using a dataset *OQFS_NEW.xlsx* which pertains to a major online food service provider in India who belong to the former category of service providers. Customers mostly use mobile apps to make their choices and place orders. Customers may conclude mostly with a vote which rates the restaurant food and overall experience. This data represents a sample of 1038 cases from India that were selected from a much larger sample that includes reviews and rating of restaurants in multiple cities and international locations. The customer rating ranges from 1 to 5 which has been transformed into a binary rating of 0 and 1 for the purpose of this illustration. Ratings that exceed 3 have been put as 1, and values equal to or less than 3 have been put as 0. Among these 1038 restaurant ratings, 705 (i.e., 68%) have been rated for services above 3. The data also includes details about the restaurant, which includes city, average cost, price range, voting count of customers, and average rating (Table 10.1). The analytical goal is to build a model that identifies dimensions of the service restaurant and can predict a likely customer rating.

TABLE 10.1 DESCRIPTION OF VARIABLES FOR SATISFOACTORY RATING OF ONLINE QUICK SERVICE RESTAURANTS (QSRs)

RestaurantID	Unique Identifier Restaurant
City	Restaurant Location
Price_Range	1 to 4, 1 for average lowest price and 4 for average highest price (predictor)
FoodVariety	Coded FoodVariety1 as 1(single type cuisine), FoodVariety2 as 2 (two types of dstinct cuisines) and FoodVariety3 as 3(three or more types of distinct cuisines (predictor)
Average_Billing	Average bill of purchase transaction in Indian rupees for two which has been transformed into categories with levels 1 to 5 (predictor)
Votes	Number of customers rated which has been transformed into categories with levels 1 to 5 (predictor)
Satisfactory_Rating	1: Satisfactory rating 0: Unsatisfactory rating (dependent variable target) It has been curated by categorizing original ratings from 1 to 5 into 1 for ratings above 3 otherwise 0 (target or dependent variable).

Model with a Single Predictor

Consider first a simple logistic regression model with just one predictor. This is conceptually analogous to the simple linear regression model in which we fit a straight line to relate the *Satisfactory_Rating*, *Y*, to a single predictor, *X*.

Let us construct a simple logistic regression model for classification of restaurants using the single predictor *Price_Range*. The equation relating the outcome variable to the predictor in terms of probabilities is

$$P(\text{Satisfactory\_Rating} = 1 \,|\, \text{Price\_Range} = x) = \frac{1}{1 + e^{-(\beta_0 + \beta_1 x)}},$$

or equivalently, in terms of odds,

$$\text{Odds}(\text{Satisfactory\_Rating} = 1 \,|\, \text{Price\_Range} = x) = e^{\beta_0 + \beta_1 x}. \tag{10.7}$$

Suppose the estimated coefficients for the model are $\hat{\beta}_0 = -3.964$ and $\hat{\beta}_1 = 2.292$. So the fitted model is

$$P(\text{Satisfactory\_Rating} = 1 \,|\, \text{Price\_Range} = x) = \frac{1}{1 + e^{(3.964 - 2.292x)}}. \tag{10.8}$$

Although logistic regression can be used for prediction in the sense that we predict the *probability* of a categorical outcome, it is most often used for classification. To see the difference between the two, consider predicting the probability of a restaurant getting a satisfactory rating as opposed to classifying the rating as a satisfactory/non-satisfactory event. From Figure 10.2, it can be seen that the satisfactory rating probabilities produced by the logistic regression model (the s-shaped curve in Figure 10.2) can yield values between 0 and 1. To end up with classifications into either 1 or 0 (e.g., a restaurant either gets a satisfactory rating or does not get satisfactory rating), we need a threshold, or cutoff value (see section on "Propensities and Cutoff for Classification" in Chapter 5). This is true in the case of multiple predictor variables as well.

In the online quick food service example, in order to classify a new restaurant likely to be rated satisfactory, we use the information about its prices by factoring it into the fitted equation in (10.8). This yields an estimated probability of a satisfactory rating. We then compare it to the cutoff value. The restaurant is classified as a qualifier for higher customer acceptance if the probability of its *Satisfactory_Rating* is above the cutoff.[5]

[5]Here we compared the probability to a cutoff c. If we prefer to look at *odds* of accepting rather than the probability, an equivalent method is to use the equation in (10.7) and compare the odds to $c/(1-c)$. If the odds are higher than this number, the rating is classified as satisfactory otherwise unsatisfactory.

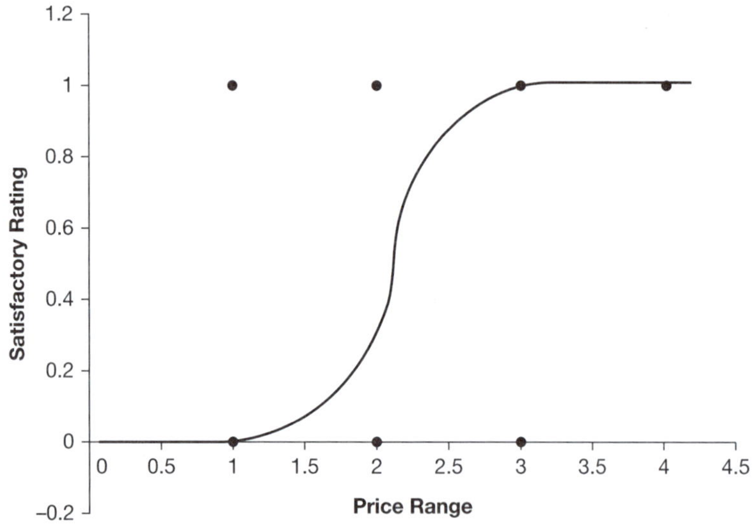

FIGURE 10.2 PLOT OF DATA POINTS (SATISFACTORY RATING AS A FUNCTION OF PRICE RANGE)

Estimating the Logistic Model from Data: Computing Parameter Estimates

In logistic regression, the relation between Y and the β parameters is nonlinear. For this reason, the β parameters are not estimated using the method of least squares (as in multiple linear regression). Instead, a method called *maximum likelihood* is used. The idea, in brief, is to find the estimates that maximize the chance of obtaining the data that we have. This requires iterations using a computer program.[6]

Algorithms to compute the coefficient estimates are less robust than algorithms for linear regression. Computed estimates are generally reliable for well-behaved datasets where the number of records with outcome variable values of both 0 and 1 are large; their ratio is "not too close" to either 0 or 1; and when the number of coefficients in the logistic regression model is small relative to the sample size (say, no more than 10%). As with linear regression, collinearity (strong correlation among the predictors) can lead to computational difficulties. Computationally intensive algorithms have been developed recently that circumvent some of these difficulties. For technical details on the maximum likelihood estimation in logistic regression, see Hosmer and Lemeshow (2000).

[6]The method of maximum likelihood ensures good asymptotic (large sample) properties for the estimates. Under very general conditions, maximum likelihood estimators are: (1) *Consistent*—The probability of the estimator differing from the true value approaches zero with increasing sample size. (2) *Asymptotically efficient*—The variance is the smallest possible among consistent estimators. (3) *Asymptotically normally distributed*—This allows us to compute confidence intervals and perform statistical tests in a manner analogous to the analysis of multiple linear regression models, provided that the sample size is *large*.

To illustrate a typical output from such a procedure, we fit a logistic model to the training set of 1038 online food service restaurants. The outcome variable is *Satisfactory_Rating*, with 1 defined as the satisfactory and 0 for a unsatisfactory.

Data Preprocessing We usually start by converting predictor variable into a set of dummy variables. In the dataset, if it is coded as an integer, like values 1, 2, or 3 or something similar. To turn it into a dummy variable, we first convert it into a categorical variable using the pandas methods *astype('category')* and *rename_categories*. Then we apply the function *pd.get_dummies* on the data frame to create appropriate dummies like if there are three categories we will create two dummy variables and logistic regression will only use two of the three categories because using all three would create a multicollinearity issue (see Chapter 6). Together with the three numerical predictors, we have a total of five predictors.

Next, we partition the data randomly into training (60%) and validation (40%) sets. We use the training set to fit a logistic regression model and the validation set to assess the model's performance.

Estimated Model Table 10.2 presents the output from running a logistic regression using the 5 predictors on the training data. Ignoring *p*-values for the coefficients, a model based on all 5 predictors has the estimated logistic equation

$$\begin{aligned}
&\text{Logit(Satisfactory_Rating} = 1)\\
&\quad = -6.9356 + 1.7297\text{Votes}\\
&\qquad - 1.11019\ \text{Food_Varieties_TwoVarieties}\\
&\qquad - 0.50293\ \text{FoodVariety_MultipleVarieties}\\
&\qquad - 0.15471\ \text{Average_Billing} + 2.16242\ \text{Price_Range}
\end{aligned} \tag{10.9}$$

TABLE 10.2 LOGISTIC REGRESSION MODEL FOR OQFS SATISFACTORY RATING

code for fitting a logistic regression model

```
# read csv file OQFS.csv and drop irrelevant columns
oqfs=pd.read_csv('OQFS.csv')
oqfs.drop(columns=['Restaurant ID', 'City', 'Unnamed: 7'], inplace=True)

# Treat education as categorical, convert to dummy variables
oqfs.FoodVariety= oqfs['FoodVariety'].astype('category')
oqfs.Average_Billing= oqfs['Average_Billing'].astype('category')
oqfs.Price_Range= oqfs['Price_Range'].astype('category')
```

(Continued)

TABLE 10.2 LOGISTIC REGRESSION MODEL FOR OQFS SATISFACTORY RATING (*Continued*)

```
oqfs.Votes= oqfs['Votes'].astype('category')
oqfs.Satisfactory_Rating= oqfs['Satisfactory_Rating'].astype('category')
NewCategories= {1: 'SingleVariety', 2: 'TwoVarieties', 3: 'MultipleVarieties'}
oqfs.FoodVariety.cat.rename_categories(NewCategories, inplace=True)
oqfs= pd.get_dummies(oqfs, columns=['FoodVariety'],prefix_sep='_', drop_first=True)
y = oqfs['Satisfactory_Rating']
X = oqfs.drop(columns=['Satisfactory_Rating'])
train_X, valid_X, train_y, valid_y = train_test_split(X, y,test_size=0.4, random_state=1)

# fit a logistic regression (set penalty=l2 and C=1e42 to avoid regularization)
logit_reg = LogisticRegression(penalty=''l2'', C=1e42, solver='liblinear')
logit_reg.fit(train_X, train_y)

print('intercept', logit_reg.intercept_[0])
print(pd.DataFrame({'coeff': logit_reg.coef_[0]}, index=X.columns).transpose())

print('AIC', AIC_score(valid_y, logit_reg.predict(valid_X), df = len(train_X.columns) + 1))
```

Output

```
intercept -6.93558760647607
        Average_Billing Price_Range Votes FoodVariety_TwoVarieties \
coeff -0.154712 2.162422 1.729702 -1.110194
        FoodVariety_MultipleVarieties
coeff -0.50293
AIC 313.19336161571084
```

The negative coefficients for the dummy variables *FoodVariety_TwoVarieties* and *FoodVariety_MultipleVarieties* means that restaurants offering two types and different types of cuisine are less likely to be ranked as Satisfactory. (All marked by 1 in the dummy variables) are associated with lesser probabilities of getting high ratings from customers versus *FoodVariety_SingleVariety* offers. For the continuous predictors, positive coefficients indicate that a higher value on that predictor is associated with a higher probability of getting of higher rating (e.g., Votes: More votes are likely to result in higher rating indicative of sustained service performance could result in better rating). Similarly, positive coefficient of Price_Range indicates likelihood of higher rating at higher price point of cuisine/s on offer online. Negative coefficient of Average_Billing, though insignificant, indicate inverse association rating by customers. Which means if average billing charges of a QFS restaurant are higher, it is likely to get slightly lesser rating.

Interpreting Results in Terms of Odds (for a Higher Customer Rating Goal)

Logistic models, when they are appropriate for the data, can give useful information about the roles played by different predictor variables. For example, suppose we want to know how increase in offered cuisine prices by one level will affect the probability of Satisfactory_Rating. This can be found straightforwardly if we consider not probabilities, but odds.

Recall that the odds are given by

$$\text{Odds} = e^{\beta_0+\beta_1 x_1+\beta_2 x_2+\cdots+\beta_q x_q}.$$

At first, let us return to the single predictor example, where we model Satisfactory_Rating as a function of the restaurant's offered Price_Range:

$$\text{Odds(Satisfactory\_Rating} = 1 \mid \text{Price\_Range)} = e^{\beta_0+\beta_1 \text{Price\_Range}}.$$

We can think of the model as a multiplicative model of odds. The odds that a restaurant with offered price range at level 1 will have likelihood of rating estimated by $e^{3.964-(2.292)(1)} = 5.322$. These are the *base-case odds*. The odds of offered price range increased by one level will increase odds of increased satisfactory rating by a factor of $e^{2.292} = 9.894$.

Suppose that the value of Price_Range, or in general X_1, is increased by one unit from x_1 to $x_1 + 1$, while the other predictors are held at their current value $(x_2, \ldots, x_{10})$. We get the odds ratio

$$\frac{\text{odds}(x_1 + 1, x_2, \ldots, x_{10})}{\text{odds}(x_1, \ldots, x_{10})} = \frac{e^{\beta_0+\beta_1(x_1+1)+\beta_2 x_2+\cdots+\beta_{10} x_{10}}}{e^{\beta_0+\beta_1 x_1+\beta_2 x_2+\cdots+\beta_{10} x_{10}}} = e^{\beta_1}.$$

This tells us that a single unit increase in X_1, holding $X_2, \ldots, X_{10}$ constant, is associated with an increase in the odds that a restaurant gets a satisfactory rating by a factor of e^{β_1}. In other words, e^{β_1} is the multiplicative factor by which the odds (of belonging to class 1) increase when the value of X_1 is increased by 1 unit, *holding all other predictors constant*. If $\beta_1 < 0$, an increase in X_1 is associated with a decrease in the odds of belonging to class 1, whereas a positive value of β_1 is associated with an increase in the odds.

When a predictor is a dummy variable, the interpretation is technically the same but has a different practical meaning. For instance, the coefficient for *FoodVariety_MultipleVarieties* was estimated from the training data to be –0.50293. Recall that the reference group is restaurants in *FoodVariety_SingleVariety* which means restaurants who offer only one type of cuisine. We interpret this coefficient as follows: $e^{-0.50293} = 0.6047$. Therefore odds of restaurant to get a satisfactory rating with single cuisine is more than one and half times higher (1/0.6047) than restaurants who offer multiple cuisine.

The advantage of reporting results in odds as opposed to probabilities is that statements such as those above are true for any value of X_1. Unless X_1 is a dummy variable, we cannot apply such statements about the effect of increasing X_1 by a single unit to probabilities. This is because the result depends on the actual value of X_1. So if we increase X_1 from, say, 3 to 4, the effect on p, the probability of belonging to class 1, will be different than if we increase X_1 from 30 to 31. In short, the change in the probability, p, for a unit increase in a particular predictor variable, while holding all other predictors constant, is not a constant—it depends on the specific values of the predictor variables. We therefore talk about probabilities only in the context of specific records.

10.4 | EVALUATING CLASSIFICATION PERFORMANCE

The general measures of performance that were described in Chapter 5 are used to assess the logistic model performance. Recall that there are several performance measures, the most popular being those based on the confusion matrix (accuracy alone or combined with costs) and the lift chart. As in other classification methods, the goal is to find a model that accurately classifies records to their class, using only the predictor information. A variant of this goal is *ranking*, or finding a model that does a superior job of identifying the members of a particular class of interest for a set of new records (which might come at some cost to overall accuracy). Since the training data are used for selecting the model, we expect the model to perform quite well for those data, and therefore prefer to test its performance on the validation set. Recall that the data in the validation set were not involved in the model building, and thus we can use them to test the model's ability to classify data that it has not "seen" before.

To obtain the confusion matrix from a logistic regression analysis, we use the estimated equation to predict the probability of class membership (the *propensities*) for each record in the validation set, and use the cutoff value to decide on the class assignment of these records. We then compare these classifications to the actual class memberships of these records. In the online quick food service case, we use the estimated model in equation (10.9) to predict the probability of satisfactory rating in a validation set that contains 415 restaurants (these data were not used in the modeling step). Technically, this is done by predicting the *logit* using the estimated model in equation (10.9) and then obtaining the probabilities p through the relation $p = e^{\text{logit}}/(1+e^{\text{logit}})$. We then compare these probabilities to our chosen cutoff value in order to classify each of the 415 validation records as potential restaurants for satisfactory rating.

Table 10.3 shows propensities for the first five selected records in the validation set. Suppose that we use a cutoff of 0.5. We see that the four restaurants have probability of getting satisfactory rating being more than the cutoff of 0.5, and therefore they are classified as High_Rating_Resturatnt. First three and fifth listed restaurant has got higher rating coded as 1. These four positive cases are True Positives and remaining cases is a True Negative. Hence, there could be four possibilities resulting into True Positives (Both Actual and Predicted are 1), False Positives (Actual 0 but Predicted 1), True Negatives (Both Actual and Predicted are 0), and False Negative (Actual 1 but Predicted 0).

TABLE 10.3 PROPENSITIES FOR FOUR CUSTOMERS IN VALIDATION DATA

code for using logistic regression to generate predicted probabilities

```
logit_reg_pred = logit_reg.predict(valid_X)
logit_reg_proba = logit_reg.predict_proba(valid_X)
logit_result = pd.DataFrame({'actual': valid_y,
                             'p(0)': [p[0] for p in logit_reg_proba],
                             'p(1)': [p[1] for p in logit_reg_proba],
                             'predicted': logit_reg_pred })

# display first five cases
print(logit_result.iloc[0:5,])
```

Output

```
     actual      p(0)      p(1)  predicted
589       1  0.000013  0.999987          1
718       1  0.000016  0.999984          1
677       1  0.000011  0.999989          1
957       0  0.999989  0.000011          0
314       1  0.000024  0.999976          1
```

Another useful tool for assessing model classification performance are the lift (gains) chart and decile-wise lift chart (see Chapter 5). Figure 10.3 illustrates the lift chart obtained for the online QFS customer rating logistic model using the validation set. The "lift" over the base curve indicates for a given number of cases (read on the *x*-axis), the additional responders that you can identify by using the model. The same information is portrayed in Figure 10.3: Taking the 10% of the records that are ranked by the model as "most probable 1's" yields 1.5 times as many 1's as would simply selecting 10% of the records at random.

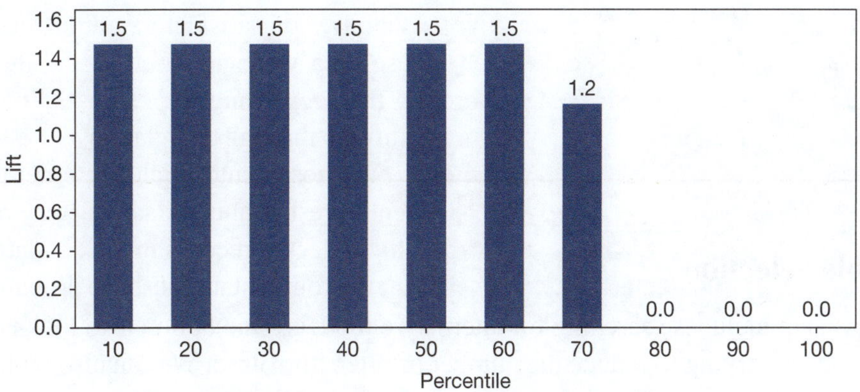

FIGURE 10.3 DECILE-WISE LIFT CHART FOR THE VALIDATION DATA FOR QFS CUSTOMER RATING

code for creating decile lift chart

```
# df = logit_result.sort_values(by=['p(1)'], ascending=False)
fig, axes = plt.subplots(nrows=1, ncols=1, figsize=(10, 4))

liftChart(df['p(1)'], title=False)

plt.show()
```

TABLE 10.4 TRAINING AND VALIDATION CONFUSION MATRICES

code for using logistic regression to generate confusion matrices

```
# training confusion matrix
print('Training Data')
a=classificationSummary(train_y, logit_reg.predict(train_X))

# validation confusion matrix
print('Validation Data')
b=classificationSummary(valid_y, logit_reg.predict(valid_X))
```

Output

```
Training Data
Confusion Matrix (Accuracy 1.0000)

       Prediction
Actual   0   1
     0 200   0
     1   0 422
Validation Data
Confusion Matrix (Accuracy 1.0000)

        Prediction
 Actual    0   1
      0  133   0
      1    0 283
```

Variable Selection

The next step includes searching for alternative models. One option is to look for simpler models by trying to reduce the number of predictors used. We can also build more complex models that reflect interactions among predictors by creating and including new variables that are derived from the predictors. For example, if we hypothesize that there is an interaction effect between Average_Billing and Votes, we should add an interaction term of the form Average_Billing × Votes. The choice among the set of alternative models is guided primarily by performance on the validation data. For models that perform roughly equally well, simpler models are generally preferred over more complex models. Note also that performance on validation data may be overly optimistic when it comes to predicting performance on data that have not been exposed to the model at all. This is because when the validation data are used to select a final model among a set of model, we are selecting based on how well the model performs with those data and therefore may be incorporating some of the random idiosyncrasies of the validation data into the judgment about the best model. The model still may be the best for the validation data among those considered, but it will probably not do as well with the unseen data. Therefore, it is useful to evaluate the chosen model on a new test dataset to get a sense of how well it will perform on new data. In addition, one must consider practical issues such as costs of collecting variables, error-proneness, and model complexity in the selection of the final model.

As in linear regression and in logistic regression we can use automated variable selection heuristics such as stepwise regression, forward selection, and backward elimination (See Section 6.4 in Chapter 6).

10.5 | LOGISTIC REGRESSION FOR MULTI-CLASS CLASSIFICATION

The logistic model for a binary outcome can be extended for more than two classes. Suppose that there are m classes. Using a logistic regression model, for each record we would have m probabilities of belonging to each of the m classes. Since the m probabilities must add up to 1, we need estimate only $m - 1$ probabilities.

Ordinal Classes

Ordinal classes are classes that have a meaningful order. For example, in stock recommendations, the three classes *buy*, *hold*, and *sell* can be treated as ordered. As a simple rule, if classes can be numbered in a meaningful way, we consider them ordinal. When the number of classes is large (typically, more than 5), we can treat the outcome variable as continuous and perform multiple linear regression. When $m = 2$, the logistic model described above is used. We therefore need an extension of the logistic regression for a small number of ordinal classes ($3 \leq m \leq 5$). There are several ways to extend the binary-class case. Here, we describe the *proportional odds* or *cumulative logit method*. For other methods, see Hosmer and Lemeshow (2000).

For simplicity of interpretation and computation, we look at *cumulative* probabilities of class membership. For example, in the stock recommendations, we have $m = 3$ classes. Let us denote them by 1 = *buy*, 2 = *hold*, and 3 = *sell*. The probabilities estimated by the model are $P(Y \leq 1)$, (the probability of a *buy* recommendation) and $P(Y \leq 2)$

(the probability of a *buy* or *hold* recommendation). The three noncumulative probabilities of class membership can easily be recovered from the two cumulative probabilities:

$$P(Y = 1) = P(Y \leq 1),$$
$$P(Y = 2) = P(Y \leq 2) - P(Y \leq 1),$$
$$P(Y = 3) = 1 - P(Y \leq 2).$$

Next, we want to model each logit as a function of the predictors. Corresponding to each of the $m - 1$ cumulative probabilities is a logit. In our example, we would have

$$\text{logit}(buy) = \log \frac{P(Y \leq 1)}{1 - P(Y \leq 1)},$$
$$\text{logit}(buy \text{ or } hold) = \log \frac{P(Y \leq 2)}{1 - P(Y \leq 2)}.$$

Each of the logits is then modeled as a linear function of the predictors (as in the two-class case). If in the stock recommendations we have a single predictor value x, we compute two logit values using two equations

$$\text{logit}(buy) = \alpha_0 + \beta_1 x,$$
$$\text{logit}(buy \text{ or } hold) = \beta_0 + \beta_1 x.$$

This means that both lines have the same slope (β_1) but different intercepts. Once the coefficients $\alpha_0, \beta_0, \beta_1$ are estimated, we can compute the class membership probabilities by rewriting the logit equations in terms of probabilities. For the three-class case, for example, we would have

$$P(Y = 1) = P(Y \leq 1) = \frac{1}{1 + e^{-(a_0 + b_1 x)}},$$
$$P(Y = 2) = P(Y \leq 2) - P(Y \leq 1) = \frac{1}{1 + e^{-(b_0 + b_1 x)}} - \frac{1}{1 + e^{-(a_0 + b_1 x)}},$$
$$P(Y = 3) = 1 - P(Y \leq 2) = 1 - \frac{1}{1 + e^{-(b_0 + b_1 x)}},$$

where a_0, b_0, and b_1 are the estimates obtained from the training set.

For each record, we now have the estimated probabilities that it belongs to each of the classes. In our example, each stock would have three probabilities: for a *buy* recommendation, a *hold* recommendation, and a *sell* recommendation. The last step is to classify the record into one of the classes. This is done by assigning it to the class with the highest membership probability. For example, if a stock had estimated probabilities $P(Y = 1) = 0.2$, $P(Y = 2) = 0.3$, and $P(Y = 3) = 0.5$, we would classify it as getting a *sell* recommendation.

Nominal Classes

When the classes cannot be ordered and are simply different from one another, we are in the case of nominal classes. An example is the choice between several brands of cereal. A simple way to verify that the classes are nominal is when it makes sense to tag them as $A, B, C, \ldots$, and the assignment of letters to classes does not matter. For simplicity, let us assume that there are $m = 3$ brands of cereal that consumers can choose from (assuming that each consumer chooses one). Then we estimate the probabilities $P(Y = A)$, $P(Y = B)$, and $P(Y = C)$. As before, if we know two of the probabilities, the third probability is determined. We therefore use one of the classes as the reference class. Let us use C as the reference brand.

The goal, once again, is to model the class membership as a function of predictors. So in the cereals example, we might want to predict which cereal will be chosen if we know the cereal's price x.

Next, we form $m - 1$ pseudologit equations that are linear in the predictors. In our example, we would have

$$\text{logit}(A) = \log \frac{P(Y = A)}{P(Y = C)} = \alpha_0 + \alpha_1 x,$$

$$\text{logit}(B) = \log \frac{P(Y = B)}{P(Y = C)} = \beta_0 + \beta_1 x.$$

Once the four coefficients are estimated from the training set, we can estimate the class membership probabilities[7]:

$$P(Y = A) = \frac{e^{a_0 + a_1 x}}{1 + e^{a_0 + a_1 x} + e^{b_0 + b_1 x}},$$

$$P(Y = B) = \frac{e^{b_0 + b_1 x}}{1 + e^{a_0 + a_1 x} + e^{b_0 + b_1 x}},$$

$$P(Y = C) = 1 - P(Y = A) - P(Y = B),$$

where a_0, a_1, b_0, and b_1 are the coefficient estimates obtained from the training set. Finally, a record is assigned to the class that has the highest probability.

---

[7]From the two logit equations, we see that $P(Y = A) = P(Y = C) \cdot e^{\alpha_0 + \alpha_1 x}$ and $P(Y = B) = P(Y = C) \cdot e^{\beta_0 + \beta_1 x}$. Since $P(Y = A) + P(Y = B) + P(Y = C) = 1$, we get

$$P(Y = C) = 1 - P(Y = C)e^{\alpha_0 + \alpha_1 x} - P(Y = C)e^{\beta_0 + \beta_1 x} = \frac{1}{e^{\alpha_0 + \alpha_1 x + e^{\beta_0 + \beta_1 x}}}. \tag{10.10}$$

By plugging this form into the two equations above it, we also obtain the membership probabilities in classes A and B.

Comparing Ordinal and Nominal Models

The estimated logistic models will differ, depending on whether the outcome variable is coded as ordinal or nominal. Lets take, for example, data on accidents from the US Bureau of Transportation Statistics. These data can be used to predict whether an accident will result in injuries or fatalities based on predictors such as alcohol involvement, time of day, and road condition. The severity of the accident has three classes: 0 = No Injury, 1 = Nonfatal Injuries, 2 = Fatalities.

We first consider severity as an ordinal variable, and fit a simple model with two nominal predictors, alcohol and weather. Each of these predictors is coded as No (not involved in the accident) or Yes (involved in the accident). Next we change the modeling type for severity to nominal, and fit a model with the same predictors. The reference severity level, in both models, is severity = 2.

Table 10.5 presents Python code for ordinal and nominal multinomial regression applied to the accidents data, displaying the resulting estimated models and predicted probabilities for a few sample records.

TABLE 10.5 ORDINAL AND NOMINAL (MULTI-CLASS) REGRESSION IN PYTHON

code for logistic regression with more than 2 classes

```
data = pd.read_csv('accidentsFull.csv')
outcome = 'MAX_SEV_IR'
predictors = ['ALCHL_I', 'WEATHER_R']

y = data[outcome]
X = data[predictors]
train_X, train_y = X, y

print('Nominal logistic regression')
logit = LogisticRegression(penalty="l2", solver='lbfgs', C=1e24, multi_class='multinomial')
logit.fit(X, y)
print('  intercept', logit.intercept_)
print('  coefficients', logit.coef_)
print()
probs = logit.predict_proba(X)
results = pd.DataFrame({
    'actual': y, 'predicted': logit.predict(X),
    'P(0)': [p[0] for p in probs],
    'P(1)': [p[1] for p in probs],
    'P(2)': [p[2] for p in probs],
})
print(results.head())
print()
```

TABLE 10.5 **ORDINAL AND NOMINAL (MULTI-CLASS) REGRESSION IN PYTHON (*Continued*)**

```
print('Ordinal logistic regression')
logit = LogisticIT(alpha=0)
logit.fit(X, y)
print('  theta', logit.theta_)
print('  coefficients', logit.coef_)
print()
probs = logit.predict_proba(X)
results = pd.DataFrame({
    'actual': y, 'predicted': logit.predict(X),
    'P(0)': [p[0] for p in probs],
    'P(1)': [p[1] for p in probs],
    'P(2)': [p[2] for p in probs],
})
print(results.head())
```

Output

```
Nominal logistic regression
  intercept
    [-0.09100315  0.9036454  -0.81264225]
  coefficients [[ 0.51606685  0.3391015 ]
 [ 0.14900396  0.09543369]
 [-0.66507082 -0.43453518]]

   actual  predicted   P(0)   P(1)   P(2)
0       1          1  0.491  0.499  0.010
1       0          0  0.553  0.441  0.005
2       0          0  0.553  0.441  0.005
3       0          1  0.491  0.499  0.010
4       0          1  0.394  0.579  0.027
```

```
Ordinal logistic regression
  theta
    [-1.06916285  2.77444326]
  coefficients
    [-0.40112008 -0.25174207]

   actual  predicted   P(0)   P(1)   P(2)
0       1          1  0.496  0.483  0.021
1       0          0  0.559  0.425  0.017
2       0          0  0.559  0.425  0.017
3       0          1  0.496  0.483  0.021
4       0          1  0.397  0.571  0.031
```

The ordinal logistic model has estimates for two intercepts (the first for severity = 0 and and the second for severity = 1), but one estimate for each predictor. In contrast, the nominal logistic model has estimates for the three intercepts, and also has three separate sets of coefficients for the predictors for each level of the outcome variable.

Finally, the resulting predicted probabilities also differ across the two models. Hence, it is useful to determine which model is more suitable for the outcome at hand, and to evaluate predictive performance on a validation set.

10.6 EXAMPLE OF COMPLETE ANALYSIS: PREDICTING DELAYED FLIGHTS

Predicting flight delays can be useful to a variety of organizations: airport authorities, airlines, aviation authorities. At times, joint task forces have been formed to address the problem. Such an organization, if it were to provide ongoing real-time assistance with flight delays,would benefit from some advance notice about flights likely to be delayed.

In this simplified illustration, we look at six predictors (see Table 10.6). The outcome of interest is whether the flight is delayed or not (*delayed* means more than 15 minutes late). Our data consist of all flights from the Washington, DC area into the New York City area during January 2004. The percent of delayed flights among these 2201 flights is 19.5%. The data were obtained from the Bureau of Transportation Statistics website (www.transtats.bts.gov).

TABLE 10.6 DESCRIPTION OF PREDICTORS FOR FLIGHT DELAYS EXAMPLE

Day of week	Coded as 1 = Monday, 2 = Tuesday,..., 7 = Sunday
Departure time	Broken down into 18 intervals between 6:00 AM and 10:00 PM
Origin	Three airport codes: DCA (Reagan National), IAD (Dulles), BWI (Baltimore–Washington Int'l)
Destination	Three airport codes: JFK (Kennedy), LGA (LaGuardia), EWR (Newark)
Carrier	Eight airline codes: CO (Continental), DH (Atlantic Coast), DL (Delta), MQ (American Eagle), OH (Comair), RU (Continental Express), UA (United), and US (USAirways)
Weather	Coded as 1 if there was a weather-related delay

The goal is to predict accurately whether a new flight, not in this dataset, will be delayed or not. The outcome variable is a variable called Flight Status, coded as *delayed* or *ontime*.

Other information available on the website, such as distance and arrival time, is irrelevant because we are looking at a certain route (distance, flight time, etc. should be approximately equal for all flights in the data). A sample of the data for 20 flights is shown in Table 10.7. Figures 10.4 and 10.5 show visualizations of the relationships between flight delays and different predictors or combinations of predictors. From Figure 10.4, we see that Sundays and Mondays saw the largest proportion of delays. Delay rates also seem to differ by carrier, by time of day, as well as by origin and destination airports. For Weather, we see a strong distinction between delays when Weather = 1 (in that case there is always a delay) and Weather = 0. The heatmap in Figure 10.5 reveals some specific combinations with high rates of delays, such as Sunday flights by carrier RU, departing from BWI, or Sunday flights by MQ departing from DCA. We can also see combinations with very low delay rates.

Our main goal is to find a model that can obtain accurate classifications of new flights based on their predictor information. An alternative goal is finding a certain percentage of flights that are most/least likely to get delayed (*ranking*). And a third different goal is profiling flights: finding out which factors are associated with a delay (not only in this sample but in the entire population of flights on this route), and for those factors we would like to quantify these effects. A logistic regression model can be used for all these goals, albeit in different ways.

TABLE 10.7 SAMPLE OF 20 FLIGHTS

Flight status	Carrier	Day of week	Departure time	Destination	Origin	Weather
Ontime	DL	2	728	LGA	DCA	0
Delayed	US	3	1600	LGA	DCA	0
Ontime	DH	5	1242	EWR	IAD	0
Ontime	US	2	2057	LGA	DCA	0
Ontime	DH	3	1603	JFK	IAD	0
Ontime	CO	6	1252	EWR	DCA	0
Ontime	RU	6	1728	EWR	DCA	0
Ontime	DL	5	1031	LGA	DCA	0
Ontime	RU	6	1722	EWR	IAD	0
Delayed	US	1	627	LGA	DCA	0
Delayed	DH	2	1756	JFK	IAD	0
Ontime	MQ	6	1529	JFK	DCA	0
Ontime	US	6	1259	LGA	DCA	0
Ontime	DL	2	1329	LGA	DCA	0
Ontime	RU	2	1453	EWR	BWI	0
Ontime	RU	5	1356	EWR	DCA	0
Delayed	DH	7	2244	LGA	IAD	0
Ontime	US	7	1053	LGA	DCA	0
Ontime	US	2	1057	LGA	DCA	0
Ontime	US	4	632	LGA	DCA	0

Data Preprocessing

Create a binary outcome variable called is Delay that takes the value 1 if Flight Status = *delayed* and 0 otherwise. Transform day of week into a categorical variable, and bin and categorize the departure time into hourly intervals between 6:00 AM and 10:00 PM. Set reference categories for categorical variables: IAD for departure airport, LGA for arrival, USAirways for carrier, and Wednesday for day (see Table 10.8 for Python code). This yields a total of 34 dummies. In addition, we have a single dummy for Weather. While this is a large number of predictors, we start by using all of them, look at performance, and then explore reducing the dimension. We then partition the data into training set (60%) and validation set (40%). We use the training set to fit a model and the validation set to assess the model's performance.

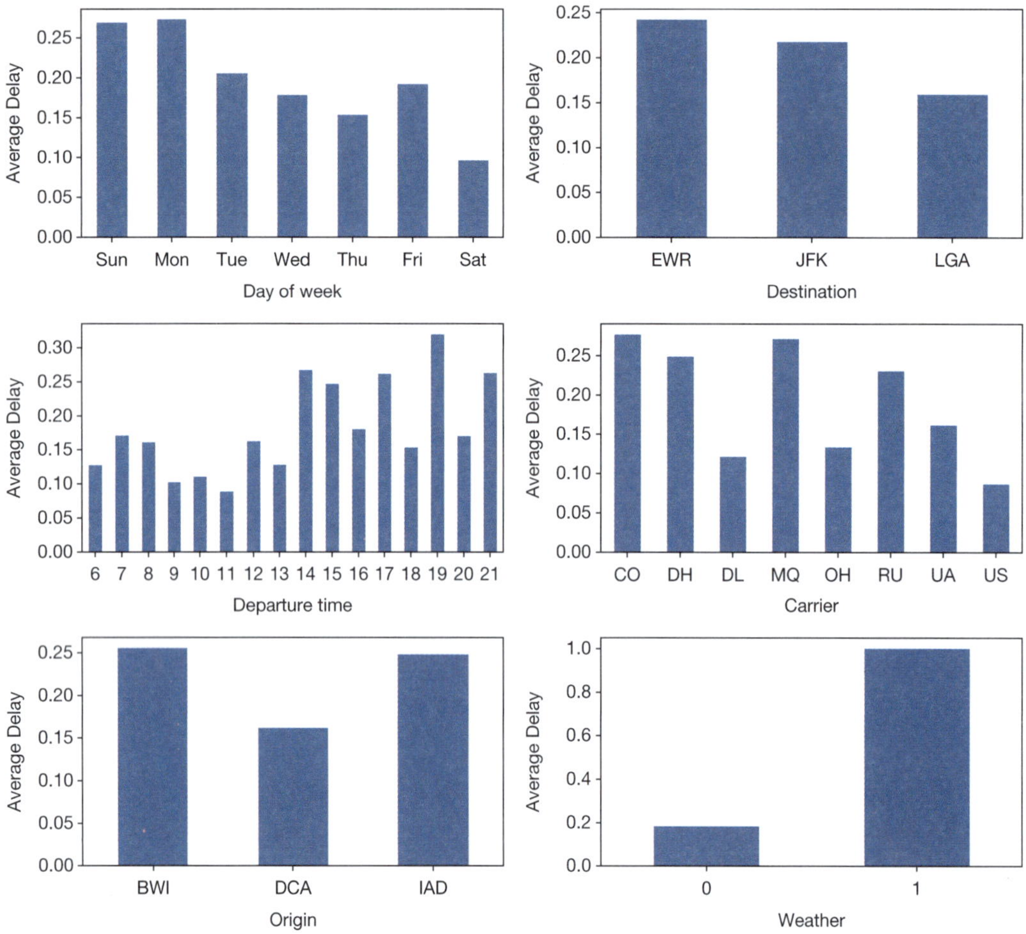

FIGURE 10.4 PROPORTION OF DELAYED FLIGHTS BY EACH OF THE SIX PREDICTORS. TIME OF DAY IS DIVIDED INTO HOURLY BINS

code for generating bar charts of average delay vs. predictors

```
delays_df = pd.read_csv('FlightDelays.csv')
# Create an indicator variable
delays_df['isDelayed'] = [1 if status == 'delayed' else 0
                          for status in delays_df['Flight Status']]

def createGraph(group, xlabel, axis):
    groupAverage = delays_df.groupby([group])['isDelayed'].mean()
    if group == 'DAY_WEEK': # rotate so that display starts on Sunday
        groupAverage = groupAverage.reindex(index=np.roll(groupAverage.index,1))
        groupAverage.index = ['Sun', 'Mon', 'Tue', 'Wed', 'Thu', 'Fri', 'Sat']
    ax = groupAverage.plot.bar(color='C0', ax=axis)
    ax.set_ylabel('Average Delay')
    ax.set_xlabel(xlabel)
    return ax
```

```
def graphDepartureTime(xlabel, axis):
    temp_df = pd.DataFrame({'CRS_DEP_TIME': delays_df['CRS_DEP_TIME'] // 100,
                            'isDelayed': delays_df['isDelayed']})
    groupAverage = temp_df.groupby(['CRS_DEP_TIME'])['isDelayed'].mean()
    ax = groupAverage.plot.bar(color='C0', ax=axis)
    ax.set_xlabel(xlabel); ax.set_ylabel('Average Delay')

fig, axes = plt.subplots(nrows=3, ncols=2, figsize=(10, 10))

createGraph('DAY_WEEK', 'Day of week', axis=axes[0][0])
createGraph('DEST', 'Destination', axis=axes[0][1])
graphDepartureTime('Departure time', axis=axes[1][0])
createGraph('CARRIER', 'Carrier', axis=axes[1][1])
createGraph('ORIGIN', 'Origin', axis=axes[2][0])
createGraph('Weather', 'Weather', axis=axes[2][1])
plt.tight_layout()
```

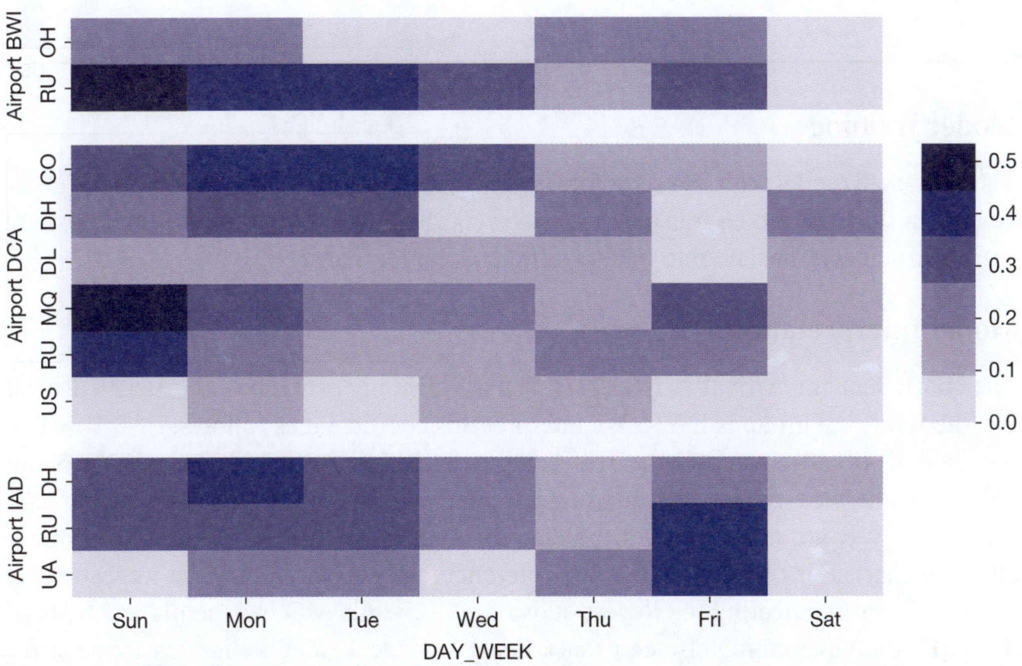

FIGURE 10.5 PERCENT OF DELAYED FLIGHTS (DARKER = HIGHER % DELAYS) BY DAY OF WEEK, ORIGIN, AND CARRIER

code for generating heatmap for exploring flight delays

```
agg = delays_df.groupby(['ORIGIN', 'DAY_WEEK', 'CARRIER']).isDelayed.mean()
agg = agg.reset_index()

# Define the layout of the graph
height_ratios = []
```

```
for i, origin in enumerate(sorted(delays_df.ORIGIN.unique())):
    height_ratios.append(len(agg[agg.ORIGIN == origin].CARRIER.unique()))
gridspec_kw = {'height_ratios': height_ratios, 'width_ratios': [15, 1]}
fig, axes = plt.subplots(nrows=3, ncols=2, figsize=(10, 6),
                         gridspec_kw = gridspec_kw)
axes[0, 1].axis('off')
axes[2, 1].axis('off')

maxIsDelay = agg.isDelayed.max()
for i, origin in enumerate(sorted(delays_df.ORIGIN.unique())):
    data = pd.pivot_table(agg[agg.ORIGIN == origin], values='isDelayed', aggfunc=np.sum,
                          index=['CARRIER'], columns=['DAY_WEEK'])
    data = data[[7, 1, 2, 3, 4, 5, 6]]  # Shift last columns to first
    ax = sns.heatmap(data, ax=axes[i][0], vmin=0, vmax=maxIsDelay,
                     cbar_ax=axes[1][1], cmap=sns.light_palette("navy"))
    ax.set_xticklabels(['Sun', 'Mon', 'Tue', 'Wed', 'Thu', 'Fri', 'Sat'])
    if i != 2:
        ax.get_xaxis().set_visible(False)
    ax.set_ylabel('Airport ' + origin)
plt.show()
```

Model Training

The estimated model with 34 predictors is shown in Table 10.8. Note that negative coefficients in the logit model translate into odds coefficients $e^{\hat{\beta}}$ lower than 1, and positive logit coefficients translate into odds coefficients larger than 1.

Model Interpretation

The coefficient for Arrival Airport JFK (DEST_JFK) is estimated as −0.524. Recall that the reference group is EWR. We interpret this coefficient as follows: $e^{-0.524} = 0.59$ are the odds of a flight arriving at JFK being delayed relative to a flight to EWR being delayed (=the base-case odds), holding all other variables constant. This means that flights to EWR are more likely to be delayed than those to JFK (holding everything else constant). For carriers (CO is the reference category), US has the largest negative coefficient, indicating the lowest odds of delay, while MQ has the highest odds of delay (holding everything else constant). For day of week, all coefficients are negative indicating that Monday (DAY_WEEK_1, the reference category) has the highest odds of delay, while Saturdays have the largest negative coefficient, and thereby the lowest odds of delay (holding everything else constant). Also, odds of delays appear to change over the course of the day, with the most noticeable difference from the reference category (6–7 AM) being 7–8 PM. Finally, Weather has the largest coefficient, indicating a large gap between flights with Weather = 0 and Weather = 1. Note that we have considered above only coefficient magnitude and not statistical significance. Since our eventual goal is prediction, we will rely instead on predictive performance.

TABLE 10.8 ESTIMATED LOGISTIC REGRESSION MODEL FOR DELAYED FLIGHTS (BASED ON THE TRAINING SET)

code for data preprocessing and running logistic regression

```
delays_df = pd.read_csv('FlightDelays.csv')
# Create an indicator variable
delays_df['isDelayed'] = [1 if status == 'delayed' else 0 for status in delays_df['Flight Status']]

# convert to categorical
delays_df.DAY_WEEK = delays_df.DAY_WEEK.astype('category')

# create hourly bins departure time
delays_df.CRS_DEP_TIME = [round(t / 100) for t in delays_df.CRS_DEP_TIME]
delays_df.CRS_DEP_TIME = delays_df.CRS_DEP_TIME.astype('category')

predictors = ['DAY_WEEK', 'CRS_DEP_TIME', 'ORIGIN', 'DEST', 'CARRIER', 'Weather']
outcome = 'isDelayed'

X = pd.get_dummies(delays_df[predictors], drop_first=True)
y = delays_df[outcome]
classes = ['ontime', 'delayed']

# split into training and validation
train_X, valid_X, train_y, valid_y = train_test_split(X, y, test_size=0.4, random_state=1)

logit_full = LogisticRegression(penalty="l2", C=1e42, solver='liblinear')
logit_full.fit(train_X, train_y)

print('intercept ', logit_full.intercept_[0])
print(pd.DataFrame({'coeff': logit_full.coef_[0]}, index=X.columns).transpose())

print('AIC', AIC_score(valid_y, logit_full.predict(valid_X), df = len(train_X.columns) + 1))
```

Partial output

```
intercept  -1.2190975950944987

      Weather  DAY_WEEK_2  DAY_WEEK_3  DAY_WEEK_4  DAY_WEEK_5  DAY_WEEK_6  DAY_WEEK_7
coeff   9.325      -0.598      -0.705      -0.799      -0.296      -1.129      -0.135

      CRS_DEP_TIME_7  CRS_DEP_TIME_8  CRS_DEP_TIME_9  CRS_DEP_TIME_10  CRS_DEP_TIME_11
coeff          0.631           0.382          -0.365            0.337            0.078

      CRS_DEP_TIME_12  CRS_DEP_TIME_13  CRS_DEP_TIME_14  CRS_DEP_TIME_15  CRS_DEP_TIME_16
coeff           0.399            0.175            0.202            1.265            0.628

      CRS_DEP_TIME_17  CRS_DEP_TIME_18  CRS_DEP_TIME_19  CRS_DEP_TIME_20  CRS_DEP_TIME_21
coeff           1.093            0.285            1.655            1.023            1.077

      ORIGIN_DCA  ORIGIN_IAD  DEST_JFK  DEST_LGA  CARRIER_DH  CARRIER_DL  CARRIER_MQ
coeff      -0.01      -0.134    -0.524    -0.546       0.352      -0.685       0.743

      CARRIER_OH  CARRIER_RU  CARRIER_UA  CARRIER_US
coeff     -0.711      -0.194       0.315      -0.971

AIC 1004.5346225948085
```

Model Performance

How should we measure the performance of models? One possible measure is "percent of flights correctly classified." Accurate classification can be obtained from the confusion matrix for the validation data. The confusion matrix gives a sense of the classification accuracy and what type of misclassification is more frequent. From the confusion matrix and error rates in Figure 10.6, it can be seen that the model more accurately classifies ontime flights and is less accurate in classifying flights that were delayed. (*Note*: The same pattern appears in the confusion matrix for the training data, so it is not surprising to see it emerge for new data.) If there is an asymmetric cost structure so that one type of misclassification is more costly than the other, the cutoff value can be selected to minimize the cost. Of course, this tweaking should be carried out on the training data and assessed only using the validation data.

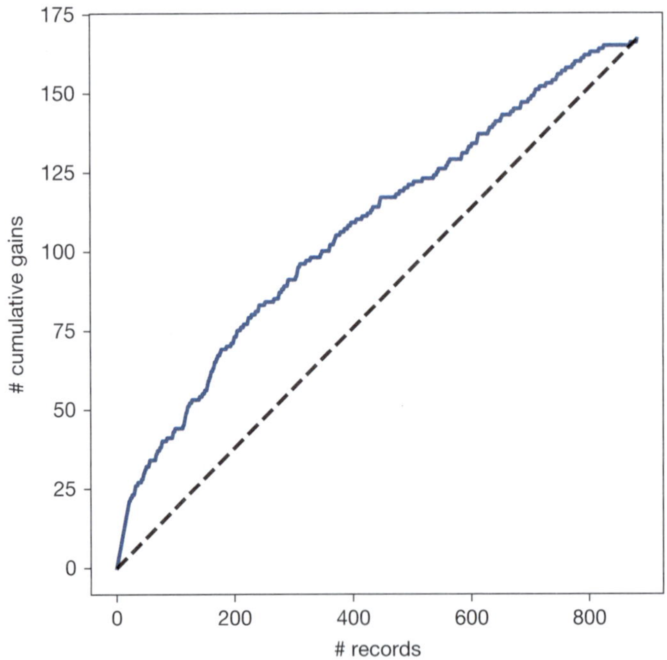

FIGURE 10.6 CONFUSION MATRIX AND CUMULATIVE GAINS CHART FOR THE FLIGHT DELAYS VALIDATION DATA USING ALL PREDICTORS

code for evaluating performance of all-predictor model on validation

```
logit_reg_pred = logit_full.predict_proba(valid_X)
full_result = pd.DataFrame({'actual': valid_y,
                            'p(0)': [p[0] for p in logit_reg_pred],
                            'p(1)': [p[1] for p in logit_reg_pred],
                            'predicted': logit_full.predict(valid_X)})
```

```
full_result = full_result.sort_values(by=['p(1)'], ascending=False)

# confusion matrix
classificationSummary(full_result.actual, full_result.predicted, class_names=classes)

gainsChart(full_result.actual, figsize=[5, 5])
plt.show()
```

Output

```
Confusion Matrix (Accuracy 0.8309)

       Prediction
 Actual  ontime delayed
 ontime     705       9
delayed     140      27
```

In most conceivable situations, the purpose of the model would be to identify those flights most likely to be delayed among a set of flights, so that resources can be directed toward either reducing the delay or mitigating its effects. Air traffic controllers might work to open up additional air routes or allocate more controllers to a specific area for a short time. Airlines might bring on personnel to rebook passengers and to activate standby flight crews and aircraft. Hotels might allocate space for stranded travellers. In all cases, the resources available are going to be limited and might vary over time and from organization to organization. In this situation, the most useful model would provide an ordering of flights by their probability of delay, letting the model users decide how far down that list to go in taking action. Therefore, model lift is a useful measure of performance—as you move down that list of flights, ordered by their delay probability, how much better does the model do in predicting delay than would a naive model which is simply the average delay rate for all flights? From the gains curve for the validation data (Figure 10.6), we see that our model is superior to the baseline (simple random selection of flights).

Variable Selection

From the data exploration charts (Figures 10.4 and 10.5) and from the coefficient table for the flights delay model (Table 10.8), it appears that several of the predictors could be dropped or coded differently. Additionally, we look at the number of flights in different categories to identify categories with very few or no flights—such categories are candidates for removal or merger (see Table 10.9).

TABLE 10.9 NUMBER OF FLIGHTS BY CARRIER AND ORIGIN

	BWI	DCA	IAD	Total
CO		94		94
DH		27	524	551
DL		388		388
MQ		295		295
OH	30			30
RU	115	162	131	408
UA			31	31
US		404		404
Total	145	1370	686	2201

First, we find that most carriers depart from a single airport (DCA): For those that depart from all three airports, the delay rates are similar regardless of airport. We therefore drop the departure airport distinction by excluding Origin dummies and find that the model performance and fit is not harmed. We also drop the destination airport for a practical reason: Not all carriers fly to all airports. Our model would then be invalid for prediction in nonexistent combinations of carrier and destination airport. We also try grouping carriers, day of week, and hour of day into fewer categories that are more distinguishable with respect to delays. For example, Sundays and Mondays seem to have a similar rate of delays, which differs from the lower rate on Tuesday–Saturday. We therefore group the days of week into Sunday + Monday and Other, resulting in a single dummy variable.

Finally, we try an automated variable selection approach, by using regularization with L1 penalty. The regularized model includes only seven predictors and has the advantage of being more parsimonious.

Table 10.10 displays the estimated smaller model, with its validation confusion matrix and AIC. Figure 10.7 presents the cumulative gains chart on the validation set. It can be seen that this model competes well with the larger model in terms of classification accuracy and lift, while using much less information.

We therefore conclude with a seven-predictor model that requires only knowledge of the carrier, the day of week, the hour of the day, and whether it is likely that there will be a delay due to weather. However, this weather variable refers to actual weather at flight time, not a forecast, and is not known in advance! If the aim is to predict in advance whether a particular flight will be delayed, a model without Weather must be used. In contrast, if the goal is profiling (describing) delayed vs. ontime flights, we can keep Weather in the model to allow evaluating the impact of the other factors while holding weather constant [that is, (approximately) comparing days with weather delays to days without weather delays].

TABLE 10.10 LOGISTIC REGRESSION MODEL WITH FEWER PREDICTORS

code for logistic regression with fewer predictors

```
delays_df = pd.read_csv('FlightDelays.csv')
delays_df['isDelayed'] = [1 if status == 'delayed' else 0
                          for status in delays_df['Flight Status']]
delays_df['CRS_DEP_TIME'] = [round(t / 100) for t in delays_df['CRS_DEP_TIME']]
delays_red_df = pd.DataFrame({
    'Sun_Mon' : [1 if d in (1, 7) else 0 for d in delays_df.DAY_WEEK],
    'Weather' : delays_df.Weather,
    'CARRIER_CO_MQ_DH_RU' : [1 if d in ("CO", "MQ", "DH", "RU") else 0
                             for d in delays_df.CARRIER],
    'MORNING' : [1 if d in (6, 7, 8, 9) else 0 for d in delays_df.CRS_DEP_TIME],
    'NOON' : [1 if d in (10, 11, 12, 13) else 0 for d in delays_df.CRS_DEP_TIME],
    'AFTER2P' : [1 if d in (14, 15, 16, 17, 18) else 0 for d in delays_df.CRS_DEP_TIME],
    'EVENING' : [1 if d in (19, 20) else 0 for d in delays_df.CRS_DEP_TIME],
    'isDelayed' : [1 if status == 'delayed' else 0 for status in delays_df['Flight Status']],
})

X = delays_red_df.drop(columns=['isDelayed'])
y = delays_red_df['isDelayed']
classes = ['ontime', 'delayed']

# split into training and validation
train_X, valid_X, train_y, valid_y = train_test_split(X, y, test_size=0.4,
                                                      random_state=1)

logit_red = LogisticRegressionCV(penalty="l1", solver='liblinear', cv=5)
logit_red.fit(train_X, train_y)

print('intercept ', logit_red.intercept_[0])
print(pd.DataFrame({'coeff': logit_red.coef_[0]}, index=X.columns).transpose())

print('AIC', AIC_score(valid_y, logit_red.predict(valid_X), df=len(train_X.columns) + 1))

# confusion matrix
classificationSummary(valid_y, logit_red.predict(valid_X), class_names=classes)
```

Modified output

```
intercept  -2.2872748179110203
       Sun_Mon  Weather  CARRIER_CO_MQ_DH_RU  MORNING   NOON  AFTER2P  EVENING
coeff    0.578    4.978                1.299   -0.583 -0.666   -0.055    0.561

AIC 934.6153607819033

Confusion Matrix (Accuracy 0.8343)

       Prediction
 Actual  ontime delayed
 ontime     711       3
delayed     143      24
```

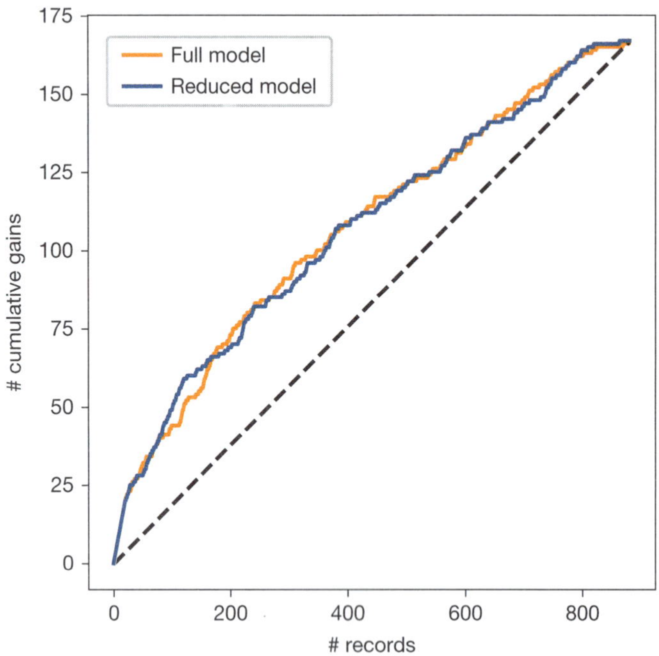

FIGURE 10.7 CUMULATIVE GAINS CHART FOR LOGISTIC REGRESSION MODEL WITH FEWER PREDICTORS ON THE VALIDATION SET. RESULT FOR THE FULL MODEL IS SHOWN FOR COMPARISON

```
logit_reg_proba = logit_red.predict_proba(valid_X)
red_result = pd.DataFrame({'actual': valid_y,
                           'p(0)': [p[0] for p in logit_reg_proba],
                           'p(1)': [p[1] for p in logit_reg_proba],
                           'predicted': logit_red.predict(valid_X),
                          })
red_result = red_result.sort_values(by=['p(1)'], ascending=False)

ax = gainsChart(full_result.actual, color='C1', figsize=[5, 5])
gainsChart(red_result.actual, color='C0', ax=ax)
```

To conclude, based on the model built from January 2004 data, the highest chance of an ontime flight from DC to New York is on Tuesday–Saturday in the morning on Delta, Comair, United, or USAirways. And clearly, good weather is advantageous!

APPENDIX: USING STATMODELS

An alternative to `scikit`'s *LogisticRegression* is method *sm.glm* in `statmodels`. The latter produces a more extensive output of the statistical properties of the model, suitable for non-predictive tasks such as statistical inference. Table 10.11 shows the same model for loan acceptance from Table 10.2 run using *sm.glm*. For regularization, use `statmodels` method *Logit.fit_regularized*, which uses a penalty based on $\sum_{j=1}^{p} |\beta_j|$ (L1 penalty).

TABLE 10.11 LOGISTIC REGRESSION MODEL FOR LOAN ACCEPTANCE USING STATMODELS

code for fitting a logistic regression model using Statmodels

```
# same initial preprocessing and creating dummies

# add constant column
bank_df = sm.add_constant(bank_df, prepend=True)

y = bank_df['Personal_Loan']
X = bank_df.drop(columns=['Personal_Loan'])

# partition data
train_X, valid_X, train_y, valid_y = train_test_split(X, y, test_size=0.4, random_state=1)

# use GLM (general linear model) with the binomial family to fit a logistic regression
logit_reg = sm.GLM(train_y, train_X, family=sm.families.Binomial())
logit_result = logit_reg.fit()
logit_result.summary()
```

Output

```
                 Generalized Linear Model Regression Results
==============================================================================
Dep. Variable:          Personal_Loan   No. Observations:                 3000
Model:                            GLM   Df Residuals:                     2987
Model Family:                Binomial   Df Model:                           12
Link Function:                  logit   Scale:                          1.0000
Method:                          IRLS   Log-Likelihood:                -340.15
Date:                Tue, 19 Feb 2019   Deviance:                       680.30
Time:                        18:00:41   Pearson chi2:                 8.10e+03
No. Iterations:                     8   Covariance Type:             nonrobust
===============================================================================================
                                   coef    std err          z      P>|z|     [0.025     0.975]
-----------------------------------------------------------------------------------------------
const                          -12.5634      2.336     -5.377      0.000    -17.143     -7.984
Age                             -0.0354      0.086     -0.412      0.680     -0.204      0.133
Experience                       0.0369      0.086      0.431      0.666     -0.131      0.205
Income                           0.0589      0.004     15.044      0.000      0.051      0.067
Family                           0.6128      0.103      5.931      0.000      0.410      0.815
CCAvg                            0.2408      0.060      4.032      0.000      0.124      0.358
Mortgage                         0.0010      0.001      1.301      0.193     -0.001      0.003
Securities_Account              -1.0305      0.422     -2.443      0.015     -1.857     -0.204
CD_Account                       3.6628      0.460      7.961      0.000      2.761      4.565
Online                          -0.6794      0.216     -3.140      0.002     -1.103     -0.255
CreditCard                      -0.9609      0.274     -3.507      0.000     -1.498     -0.424
Education_Graduate               4.2075      0.364     11.573      0.000      3.495      4.920
Education_Advanced/Professional  4.3580      0.365     11.937      0.000      3.642      5.074
```

PROBLEMS

10.1 Financial Condition of Banks. The file *Banks.csv* includes data on a sample of 20 banks. The "Financial Condition" column records the judgment of an expert on the financial condition of each bank. This outcome variable takes one of two possible values— *weak* or *strong*—according to the financial condition of the bank. The predictors are two ratios used in the financial analysis of banks: TotLns&Lses/Assets is the ratio of total loans and leases to total assets and TotExp/Assets is the ratio of total expenses to total assets. The target is to use the two ratios for classifying the financial condition of a new bank.

Run a logistic regression model (on the entire dataset) that models the status of a bank as a function of the two financial measures provided. Specify the *success* class as *weak* (this is similar to creating a dummy that is 1 for financially weak banks and 0 otherwise), and use the default cutoff value of 0.5.

a. Write the estimated equation that associates the financial condition of a bank with its two predictors in three formats:

i. The logit as a function of the predictors

ii. The odds as a function of the predictors

iii. The probability as a function of the predictors

b. Consider a new bank whose total loans and leases/assets ratio = 0.6 and total expenses/assets ratio = 0.11. From your logistic regression model, estimate the following four quantities for this bank (use Python to do all the intermediate calculations; show your final answers to four decimal places): the logit, the odds, the probability of being financially weak, and the classification of the bank (use cutoff = 0.5).

c. The cutoff value of 0.5 is used in conjunction with the probability of being financially weak. Compute the threshold that should be used if we want to make a classification based on the odds of being financially weak, and the threshold for the corresponding logit.

d. Interpret the estimated coefficient for the total loans & leases to total assets ratio (TotLns&Lses/Assets) in terms of the odds of being financially weak.

e. When a bank that is in poor financial condition is misclassified as financially strong, the misclassification cost is much higher than when a financially strong bank is misclassified as weak. To minimize the expected cost of misclassification, should the cutoff value for classification (which is currently at 0.5) be increased or decreased?

10.2 Identifying Good System Administrators. A management consultant is studying the roles played by experience and training in a system administrator's ability to complete a set of tasks in a specified amount of time. In particular, she is interested in discriminating between administrators who are able to complete given tasks within a specified time and those who are not. Data are collected on the performance of 75 randomly selected administrators. They are stored in the file *SystemAdministrators.csv*.

The variable Experience measures months of full-time system administrator experience, while Training measures the number of relevant training credits. The outcome variable Completed is either *Yes* or *No*, according to whether or not the administrator completed the tasks.

a. Create a scatter plot of Experience vs. Training using color or symbol to distinguish programmers who completed the task from those who did not complete it. Which predictor(s) appear(s) potentially useful for classifying task completion?

b. Run a logistic regression model with both predictors using the entire dataset as training data. Among those who completed the task, what is the percentage of programmers incorrectly classified as failing to complete the task?

c. To decrease the percentage in part (b), should the cutoff probability be increased or decreased?

d. How much experience must be accumulated by a programmer with 4 years of training before his or her estimated probability of completing the task exceeds 0.5?

10.3 Sales of Riding Mowers. A company that manufactures riding mowers wants to identify the best sales prospects for an intensive sales campaign. In particular, the manufacturer is interested in classifying households as prospective owners or nonowners on the basis of Income (in \$1000s) and Lot Size (in 1000 ft^2). The marketing expert looked at a random sample of 24 households, given in the file *RidingMowers.csv*. Use all the data to fit a logistic regression of ownership on the two predictors.

a. What percentage of households in the study were owners of a riding mower?

b. Create a scatter plot of Income vs. Lot Size using color or symbol to distinguish owners from nonowners. From the scatter plot, which class seems to have a higher average income, owners or nonowners?

c. Among nonowners, what is the percentage of households classified correctly?

d. To increase the percentage of correctly classified nonowners, should the cutoff probability be increased or decreased?

e. What are the odds that a household with a \$60K income and a lot size of 20,000 ft^2 is an owner?

f. What is the classification of a household with a \$60K income and a lot size of 20,000 ft^2? Use cutoff = 0.5.

g. What is the minimum income that a household with 16,000 ft^2 lot size should have before it is classified as an owner?

10.4 Competitive Auctions on eBay.com. The file *eBayAuctions.csv* contains information on 1972 auctions transacted on eBay.com during May–June 2004. The goal is to use these data to build a model that will distinguish competitive auctions from noncompetitive ones. A competitive auction is defined as an auction with at least two bids placed on the item being auctioned. The data include variables that describe the item (auction category), the seller (his or her eBay rating), and the auction terms that the seller selected (auction duration, opening price, currency, day of week of auction close). In addition, we have the price at which the auction closed. The goal is to predict whether or not an auction of interest will be competitive.

Data preprocessing. Create dummy variables for the categorical predictors. These include Category (18 categories), Currency (USD, GBP, Euro), EndDay (Monday–Sunday), and Duration (1, 3, 5, 7, or 10 days).

a. Create pivot tables for the mean of the binary outcome (Competitive?) as a function of the various categorical variables (use the original variables, not the dummies). Use the information in the tables to reduce the number of dummies that will be used in the model. For example, categories that appear most similar with respect to the distribution of competitive auctions could be combined.

b. Split the data into training (60%) and validation (40%) datasets. Run a logistic model with all predictors with a cutoff of 0.5.

c. If we want to predict at the start of an auction whether it will be competitive, we cannot use the information on the closing price. Run a logistic model with all predictors as above, excluding price. How does this model compare to the full model with respect to predictive accuracy?

d. Interpret the meaning of the coefficient for closing price. Does closing price have a practical significance? Is it statistically significant for predicting competitiveness of auctions? (Use a 10% significance level.)

e. Use stepwise regression as described in Section 6.4 to find the model with the best fit to the training data (highest accuracy). Which predictors are used?

f. Use stepwise regression to find the model with the highest accuracy on the validation data. Which predictors are used?

g. What is the danger of using the best predictive model that you found?

h. Explain how and why the best-fitting model and the best predictive models are the same or different.

i. Use regularized logistic regression with L1 penalty on the training data. Compare its selected predictors and classification performance to the best-fitting and best predictive models.

j. If the major objective is accurate classification, what cutoff value should be used?

k. Based on these data, what auction settings set by the seller (duration, opening price, ending day, currency) would you recommend as being most likely to lead to a competitive auction?

CHAPTER 11

Neural Nets

In this chapter, we describe neural networks, a flexible data-driven (albeit blackbox) method that can be used for classification, prediction and feature extraction, and is the basis for deep learning—a powerful technique that lies behind many artificial intelligence applications like image and voice recognition. We discuss the concepts of "nodes" and "layers" (input layers, output layers, and hidden layers) and how they connect to form the structure of the network. We then explain how a neural network is fitted to data using a numerical example. Because overfitting is a major danger with neural nets, we present a strategy for avoiding it. We describe the different parameters that a user must specify and explain the effect of each on the process. Finally, we move from a detailed description of a basic neural net to a more general discussion of the deeper and more complex neural nets that power deep learning.

Python

In this chapter, we will use pandas for data handling and `scikit-learn` for the models. We will also make use of the utility functions from the Python Utilities Functions Appendix. Use the following import statements for the Python code in this chapter.

import required functionality for this chapter

```
import pandas as pd
from sklearn.model_selection import train_test_split
from sklearn.neural_network import MLPClassifier
from dmba import classificationSummary
```

11.1 | INTRODUCTION

Neural networks, also called *artificial neural networks*, are models for classification and prediction. Complex and deep neural networks (deep learning) can also be used for unsupervised tasks such as feature extraction. The neural network is based on a model of biological activity in the brain, where neurons are interconnected and learn from experience. Neural networks mimic the way that human experts learn. The learning and memory properties of neural networks resemble the properties of human learning and memory, and they also have a capacity to generalize from particulars.

A number of successful applications have been reported in financial applications (see Trippi and Turban, 1996) such as bankruptcy predictions, currency market trading, picking stocks and commodity trading, detecting fraud in credit card and monetary transactions, and customer relationship management (CRM). There have also been a number of successful applications of neural nets in engineering applications. One of the best known is ALVINN, an autonomous vehicle driving application for normal speeds on highways. Using as input a 30×32 grid of pixel intensities from a fixed camera on the vehicle, the classifier provides the direction of steering. The outcome variable is a categorical one with 30 classes, such as *sharp left*, *straight ahead*, and *bear right*.

The main strength of neural networks is their high predictive performance. Their structure supports capturing very complex relationships between predictors and an outcome variable, which is often not possible with other predictive models.

11.2 | CONCEPT AND STRUCTURE OF A NEURAL NETWORK

The idea behind neural networks is to combine the predictor information in a very flexible way that captures complicated relationships among these variables and between them and the outcome variable. For instance, recall that in linear regression models, the form of the relationship between the outcome and the predictors is specified directly by the user (see Chapter 6). In many cases, the exact form of the relationship is very complicated, or is generally unknown. In linear regression modeling, we might try different transformations of the predictors, interactions between predictors, and so on, but the specified form of the relationship remains linear. In comparison, in neural networks the user is not required to specify the correct form. Instead, the network tries to learn about such relationships from the data. In fact, linear regression and logistic regression can be thought of as special cases of very simple neural networks that have only input and output layers and no hidden layers.

Although researchers have studied numerous different neural network architectures, the most successful applications of neural networks in data mining have been *multilayer feedforward networks*. These are networks in which there is an *input layer* consisting of nodes (sometimes called *neurons*) that simply accept the predictor values, and successive layers of nodes that receive input from the previous layers. The outputs of nodes in each layer are inputs to nodes in the next layer. The last layer is called the *output layer*. Layers between the input and output layers are known as *hidden layers*. A feedforward network is a fully connected network with a one-way flow and no cycles. Figure 11.1 shows a diagram for this architecture, with two hidden layers and one node in the output layer representing the outcome value to be predicted. In a classification problem with m classes, there would be m output nodes (or $m - 1$ output nodes, depending on the software).

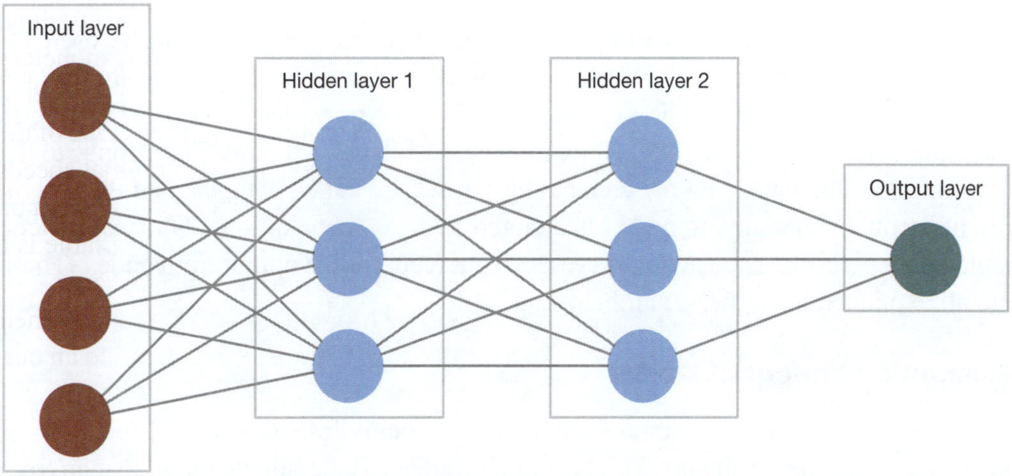

FIGURE 11.1 MULTILAYER FEEDFORWARD NEURAL NETWORK

11.3 | FITTING A NETWORK TO DATA

To illustrate how a neural network is fitted to data, we start with a very small illustrative example. Although the method is by no means operational in such a small example, it is useful for explaining the main steps and operations, for showing how computations are done, and for integrating all the different aspects of neural network data fitting. We will later discuss a more realistic setting.

Example 1: Tiny Dataset

Consider the following very small dataset. Table 11.1 includes information on a tasting score for a certain processed cheese. The two predictors are scores for fat and salt, indicating the relative presence of fat and salt in the particular cheese sample (where 0 is the minimum amount possible in the manufacturing process, and 1 the maximum). The outcome variable is the cheese sample's consumer taste preference, where *like* or *dislike* indicate whether the consumer likes the cheese or not.

TABLE 11.1 TINY EXAMPLE ON TASTING SCORES FOR SIX CONSUMERS WITH TWO PREDICTORS

Obs.	Fat score	Salt score	Acceptance
1	0.2	0.9	like
2	0.1	0.1	dislike
3	0.2	0.4	dislike
4	0.2	0.5	dislike
5	0.4	0.5	like
6	0.3	0.8	like

Figure 11.2 describes an example of a typical neural net that could be used for predicting cheese preference (*like/dislike*) by new consumers, based on these data. We numbered the nodes in the example from N1 to N6. Nodes N1 and N2 belong to the input layer, nodes N3 to N5 belong to the hidden layer, and node N6 belongs to the output layer. The values on the connecting arrows are called *weights*, and the weight on the arrow from node *i* to node *j* is denoted by $w_{i,j}$. The additional *bias* parameters, denoted by θ_j (inside each node), serve as an intercept for the output from node *j*. These are all explained in further detail below.

Computing Output of Nodes

We discuss the input and output of the nodes separately for each of the three types of layers (input, hidden, and output). The main difference is the function used to map from the input to the output of the node.

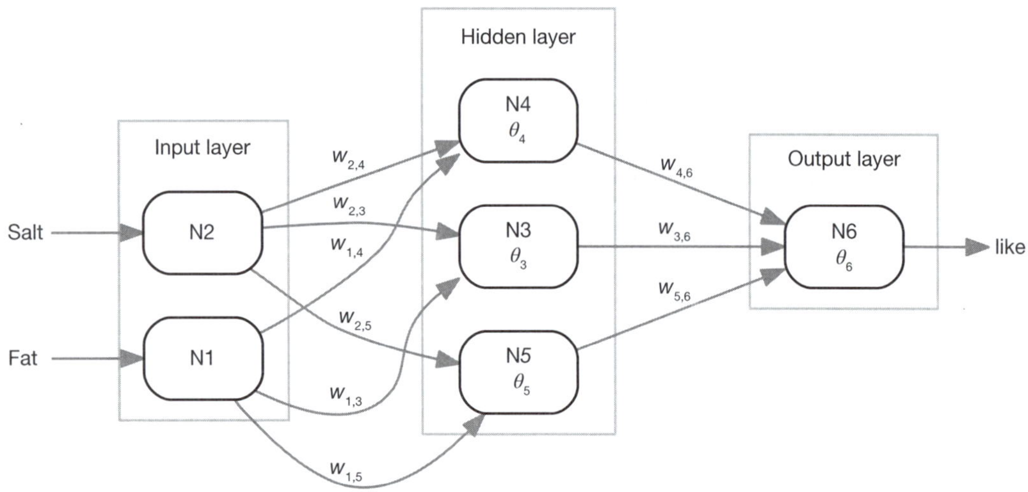

FIGURE 11.2 NEURAL NETWORK FOR THE TINY EXAMPLE. RECTANGLES REPRESENT NODES ("NEURONS"), $w_{i,j}$ ON ARROWS ARE WEIGHTS, AND θ_j INSIDE NODES ARE BIAS VALUES

Input nodes take as input the values of the predictors. Their output is the same as the input. If we have p predictors, the input layer will usually include p nodes. In our example, there are two predictors, and therefore the input layer (shown in Figure 11.2) includes two nodes, each feeding into each node of the hidden layer. Consider the first record: The input into the input layer is Fat = 0.2 and Salt = 0.9, and the output of this layer is also $x_1 = 0.2$ and $x_2 = 0.9$.

Hidden layer nodes take as input the output values from the input layer. The hidden layer in this example consists of three nodes, each receiving input from all the input nodes. To compute the output of a hidden layer node, we compute a weighted sum of the inputs and apply a certain function to it. More formally, for a set of input values $x_1, x_2, \ldots, x_p$, we compute the output of node j by taking the weighted sum[1] $\theta_j + \sum_{i=1}^{p} w_{ij}x_i$, where $\theta_j, w_{1,j}, \ldots, w_{p,j}$ are weights that are initially set randomly, then adjusted as the network "learns." Note that θ_j, also called the *bias* of node j, is a constant that controls the level of contribution of node j.

In the next step, we take a function g of this sum. The function g, also called a *transfer function* or *activation function* is some monotone function. Examples include the linear function $[g(s) = bs]$, an exponential function $[g(s) = \exp(bs)]$, and a logistic/sigmoidal function $[g(s) = 1/1 + e^{-s}]$. This last function used to be by far the most popular one in neural networks. Its practical value arises from the fact that it has a squashing effect on very small or very large values but is almost linear in the range where the value of the function is between 0.1 and 0.9. Deep learning uses mostly the ReLU (rectified linear unit) activation function or variants of it. This function is identical to the linear function, but set to zero for $s < 0$.

If we use a logistic activation function, we can write the output of node j in the hidden layer as

$$\text{Output}_j = g\left(\theta_j + \sum_{i=1}^{p} w_{ij}x_i\right) = \frac{1}{1 + e^{-\left(\theta_j + \sum_{i=1}^{p} w_{ij}x_i\right)}}. \tag{11.1}$$

Initializing the Weights and Bias The values of θ_j and w_{ij} are initialized to small, usually random, numbers around zero. Such values represent a state of no knowledge by the network, similar to a model with no predictors. The initial weights are used in the first round of training.

Returning to our example, suppose that the initial bias and weights for node N3 are $\theta_3 = -0.3$, $w_{1,3} = 0.05$, and $w_{2,3} = 0.01$ (as shown in Figure 11.3). Using the logistic function, we can compute the output of node N3 in the hidden layer (using the first record) as

[1]Other options exist for combining inputs, such as taking the maximum or minimum of the weighted inputs rather than their sum, but they are much less popular.

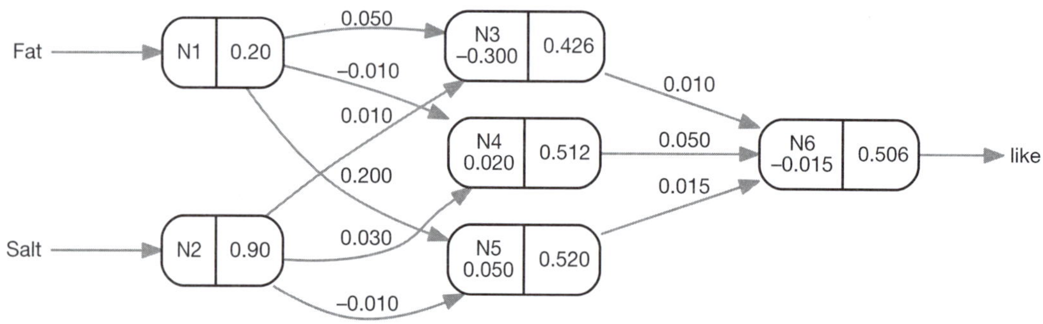

FIGURE 11.3 COMPUTING NODE OUTPUTS (VALUES ARE ON RIGHT SIDE WITHIN EACH NODE) USING THE FIRST RECORD IN THE TINY EXAMPLE AND A LOGISTIC FUNCTION

$$\text{Output}_{N3} = \frac{1}{1 + e^{-[-0.3+(0.05)(0.2)+(0.01)(0.9)]}} = 0.43.$$

Figure 11.3 shows the initial weights, bias, inputs, and outputs for the first record in our tiny example. If there is more than one hidden layer, the same calculation applies, except that the input values for the second, third, and so on, hidden layers would be the output of the preceding hidden layer. This means that the number of input values into a certain node is equal to the number of nodes in the preceding layer. (If there was an additional hidden layer in our example, its nodes would receive input from the three nodes in the first hidden layer.)

Finally, the output layer obtains input values from the (last) hidden layer. It applies the same function as above to create the output. In other words, it takes a weighted sum of its input values and then applies the function g. In our example, output node N6 receives input from the three hidden layer nodes. We can compute the output of this node by

$$\text{Output}_{N6} = \frac{1}{1 + e^{-[-0.015+(0.01)(0.43)+(0.05)(0.51)+(0.015)(0.52)]}} = 0.506.$$

This is the propensity $P(Y = like)$ for this record. For classification, we use a cutoff value (for a binary outcome) on the propensity. Using a cutoff of 0.5, we would classify this record as *like*. For applications with more than two classes, we choose the output node with the largest value.

Relation to Linear and Logistic Regression Consider a neural network with a single output node and no hidden layers. For a dataset with p predictors, the output node receives $x_1, x_2, \ldots, x_p$, takes a weighted sum of these, and applies the g function. The output of the neural network is therefore $g\left(\theta + \sum_{i=1}^{p} w_i x_i\right)$.

First, consider a numerical outcome variable Y. If g is the identity function [$g(s) = s$], the output is simply

$$\hat{Y} = \theta + \sum_{i=1}^{p} w_i x_i.$$

This is exactly equivalent to the formulation of a multiple linear regression! This means that a neural network with no hidden layers, a single output node, and an identity function g searches only for linear relationships between the outcome and the predictors.

Now consider a binary output variable Y. If g is the logistic function, the output is simply

$$\hat{P}(Y = 1) = \frac{1}{1 + e^{-\left(\theta + \sum_{i=1}^{p} w_i x_i\right)}},$$

which is equivalent to the logistic regression formulation!

In both cases, although the formulation is equivalent to the linear and logistic regression models, the resulting estimates for the bias and weights (*coefficients* in linear and logistic regression) can differ, because the estimation method is different. The neural net estimation method is different from *least squares*, the method used to calculate coefficients in linear regression, or the *maximum likelihood* method used in logistic regression. We explain below the method by which the neural network learns.

Preprocessing the Data

When using a logistic activation function (option *activation = 'logistic'* in scikit-learn), neural networks perform best when the predictors and outcome variable are on a scale of [0, 1]. For this reason, all variables should be scaled to a [0, 1] interval before entering them into the network. For a numerical variable X that takes values in the range $[a, b]$ where $a < b$, we normalize the measurements by subtracting a and dividing by $b - a$. The normalized measurement is then

$$X_{\text{norm}} = \frac{X - a}{b - a}.$$

Note that if $[a, b]$ is within the [0, 1] interval, the original scale will be stretched.

If a and b are unknown, we can estimate them from the minimal and maximal values of X in the data. Even if new data exceed this range by a small amount, yielding normalized values slightly lower than 0 or larger than 1, this will not affect the results much.

For binary variables, no adjustment is needed other than creating dummy variables. For categorical variables with m categories, if they are ordinal in nature, a choice of m

fractions in [0, 1] should reflect their perceived ordering. For example, if four ordinal categories are equally distant from each other, we can map them to [0, 0.25, 0.5, 1]. If the categories are nominal, transforming into $m - 1$ dummies is a good solution.

Another operation that improves the performance of the network is to transform highly skewed predictors. In business applications, there tend to be many highly right-skewed variables (such as income). Taking a log transform of a right-skewed variable (before converting to a [0, 1] scale) will usually spread out the values more symmetrically.

Another common sigmoidal function is the hyperbolic tangent (option *activation* = *'tanh'* in scikit-learn). When using this function, it is usually better to scale predictors to a [−1, 1] scale.

Training the Model

Training the model means estimating θ_j and w_{ij} (bias and weights) that lead to the best predictive results. The process that we described earlier (Section 11.1) for computing the neural network output for a record is repeated for all records in the training set. For each record, the model produces a prediction which is then compared with the actual outcome value. Their difference is the error for the output node. However, unlike least squares or maximum likelihood, where a global function of the errors (e.g., sum of squared errors) is used for estimating the coefficients, in neural networks, the estimation process uses the errors iteratively to update the estimated parameters (bias and weights).

In particular, the error for the output node is distributed across all the hidden nodes that led to it, so that each node is assigned "responsibility" for part of the error. Each of these node-specific errors is then used for updating the weights and bias values.

Back Propagation of Error The most popular method for using model errors to update weights ("learning") is an algorithm called *back propagation*. As the name implies, errors are computed from the last layer (the output layer) back to the hidden layers.

Let us denote by $\hat{y}_k$ the output from output node k. y_k is 1 or 0 depending on whether the actual class of the observation coincides with node k's label or not (e.g., in Figure 11.3, for a person with output class "like" we have $y_6 = 0$ and $y_1 = 1$). The error associated with output node k is computed by

$$\text{err}_k = \hat{y}_k(1 - \hat{y}_k)(y_k - \hat{y}_k).$$

Notice that this is similar to the ordinary definition of an error $(y_k - \hat{y}_k)$ multiplied by a correction factor. The bias and weights are then updated as follows:

$$\theta_j^{\text{new}} = \theta_j^{\text{old}} + l \times \text{err}_j, \tag{11.2}$$

$$w_{i,j}^{\text{new}} = w_{i,j}^{\text{old}} + l \times \text{err}_j,$$

where l is a *learning rate* or *weight decay* parameter, a constant ranging typically between 0 and 1, which controls the amount of change in weights from one iteration to the next.

In our example, the error associated with output node N6 for the first record is (0.506)(1 – 0.506)(1 – 0.506) = 0.123. This error is then used to compute the errors associated with the hidden layer nodes, and those bias and weights are updated accordingly using a formula similar to equation (11.2).

Two methods for updating the bias and weights are *case updating* and *batch updating*. In case updating, the parameter values are updated after each record is run through the network (called a *trial*). For example, if we used case updating in the tiny example, the bias and weights would first be updated after running record 1 as follows: Using a learning rate of 0.5, $\theta_6, w_{3,6}, w_{4,6}$, and $w_{5,6}$ are updated to

$$\begin{aligned}
\theta_6 &= -0.015 + (0.5)(0.123) = 0.047, \\
w_{3,6} &= 0.01 + (0.5)(0.123) = 0.072, \\
w_{4,6} &= 0.05 + (0.5)(0.123) = 0.112, \\
w_{5,6} &= 0.015 + (0.5)(0.123) = 0.077.
\end{aligned}$$

These new values are next updated after the second record is run through the network, the third, and so on, until all records are used. This is called one *epoch*, *sweep*, or *iteration* through the data. Typically, there are many iterations.

In batch updating, the entire training set is run through the network before each updating of the bias and weights takes place. In that case, the errors err_k in the updating equation is the sum of the errors from all records. In practice, case updating tends to yield more accurate results than batch updating, but requires a longer run time. This is a serious consideration, since even in batch updating, hundreds or even thousands of sweeps through the training data are executed.

When does the updating stop? The most common conditions are one of the following:

1. When the new values of the bias and weights are only incrementally different from those of the preceding iteration
2. When the misclassification rate reaches a required threshold
3. When the limit on the number of runs is reached

Python has several packages for neural nets. For basic neural networks, the most common one is `scikit-learn`. For deep learning applications, you can use `keras`, `pytorch`, or `tensorflow`.

Let us examine the output from running a neural network on the tiny data. Following Figures 11.2 and 11.3, we used a single hidden layer with three nodes. We used `scikit-learn`'s *MLPClassifier* in this example.[2] The final bias and weights and the network's predictions are shown in Table 11.2. Figure 11.4 shows the final bias and weights in a format similar to that of our previous diagrams.

The first part of the output shows the estimated parameters that connect the input layer and the hidden layer and then those connecting the hidden layer and output layer. *Intercepts* are the *bias nodes* and correspond to θ_3, θ_4, θ_5, and θ_6. The *Intercepts* and *Weights* are used to compute the output of the hidden layer nodes. They were computed iteratively after choosing a random initial set of values (like the set we chose in Figure 11.3). We use the bias and weights in the way we described earlier to compute the hidden layer's output. For instance, for the first record, the output of our previous node N3 is:

$$\text{Output}_{\text{N3}} = \frac{1}{1 + e^{-[0.134 + (-1.307)(0.2) + (-0.044)(0.9)]}} = 0.458.$$

Similarly, we can compute the output from the two other hidden nodes for the same record and get $\text{Output}_{\text{N4}} = 0.233$ and $\text{Output}_{\text{N5}} = 0.253$. The second set of intercepts and weights are for connecting the hidden and output layer nodes. To compute the probability (=propensity) for the *like* output node (N6) for the first record, we use the outputs from the hidden layer that we computed above, and get

$$\begin{aligned}\text{Output}_{\text{N6}} &= \frac{1}{1 + e^{-[14.307 + (-0.273)(0.458) + (-9.012)(0.233) + (-17.635)(0.253)]}}\\ &= 1.00.\end{aligned}$$

(More accurately, using all decimals shown in Table 11.2 leads to $\text{Output}_{\text{N6}} = 0.9995$.)

The probabilities for the other five records are computed in the same manner, replacing the input value in the computation of the hidden layer outputs and then plugging these outputs into the computation for the output layer. These probabilities, and classifications based on a cutoff of 0.5, are shown at the bottom of Table 11.2. The confusion matrix based on these classifications is given in Table 11.3. We can see that the network correctly classifies all six records.

[2]Method *MLPClassifier* can use different optimization functions. While beyond the scope of this chapter, we note that the default solver = 'adam' is suitable for relatively large datasets (with at least thousands of training records) in terms of both training time and validation performance. For small datasets, solver = 'lbfgs' can converge faster and perform better.

TABLE 11.2 NEURAL NETWORK WITH A SINGLE HIDDEN LAYER (THREE NODES) FOR THE TINY DATA EXAMPLE

code for running a neural network

```
example_df = pd.read_csv('TinyData.csv')

predictors = ['Fat', 'Salt']
outcome = 'Acceptance'

X = example_df[predictors]
y = example_df[outcome]
classes = sorted(y.unique())

clf = MLPClassifier(hidden_layer_sizes=(3), activation='logistic', solver='lbfgs',
                    random_state=1)
clf.fit(X, y)
clf.predict(X)

# Network structure
print('Intercepts')
print(clf.intercepts_)

print('Weights')
print(clf.coefs_)

# Prediction
print(pd.concat([
    example_df,
    pd.DataFrame(clf.predict_proba(X), columns=classes)
], axis=1))
```

Output

```
Intercepts
[array([0.13368045, 4.07247552, 7.00768104]),
 array([14.30748676])]
Weights
[array([
    [ -1.30656481,  -4.20427792, -13.29587332],
    [ -0.04399727,  -4.91606924,  -6.03356987]
]),
array([
    [ -0.27348313],
    [ -9.01211573],
    [-17.63504694]
])]

   Fat  Salt Acceptance   dislike      like
0  0.2   0.9       like  0.000490  0.999510
1  0.1   0.1    dislike  0.999994  0.000006
2  0.2   0.4    dislike  0.999741  0.000259
3  0.2   0.5    dislike  0.997368  0.002632
4  0.4   0.5       like  0.002133  0.997867
5  0.3   0.8       like  0.000075  0.999925
```

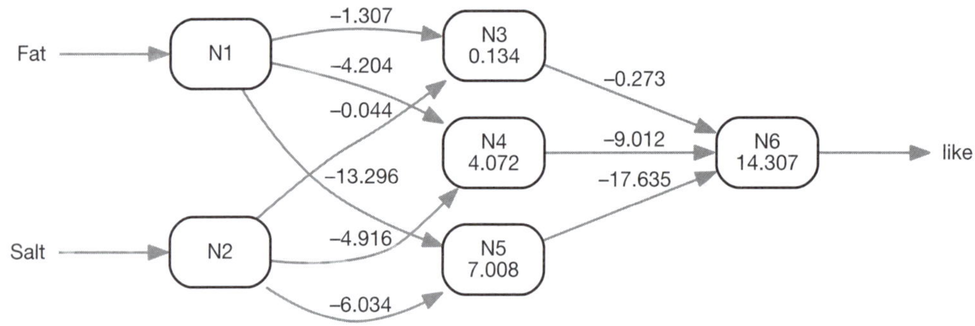

FIGURE 11.4 NEURAL NETWORK FOR THE TINY EXAMPLE WITH FINAL WEIGHTS AND BIAS VALUES (VALUES FROM TABLE 11.2).

TABLE 11.3 CONFUSION MATRIX FOR THE TINY EXAMPLE

code for the confusion matrix

```
classificationSummary(y, clf.predict(X), class_names=classes)
```

Output

```
Confusion Matrix (Accuracy 1.0000)

       Prediction
 Actual dislike    like
dislike       3       0
   like       0       3
```

Example 2: Classifying Accident Severity

Let's apply the network training process to some real data: US automobile accidents that have been classified by their level of severity as *no injury*, *injury*, or *fatality*. A firm might be interested in developing a system for quickly classifying the severity of an accident, based on initial reports and associated data in the system (some of which rely on GPS-assisted reporting). Such a system could be used to assign emergency response team priorities. Table 11.4 shows a small extract (10 records, 4 predictor variables) from a US government database.

The explanation of the four predictor variables and outcome variable is given in Table 11.5. For the analysis, we converted ALCHL_I to a 0/1 dummy variable (1 = presence of alcohol) and created four dummies for SUR_COND. This gives us a total of seven predictors.

With the exception of alcohol involvement and a few other variables in the larger database, most of the variables are ones that we might reasonably expect to be available

TABLE 11.4 SUBSET FROM THE ACCIDENTS DATA, FOR A HIGH-FATALITY REGION

Obs.	ALCHL_I	PROFIL_I_R	SUR_COND	VEH_INVL	MAX_SEV_IR
1	1	1	1	1	1
2	2	1	1	1	0
3	2	1	1	1	1
4	1	1	1	1	0
5	2	1	1	1	2
6	2	0	1	1	1
7	2	0	1	3	1
8	2	0	1	4	1
9	2	0	1	2	0
10	2	0	1	2	0

TABLE 11.5 DESCRIPTION OF VARIABLES FOR AUTOMOBILE ACCIDENT EXAMPLE

ALCHL_I	Presence (1) or absence (2) of alcohol
PROFIL_I_R	Profile of the roadway: level (1), other (0)
SUR_COND	Surface condition of the road: dry (1), wet (2), snow/slush (3), ice (4), unknown (9)
VEH_INVL	Number of vehicles involved
MAX_SEV_IR	Presence of injuries/fatalities: no injuries (0), injury (1), fatality (2)

at the time of the initial accident report, before accident details and severity have been determined by first responders. A data mining model that could predict accident severity on the basis of these initial reports would have value in allocating first responder resources.

To use a neural net architecture for this classification problem, we use seven nodes in the input layer, one for each of the seven predictors, and three neurons (one for each class) in the output layer. We use a single hidden layer and experiment with the number of nodes. If we increase the number of nodes from one to five and examine the resulting confusion matrices, we find that two nodes gives a good balance between improving the predictive performance on the training set without deteriorating the performance on the validation set. (Networks with more than two nodes in the hidden layer performed as well as the two-node network, but add undesirable complexity.) Table 11.6 shows the Python code and performance for the accidents data. We see that classes 0 and 1 are perfectly classified in both the training and validation data. However, class 2 has a high rate of misclassification.

Our results can depend on how we set the different parameters, and there are a few pitfalls to avoid. We discuss these next.

Avoiding Overfitting

A weakness of the neural network is that it can easily overfit the data, causing the error rate on validation data (and most important, on new data) to be too large. It is therefore important to limit the number of training iterations and not to over-train on the data

TABLE 11.6 A NEURAL NETWORK WITH TWO NODES IN THE HIDDEN LAYER (ACCIDENTS DATA)

code for running and evaluating a neural net on the accidents data

```
accidents_df = pd.read_csv('accidentsnn.csv')
input_vars = ['ALCHL_I', 'PROFIL_I_R', 'VEH_INVL']

accidents_df.SUR_COND = accidents_df.SUR_COND.astype('category')
accidents_df.MAX_SEV_IR = accidents_df.MAX_SEV_IR.astype('category')

# convert the categorical data into dummy variables
# exclude the column for SUR_COND 9 = unknown
processed = pd.get_dummies(accidents_df, columns=['SUR_COND'])
processed = processed.drop(columns=['SUR_COND_9'])

outcome = 'MAX_SEV_IR'
predictors = [c for c in processed.columns if c != outcome]

# partition data
X = processed[predictors]
y = processed[outcome]
train_X, valid_X, train_y, valid_y = train_test_split(X, y, test_size=0.4,
                                                      random_state=1)

# train neural network with 2 hidden nodes
clf = MLPClassifier(hidden_layer_sizes=(2), activation='logistic', solver='lbfgs',
                    random_state=1)
clf.fit(train_X, train_y.values)

# training performance (use idxmax to revert the one-hot-encoding)
classificationSummary(train_y, clf.predict(train_X))

# validation performance
classificationSummary(valid_y, clf.predict(valid_X))
```

Output

```
Training set
Confusion Matrix (Accuracy 0.8664)

       Prediction
Actual   0   1   2
     0 331   0   1
     1   0 180   0
     2  30  49   8

Validation set
Confusion Matrix (Accuracy 0.8550)

       Prediction
Actual   0   1   2
     0 218   0   1
     1   0 119   0
     2  24  33   5
```

(e.g., in Python's *MLPClassify()* method you can control the number of iterations using argument *max_iter*). As in classification and regression trees, overfitting can be detected by examining the performance on the validation set, or better, on a cross-validation set, and seeing when it starts deteriorating, while the training set performance is still improving. This approach is used in some algorithms to limit the number of training iterations. The validation error decreases in the early iterations of the training but after a while, it begins to increase. The point of minimum validation error is a good indicator of the best number of iterations for training, and the weights at that stage are likely to provide the best error rate in new data.

Using the Output for Prediction and Classification

When the neural network is used for predicting a numerical outcome variable, *MLPRegressor()* uses an identity activation function (i.e., no activation function). Both predictor and outcome variables should be scaled to a [0, 1] interval before training the network. The output will therefore also be on a [0, 1] scale. To transform the prediction back to the original y units, which were in the range $[a, b]$, we multiply the network output by $b - a$ and add a.

In the case of a binary outcome ($m = 2$), we saw that *MLPClassifier()* uses a single output node to produce $P(Y = 1)$. The *predict_proba()* method returns probabilities for both classes. Although we typically use a cutoff of 0.5 with other classifiers, in neural networks there is a tendency for values to cluster around 0.5 (from above and below). An alternative is to use the validation set to determine a cutoff that produces reasonable predictive performance.

When *MLPClassifier* is used for classification and we have $m > 2$ classes, we use in general a network with m output nodes, one for each class. How do we translate these m outputs into a classification rule? Usually, the output node with the largest value (largest probability) determines the net's classification.

Scikit-learn's *MLPClassifier* can also be used for classifying a multi-class outcome, where classes are not mutually exclusive. This means that for each record more than one class can take the value of 1 (e.g., the variable Race). In this case, *MLPClassifier* produces class probabilities that do not necessarily add up to 1.

11.4 | REQUIRED USER INPUT

One of the time-consuming and complex aspects of training a model using back propagation is that we first need to decide on a network architecture. This means specifying the number of hidden layers and the number of nodes in each layer. The usual procedure is to make intelligent guesses using past experience and to do several trial-and-error runs on different architectures. Algorithms exist that grow the number of nodes selectively during training or trim them in a manner analogous to what is done in classification and regression trees (see Chapter 9). Research continues on such methods. As of now, no automatic method seems clearly superior to the trial-and-error approach. A few general guidelines for choosing an architecture follow.

Number of hidden layers: The most popular choice for the number of hidden layers is one. A single hidden layer is usually sufficient to capture even very complex relationships between the predictors.

Size of hidden layer: The number of nodes in the hidden layer also determines the level of complexity of the relationship between the predictors that the network captures. The trade-off is between under- and overfitting. On the one hand, using too few nodes might not be sufficient to capture complex relationships (recall the special cases of a linear relationship such as in linear and logistic regression, in the extreme case of zero nodes or no hidden layer). On the other hand, too many nodes might lead to overfitting. A rule of thumb is to start with p (number of predictors) nodes and gradually decrease or increase while checking for overfitting. The number of hidden layers and the size of each hidden layer can be specified in scikit-learns' *MLPClassifier()* and *MLPRegressor()* methods using argument *hidden_layer_sizes*.

Number of output nodes: For a categorical outcome with m classes, the number of nodes should equal m or $m - 1$. For a numerical outcome, typically a single output node is used unless we are interested in predicting more than one function.

In addition to the choice of architecture, the user should pay attention to the *choice of predictors*. Since neural networks are highly dependent on the quality of their input, the choice of predictors should be done carefully, using domain knowledge, variable selection, and dimension reduction techniques before using the network. We return to this point in the discussion of advantages and weaknesses.

A key parameter that the user can control is the *learning rate* (a.k.a. weight decay), l, which is used primarily to avoid overfitting, by down-weighting new information. This helps to tone down the effect of outliers on the weights and avoids getting stuck in local optima. This parameter typically takes a value in the range [0, 1]. Berry and Linoff (2000) suggest starting with a large value (moving away from the random initial weights, thereby "learning quickly" from the data) and then slowly decreasing it as the iterations progress and as the weights are more reliable. Han and Kamber (2001) suggest the more concrete rule of thumb of setting $l = 1/(\text{current number of iterations})$. This means that at the start, $l = 1$, during the second iteration it is $l = 0.5$, and then it keeps decaying toward $l = 0$. In `scikit-learn`, you can set the learning rate in *MLPClassifier()* and *MLPRegressor* using argument *learning_rate*.

11.5 | EXPLORING THE RELATIONSHIP BETWEEN PREDICTORS AND OUTCOME

Neural networks are known to be "black boxes" in the sense that their output does not shed light on the patterns in the data that it models (like our brains). In fact, that is one of the biggest criticisms of the method. However, in some cases, it is possible to learn more about the relationships that the network captures by conducting a sensitivity analysis on the validation set. This is done by setting all predictor values to their mean and obtaining the network's prediction. Then, the process is repeated by setting each predictor sequentially to its minimum, and then maximum, value. By comparing the predictions from different levels of the predictors, we can get a sense of which predictors affect predictions more and in what way.

11.6 | DEEP LEARNING[3]

Neural nets had their greatest impact in the period from 2006 onward, with a paper published by AI researcher Geoffrey Hinton, and the rapidly growing popularity of what came to be called *deep learning*. Deep learning involves complex networks with many layers, incorporating processes for dimension reduction and feature discovery.

The data we have dealt with so far in this book are structured data, typically from organizational databases. The predictor variables, or features, that we think might be meaningful in predicting an outcome of interest already exist in our data. In predicting possible bank failure, for example, we would guess that certain financial ratios (return on assets, return on equity, etc.) might have predictive value. In predicting insurance fraud, we might guess that policy age would be predictive. We are not limited, of course, to variables that we know are predictive; sometimes a useful predictor emerges in an unexpected way.

With tasks like voice and image recognition, structured high-level predictor information like this is not available. All we have are individual "low-level" sound wave frequency and amplitude, or pixel values indicating intensity and color. You'd like to be able to tell the computer "just look for two eyes," and then provide further detail on how an eye appears—a small solid circle (pupil), surrounded by a ring (iris), surrounded by a white area. But, again, all the computer has are columns of (low-level) pixel values—you'd need to do a lot of extra work to define all the different (higher-level) pixel patterns that correspond to eyes. That's where deep learning comes in—it can "learn" how to identify these higher level features by itself.

[3]This section copyright ©2019 Datastats, LLC, Galit Shmueli, and Peter Gedeck. Used by permission.

Deep learning is a rapidly growing and evolving field, with many aspects that distinguish it from simpler predictive models. A full examination of the field of deep learning is beyond the scope of this book, but let us consider one key innovation in the area of algorithmic design that is associated with deep learning, and extends the ability of simple neural networks to perform the tasks of supervised and unsupervised learning that we have been discussing. This innovation is "convolution." Convolutional neural networks are used in many different applications and fields, and have enabled major advances in voice recognition, and the extraction of meaning from text via natural language processing (see Section 20.3, and the discussion of latent semantic indexing in Section 20.4 for a brief discussion of this topic). The basic idea of convolution is illustrated well in the context of image recognition.

Convolutional Neural Networks (CNNs)

In a standard neural network, each predictor gets its own weight at each layer of the network. A convolution, by contrast, selects a subset of predictors (pixels), and applies the same operation to the entire subset. It is this grouping that fosters the automated discovery of features. Recall that the data in image recognition tasks consist of a large number of pixel values, which, in a black and white image, range from 0 (black) to 255 (white). Since we are interested in detecting the black lines and shadings, we will reverse this to 255 for black and 0 for white.

Consider the line drawing in Figure 11.5, from a 1893 Funk and Wagnalls publication. Before the computer can begin to identify complex features like eyes, ears, noses, heads, it needs to master very simple features like lines and borders. For example, the line of the man's chin (Figure 11.6). In a typical convolution, the algorithm considers a small area at a time, say 3 pixels × 3 pixels. Figure 11.7 illustrates such a case. The line at the chin might look like the Figure 11.7a; The matrix in Figure 11.7b might be our pixel values. In its first convolution operation, the network could apply a filter operation by multiplying the pixel values by a 3×3 matrix of values that happens to be good at identifying vertical lines, such as the matrix in Figure 11.7c. The sum of the individual cell multiplications is $[0 + 0 + 0 + 200 + 225 + 225 + 0 + 0 + 0] = 650$. This is a relatively high value, compared to what another arrangement of the filter matrix might produce, because both the image section and the filter have high values in the center column and low values elsewhere. (A little experimentation with other 3×3 arrangements of three 1's and six 0's will reveal why this particular matrix is good at identifying vertical lines.) So, for this initial filter action, we can say that the filter has detected a vertical line, and thus we can consolidate the initial nine values of the image section into a single value (say a value between 0 and 1 to indicate the absence or presence of a vertical line).

FIGURE 11.5 LINE DRAWING, FROM A 1893 FUNK AND WAGNALLS PUBLICATION

FIGURE 11.6 FOCUSING ON THE LINE OF THE MAN'S CHIN

(a)

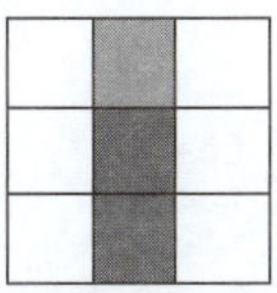

(b)

25	200	25
25	225	25
25	225	25

(c)

0	1	0
0	1	0
0	1	0

FIGURE 11.7 3×3 PIXELS REPRESENTATION OF LINE ON MAN'S CHIN USING SHADING (a) AND VALUES (b). THE FILTER (c) IDENTIFIES VERTICAL LINES

Local Feature Map

The "vertical line detector" filter moves across and down the original image matrix, recalculating and producing a single output each time. We end up with a smaller matrix;

how much smaller depends on whether the filter moves one pixel at a time, two, or more. While the original image values were simply individual pixel values, the new, smaller matrix is a map of features, answering the question "is there a vertical line in this section?"

The fact that the frame for the convolution is relatively small means that the overall operation can identify features that are local in character. We could imagine other local filters to discover horizontal lines, diagonal lines, curves, boundaries, etc. Further layers of different convolutional operations, taking these local feature maps as inputs, can then successively build up higher level features (corners, rectangles, circles, etc.).

A Hierarchy of Features

The first feature map is of vertical lines; we could repeat the process to identify horizontal lines and diagonal lines. We could also imagine filters to identify boundaries between light and dark areas. Then, having produced a set of initial low-level feature maps, the process could repeat, except this time working with these feature maps instead of the original pixel values. This iterative process continues, building up multidimensional matrix maps, or tensors, of higher and higher level features. As the process proceeds, the matrix representation of higher level features becomes somewhat abstract, so it is not necessarily possible to peer into a deep network and identify, for example, an eye.

In this process, the information is progressively compressed (simplified) as the higher level features emerge, as illustrated in Figure 11.8.

The Learning Process

How does the net know which convolutional operations to do? Put simply, it retains the ones that lead to successful classifications. In a basic neural net, the individual weights are what get adjusted in the iterative learning process. In a convolutional network, the net also learns which convolutions to do.

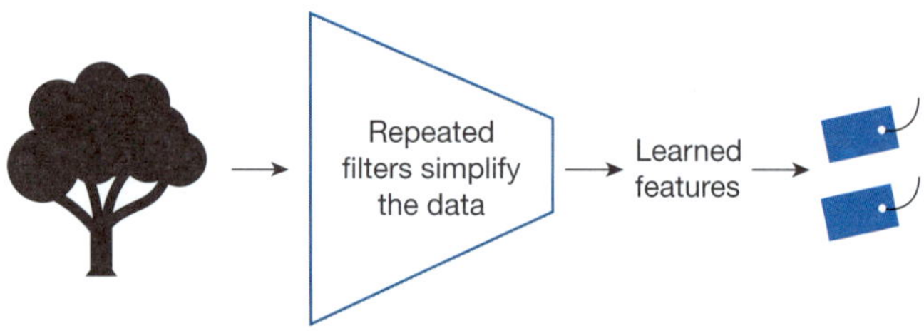

FIGURE 11.8 CONVOLUTION NETWORK PROCESS, SUPERVISED LEARNING: THE REPEATED FILTERING IN THE NETWORK CONVOLUTION PROCESS PRODUCES HIGH LEVEL FEATURES THAT FACILITATE THE APPLICATION OF CLASS LABELS, WHICH ARE COMPARED TO ACTUAL CLASSES TO TRAIN THE NETWORK

In a supervised learning setting, the network keeps building up features up to the highest level, which might be the goal of the learning task. Consider the task of deciding whether an image contains a face. You have a training set of labeled images with faces, and images without faces. The training process yields convolutions that identify hierarchies of features (e.g., edges > circles > eyes) that lead to success in the classification process. Other hierarchies that the net might conceivably encounter (e.g., edges > rectangles > houses) get dropped because they do not contribute to success in the identification of faces. Sometimes it is the case that the output of a single neuron in the network is an effective classifier, an indication that this neuron codes for the feature you are focusing on.

Unsupervised Learning

The most magical-seeming accomplishment of deep learning is its ability to identify features and, hence, objects in an unsupervised setting. Famous examples include identifying images with faces, and identifying dogs and cats in images (see, e.g., Le et al., 2012). How is this done?

One method is to use a so-called autoencoder network. These networks are trained to reproduce the input that is fed into them, by first creating a lower-dimension representation of the data and then using the created representation to reproduce the original data. The network is trained to retain the features that facilitate accurate reproduction of the input.

Viewed in the context of our image example, autoencoders have the high level architecture shown in Figure 11.9.

Up to the learned features point (the bottleneck in the image), the network is similar to the supervised network. Once it has developed the learned features, which are a low-dimension representation of the data, it expands those features into an image by a reverse process. The output image is compared to the input image, and if they are not similar, the network keeps working (using the same backpropagation method we

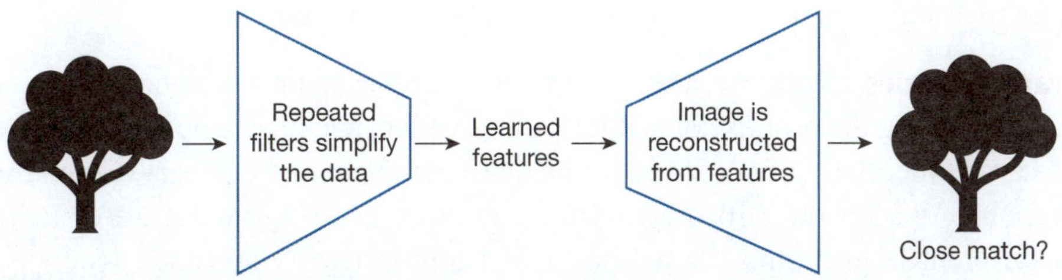

FIGURE 11.9 AUTOENCODER NETWORK PROCESS: THE REPEATED FILTERING IN THE NETWORK CONVOLUTION PROCESS PRODUCES HIGH LEVEL FEATURES THAT ARE THEN USED TO RECONSTRUCT THE IMAGE. THE RECONSTRUCTED IMAGE IS COMPARED TO THE ORIGINAL; NETWORK ARCHITECTURES THAT PRODUCE CLOSE MATCHES ARE SAVED AS THE NETWORK IS "TRAINED" WITHOUT BENEFIT OF LABELED DATA

discussed earlier). Once the network reliably produces output images that are similar to the inputs, the process stops.

This internal representation at the bottleneck now has useful information about the general domain (here, images) on which the network was trained. It turns out that the learned features (outputs of neurons at the bottleneck) that emerge in this process are often useful. Since the features can be considered a low-dimensional representation of the original data (similar in spirit to principal components in PCA—see Chapter 4), they can be used, for example, for building a supervised predictive model or for unsupervised clustering.

Conclusion

The key to convolutional networks' success is their ability to build, through iteration, multidimensional feature maps of great complexity (requiring substantial computing power and capacity) leading to the development of learned features that form a lower-dimension representation of the data. You can see that different convolutional architectures (e.g., types of filtering operations) would be suitable for different tasks. The AI community shares pre-trained networks that allow analysts to short-circuit the lengthy and complex training process that is required, as well as datasets that allow training and benchmarking to certain tasks (e.g., datasets of generic images in many different classes, images specifically of faces, satellite imagery, text data, voice data, etc.).

Finally, you may have heard of other types of deep learning. At the time of writing, Recurrent Neural Networks (RNN) are very popular. They are usually implemented with either Long Short-Term Memory (LSTM) or Gated Recurrent Units (GRU) building blocks. These networks are especially useful for data that are sequential in nature or have temporal behavior, such as time series, music, text and speech (where the order of words in a sentence matters) and user or robot behavior (e.g., clickstream data, where the order of a user's actions can be important). These networks' memory help them capture such sequences. In deciding whether to use such methods in a given business analytics application, a key consideration is their performance relative to other methods, and their required resources (in terms of data and computing).

Software Libraries With the advent of deep learning, neural nets have made great strides in fulfilling the promise of artificial intelligence, and have enjoyed a resurgence. At the same time, their architecture can be quite complex, and can vary, depending on the domain. As a result, software environments like TensorFlow, Keras, or PyTorch, where different architectures can be chosen and appropriate Python code generated, are very popular. Tensorflow has a nice visualization/demo of a simple neural network at https://playground.tensorflow.org.

11.7 | ADVANTAGES AND WEAKNESSES OF NEURAL NETWORKS

The most prominent advantage of neural networks is their good predictive performance. They are known to have high tolerance to noisy data and the ability to capture highly complicated relationships between the predictors and an outcome variable. Their weakest point is in providing insight into the structure of the relationship, hence their black-box reputation.

Several considerations and dangers should be kept in mind when using neural networks. First, although they are capable of generalizing from a set of examples, extrapolation is still a serious danger. If the network sees only records in a certain range, its predictions outside this range can be completely invalid.

Second, neural networks do not have a built-in variable selection mechanism. This means that there is a need for careful consideration of predictors. Combination with classification and regression trees (see Chapter 9) and other dimension reduction techniques (e.g., principal components analysis in Chapter 4) is often used to identify key predictors.

Third, the extreme flexibility of the neural network relies heavily on having sufficient data for training purposes. A related issue is that in classification problems, the network requires sufficient records of the minority class in order to learn it. This is achieved by oversampling, as explained in Chapter 2.

Finally, a practical consideration that can determine the usefulness of a neural network is the computation time. Neural networks are relatively heavy on computation time, requiring a longer runtime than other classifiers. This runtime grows greatly when the number of predictors is increased (as there will be many more weights to compute). In applications where real-time or near-real-time prediction is required, runtime should be measured to make sure that it does not cause unacceptable delay in the decision-making.

PROBLEMS

11.1 Credit Card Use. Consider the hypothetical bank data in Table 11.7 on consumers' use of credit card credit facilities. Create a small worksheet in Excel or a Python program to illustrate one pass through a simple neural network. (Randomly generate initial weight values.)

TABLE 11.7 DATA FOR CREDIT CARD EXAMPLE AND VARIABLE DESCRIPTIONS

Years	Salary	Used credit
4	43	0
18	65	1
1	53	0
3	95	0
15	88	1
6	112	1

Years: number of years the customer has been with the bank.

Salary: customer's salary (in thousands of dollars).

Used Credit: 1 = customer has left an unpaid credit card balance at the end of at least one month in the prior year, 0 = balance was paid off at the end of each month.

11.2 Neural Net Evolution. A neural net typically starts out with random values for bias and weights; hence, it produces essentially random predictions when presented with its first case. What is the key ingredient by which the net evolves to produce a more accurate prediction?

11.3 Car Sales. Consider the data on used cars (*ToyotaCorolla.csv*) with 1436 records and details on 38 attributes, including Price, Age, KM, HP, and other specifications. The goal is to predict the price of a used Toyota Corolla based on its specifications.

a. Fit a neural network model to the data. Use a single hidden layer with two nodes.

- Use predictors Age_08_04, KM, Fuel_Type, HP, Automatic, Doors, Quarterly_Tax, Mfr_Guarantee, Guarantee_Period, Airco, Automatic_airco, CD_Player, Powered_Windows, Sport_Model, and Tow_Bar.
- Use the scikit-learn transformer *MinMaxScaler()* to scale the data to the range [0, 1]. Use separate transformers for the input and output data. To create the dummy variables, use the pandas function *pd.get_dummies()*.

Record the RMS error for the training data and the validation data. Repeat the process, changing the number of hidden layers and nodes to {single layer with five nodes}, {two layers, five nodes in each layer}.

i. What happens to the RMS error for the training data as the number of layers and nodes increases?

ii. What happens to the RMS error for the validation data?

iii. Comment on the appropriate number of layers and nodes for this application.

11.4 Direct Mailing to Airline Customers. East–West Airlines has entered into a partnership with the wireless phone company Telcon to sell the latter's service via direct mail. The file *EastWestAirlinesNN.csv* contains a subset of a data sample of who has already received a test offer. About 13% accepted.

You are asked to develop a model to classify East–West customers as to whether they purchase a wireless phone service contract (outcome variable Phone_Sale). This model will be used to classify additional customers.

a. Run a neural net model on these data, using a single hidden layer with five nodes. Remember to first convert categorical variables into dummies and scale numerical predictor variables to 0–1 (use the scikit-learn transformer *MinMaxScaler()*). Create a decile lift chart for the training and validation sets. Interpret the meaning (in business terms) of the leftmost bar of the validation decile lift chart.

b. Comment on the difference between the training and validation lift charts.

c. Run a second neural net model on the data, this time setting the number of hidden nodes to 1. Comment now on the difference between this model and the model you ran earlier, and how overfitting might have affected results.

d. What sort of information, if any, is provided about the effects of the various variables?

CHAPTER 12

Discriminant Analysis

In this chapter, we describe the method of discriminant analysis, which is a model-based approach to classification. We discuss the main principle, where classification is based on the distance of a record from each of the class means. We explain the underlying measure of "statistical distance", which takes into account the correlation between predictors. The output of a discriminant analysis procedure generates estimated "classification functions", which are then used to produce classification scores that can be translated into classifications or propensities (probabilities of class membership). One can also directly integrate misclassification costs into the discriminant analysis setup, and we explain how this is achieved. Finally, we discuss the underlying model assumptions, the practical robustness to some assumption violations, and the advantages of discriminant analysis when the assumptions are reasonably met (e.g., the sufficiency of a small training sample).

Python

In this chapter, we will use `pandas` for data handling and `scikit-learn` for the models. We will also make use of the utility functions from the Python Utilities Functions Appendix. Use the following import statements for the Python code in this chapter.

import required functionality for this chapter

```
import numpy as np
import pandas as pd
from sklearn.discriminant_analysis import LinearDiscriminantAnalysis
import matplotlib.pylab as plt
from dmba import classificationSummary
```

12.1 | INTRODUCTION

Discriminant analysis is a classification method. Like logistic regression, it is a classical statistical technique that can be used for classification and profiling. It uses sets of measurements on different classes of records to classify new records into one of those classes (*classification*). Common uses of the method have been in classifying organisms into species and subspecies; classifying applications for loans, credit cards, and insurance into low- and high-risk categories; classifying customers of new products into early adopters, early majority, late majority, and laggards; classifying bonds into bond rating categories; classifying skulls of human fossils; as well as in research studies involving disputed authorship, decisions on college admission, medical studies involving alcoholics and nonalcoholics, and methods to identify human fingerprints. Discriminant analysis can also be used to highlight aspects that distinguish the classes (*profiling*).

We return to two examples that were described in earlier chapters, the Riding Mowers and Personal Loan Acceptance examples. In each of these, the outcome variable has two classes. We close with a third example involving more than two classes.

Example 1: Riding Mowers

We return to the example from Chapter 7, where a riding mower manufacturer would like to find a way of classifying families in a city into those likely to purchase a riding mower and those not likely to purchase one. A pilot random sample of 12 owners and 12 nonowners in the city is undertaken. The data are given in Table 7.1 in Chapter 7, and a scatter plot is shown in Figure 12.1. We can think of a linear classification rule as a line that separates the two-dimensional region into two parts, with most of the owners in one half-plane and most nonowners in the complementary half-plane. A good classification rule would separate the data so that the fewest points are misclassified: The line shown in Figure 12.1 seems to do a good job in discriminating between the two classes as it makes four misclassifications out of 24 points. Can we do better?

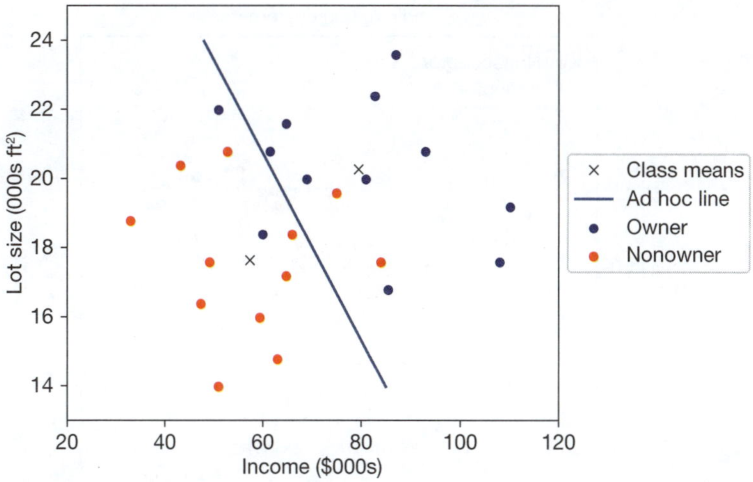

FIGURE 12.1 SCATTER PLOT OF LOT SIZE VS. INCOME FOR 24 OWNERS AND NONOWNERS OF RIDING MOWERS. THE (AD HOC) LINE TRIES TO SEPARATE OWNERS FROM NONOWNERS

Example 2: Personal Loan Acceptance

The riding mowers example is a classic example and is useful in describing the concept and goal of discriminant analysis. However, in today's business applications, the number of records is much larger, and their separation into classes is much less distinct. To illustrate this, we return to the Universal Bank example described in Chapter 9, where the bank's goal is to identify new customers most likely to accept a personal loan. For simplicity, we will consider only two predictor variables: the customer's annual income (Income, in $000s), and the average monthly credit card spending (CCAvg, in $000s). The first part of Figure 12.2 shows the acceptance of a personal loan by a subset of 200 customers from the bank's database as a function of Income and CCAvg. We use a logarithmic scale on both axes to enhance visibility because there are many points condensed in the low-income, low-CC spending area. Even for this small subset, the separation is not clear. The second figure shows all 5000 customers and the added complexity of dealing with large numbers of records.

12.2 | DISTANCE OF A RECORD FROM A CLASS

Finding the best separation between records involves measuring their distance from their class. The general idea is to classify a record to the class to which it is closest. Suppose that we are required to classify a new customer of Universal Bank as being an *acceptor* or a *nonacceptor* of their personal loan offer, based on an income of x. From the bank's database, we find that the mean income for loan acceptors was $144.75K and for nonacceptors $66.24K. We can use Income as a predictor of loan

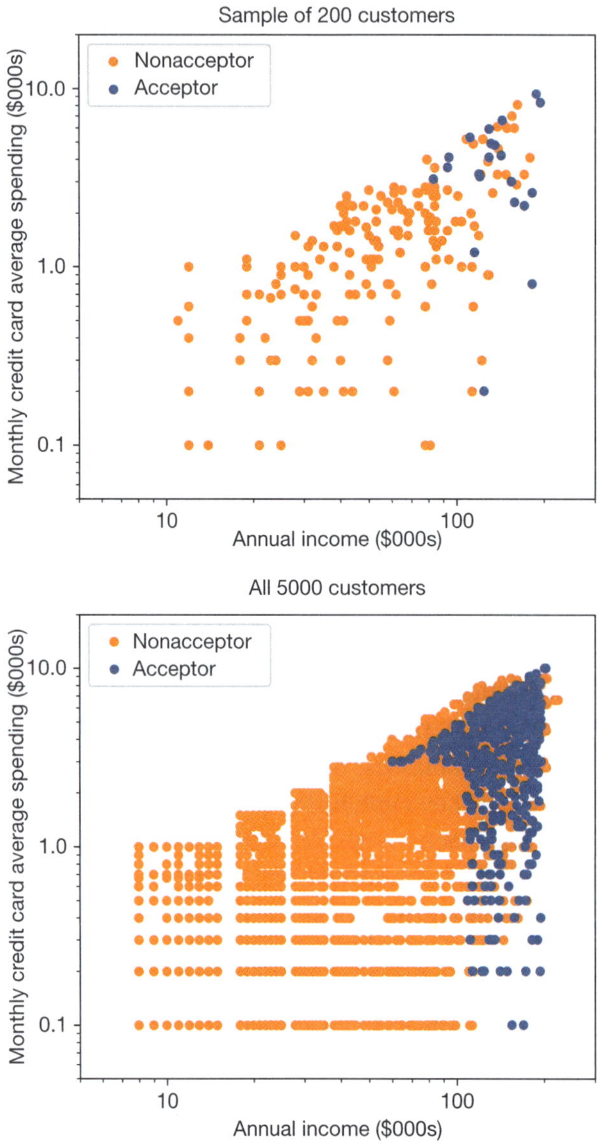

FIGURE 12.2 PERSONAL LOAN ACCEPTANCE AS A FUNCTION OF INCOME AND CREDIT CARD SPENDING FOR 5000 CUSTOMERS OF THE UNIVERSAL BANK (IN LOG SCALE)

acceptance via a simple *Euclidean distance rule*: If x is closer to the mean income of the acceptor class than to the mean income of the nonacceptor class, classify the customer as an *acceptor*; otherwise, classify the customer as a *nonacceptor*. In other words, if $|x - 144.75| < |x - 66.24|$, then classification = *acceptor*; otherwise, *nonacceptor*. Moving from a single predictor variable (income) to two or more predictor variables, the equivalent of the mean of a class is the *centroid* of a class. This is simply the vector of means $\overline{\mathbf{x}} = [\overline{x}_1, \ldots, \overline{x}_p]$. The Euclidean distance between a record with p measurements $\mathbf{x} = [x_1, \ldots, x_p]$ and the centroid $\overline{\mathbf{x}}$ is defined as the square root of the sum of the squared differences between the individual values and the means:

$$D_{\text{Euclidean}}(\mathbf{x}, \overline{\mathbf{x}}) = \sqrt{(x_1 - \overline{x}_1)^2 + \cdots + (x_p - \overline{x}_p)^2}. \tag{12.1}$$

Using the Euclidean distance has three drawbacks. First, the distance depends on the units we choose to measure the predictor variables. We will get different answers if we decide to measure income in dollars, for instance, rather than in thousands of dollars.

Second, Euclidean distance does not take into account the variability of the variables. For example, if we compare the variability in income in the two classes, we find that for acceptors, the standard deviation is lower than for nonacceptors (\$31.6K vs. \$40.6K). Therefore, the income of a new customer might be closer to the acceptors' mean income in dollars, but because of the large variability in income for nonacceptors, this customer is just as likely to be a nonacceptor. We therefore want the distance measure to take into account the variance of the different variables and measure a distance in standard deviations rather than in the original units. This is equivalent to z-scores.

Third, Euclidean distance ignores the correlation between the variables. This is often a very important consideration, especially when we are using many predictor variables to separate classes. In this case, there will often be variables, which by themselves are useful discriminators between classes, but in the presence of other predictor variables are practically redundant, as they capture the same effects as the other variables.

A solution to these drawbacks is to use a measure called *statistical distance* (or *Mahalanobis distance*). Let us denote by S the covariance matrix between the p variables. The definition of a statistical distance is

$$\begin{aligned} D_{\text{Statistical}}(\mathbf{x}, \overline{\mathbf{x}}) &= [\mathbf{x} - \overline{\mathbf{x}}]' S^{-1} [\mathbf{x} - \overline{\mathbf{x}}] \\ &= \left[(x_1 - \overline{x}_1), (x_2 - \overline{x}_2), \ldots, (x_p - \overline{x}_p)\right] S^{-1} \begin{bmatrix} x_1 - \overline{x}_1 \\ x_2 - \overline{x}_2 \\ \vdots \\ x_p - \overline{x}_p \end{bmatrix} \end{aligned} \tag{12.2}$$

(the notation $'$, which represents *transpose operation*, simply turns the column vector into a row vector). S^{-1} is the inverse matrix of S, which is the p-dimension extension to division. When there is a single predictor ($p = 1$), this formula reduces to a (squared) z-score calculation, since we subtract the mean and divide by the standard deviation. The statistical distance takes into account not only the predictor means, but also the spread of the predictor values and the correlations between the different predictors.

To compute a statistical distance between a record and a class, we must compute the predictor means (the centroid) and the covariances between each pair of predictors. These are used to construct the distances. The method of discriminant analysis uses statistical distance as the basis for finding a separating line (or, if there are more than two variables, a separating hyperplane) that is equally distant from the different class means.[1] It is based on measuring the statistical distances of a record to each of the classes and allocating it to the closest class. This is done through *classification functions*, which are explained next.

12.3 | FISHER'S LINEAR CLASSIFICATION FUNCTIONS

Linear classification functions were proposed in 1936 by the noted statistician R. A. Fisher as the basis for improved separation of records into classes. The idea is to find linear functions of the measurements that maximize the ratio of between-class variability to within-class variability. In other words, we would obtain classes that are very homogeneous and differ the most from each other. For each record, these functions are used to compute scores that measure the proximity of that record to each of the classes. A record is classified as belonging to the class for which it has the highest classification score (equivalent to the smallest statistical distance).

USING CLASSIFICATION FUNCTION SCORES TO CLASSIFY RECORDS

For each record, we calculate the value of the classification function (one for each class); whichever class' function has the highest value (= score) is the class assigned to that record. In scikit-learn's *LinearDiscriminantAnalysis* method, for a two-class problem, use the sign of the decision function to assign the predicted class: classify as "1" if positive and "0" if negative. In multi-class problems, assign to the class with the highest value.

The classification functions are estimated using software. For a two-class outcome, Scikit-learn's *LinearDiscriminantAnalysis()* method does not provide details for the class-specific linear classification functions. Instead, it returns the *difference* between the two individual classification functions as a decision function. For example, Table 12.1 shows the decision function obtained from running discriminant analysis on the riding mowers data, using two predictors. A negative decision score leads to a "0" classification, while a positive score leads to "1" classification. For more than two classes, individual decision functions are returned (see Section 12.7).

[1]An alternative approach finds a separating line or hyperplane that is "best" at separating the different clouds of points. In the case of two classes, the two methods coincide.

TABLE 12.1 DISCRIMINANT ANALYSIS FOR RIDING-MOWER DATA, DISPLAYING THE ESTIMATED CLASSIFICATION FUNCTIONS

code for linear discriminant analysis

```
mower_df = pd.read_csv('RidingMowers.csv')

da_reg = LinearDiscriminantAnalysis()
da_reg.fit(mower_df.drop(columns=['Ownership']), mower_df['Ownership'])

print('Coefficients', da_reg.coef_)
print('Intercept', da_reg.intercept_)
```

Output

```
Coefficients [[0.1002303  0.78518471]]
Intercept [-21.73876167]
```

To classify a family into the class of *owners* or *nonowners*, we use the classification functions to compute the family's classification scores: A family is classified into the class of *owners* if the owner function score is higher than the nonowner function score, and into *nonowners* if the reverse is the case. These functions are specified in a way that can be easily generalized to more than two classes. The values given for the functions are simply the weights to be associated with each variable in the linear function in a manner analogous to multiple linear regression. For instance, the first household has an income of \$60K and a lot size of 18.4K ft^2. The decision function is therefore $(0.1)(60) + (0.79)(18.4) - 21.74 = -1.28$. Since the value is negative, the household is (mis)classified by the model as a nonowner. Such calculations are done by the software and do not need to be done manually. For example, the scores and classifications for all 24 households produced by scikit-learns *LinearDiscriminantAnalysis* are given in Table 12.2.

TABLE 12.2 CLASSIFICATION SCORES, PREDICTED CLASSES, AND PROBABILITIES FOR RIDING-MOWER DATA

code for obtaining decision function, predicted classes, and probabilities

```
da_reg = LinearDiscriminantAnalysis()
da_reg.fit(mower_df.drop(columns=['Ownership']), mower_df['Ownership'])

result_df = mower_df.copy()
result_df['Dec. Function'] = da_reg.decision_function(mower_df.drop(columns=['Ownership']))
result_df['Prediction'] = da_reg.predict(mower_df.drop(columns=['Ownership']))
result_df['p(Owner)'] = da_reg.predict_proba(mower_df.drop(columns=['Ownership']))[:, 1]
result_df
```

(Continued)

TABLE 12.2 CLASSIFICATION SCORES, PREDICTED CLASSES, AND PROBABILITIES FOR RIDING-MOWER DATA (*Continued*)

Output

	Income	Lot_Size	Ownership	Dec. Function	Prediction	p(Owner)
1	60.0	18.4	Owner	-1.277545	Nonowner	0.217968
2	85.5	16.8	Owner	0.022032	Owner	0.505508
3	64.8	21.6	Owner	1.716152	Owner	0.847632
4	61.5	20.8	Owner	0.757244	Owner	0.680755
5	87.0	23.6	Owner	5.511634	Owner	0.995977
6	110.1	19.2	Owner	4.372141	Owner	0.987533
7	108.0	17.6	Owner	2.905362	Owner	0.948111
8	82.8	22.4	Owner	4.148445	Owner	0.984456
9	69.0	20.0	Owner	0.880823	Owner	0.706993
10	93.0	20.8	Owner	3.914499	Owner	0.980440
11	51.0	22.0	Owner	0.647047	Owner	0.656345
12	81.0	20.0	Owner	2.083587	Owner	0.889298
13	75.0	19.6	Nonowner	1.168131	Owner	0.762807
14	52.8	20.8	Nonowner	-0.114760	Nonowner	0.471342
15	64.8	17.2	Nonowner	-1.738661	Nonowner	0.149483
16	43.2	20.4	Nonowner	-1.391044	Nonowner	0.199241
17	84.0	17.6	Nonowner	0.499835	Owner	0.622420
18	49.2	17.6	Nonowner	-2.988180	Nonowner	0.047963
19	59.4	16.0	Nonowner	-3.222126	Nonowner	0.038342
20	66.0	18.4	Nonowner	-0.676163	Nonowner	0.337118
21	47.4	16.4	Nonowner	-4.110816	Nonowner	0.016130
22	33.0	18.8	Nonowner	-3.669689	Nonowner	0.024851
23	51.0	14.0	Nonowner	-5.634430	Nonowner	0.003560
24	63.0	14.8	Nonowner	-3.803519	Nonowner	0.021806

An alternative way for classifying a record into one of the classes is to compute the probability of belonging to each of the classes and assigning the record to the most likely class. If we have two classes, we need only compute a single probability for each record (of belonging to *owners*, for example). Using a cutoff of 0.5 is equivalent to assigning the record to the class with the highest classification score. The advantage of this approach is that we obtain propensities, which can be used for goals such as ranking: we sort the records in order of descending probabilities and generate lift curves.

Let us assume that there are m classes. To compute the probability of belonging to a certain class k, for a certain record i, we need to compute all the classification scores $c_1(i), c_2(i), \dots, c_m(i)$ and combine them using the following formula:

$$P[\text{record } i \text{ (with measurements } x_1, x_2, ..., x_p) \text{ belongs to class } k]$$

$$= \frac{e^{c_k(i)}}{e^{c_1(i)} + e^{c_2(i)} + \cdots + e^{c_m(i)}}.$$

These probabilities and their computation for the riding mower data are given in Table 12.2. In scikit-learn, *LinearDiscriminantAnalysis* provides scores (`decision_function`), classifications (`predict`), and propensities (`predict_proba`).

We now have three misclassifications, compared to four in our original (ad hoc) classification. This can be seen in Figure 12.3, which includes the line resulting from the discriminant model.[2]

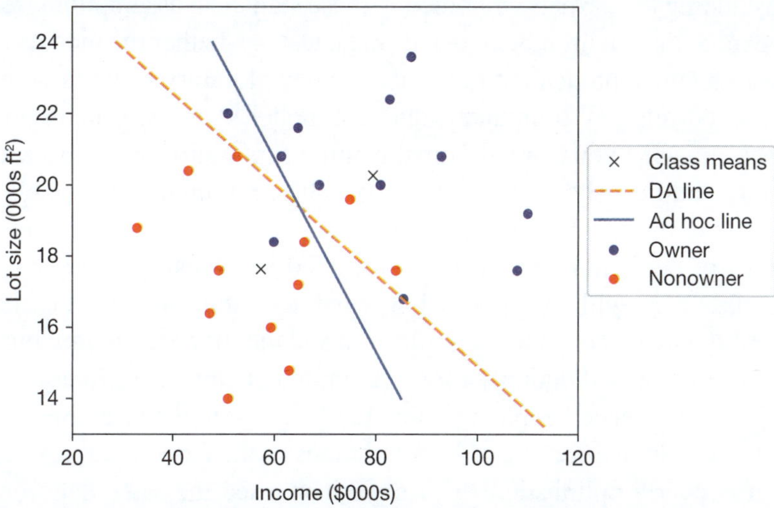

FIGURE 12.3 CLASS SEPARATION OBTAINED FROM THE DISCRIMINANT MODEL (COMPARED TO AD HOC LINE FROM FIGURE 12.1)

12.4 | CLASSIFICATION PERFORMANCE OF DISCRIMINANT ANALYSIS

The discriminant analysis method relies on two main assumptions to arrive at classification scores: First, it assumes that the predictor measurements in all classes come from a multivariate normal distribution. When this assumption is reasonably met, discriminant analysis is a more powerful tool than other classification methods, such as logistic regression. In fact, Efron (1975) showed that discriminant analysis is 30% more efficient than logistic regression if the data are multivariate normal, in the sense that we require 30% less records to arrive at the same results. In practice, it has been shown that this method is relatively robust to departures from normality in the sense that predictors can be non-normal and even dummy variables. This is true as long as the smallest class is sufficiently large (approximately more than 20 records). This method is also known to be sensitive to outliers in both the univariate space of single predictors and in the multivariate space. Exploratory analysis should therefore be used to locate extreme cases and determine whether they can be eliminated.

The second assumption behind discriminant analysis is that the correlation structure between the different predictors within a class is the same across classes. This can be roughly checked by computing the correlation matrix between the predictors separately for each class and comparing matrices. If the correlations differ substantially

[2]The slope of the line is given by $-a_1/a_2$ and the intercept is $-intercept/a_2$, where a_i are the coefficients of the decision function (e.g., here $\frac{21.74}{0.79} + \frac{-0.1}{0.79}$Lot_Size or 27.5 – 0.13Lot_Size).

across classes, the classifier will tend to classify records into the class with the largest variability. When the correlation structure differs significantly and the dataset is very large, an alternative is to use quadratic discriminant analysis.[3]

Notwithstanding the caveats embodied in these statistical assumptions, recall that in a predictive modeling environment, the ultimate test is whether the model works effectively. A reasonable approach is to conduct some exploratory analysis with respect to normality and correlation, train and evaluate a model, then, depending on classification accuracy and what you learned from the initial exploration, circle back and explore further whether outliers should be examined or choice of predictor variables revisited.

With respect to the evaluation of classification accuracy, we once again use the general measures of performance that were described in Chapter 5 (judging the performance of a classifier), with the principal ones based on the confusion matrix (accuracy alone or combined with costs) for classification and the lift chart for ranking. The same argument for using the validation set for evaluating performance still holds. For example, in the riding mowers example, families 1, 13, and 17 are misclassified. This means that the model yields an error rate of 12.5% for these data. However, this rate is a biased estimate—it is overly optimistic, because we have used the same data for fitting the classification functions and for estimating the error. Therefore, as with all other models, we test performance on a validation set that includes data that were not involved in estimating the classification functions.

To obtain the confusion matrix from a discriminant analysis, we either use the classification scores directly or the propensities (probabilities of class membership) that are computed from the classification scores. In both cases, we decide on the class assignment of each record based on the highest score or probability. We then compare these classifications to the actual class memberships of these records. This yields the confusion matrix.

12.5 | PRIOR PROBABILITIES

So far we have assumed that our objective is to minimize the classification error. The method presented above assumes that the chances of encountering a record from either class is the same. If the probability of encountering a record for classification in the future is not equal for the different classes, we should modify our functions to reduce our expected (long-run average) error rate. The modification is done as follows: Let us denote by p_j the prior or future probability of membership in class j (in the two-class

[3]In practice, quadratic discriminant analysis has not been found useful except when the difference in the correlation matrices is large and the number of records available for training and testing is large. The reason is that the quadratic model requires estimating many more parameters that are all subject to error [for m classes and p variables, the total number of parameters to be estimated for all the different correlation matrices is $mp(p + 1)/2$].

case we have p_1 and $p_2 = 1 - p_1$). We modify the classification function for each class by adding $\log(p_j)$. To illustrate this, suppose that the percentage of riding mower owners in the population is 15%, compared to 50% in the sample. This means that the model should classify fewer households as *owners*. To account for this distortion, we adjust the constant in the decision function from Table 12.1 and obtain the adjusted constants $-21.74 + \log(0.15) - \log(0.85) = -23.47$. To see how this can affect classifications, consider families 13 and 17, which were misclassified as an owner in the case involving equal probability of class membership. When we account for the lower probability of owning a mower in the population, both families are classified properly as a nonowner.

In addition to shifting the intercept, `scikit-learn` also uses the priors when averaging the class covariance matrices.

12.6 | UNEQUAL MISCLASSIFICATION COSTS

A second practical modification is needed when misclassification costs are not symmetrical. If the cost of misclassifying a class 1 record is very different from the cost of misclassifying a class 2 record, we may want to minimize the expected cost of misclassification rather than the simple error rate (which does not account for unequal misclassification costs). In the two-class case, it is easy to manipulate the classification functions to account for differing misclassification costs (in addition to prior probabilities). We denote by q_1 the cost of misclassifying a class 1 member (into class 2). Similarly, q_2 denotes the cost of misclassifying a class 2 member (into class 1). These costs are integrated into the constants of the classification functions by adding $\log(q_1)$ to the constant for class 1 and $\log(q_2)$ to the constant of class 2. To incorporate both prior probabilities and misclassification costs, add $\log(p_1 q_1)$ to the constant of class 1 and $\log(p_2 q_2)$ to that of class 2.

In practice, it is not always simple to come up with misclassification costs q_1 and q_2 for each class. It is usually much easier to estimate the *ratio of costs* q_2/q_1 (e.g., the cost of misclassifying a credit defaulter is 10 times more expensive than that of misclassifying a nondefaulter). Luckily, the relationship between the classification functions depends only on this ratio. Therefore, we can set $q_1 = 1$ and $q_2 = ratio$ and simply add $\log(q_2/q_1)$ to the constant for class 2.

12.7 | CLASSIFYING MORE THAN TWO CLASSES

Example 3: Medical Dispatch to Accident Scenes

Ideally, every automobile accident call to the emergency number 911 results in the immediate dispatch of an ambulance to the accident scene. However, in some cases the dispatch might be delayed (e.g., at peak accident hours or in some resource-strapped

TABLE 12.3 SAMPLE OF 20 AUTOMOBILE ACCIDENTS FROM THE 2001 DEPARTMENT OF TRANSPORTATION DATABASE. EACH ACCIDENT IS CLASSIFIED AS ONE OF THREE INJURY TYPES (NO-INJURY, NONFATAL, OR FATAL), AND HAS 10 MORE MEASUREMENTS (EXTRACTED FROM A LARGER SET OF MEASUREMENTS)

Accident #	Rush Hour	WRK_ ZONE	WKDY	INT_ HWY	LGTCON	LEVEL	SPD_ LIM	SUR_ COND	TRAF_ WAY	WEATHER	MAX_SEV
1	1	0	1	1	dark_light	1	70	ice	one_way	adverse	no-injury
2	1	0	1	0	dark_light	0	70	ice	divided	adverse	no-injury
3	1	0	1	0	dark_light	0	65	ice	divided	adverse	non-fatal
4	1	0	1	0	dark_light	0	55	ice	two_way	not_adverse	non-fatal
5	1	0	0	0	dark_light	0	35	snow	one_way	adverse	no-injury
6	1	0	1	0	dark_light	1	35	wet	divided	adverse	no-injury
7	0	0	1	1	dark_light	1	70	wet	divided	adverse	non-fatal
8	0	0	1	0	dark_light	1	35	wet	two_way	adverse	no-injury
9	1	0	1	0	dark_light	0	25	wet	one_way	adverse	non-fatal
10	1	0	1	0	dark_light	0	35	wet	divided	adverse	non-fatal
11	1	0	1	0	dark_light	0	30	wet	divided	adverse	non-fatal
12	1	0	1	0	dark_light	0	60	wet	divided	not_adverse	no-injury
13	1	0	1	0	dark_light	0	40	wet	two_way	not_adverse	no-injury
14	0	0	1	0	day	1	65	dry	two_way	not_adverse	fatal
15	1	0	0	0	day	0	55	dry	two_way	not_adverse	fatal
16	1	0	1	0	day	0	55	dry	two_way	not_adverse	non-fatal
17	1	0	0	0	day	0	55	dry	two_way	not_adverse	non-fatal
18	0	0	1	0	dark	0	55	ice	two_way	not_adverse	no-injury
19	0	0	0	0	dark	0	50	ice	two_way	adverse	no-injury
20	0	0	0	0	dark	1	55	snow	divided	adverse	no-injury

towns or shifts). In such cases, the 911 dispatchers must make decisions about which units to send based on sketchy information. It is useful to augment the limited information provided in the initial call with additional information in order to classify the accident as minor injury, serious injury, or death. For this purpose, we can use data that were collected on automobile accidents in the United States in 2001 that involved some type of injury. For each accident, additional information is recorded, such as day of week, weather conditions, and road type. Table 12.3 shows a small sample of records with 11 measurements of interest.

The goal is to see how well the predictors can be used to classify injury type correctly. To evaluate this, a reduced sample of 600 records was drawn (with categories combined so that most predictors are binary) and partitioned into training and validation sets, and a discriminant analysis was performed on the training data. The output structure is very similar to that for the two-class case. The only difference is that each record now has three classification functions (one for each injury type), and the confusion and error matrices are of size 3×3 to account for all the combinations of correct and incorrect classifications (see Table 12.4). The rule for classification is still to classify a record to the class that has the highest corresponding classification score. The classification scores are computed, as before, using the classification function coefficients. This can be seen in Table 12.5. For instance, the *no-injury* classification score for the first accident in the training set is $-0.89 + (0.03)(1) + (0.03)(0) + \cdots + (0.08)(1) = -0.46$. The *nonfatal* score is similarly computed as -0.96 and the *fatal* score as -5.94. Since the *no-injury* score is highest, this accident is (correctly) classified as having no injuries.

TABLE 12.4 DISCRIMINANT ANALYSIS FOR THE THREE-CLASS INJURY EXAMPLE: CLASSIFICATION FUNCTIONS AND CONFUSION MATRIX FOR TRAINING SET

code for running linear discriminant analysis on the accidents data

```
accidents_df = pd.read_csv('accidents.csv')
lda_reg = LinearDiscriminantAnalysis()
lda_reg.fit(accidents_df.drop(columns=['MAX_SEV']), accidents_df['MAX_SEV'])

print('Coefficients and intercept')
fct = pd.DataFrame([lda_reg.intercept_], columns=lda_reg.classes_, index=['constant'])
fct = fct.append(pd.DataFrame(lda_reg.coef_.transpose(), columns=lda_reg.classes_,
                              index=list(accidents_df.columns)[:-1]))
print(fct)
print()
classificationSummary(accidents_df['MAX_SEV'],
                      lda_reg.predict(accidents_df.drop(columns=['MAX_SEV'])),
                      class_names=lda_reg.classes_)
```

(Continued)

TABLE 12.4 DISCRIMINANT ANALYSIS FOR THE THREE-CLASS INJURY EXAMPLE: CLASSIFICATION FUNCTIONS AND CONFUSION MATRIX FOR TRAINING SET (*Continued*)

Output

```
Coefficients and intercept
                    fatal  no-injury  non-fatal
constant        -1.972659  -0.891172  -0.610471
RushHour        -0.996411   0.033430  -0.015774
WRK_ZONE        -0.457188   0.220012  -0.204480
WKDY            -1.471777   0.165707  -0.135404
INT_HWY          0.755344  -0.075816   0.060599
LGTCON_day       0.009515  -0.031421   0.030124
LEVEL            0.976626  -0.082717   0.063598
SPD_LIM          0.048033   0.004381  -0.005014
SUR_COND_dry    -5.999809  -0.164874   0.257895
TRAF_two_way     0.752985  -0.012844  -0.000048
WEATHER_adverse -6.596690   0.079166   0.032564

Confusion Matrix (Accuracy 0.5283)

           Prediction
   Actual      fatal no-injury non-fatal
    fatal          1         1         3
no-injury          6       114       172
non-fatal          6        95       202
```

TABLE 12.5 CLASSIFICATION SCORES, MEMBERSHIP PROBABILITIES, AND CLASSIFICATIONS FOR THE THREE-CLASS INJURY TRAINING DATASET

code for producing linear discriminant analysis scores and propensities

```
result = pd.concat([
    pd.DataFrame({'Classification': lda_reg.predict(accidents_df.drop(columns=['MAX_SEV'])),
                  'Actual': accidents_df['MAX_SEV']}),
    pd.DataFrame(lda_reg.decision_function(accidents_df.drop(columns=['MAX_SEV'])),
                 columns=['Score {}'.format(cls) for cls in lda_reg.classes_]),
    pd.DataFrame(lda_reg.predict_proba(accidents_df.drop(columns=['MAX_SEV'])),
                 columns=['Propensity {}'.format(cls) for cls in lda_reg.classes_])
], axis=1)

pd.set_option('precision',2)
pd.set_option('chop_threshold', .01)
print(result.head())
```

(*Continued*)

TABLE 12.5 CLASSIFICATION SCORES, MEMBERSHIP PROBABILITIES, AND CLASSIFICATIONS FOR THE THREE-CLASS INJURY TRAINING DATASET (*Continued*)

Output

```
  Classification      Actual  Score fatal  Score no-injury  Score non-fatal  \
0      no-injury   no-injury        -5.94            -0.46            -0.96
1      no-injury  non-fatal         -1.05            -0.46            -1.04
2      no-injury   no-injury        -7.88            -0.63            -0.77
3      no-injury   no-injury        -8.38            -0.54            -0.84
4      no-injury  non-fatal         -9.84            -0.50            -0.85

  Propensity fatal  Propensity no-injury  Propensity non-fatal
0         0.00e+00                  0.58                  0.42
1         2.86e-01                  0.43                  0.29
2         0.00e+00                  0.52                  0.48
3         0.00e+00                  0.55                  0.45
4         0.00e+00                  0.56                  0.44
```

We can also compute for each accident, the propensities (estimated probabilities) of belonging to each of the three classes using the same relationship between classification scores and probabilities as in the two-class case. For instance, the probability of the above accident involving nonfatal injuries is estimated by the model as

$$\frac{e^{-0.96}}{e^{-5.94} + e^{-0.46} + e^{-0.96}} = 0.42. \tag{12.3}$$

The probabilities of an accident involving no injuries or fatal injuries are computed in a similar manner. For the first accident in the training set, the highest probability is that of involving no injuries, and therefore it is classified as a *no-injury* accident.

12.8 | ADVANTAGES AND WEAKNESSES

Discriminant analysis is typically considered more of a statistical classification method than a data mining method. This is reflected in its absence or short mention in many data mining resources. However, it is very popular in social sciences and has shown good performance. The use and performance of discriminant analysis are similar to those of multiple linear regression. The two methods therefore share several advantages and weaknesses.

Like linear regression, discriminant analysis searches for the optimal weighting of predictors. In linear regression, weighting is with relation to the numerical outcome variable, whereas in discriminant analysis, it is with relation to separating the classes. Both use least squares for estimation and the resulting estimates are robust to local optima.

In both methods, an underlying assumption is normality. In discriminant analysis, we assume that the predictors are approximately from a multivariate normal distribution. Although this assumption is violated in many practical situations (such as with commonly-used binary predictors), the method is surprisingly robust. According to Hastie et al. (2001), the reason might be that data can usually support only simple separation boundaries, such as linear boundaries. However, for continuous variables that are found to be very skewed (as can be seen through a histogram), transformations such as the log transform can improve performance. In addition, the method's sensitivity to outliers commands exploring the data for extreme values and removing those records from the analysis.

An advantage of discriminant analysis as a classifier (like logistic regression in this respect) is that it provides estimates of single-predictor contributions.[4] This is useful for obtaining a ranking of predictor importance, and for variable selection.

Finally, the method is computationally simple, parsimonious, and especially useful for small datasets. With its parametric form, discriminant analysis makes the most out of the data and is therefore especially useful with small samples (as explained in Section 12.4).

PROBLEMS

12.1 Personal Loan Acceptance. Universal Bank is a relatively young bank growing rapidly in terms of overall customer acquisition. The majority of these customers are liability customers with varying sizes of relationship with the bank. The customer base of asset customers is quite small, and the bank is interested in expanding this base rapidly to bring in more loan business. In particular, it wants to explore ways of converting its liability customers to personal loan customers.

A campaign the bank ran for liability customers last year showed a healthy conversion rate of over 9% successes. This has encouraged the retail marketing department to devise smarter campaigns with better target marketing. The goal of our analysis is to model the previous campaign's customer behavior to analyze what combination of factors make a customer more likely to accept a personal loan. This will serve as the basis for the design of a new campaign.

The file *UniversalBank.csv* contains data on 5000 customers. The data include customer demographic information (e.g., age, income), the customer's relationship with the bank (e.g., mortgage, securities account), and the customer response to the last personal loan campaign (Personal Loan). Among these 5000 customers, only 480 (= 9.6%) accepted the personal loan that was offered to them in the previous campaign.

[4]Comparing predictor contribution requires normalizing all the predictors before running discriminant analysis. Then, compare each coefficient across the two classification functions: coefficients with large differences indicate a predictor with high separation power.

Partition the data (60% training and 40% validation) and then perform a discriminant analysis that models Personal Loan as a function of the remaining predictors (excluding zip code). Remember to turn categorical predictors with more than two categories into dummy variables first. Specify the success class as 1 (personal loan acceptance), and use the default cutoff value of 0.5.

a. Compute summary statistics for the predictors separately for loan acceptors and nonacceptors. For continuous predictors, compute the mean and standard deviation. For categorical predictors, compute the percentages. Are there predictors where the two classes differ substantially?

b. Examine the model performance on the validation set.

  i. What is the accuracy rate?

  ii. Is one type of misclassification more likely than the other?

  iii. Select three customers who were misclassified as *acceptors* and three who were misclassified as *nonacceptors*. The goal is to determine why they are misclassified. First, examine their probability of being classified as acceptors: is it close to the threshold of 0.5? If not, compare their predictor values to the summary statistics of the two classes to determine why they were misclassified.

c. As in many marketing campaigns, it is more important to identify customers who will accept the offer rather than customers who will not accept it. Therefore, a good model should be especially accurate at detecting acceptors. Examine the lift chart and decile-wise lift chart for the validation set and interpret them in light of this ranking goal.

d. Compare the results from the discriminant analysis with those from a logistic regression (both with cutoff 0.5 and the same predictors). Examine the confusion matrices, the lift charts, and the decile charts. Which method performs better on your validation set in detecting the acceptors?

e. The bank is planning to continue its campaign by sending its offer to 1000 additional customers. Suppose that the cost of sending the offer is $1 and the profit from an accepted offer is $50. What is the expected profitability of this campaign?

f. The cost of misclassifying a loan acceptor customer as a nonacceptor is much higher than the opposite misclassification cost. To minimize the expected cost of misclassification, should the cutoff value for classification (which is currently at 0.5) be increased or decreased?

12.2 Identifying Good System Administrators. A management consultant is studying the roles played by experience and training in a system administrator's ability to complete a set of tasks in a specified amount of time. In particular, she is interested in discriminating between administrators who are able to complete given tasks within a specified time and those who are not. Data are collected on the performance of 75 randomly selected administrators. They are stored in the file *SystemAdministrators.csv*.

Using these data, the consultant performs a discriminant analysis. The variable Experience measures months of full time system administrator experience, while Training measures number of relevant training credits. The dependent variable Completed is either *Yes* or *No*, according to whether or not the administrator completed the tasks.

a. Create a scatter plot of Experience vs. Training using color or symbol to differentiate administrators who completed the tasks from those who did not complete them. See if you can identify a line that separates the two classes with minimum misclassification.

b. Run a discriminant analysis with both predictors using the entire dataset as training data. Among those who completed the tasks, what is the percentage of administrators who are classified incorrectly as failing to complete the tasks?

c. Compute the two classification scores for an administrator with 4 months of experience and six credits of training. Based on these, how would you classify this administrator?

d. How much experience must be accumulated by an administrator with four training credits before his or her estimated probability of completing the tasks exceeds 0.5?

e. Compare the classification accuracy of this model to that resulting from a logistic regression with cutoff 0.5.

12.3 Detecting Spam E-mail (from the UCI Machine Learning Repository). A team at Hewlett-Packard collected data on a large number of e-mail messages from their postmaster and personal e-mail for the purpose of finding a classifier that can separate e-mail messages that are *spam* vs. *nonspam* (a.k.a. "ham"). The spam concept is diverse: It includes advertisements for products or websites, "make money fast" schemes, chain letters, pornography, and so on. The definition used here is "unsolicited commercial e-mail." The file *Spambase.csv* contains information on 4601 e-mail messages, among which 1813 are tagged "spam." The predictors include 57 attributes, most of them are the average number of times a certain word (e.g., mail, George) or symbol (e.g., #, !) appears in the e-mail. A few predictors are related to the number and length of capitalized words.

a. To reduce the number of predictors to a manageable size, examine how each predictor differs between the *spam* and *nonspam* e-mails by comparing the spam-class average and nonspam-class average. Which are the 11 predictors that appear to vary the most between *spam* and *nonspam* e-mails? From these 11, which words or signs occur more often in spam?

b. Partition the data into training and validation sets, then perform a discriminant analysis on the training data using only the 11 predictors.

c. If we are interested mainly in detecting spam messages, is this model useful? Use the confusion matrix, lift chart, and decile chart for the validation set for the evaluation.

d. In the sample, almost 40% of the e-mail messages were tagged as spam. However, suppose that the actual proportion of spam messages in these e-mail accounts is 10%. Compute the intercept of the classification function to account for this information.

e. A spam filter that is based on your model is used, so that only messages that are classified as *nonspam* are delivered, while messages that are classified as *spam* are quarantined. In this case, misclassifying a nonspam e-mail (as spam) has much heftier results. Suppose that the cost of quarantining a nonspam e-mail is 20 times that of not detecting a spam message. Compute the intercept of the classification functions to account for these costs (assume that the proportion of spam is reflected correctly by the sample proportion).

CHAPTER 13

Combining Methods: Ensembles and Uplift Modeling

In this chapter, we look at two useful approaches that combine methods for improving predictive power: *ensembles* and *uplift modeling*. An ensemble combines multiple supervised models into a "supermodel." The previous chapters in this part of the book introduced different supervised methods for prediction and classification. Earlier, in Chapter 5, we learned about evaluating predictive performance, which can be used to compare several models and choose the best one. An ensemble is based on the powerful notion of *combining models*. Instead of choosing a single predictive model, we can combine several models to achieve improved predictive accuracy. In this chapter, we explain the underlying logic of why ensembles can improve predictive accuracy and introduce popular approaches for combining models, including simple averaging, bagging, and boosting.

In *uplift modeling*, we combine supervised modeling with A–B testing, which is a simple type of a randomized experiment. We describe the basics of A–B testing and how it is used along with predictive models in persuasion messaging not to predict outcomes but to predict who should receive which message or treatment.

Python

In this chapter, we will use `pandas` for data handling and `scikit-learn` for the models. We will also make use of the utility functions from the Python Utilities Functions Appendix. Use the following import statements for the Python code in this chapter.

import required functionality for this chapter

```
import pandas as pd
from sklearn.model_selection import train_test_split
from sklearn.tree import DecisionTreeClassifier
from sklearn.ensemble import AdaBoostClassifier
from sklearn.ensemble import BaggingClassifier
from sklearn.ensemble import RandomForestClassifier
from dmba import classificationSummary
```

13.1 | ENSEMBLES[1]

Ensembles played a major role in the million-dollar Netflix Prize contest that started in 2006. At the time, Netflix, the largest DVD rental service in the United States, wanted to improve their movie recommendation system (from www.netflixprize.com):

> Netflix is all about connecting people to the movies they love. To help customers find those movies, we've developed our world-class movie recommendation system: Cinematch℠...And while Cinematch is doing pretty well, it can always be made better.

In a bold move, the company decided to share a large amount of data on movie ratings by their users, and set up a contest, open to the public, aimed at improving their recommendation system:

> We provide you with a lot of anonymous rating data, and a prediction accuracy bar that is 10% better than what Cinematch can do on the same training data set.

During the contest, an active leader-board showed the results of the competing teams. An interesting behavior started appearing: Different teams joined forces to create combined, or *ensemble* predictions, which proved more accurate than the individual predictions. The winning team, called "BellKor's Pragmatic Chaos" combined results from the "BellKor" and "Big Chaos" teams alongside additional members. In a 2010 article in *Chance* magazine, the Netflix Prize winners described the power of their ensemble approach:

---

[1] This and subsequent sections in this chapter copyright © 2019 Datastats, LLC, and Galit Shmueli. Used by permission.

An early lesson of the competition was the value of combining sets of predictions from multiple models or algorithms. If two prediction sets achieved similar RMSEs, it was quicker and more effective to simply average the two sets than to try to develop a new model that incorporated the best of each method. Even if the RMSE for one set was much worse than the other, there was almost certainly a linear combination that improved on the better set.

Why Ensembles Can Improve Predictive Power

The principle of combining methods is popular for reducing risk. For example, in finance, portfolios are created for reducing investment risk. The return from a portfolio is typically less risky, because the variation is smaller than each of the individual components.

In predictive modeling, "risk" is equivalent to variation in prediction error. The more our prediction errors vary, the more volatile our predictive model. Consider predictions from two different models for a set of n records. $e_{1,i}$ is the prediction error for the ith record by method 1 and $e_{2,i}$ is the prediction error for the same record by method 2.

Suppose that each model produces prediction errors that are, on average, zero (for some records the model over-predicts and for some it under-predicts, but on average the error is zero):

$$E(e_{1,i}) = E(e_{2,i}) = 0.$$

If, for each record, we take an average of the two predictions: $\overline{y}_i = \frac{\hat{y}_{1,i}+\hat{y}_{2,i}}{2}$, then the expected mean error will also be zero:

$$\begin{aligned} E\left(y_i - \overline{y}_i\right) &= E\left(y_i - \frac{\hat{y}_{1,i} + \hat{y}_{2,i}}{2}\right) \\ &= E\left(\frac{y_i - \hat{y}_{1,i}}{2} + \frac{y_i - \hat{y}_{2,i}}{2}\right) = E\left(\frac{e_{1,i} + e_{2,i}}{2}\right) = 0. \end{aligned} \tag{13.1}$$

This means that the ensemble has the same mean error as the individual models. Now let us examine the variance of the ensemble's prediction errors:

$$\text{Var}\left(\frac{e_{1,i} + e_{2,i}}{2}\right) = \frac{1}{4}(\text{Var}(e_{1,i}) + \text{Var}(e_{2,i})) + \frac{1}{4} \times 2\text{Cov}(e_{1,i}, e_{2,i}). \tag{13.2}$$

This variance can be lower than each of the individual variances $\text{Var}(e_{1,i})$ and $\text{Var}(e_{2,i})$ under some circumstances. A key component is the covariance (or equivalently, correlation) between the two prediction errors. The case of no correlation leaves us with a quantity that can be smaller than each of the individual variances.

The variance of the average prediction error will be even smaller when the two prediction errors are negatively correlated.

In summary, using an average of two predictions can potentially lead to smaller error variance, and therefore better predictive power. These results generalize to more than two methods; you can combine results from multiple prediction methods or classifiers.

THE WISDOM OF CROWDS

In his book *The Wisdom of Crowds*, James Surowiecki recounts how Francis Galton, a prominent statistician from the 19th century, watched a contest at a county fair in England. The contest's objective was to guess the weight of an ox. Individual contest entries were highly variable, but the mean of all the estimates was surprisingly accurate—within 1% of the true weight of the ox. On balance, the errors from multiple guesses tended to cancel one another out. You can think of the output of a predictive model as a more informed version of these guesses. Averaging together multiple guesses will yield a more precise answer than the vast majority of the individual guesses. Note that in Galton's story, there were a few (lucky) individuals who scored better than the average. An ensemble estimate will not always be more accurate than all the individual estimates in all cases, but it will be more accurate most of the time.

Simple Averaging

The simplest approach for creating an ensemble is to combine the predictions, classifications, or propensities from multiple models. For example, we might have a linear regression model, a regression tree, and a k-NN algorithm. We use each of the three methods to score, say, a test set. We then combine the three sets of results.

The three models can also be variations that use the same algorithm. For example, we might have three linear regression models, each using a different set of predictors.

Combining Predictions In prediction tasks, where the outcome variable is numerical, we can combine the predictions from the different methods simply by taking an average. In the above example, for each record in the test set, we have three predictions (one from each model). The ensemble prediction is then the average of the three values.

One alternative to a simple average is taking the median prediction, which would be less affected by extreme predictions. Another possibility is computing a weighted average, where weights are proportional to a quantity of interest. For instance, weights can be proportional to the accuracy of the model, or if different data sources are used, the weights can be proportional to the quality of the data.

Ensembles for prediction are useful not only in cross-sectional prediction, but also in time series forecasting (see Chapters 16–18). In forecasting, the same approach of combining future forecasts from multiple methods can lead to more precise predictions. One example is the weather forecasting application Forecast.io (www.forecast.io), which describes their algorithm as follows:

> Forecast.io is backed by a wide range of data sources, which are aggregated together statistically to provide the most accurate forecast possible for a given location.

Combining Classifications In the case of classification, combining the results from multiple classifiers can be done using "voting": For each record, we have multiple classifications. A simple rule would be to choose the most popular class among these classifications. For example, we might use a classification tree, a naive Bayes classifier, and discriminant analysis for classifying a binary outcome. For each record we then generate three predicted classes. Simple voting would choose the most common class among the three.

As in prediction, we can assign heavier weights to scores from some models, based on considerations such as model accuracy or data quality. This would be done by setting a "majority rule" that is different from 50%.

Combining Propensities Similar to predictions, propensities can be combined by taking a simple (or weighted) average. Recall that some algorithms, such as naive Bayes (see Chapter 8), produce biased propensities and should therefore not be simply averaged with propensities from other methods.

Bagging

Another form of ensembles is based on averaging across multiple random data samples. *Bagging*, short for "bootstrap aggregating," comprises two steps:

1. Generate multiple random samples (by sampling with replacement from the original data)—this method is called "bootstrap sampling."
2. Running an algorithm on each sample and producing scores.

Bagging improves the performance stability of a model and helps avoid overfitting by separately modeling different data samples and then combining the results. It is therefore especially useful for algorithms such as trees and neural networks.

Boosting

Boosting is a slightly different approach to creating ensembles. Here the goal is to directly improve areas in the data where our model makes errors, by forcing the model to pay more attention to those records. The steps in boosting are:

1. Fit a model to the data.
2. Draw a sample from the data so that misclassified records (or records with large prediction errors) have higher probabilities of selection.

3. Fit the model to the new sample.
4. Repeat Steps 2–3 multiple times.

Bagging and Boosting in Python

Although bagging and boosting can be applied to any data mining method, most applications are for trees, where they have proved extremely effective. In Chapter 9, we described random forests, an ensemble based on bagged trees. We illustrated a random forest implementation for the personal loan example. `scikit-learn` has a variety of methods to combine classifiers (models for predicting categorical outcomes) and regressors (models for predicting numerical outcomes) using bagging or boosting. Here, we will demonstrate this for decision tree classifiers. Table 13.1 shows the Python code and output producing a bagged tree and a boosted tree for the personal loan data, and how they are used to generate classifications for the validation set. In this example, we see that bagging and boosting both produce better validation accuracy than the single tree.

TABLE 13.1 EXAMPLE OF BAGGING AND BOOSTING CLASSIFICATION TREES (PERSONAL LOAN DATA)

code for bagging and boosting trees

```
bank_df = pd.read_csv('UniversalBank.csv')
bank_df.drop(columns=['ID', 'ZIP Code'], inplace=True)

# split into training and validation
X = bank_df.drop(columns=['Personal Loan'])
y = bank_df['Personal Loan']
X_train, X_valid, y_train, y_valid = train_test_split(X, y, test_size=0.40, random_state=3)

# single tree
defaultTree = DecisionTreeClassifier(random_state=1)
defaultTree.fit(X_train, y_train)

classes = defaultTree.classes_
classificationSummary(y_valid, defaultTree.predict(X_valid), class_names=classes)

# bagging
bagging = BaggingClassifier(DecisionTreeClassifier(random_state=1),
                            n_estimators=100, random_state=1)
bagging.fit(X_train, y_train)

classificationSummary(y_valid, bagging.predict(X_valid), class_names=classes)

# boosting
boost = AdaBoostClassifier(DecisionTreeClassifier(random_state=1),
                           n_estimators=100, random_state=1)
```

TABLE 13.1 EXAMPLE OF BAGGING AND BOOSTING CLASSIFICATION TREES (PERSONAL LOAN DATA) (*Continued*)

```
boost.fit(X_train, y_train)

classificationSummary(y_valid, boost.predict(X_valid), class_names=classes)
```

Output

```
> # single tree
Confusion Matrix (Accuracy 0.9825)

       Prediction
Actual    0    1
     0 1778   15
     1   20  187

> # bagging
Confusion Matrix (Accuracy 0.9855)

       Prediction
Actual    0    1
     0 1781   12
     1   17  190

> # boosting
Confusion Matrix (Accuracy 0.9840)

       Prediction
Actual    0    1
     0 1779   14
     1   18  189
```

Advantages and Weaknesses of Ensembles

Combining scores from multiple models is aimed at generating more precise predictions (lowering the prediction error variance). The ensemble approach is most useful when the combined models generate prediction errors that are negatively associated, but it can also be useful when the correlation is low. Ensembles can use simple averaging, weighted averaging, voting, medians, etc. Models can be based on the same algorithm or on different algorithms, using the same sample or different samples. Ensembles have become a major strategy for participants in data mining contests, where the goal is to optimize some predictive measure. In that sense, ensembles also provide an operational way to obtain solutions with high predictive power in a fast way, by engaging multiple teams of "data crunchers" working in parallel and combining their results.

Ensembles that are based on different data samples help avoid overfitting. However, remember that you can also overfit the data with an ensemble if you tweak it (e.g., choosing the "best" weights when using a weighted average).

The major disadvantage of an ensemble is the resources that it requires: computationally, as well as in terms of software availability and the analyst's skill and time investment. Ensembles that combine results from different algorithms require developing each of the models and evaluating them. Boosting-type ensembles and bagging-type ensembles do not require such effort, but they do have a computational cost (although boosting can be parallelized easily). Ensembles that rely on multiple data sources require collecting and maintaining multiple data sources. And finally, ensembles are "blackbox" methods, in that the relationship between the predictors and the outcome variable usually becomes nontransparent.

13.2 | UPLIFT (PERSUASION) MODELING

Long before the advent of the Internet, sending messages directly to individuals (i.e., direct mail) held a big share of the advertising market. Direct marketing affords the marketer the ability to invite and monitor direct responses from consumers. This, in turn, allows the marketer to learn whether the messaging is paying off. A message can be tested with a small section of a large list and, if it pays off, the message can be rolled out to the entire list. With predictive modeling, we have seen that the rollout can be targeted to that portion of the list that is most likely to respond or behave in a certain way. None of this was possible with traditional media advertising (television, radio, newspaper, magazine).

Direct response also made it possible to test one message against another and find out which does better.

A–B Testing

A–B testing is the marketing industry's term for a standard scientific experiment in which results can be tracked for each individual. The idea is to test one treatment against another, or a treatment against a control. "Treatment" is simply the term for the intervention you are testing: In a medical trial it is typically a drug, device, or other therapy; in marketing it is typically an offering to a consumer—for example, an e-mail, or a web page shown to a consumer. A general display ad in a magazine would not generally qualify, unless it had a specific call to action that allowed the marketer to trace the action (e.g., purchase) to a given ad, plus the ability to split the magazine distribution randomly and provide a different offer to each segment.

An important element of A–B testing is random allocation—the treatments are assigned or delivered to individuals randomly. That way, any difference between treatment A and treatment B can be attributed to the treatment (unless it is due to chance).

Uplift

An A–B test tells you which treatment does better on average, but says nothing about which treatment does better for which individual. A classic example is in political campaigns. Consider the following scenario: The campaign director for Smith, a Democratic Congressional candidate, would like to know which voters should be called to encourage to support Smith. Voters that tend to vote Democratic but are not activists might be more inclined to vote for Smith if they got a call. Active Democrats are probably already supportive of him, and therefore a call to them would be wasted. Calls to Republicans are not only wasteful, but they could be harmful.

Campaigns now maintain extensive data on voters to help guide decisions about outreach to individual voters. Prior to the 2008 Obama campaign, the practice was to make rule-based decisions based on expert political judgment. Since 2008, it has increasingly been recognized that, rather than relying on judgment or supposition to determine whether an individual should be called, it is best to use the data to develop a model that can predict whether a voter will respond positively to outreach.

Gathering the Data

US states maintain publicly available files of voters, as part of the transparent oversight process for elections. The voter file contains data such as name, address, and date of birth. Political parties have "poll-watchers" at elections to record who votes, so they have additional data on which elections voters voted in. Census data for neighborhoods can be appended, based on voter address. Finally, commercial demographic data can be purchased and matched to the voter data. Table 13.2 shows a small extract of data derived from the voter file for the US state of Delaware.[2] The actual data used in this problem are in the file *Voter-Persuasion.csv* and contain 10,000 records and many additional variables beyond those shown in Table 13.2.

First, the campaign director conducts a survey of 10,000 voters to determine their inclination to vote Democratic. Then she conducts an experiment, randomly splitting the sample of 10,000 voters in half and mailing a message promoting Smith to half the list (treatment A), and nothing to the other half (treatment B). The control group that gets no message is essential, since other campaigns or news events might cause a shift in opinion. The goal is to measure the change in opinion after the message is sent out, relative to the no-message control group.

---

[2]Thanks to Ken Strasma, founder of the microtargeting firm HaystaqDNA and director of targeting for the 2004 Kerry campaign and the 2008 Obama campaign, for these data.

TABLE 13.2 DATA ON VOTERS (SMALL SUBSET OF VARIABLES AND RECORDS) AND DATA DICTIONARY

Voter	Age	NH_White	Comm_PT	H_F1	Reg_Days	PR_Pelig	E_Elig	Political_C
1	28	70	0	0	3997	0	20	1
2	23	67	3	0	300	0	0	1
3	57	64	4	0	2967	0	0	0
4	70	53	2	1	16,620	100	90	1
5	37	76	2	0	3786	0	20	0

Data Dictionary

Age	Voter age in years
NH_White	Neighborhood average of % non-Hispanic white in household
Comm_PT	Neighborhood % of workers who take public transit
H_F1	Single female household (1 = yes)
Reg_Days	Days since voter registered at current address
PR_Pelig	Voted in what % of non-presidential primaries
E_Pelig	Voted in what % of any primaries
Political_C	Is there a political contributor in the home? (1 = yes)

The next step is conducting a post-message survey of the same sample of 10,000 voters, to measure whether each voter's opinion of Smith has shifted in a positive direction. A binary variable, Moved_AD, will be added to the above data, indicating whether opinion has moved in a Democratic direction (1) or not (0).

Table 13.3 summarizes the results of the survey, by comparing the movement in a Democratic direction for each of the treatments. Overall, the message (Message = 1) is modestly effective.

TABLE 13.3 RESULTS OF SENDING A PRO-DEMOCRATIC MESSAGE TO VOTERS

	#Voters	# Moved Dem.	% Moved Dem.
Message = 1 (message sent)	5000	2012	40.2
Message = 0 (no message sent)	5000	1722	34.4

Movement in a Democratic direction among those who got no message is 34.4%. This probably reflects the approach of the election, the heightening campaign activity, and the reduction in the "no opinion" category. It also illustrates the need for a control group. Among those who did get the message, the movement in a Democratic direction is 40.2%. So, overall, the lift from the message is 5.8%.

We can now append two variables to the voter data shown earlier in Table 13.2: *message* [whether they received the message (1) or not (0)] and *Moved_AD* [whether they moved in a Democratic direction (1) or not (0)]. The augmented data are shown in Table 13.4.

TABLE 13.4 OUTCOME VARIABLE (MOVED_AD) AND TREATMENT VARIABLE (MESSAGE) ADDED TO VOTER DATA

Voter	Age	NH_White	Comm_PT	H_F1	Reg_Days	PR_Pelig	E_Elig	Political_C	Message	Moved_AD
1	28	70	0	0	3997	0	20	1	0	1
2	23	67	3	0	300	0	0	1	1	1
3	57	64	4	0	2967	0	0	0	0	0
4	70	53	2	1	16,620	100	90	1	0	0
5	37	76	2	0	3786	0	20	0	1	0

A Simple Model

We can develop a predictive model with Moved_AD as the outcome variable, and various predictor variables, *including the treatment Message*. Any classification method can be used; Table 13.5 shows the first few lines from the output of some predictive model used to predict Moved_AD.

TABLE 13.5 CLASSIFICATIONS AND PROPENSITIES FROM PREDICTIVE MODEL (SMALL EXTRACT)

Voter	Message	Actual Moved_AD	Predicted Moved_AD	Predicted Prob.
1	0	1	1	0.5975
2	1	1	1	0.5005
3	0	0	0	0.2235
4	0	0	0	0.3052
5	1	0	0	0.4140

However, our interest is not just how the message did overall, nor is it whether we can predict the probability that a voter's opinion will move in a favorable direction. Rather our goal is to predict how much (positive) impact the message will have on a specific voter. That way the campaign can direct its limited resources toward the voters who are the most persuadable—those for whom sending the message will have the greatest positive effect.

Modeling Individual Uplift

To answer the question about the message's impact on each voter, we need to model the effect of the message at the individual voter level. For each voter, uplift is defined as follows:

Uplift = increase in propensity of favorable opinion after receiving message

To build an uplift model, we follow the following steps to estimate the change in probability of "success" (propensity) that comes from receiving the treatment (the message):

1. Randomly split a data sample into treatment and control groups, conduct an A–B test, and record the outcome (in our example: Moved_AD).
2. Recombining the data sample, partition it into training and validation sets; build a predictive model with this outcome variable and include a predictor variable that denotes treatment status (in our example: Message). If logistic regression is used, additional interaction terms between treatment status and other predictors can be added as predictors to allow the treatment effect to vary across records (in data-driven methods such as trees and KNN this happens automatically).
3. Score this predictive model to a partition of the data; you can use the validation partition. This will yield, for each validation record, its propensity of success given its treatment.
4. Reverse the value of the treatment variable and re-score the same model to that partition. This will yield for each validation record its propensity of success had it received the other treatment.
5. Uplift is estimated for each individual by $P(\text{Success} \mid \text{Treatment} = 1) - P(\text{Success} \mid \text{Treatment} = 0)$.
6. For new data where no experiment has been performed, simply add a synthetic predictor variable for treatment and assign first a "1," score the model, then a "0," and score the model again. Estimate uplift for the new record(s) as above.

Continuing with the small voter example, the results from Step 3 were shown in Table 13.5—the right column shows the propensities from the model. Next, we re-train the predictive model, but with the values of the treatment variable Message reversed for each row. Table 13.6 shows the propensities with variable Message reversed (you can see the reversed values in column Message). Finally, in Step 5, we calculate the uplift for each voter.

TABLE 13.6 CLASSIFICATIONS AND PROPENSITIES FROM PREDICTIVE MODEL (SMALL EXTRACT) WITH MESSAGE VALUES REVERSED

Voter	Message	Actual Moved_AD	Predicted Moved_AD	Predicted Prob.
1	1	1	1	0.6908
2	0	1	1	0.3996
3	1	0	0	0.3022
4	1	0	0	0.3980
5	0	0	0	0.3194

Table 13.7 shows the uplift for each voter—the success (Moved_AD = 1) propensity given Message = 1 minus the success propensity given Message = 0.

TABLE 13.7 UPLIFT: CHANGE IN PROPENSITIES FROM SENDING MESSAGE VS. NOT SENDING MESSAGE

Voter	Prob. if Message = 1	Prob. if Message = 0	Uplift
1	0.6908	0.5975	0.0933
2	0.5005	0.3996	0.1009
3	0.3022	0.2235	0.0787
4	0.3980	0.3052	0.0928
5	0.4140	0.3194	0.0946

Computing Uplift with Python

This entire process that we showed manually can be done using `scikit-learn`. One difference to our manual computation is that we used a logistic regression whereas here we will use a random forest classifier. Table 13.8 shows the result of implementing the uplift analysis in `scikit-learn` using a random forest. The output shows the two conditional probabilities, $P(\text{Success} \mid \text{Treatment} = 1)$ and $P(\text{Success} \mid \text{Treatment} = 0)$, estimated for each record. The difference between the values in Tables 13.7 and 13.8 are due to the use of two different predictive algorithms (logistic regression vs. random forests).

TABLE 13.8 UPLIFT IN PYTHON APPLIED TO THE VOTERS DATA

code for uplift

```
voter_df = pd.read_csv('Voter-Persuasion.csv')

# Preprocess data frame
predictors = ['AGE', 'NH_WHITE', 'COMM_PT', 'H_F1', 'REG_DAYS',
              'PR_PELIG', 'E_PELIG', 'POLITICALC', 'MESSAGE_A']
outcome = 'MOVED_AD'

classes = list(voter_df.MOVED_AD.unique())

# Partition the data
X = voter_df[predictors]
y = voter_df[outcome]
X_train, X_valid, y_train, y_valid = train_test_split(X, y, test_size=0.40,
                                                      random_state=1)

# Train a random forest classifier using the training set
rfModel = RandomForestClassifier(n_estimators=100, random_state=1)
rfModel.fit(X_train, y_train)
```

(Continued)

TABLE 13.8 UPLIFT IN PYTHON APPLIED TO THE VOTERS DATA (*Continued*)

```
# Calculating the uplift
uplift_df = X_valid.copy()  # Need to create a copy to allow modifying data

uplift_df.MESSAGE_A = 1
predTreatment = rfModel.predict_proba(uplift_df)
uplift_df.MESSAGE_A = 0
predControl = rfModel.predict_proba(uplift_df)

upliftResult_df = pd.DataFrame({
     'probMessage': predTreatment[:,1],
     'probNoMessage': predControl[:,1],
     'uplift': predTreatment[:,1] - predControl[:,1],
}, index=uplift_df.index)
upliftResult_df.head()
```

Output

```
      probMessage  probNoMessage  uplift
9953         0.77           0.62    0.15
3850         0.39           0.39    0.00
4962         0.20           0.14    0.06
3886         0.86           0.62    0.24
5437         0.10           0.28   -0.18
```

Using the Results of an Uplift Model

Once we have estimated the uplift for each individual, the results can be ordered by uplift. The message could then be sent to all those voters with a positive uplift, or, if resources are limited, only to a subset—those with the greatest uplift.

Uplift modeling is used mainly in marketing and, more recently, in political campaigns. It has two main purposes:

- To determine whether to send someone a persuasion message, or just leave them alone.
- When a message is definitely going to be sent, to determine which message, among several possibilities, to send.

Technically this amounts to the same thing—"send no message" is simply another category of treatment, and an experiment can be constructed with multiple treatments, for example, no message, message A, and message B. However, practitioners tend to think of the two purposes as distinct, and tend to focus on the first. Marketers want to avoid sending discount offers to customers who would make a purchase anyway, or renew a subscription anyway. Political campaigns, likewise, want to avoid calling voters who would vote for their candidate in any case. And both parties especially want to avoid sending messages or offers where the effect might be antagonistic—where the uplift is negative.

13.3 | SUMMARY

In practice, the methods discussed in this book are often used not in isolation, but as building blocks in an analytic process whose goal is always to inform and provide insight.

In this chapter, we looked at two ways that multiple models are deployed. In ensembles, multiple models are weighted and combined to produce improved predictions. In uplift modeling, the results of A–B testing are folded into the predictive modeling process as a predictor variable to guide choices not just about whether to send an offer or persuasion message, but also as to who to send it to.

PROBLEMS

13.1 Acceptance of Consumer Loan. Universal Bank has begun a program to encourage its existing customers to borrow via a consumer loan program. The bank has promoted the loan to 5000 customers, of whom 480 accepted the offer. The data are available in file *UniversalBank.csv*. The bank now wants to develop a model to predict which customers have the greatest probability of accepting the loan, to reduce promotion costs and send the offer only to a subset of its customers.

We will develop several models, then combine them in an ensemble. The models we will use are (1) logistic regression, (2) k-nearest neighbors with $k = 3$, and (3) classification trees. Preprocess the data as follows:

- Bin the following variables so they can be used in Naive Bayes: Age (5 bins), Experience (10 bins), Income (5 bins), CC Average (6 bins), and Mortgage (10 bins).
- Education and Family can be used as is, without binning.
- Zip code can be ignored.
- Use one-hot-encoding to convert the categorical data into indicator variables.
- Partition the data: 60% training, 40% validation.

a. Fit models to the data for (1) logistic regression, (2) k-nearest neighbors with $k = 3$, (3) classification trees, and (4) Naive Bayes. Use Personal Loan as the outcome variable. Report the validation confusion matrix for each of the models.

b. Create a data frame with the actual outcome, predicted outcome, and each of the models. Report the first 10 rows of this data frame.

c. Add two columns to this data frame for (1) a majority vote of predicted outcomes and (2) the average of the predicted probabilities. Using the classifications generated by these two methods derive a confusion matrix for each method and report the overall accuracy.

d. Compare the error rates for the four individual methods and the two ensemble methods.

13.2 eBay Auctions—Boosting and Bagging. Using the eBay auction data (file *eBayAuctions.csv*) with variable Competitive as the outcome variable, partition the data into training (60%) and validation (40%).

a. Run a classification tree, using the default settings of *DecisionTreeClassifier*. Looking at the validation set, what is the overall accuracy? What is the lift on the first decile?

b. Run a boosted tree with the same predictors (use *AdaBoostClassifier* with *DecisionTreeClassifier* as the base estimator). For the validation set, what is the overall accuracy? What is the lift on the first decile?

c. Run a bagged tree with the same predictors (use *BaggingClassifier*). For the validation set, what is the overall accuracy? What is the lift on the first decile?

d. Run a random forest (use *RandomForestClassifier*). Compare the bagged tree to the random forest in terms of validation accuracy and lift on first decile. How are the two methods conceptually different?

13.3 Predicting Delayed Flights (Boosting). The file *FlightDelays.csv* contains information on all commercial flights departing the Washington, DC area and arriving at New York during January 2004. For each flight, there is information on the departure and arrival airports, the distance of the route, the scheduled time and date of the flight, and so on. The variable that we are trying to predict is whether or not a flight is delayed. A delay is defined as an arrival that is at least 15 minutes later than scheduled.

Data Preprocessing. Transform variable day of week info a categorical variable. Bin the scheduled departure time into eight bins (in Python use function *pd.cut()* from the `pandas` package). Partition the data into training (60%) and validation (40%).

Run a boosted classification tree for delay. With the exception of setting `n_estimators=500` and `random_state=1`, use default setting for the DecisionTreeClassifier and the AdaBoostClassifier.

a. Compared with the single tree, how does the boosted tree behave in terms of overall accuracy?

b. Compared with the single tree, how does the boosted tree behave in terms of accuracy in identifying delayed flights?

c. Explain why this model might have the best performance over the other models you fit.

13.4 Hair Care Product—Uplift Modeling. This problem uses the data set in *Hair-Care-Product.csv*, courtesy of SAS. In this hypothetical case, a promotion for a hair care product was sent to some members of a buyers club. Purchases were then recorded for both the members who got the promotion and those who did not.

a. What is the purchase propensity

  i. among those who received the promotion?

  ii. among those who did not receive the promotion?

b. Partition the data into training (60%) and validation (40%) and fit:

  i. Uplift using a Random Forest.

  ii. Uplift using k-NN.

c. Report the two models' recommendations for the first three members.

PART

V

Mining Relationships Among Records

CHAPTER 14

Association Rules and Collaborative Filtering

In this chapter, we describe the unsupervised learning methods of association rules (also called "affinity analysis" and "market basket analysis") and collaborative filtering. Both methods are popular in marketing for cross-selling products associated with an item that a consumer is considering.

In association rules, the goal is to identify item clusters in transaction-type databases. Association rule discovery in marketing is termed "market basket analysis" and is aimed at discovering which groups of products tend to be purchased together. These items can then be displayed together, offered in post-transaction coupons, or recommended in online shopping. We describe the two-stage process of rule generation and then assessment of rule strength to choose a subset. We look at the popular rule-generating Apriori algorithm, and then criteria for judging the strength of rules.

In collaborative filtering, the goal is to provide personalized recommendations that leverage user-level information. User-based collaborative filtering starts with a user, then finds users who have purchased a similar set of items or ranked items in a similar fashion, and makes a recommendation to the initial user based on what the similar users purchased or liked. Item-based collaborative filtering starts with an item being considered by a user, then locates other items that tend to be co-purchased with that first item. We explain the technique and the requirements for applying it in practice.

Python

In this chapter, we will use pandas for data handling. The package `mlxtend` is used for associative rules and `surprise` for collaborative filtering. Use the following import statements for the code in this chapter.

import required functionality for this chapter

```
import heapq
from collections import defaultdict

import pandas as pd
import matplotlib.pylab as plt
from mlxtend.frequent_patterns import apriori
from mlxtend.frequent_patterns import association_rules

from surprise import Dataset, Reader, KNNBasic
from surprise.model_selection import train_test_split
```

14.1 | ASSOCIATION RULES

Put simply, association rules, or *affinity analysis*, constitute a study of "what goes with what." This method is also called *market basket analysis* because it originated with the study of customer transactions databases to determine dependencies between purchases of different items. Association rules are heavily used in retail for learning about items that are purchased together, but they are also useful in other fields. For example, a medical researcher might want to learn what symptoms appear together. In law, word combinations that appear too often might indicate plagiarism.

Discovering Association Rules in Transaction Databases

The availability of detailed information on customer transactions has led to the development of techniques that automatically look for associations between items that are stored in the database. An example is data collected using bar-code scanners in supermarkets. Such *market basket databases* consist of a large number of transaction records. Each record lists all items bought by a customer on a single-purchase transaction. Managers are interested to know if certain groups of items are consistently purchased together. They could use such information for making decisions on store layouts and item placement, for cross-selling, for promotions, for catalog design, and for identifying customer segments based on buying patterns. Association rules provide information of this type in the form of "if–then" statements. These rules are computed from the data; unlike the if–then rules of logic, association rules are probabilistic in nature.

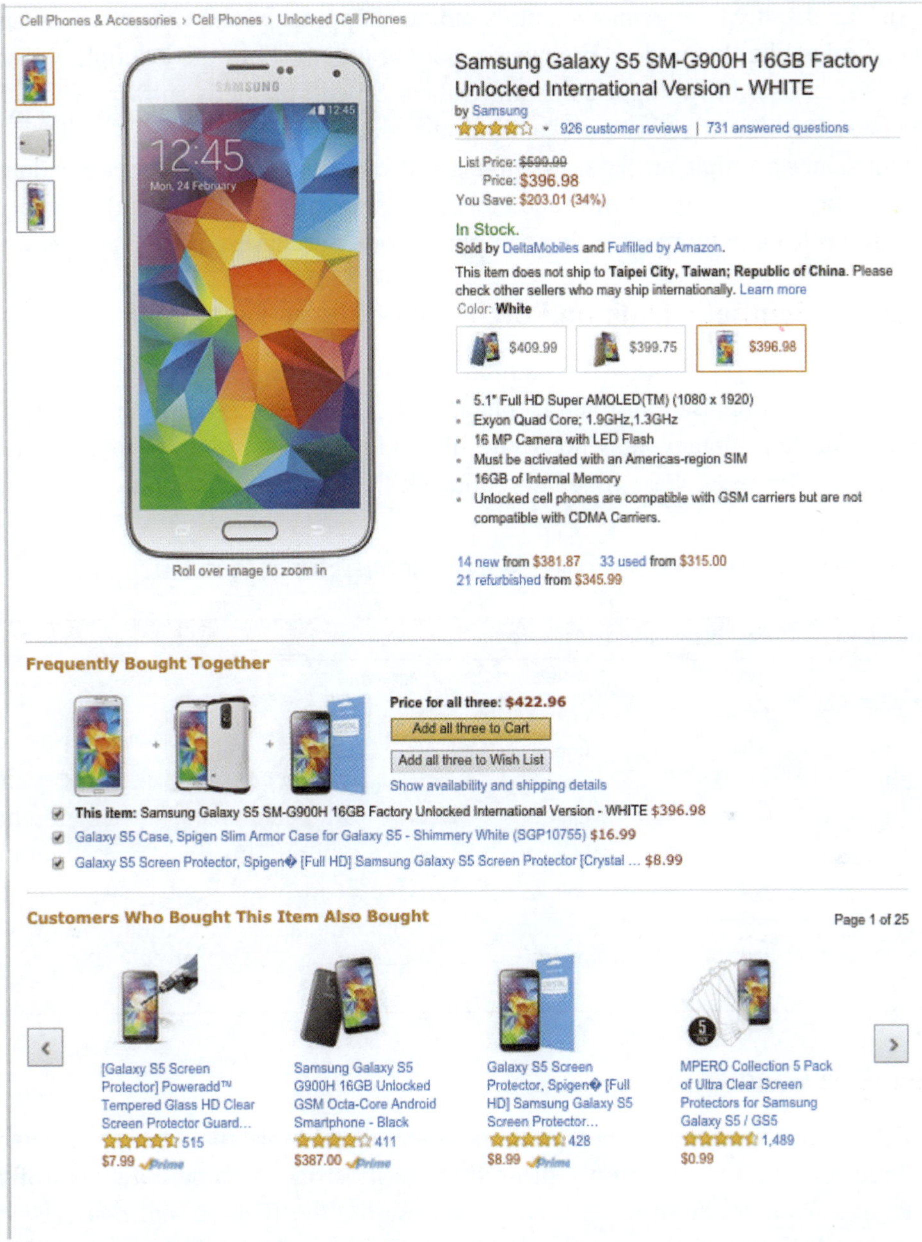

FIGURE 14.1 RECOMMENDATIONS UNDER "FREQUENTLY BOUGHT TOGETHER" ARE BASED ON ASSOCIATION RULES

Association rules are commonly encountered in online *recommendation systems* (or *recommender systems*), where customers examining an item or items for possible purchase are shown other items that are often purchased in conjunction with the first item(s). The display from Amazon.com's online shopping system illustrates the application of rules like this under "Frequently bought together." In the example shown in Figure 14.1, a user browsing a Samsung Galaxy S5 cell phone is shown a case and a screen protector that are often purchased along with this phone.

We introduce a simple artificial example and use it throughout the chapter to demonstrate the concepts, computations, and steps of association rules. We end by applying association rules to a more realistic example of book purchases.

Example 1: Synthetic Data on Purchases of Phone Faceplates

A store that sells accessories for cellular phones runs a promotion on faceplates. Customers who purchase multiple faceplates from a choice of six different colors get a discount. The store managers, who would like to know what colors of faceplates customers are likely to purchase together, collected the transaction database as shown in Table 14.1.

TABLE 14.1 TRANSACTIONS DATABASE FOR PURCHASES OF DIFFERENT-COLORED CELLULAR PHONE FACEPLATES

Transaction	Faceplate colors purchased			
1	red	white	green	
2	white	orange		
3	white	blue		
4	red	white	orange	
5	red	blue		
6	white	blue		
7	red	blue		
8	red	white	blue	green
9	red	white	blue	
10	yellow			

Generating Candidate Rules

The idea behind association rules is to examine all possible rules between items in an if–then format, and select only those that are most likely to be indicators of true dependence. We use the term *antecedent* to describe the IF part, and *consequent* to describe the THEN part. In association analysis, the antecedent and consequent are sets of items (called *itemsets*) that are disjoint (do not have any items in common). Note that itemsets are not records of what people buy; they are simply possible combinations of items, including single items.

Returning to the phone faceplate purchase example, one example of a possible rule is "if red, then white," meaning that if a red faceplate is purchased, a white one is, too.

Here the antecedent is *red* and the consequent is *white*. The antecedent and consequent each contain a single item in this case. Another possible rule is "if red and white, then green." Here the antecedent includes the itemset {*red, white*} and the consequent is {*green*}.

The first step in association rules is to generate all the rules that would be candidates for indicating associations between items. Ideally, we might want to look at all possible combinations of items in a database with p distinct items (in the phone faceplate example, $p = 6$). This means finding all combinations of single items, pairs of items, triplets of items, and so on, in the transactions database. However, generating all these combinations requires a long computation time that grows exponentially[1] in p. A practical solution is to consider only combinations that occur with higher frequency in the database. These are called *frequent itemsets*.

Determining what qualifies as a frequent itemset is related to the concept of *support*. The support of a rule is simply the number of transactions that include both the antecedent and consequent itemsets. It is called a support because it measures the degree to which the data "support" the validity of the rule. The support is sometimes expressed as a percentage of the total number of records in the database. For example, the support for the itemset {*red, white*} in the phone faceplate example is 4 (or, $100 \times \frac{4}{10} = 40\%$).

What constitutes a frequent itemset is therefore defined as an itemset that has a support that exceeds a selected minimum support, determined by the user.

The Apriori Algorithm

Several algorithms have been proposed for generating frequent itemsets, but the classic algorithm is the *Apriori algorithm* of Agrawal et al. (1993). The key idea of the algorithm is to begin by generating frequent itemsets with just one item (one-itemsets) and to recursively generate frequent itemsets with two items, then with three items, and so on, until we have generated frequent itemsets of all sizes.

It is easy to generate frequent one-itemsets. All we need to do is to count, for each item, how many transactions in the database include the item. These transaction counts are the supports for the one-itemsets. We drop one-itemsets that have support below the desired minimum support to create a list of the frequent one-itemsets.

To generate frequent two-itemsets, we use the frequent one-itemsets. The reasoning is that if a certain one-itemset did not exceed the minimum support, any larger size itemset that includes it will not exceed the minimum support. In general, generating k-itemsets uses the frequent $(k-1)$-itemsets that were generated in the preceding step.

---

[1]The number of rules that one can generate for p items is $3^p - 2^{p+1} + 1$. Computation time therefore grows by a factor for each additional item. For 6 items we have 602 rules, while for 7 items the number of rules grows to 1932.

Each step requires a single run through the database, and therefore the Apriori algorithm is very fast even for a large number of unique items in a database.

Selecting Strong Rules

From the abundance of rules generated, the goal is to find only the rules that indicate a strong dependence between the antecedent and consequent itemsets. To measure the strength of association implied by a rule, we use the measures of *confidence* and *lift ratio*, as described below.

Support and Confidence In addition to support, which we described earlier, there is another measure that expresses the degree of uncertainty about the if–then rule. This is known as the *confidence*[2] of the rule. This measure compares the co-occurrence of the antecedent and consequent itemsets in the database to the occurrence of the antecedent itemsets. Confidence is defined as the ratio of the number of transactions that include all antecedent and consequent itemsets (namely, the support) to the number of transactions that include all the antecedent itemsets:

$$\text{Confidence} = \frac{\text{no. of transactions with both antecedent and consequent itemsets}}{\text{no. of transactions with antecedent itemset}}.$$

For example, suppose that a supermarket database has 100,000 point-of-sale transactions. Of these transactions, 2000 include both orange juice and (over-the-counter) flu medication, and 800 of these include soup purchases. The association rule "IF orange juice and flu medication are purchased THEN soup is purchased on the same trip" has a support of 800 transactions (alternatively, 0.8% = 800/100,000) and a confidence of 40% (=800/2000).

To see the relationship between support and confidence, let us think about what each is measuring (estimating). One way to think of support is that it is the (estimated) probability that a transaction selected randomly from the database will contain all items in the antecedent and the consequent:

$$\text{Support} = \hat{P}(\text{antecedent AND consequent}).$$

In comparison, the confidence is the (estimated) *conditional probability* that a transaction selected randomly will include all the items in the consequent *given* that the transaction includes all the items in the antecedent:

$$\text{Confidence} = \frac{\hat{P}(\text{antecedent AND consequent})}{\hat{P}(\text{antecedent})} = \hat{P}(\text{consequent} \mid \text{antecedent}).$$

[2]The concept of confidence is different from and unrelated to the ideas of confidence intervals and confidence levels used in statistical inference.

A high value of confidence suggests a strong association rule (in which we are highly confident). However, this can be deceptive because if the antecedent and/or the consequent has a high level of support, we can have a high value for confidence even when the antecedent and consequent are independent! For example, if nearly all customers buy bananas and nearly all customers buy ice cream, the confidence level of a rule such as "IF bananas THEN ice-cream" will be high regardless of whether there is an association between the items.

Lift Ratio A better way to judge the strength of an association rule is to compare the confidence of the rule with a benchmark value, where we assume that the occurrence of the consequent itemset in a transaction is independent of the occurrence of the antecedent for each rule. In other words, if the antecedent and consequent itemsets are independent, what confidence values would we expect to see? Under independence, the support would be

$$P(\text{antecedent AND consequent}) = P(\text{antecedent}) \times P(\text{consequent}),$$

and the benchmark confidence would be

$$\frac{P(\text{antecedent}) \times P(\text{consequent})}{P(\text{antecedent})} = P(\text{consequent}).$$

The estimate of this benchmark from the data, called the *benchmark confidence value* for a rule, is computed by

$$\text{Benchmark confidence} = \frac{\text{no. of transactions with consequent itemset}}{\text{no. of transactions in database}}.$$

We compare the confidence to the benchmark confidence by looking at their ratio: this is called the *lift ratio* of a rule. The lift ratio is the confidence of the rule divided by the confidence, assuming independence of consequent from antecedent:

$$\text{lift ratio} = \frac{\text{confidence}}{\text{benchmark confidence}}.$$

A lift ratio greater than 1.0 suggests that there is some usefulness to the rule. In other words, the level of association between the antecedent and consequent itemsets is higher than would be expected if they were independent. The larger the lift ratio, the greater the strength of the association.

To illustrate the computation of support, confidence, and lift ratio for the cellular phone faceplate example, we introduce an alternative presentation of the data that is better suited to this purpose.

Other Metrics There are a large variety of other metrics for rules. The `mlxtend` library adds leverage and conviction. These are defined as follows:

$$\text{leverage} = P(\text{antecedent AND consequent}) - P(\text{antecedent}) \times P(\text{consequent}),$$

$$\text{conviction} = \frac{P(\text{antecedent}) \times P(\text{not consequent})}{P(\text{antecedent AND not consequent})}.$$

Leverage measures the deviation from independence. It ranges from −1 to 1 and is 0 if the antecedent and consequent are independent. In a sales setting, leverage tells us how much more frequently the items are bought together compared to their independent sales. Conviction is similar to confidence and ranges from 0 to ∞. If antecedent and consequent are independent, conviction is equal to 1. If the rule always holds (the items always appear together), its value is infinity.

Data Format

Transaction data are usually displayed in one of two formats: a transactions database (with each row representing a list of items purchased in a single transaction), or a binary incidence matrix in which columns are items, rows again represent transactions, and each cell has either a 1 or a 0, indicating the presence or absence of an item in the transaction. For example, Table 14.1 displays the data for the cellular faceplate purchases in a transactions database. We translate these into binary incidence matrix format in Table 14.2.

TABLE 14.2 PHONE FACEPLATE DATA IN BINARY INCIDENCE MATRIX FORMAT

Transaction	Red	White	Blue	Orange	Green	Yellow
1	1	1	0	0	1	0
2	0	1	0	1	0	0
3	0	1	1	0	0	0
4	1	1	0	1	0	0
5	1	0	1	0	0	0
6	0	1	1	0	0	0
7	1	0	1	0	0	0
8	1	1	1	0	1	0
9	1	1	1	0	0	0
10	0	0	0	0	0	1

Now suppose that we want association rules between items for this database that have a support count of at least 2 (equivalent to a percentage support of 2/10 = 20%). In other words, rules based on items that were purchased together in at least 20% of the transactions. By enumeration, we can see that only the itemsets listed in Table 14.3 have a count of at least 2.

TABLE 14.3 ITEMSETS WITH SUPPORT COUNT OF AT LEAST TWO

Itemset	Support (count)
{red}	6
{white}	7
{blue}	6
{orange}	2
{green}	2
{red, white}	4
{red, blue}	4
{red, green}	2
{white, blue}	4
{white, orange}	2
{white, green}	2
{red, white, blue}	2
{red, white, green}	2

The first itemset {*red*} has a support of 6, because six of the transactions included a red faceplate. Similarly, the last itemset {*red*, *white*, *green*} has a support of 2, because only two transactions included red, white, and green faceplates.

> In Python, we will use the apriori implementation in the library `mlxtend`. It accepts transactions as a pandas DataFrame or pandas SparseDataFrame. The latter is more efficient for a large number of possible items. The package creates rules with one or more items as antecedents and consequents.

The Process of Rule Selection

The process of selecting strong rules is based on generating all association rules that meet stipulated support and confidence requirements. This is done in two stages. The first stage, described earlier, consists of finding all "frequent" itemsets, those itemsets that have a requisite support. In the second stage, we generate, from the frequent itemsets, association rules that meet a confidence requirement. The first step is aimed at removing item combinations that are rare in the database. The second stage then filters the remaining rules and selects only those with high confidence. For most association analysis data, the computational challenge is the first stage, as described in the discussion of the Apriori algorithm.

The computation of confidence in the second stage is simple. Since any subset (e.g., {*red*} in the phone faceplate example) must occur at least as frequently as the set it belongs to (e.g., {*red*, *white*}), each subset will also be in the list. It is then straightforward to compute the confidence as the ratio of the support for the itemset to the support for each subset of the itemset. We retain the corresponding association rule only if it exceeds the desired cutoff value for confidence. For example, from the itemset {*red*, *white*, *green*} in the phone faceplate purchases, we get the following single-consequent association rules, confidence values, and lift values:

Rule	Confidence	Lift
{*red*, *white*} ⇒ {*green*}	$\frac{\text{support of } \{red, white, green\}}{\text{support of } \{red, white\}} = \frac{2}{4} = 50\%$	$\frac{\text{confidence of rule}}{\text{benchmark confidence}} = \frac{50\%}{20\%} = 2.5$
{*green*} ⇒ {*red*}	$\frac{\text{support of } \{green, red\}}{\text{support of } \{green\}} = \frac{2}{2} = 100\%$	$\frac{\text{confidence of rule}}{\text{benchmark confidence}} = \frac{100\%}{60\%} = 1.67$
{*white*, *green*} ⇒ {*red*}	$\frac{\text{support of } \{white, green, red\}}{\text{support of } \{white, green\}} = \frac{2}{2} = 100\%$	$\frac{\text{confidence of rule}}{\text{benchmark confidence}} = \frac{100\%}{60\%} = 1.67$

If the desired minimum confidence is 70%, we would report only the second and third rules.

We can generate association rules in Python from a pandas data frame formatted as a binary incidence matrix as shown in Table 14.2 or in sparse pandas data frame which keeps data in a similar format to Table 14.1. We specify the minimum support (20%) and minimum confidence level percentage (50%). Table 14.4 shows the output. The output includes information on each rule and its support, confidence, lift, leverage, and conviction. (Note that here we consider all possible itemsets, not just {*red*, *white*, *green*} as above.)

TABLE 14.4 BINARY INCIDENCE MATRIX, TRANSACTIONS DATABASE, AND RULES FOR FACEPLATE EXAMPLE

code for running the Apriori algorithm

```
# Load and preprocess data set
fp_df = pd.read_csv('Faceplate.csv')
fp_df.set_index('Transaction', inplace=True)
print(fp_df)

# create frequent itemsets
itemsets = apriori(fp_df, min_support=0.2, use_colnames=True)

# convert into rules
rules = association_rules(itemsets, metric='confidence', min_threshold=0.5)
rules.sort_values(by=['lift'], ascending=False).head(6)

print(rules.sort_values(by=['lift'], ascending=False)
      .drop(columns=['antecedent support', 'consequent support', 'conviction'])
      .head(6))
```

TABLE 14.4 BINARY INCIDENCE MATRIX, TRANSACTIONS DATABASE, AND RULES FOR FACEPLATE EXAMPLE (*Continued*)

Partial output

Transaction	Red	White	Blue	Orange	Green	Yellow
1	1	1	0	0	1	0
2	0	1	0	1	0	0
3	0	1	1	0	0	0
4	1	1	0	1	0	0
5	1	0	1	0	0	0
6	0	1	1	0	0	0
7	1	0	1	0	0	0
8	1	1	1	0	1	0
9	1	1	1	0	0	0
10	0	0	0	0	0	1

	antecedents	consequents	support	confidence	lift	leverage
14	(White, Red)	(Green)	0.2	0.5	2.500000	0.12
15	(Green)	(White, Red)	0.2	1.0	2.500000	0.12
4	(Green)	(Red)	0.2	1.0	1.666667	0.08
12	(Green, White)	(Red)	0.2	1.0	1.666667	0.08
7	(Orange)	(White)	0.2	1.0	1.428571	0.06
8	(Green)	(White)	0.2	1.0	1.428571	0.06

Interpreting the Results

We can translate each of the rules from Table 14.4 into an understandable sentence that provides information about performance. For example, we can read rule $\{orange\} \Rightarrow \{white\}$ as follows:

> If *orange* is purchased, then with confidence 100% *white* will also be purchased. This rule has a lift ratio of 1.43.

In interpreting results, it is useful to look at the various measures. The support for the rule indicates its impact in terms of overall size: How many transactions are affected? If only a small number of transactions are affected, the rule may be of little use (unless the consequent is very valuable and/or the rule is very efficient in finding it).

The lift ratio indicates how efficient the rule is in finding consequents, compared to random selection. A very efficient rule is preferred to an inefficient rule, but we must still consider support: A very efficient rule that has very low support may not be as desirable as a less efficient rule with much greater support.

The confidence tells us at what rate consequents will be found, and is useful in determining the business or operational usefulness of a rule: A rule with low confidence may find consequents at too low a rate to be worth the cost of (say) promoting the consequent in all the transactions that involve the antecedent.

Rules and Chance

What about confidence in the nontechnical sense? How sure can we be that the rules we develop are meaningful? Considering the matter from a statistical perspective, we can ask: Are we finding associations that are really just chance occurrences?

TABLE 14.5 FIFTY TRANSACTIONS OF RANDOMLY ASSIGNED ITEMS

Transaction	Items	Transaction	Items	Transaction	Items
1	8	18	8	35	3 4 6 8
2	3 4 8	19		36	1 4 8
3	8	20	9	37	4 7 8
4	3 9	21	2 5 6 8	38	8 9
5	9	22	4 6 9	39	4 5 7 9
6	1 8	23	4 9	40	2 8 9
7	6 9	24	8 9	41	2 5 9
8	3 5 7 9	25	6 8	42	1 2 7 9
9	8	26	1 6 8	43	5 8
10		27	5 8	44	1 7 8
11	1 7 9	28	4 8 9	45	8
12	1 4 5 8 9	29	9	46	2 7 9
13	5 7 9	30	8	47	4 6 9
14	6 7 8	31	1 5 8	48	9
15	3 7 9	32	3 6 9	49	9
16	1 4 9	33	7 9	50	6 7 8
17	6 7 8	34	7 8 9		

Let us examine the output from an application of this algorithm to a small database of 50 transactions, where each of the nine items is assigned randomly to each transaction. The data are shown in Table 14.5, and the association rules generated are shown in Table 14.6. In looking at these tables, remember that "lhs" and "rhs" refer to itemsets, not records.

In this example, the lift ratios highlight Rule [105] as most interesting, as it suggests that purchase of item 4 is almost five times as likely when items 3 and 8 are purchased than if item 4 was not associated with the itemset {3, 8}. Yet we know there is no fundamental association underlying these data—they were generated randomly.

Two principles can guide us in assessing rules for possible spuriousness due to chance effects:

1. The more records the rule is based on, the more solid the conclusion.
2. The more distinct rules we consider seriously (perhaps consolidating multiple rules that deal with the same items), the more likely it is that at least some will be based on chance sampling results. For one person to toss a coin 10 times and

get 10 heads would be quite surprising. If 1000 people toss a coin 10 times each, it would not be nearly so surprising to have one get 10 heads. Formal adjustment of "statistical significance" when multiple comparisons are made is a complex subject in its own right, and beyond the scope of this book. A reasonable approach is to consider rules from the top-down in terms of business or operational applicability, and not consider more than what can reasonably be incorporated in a human decision-making process. This will impose a rough constraint on the dangers that arise from an automated review of hundreds or thousands of rules in search of "something interesting."

TABLE 14.6 ASSOCIATION RULES OUTPUT FOR RANDOM DATA

```
# create frequent itemsets
itemsets = apriori(randomData, min_support=2/len(randomData), use_colnames=True)
# and convert into rules
rules = association_rules(itemsets, metric='confidence', min_threshold=0.7)
print(rules.sort_values(by=['lift'], ascending=False)
      .drop(columns=['antecedent support', 'consequent support', 'conviction'])
      .head(6))

  antecedents consequents  support  confidence      lift  leverage
3      (8, 3)         (4)     0.04         1.0  4.545455    0.0312
1      (1, 5)         (8)     0.04         1.0  1.851852    0.0184
2      (2, 7)         (9)     0.04         1.0  1.851852    0.0184
4      (3, 4)         (8)     0.04         1.0  1.851852    0.0184
5      (3, 7)         (9)     0.04         1.0  1.851852    0.0184
6      (4, 5)         (9)     0.04         1.0  1.851852    0.0184
```

We now consider a more realistic example, using a larger database and real transactional data.

Example 2: Rule for Cross Category Purchases in Online Store

The following example illustrates the application of association rules to get insights for cross-selling, product bundling, and effective merchandising decisions by retailers and in this case by online retailers. The dataset used in this example has 1500 purchase transactions and items purchased across the fourteen categories offered by the online retailer. The data, in binary incidence matrix form, are shown in Table 14.7.

For instance, the first transaction included items purchased in the categories of Baby Care, Sports-Fitness, and Beauty Personal care. Table 14.8 shows all the 16 rules generated given that we specified a minimal support of 10% and a minimal confidence of 60%. This resulted in 16 rules, which are sorted by lift values in ascending order.

TABLE 14.7 SUBSET OF ITEM TRANSACTIONS IN ONLINE MARKET PLACE

Clothing	Pens Stationery	BagBelts	Jewellery	Mobiles	Footwear	Watches	Computers	Home Furnish	Sports Fitness	BabyCare	Craft	Beauty PersonCare	Toys
0	1	1	0	0	0	0	0	0	0	1	0	0	1
0	0	0	1	0	0	0	0	1	0	0	0	0	0
0	0	1	1	0	0	0	0	0	0	1	0	0	0
0	0	0	0	0	1	0	0	0	1	0	0	1	1
1	0	0	0	0	0	0	0	0	0	1	0	0	1
0	0	0	0	1	1	0	0	1	0	1	0	0	1
1	1	1	1	1	0	1	0	0	1	1	0	1	1
0	0	1	0	0	1	0	0	1	0	0	0	0	1
0	0	0	0	0	1	1	0	1	1	1	0	1	1
0	0	0	0	0	0	0	0	1	0	1	0	0	0
0	0	0	1	0	0	0	0	0	0	1	0	0	0
0	0	1	0	0	1	0	0	1	1	0	1	1	1

code for running the Apriori algorithm

```
import heapq
from collections import defaultdict
import pandas as pd
import matplotlib.pylab as plt
from mlxtend.frequent_patterns import apriori
from mlxtend.frequent_patterns import association_rules

# load dataset
ccb = pd.read_csv('CrossCatBuying.csv')
ccb=ccb.drop(columns=['Trans_ID'])
ccb[ccb > 0] = 1

# create frequent itemsets and rules
itemsets = apriori(ccb, min_support=150/1500, use_colnames=True)
rules = association_rules(itemsets, metric='confidence', min_threshold=0.60)

# Display 25 rules with highest lift
rules.sort_values(by=['lift'], ascending=False).head(15)
```

Output

	antecedents	consequents	antecedent support	consequent support	support	confidence	lift	leverage	conviction
9	(BabyCare, SportsFitness)	(BeautyPersonCare)	0.125333	0.362000	0.119333	0.952128	2.630187	0.073963	13.327111
6	(Jewellery, Mobiles)	(PensStationery)	0.142667	0.292667	0.106000	0.742991	2.538692	0.064246	2.752170
5	(Jewellery, PensStationery)	(Mobiles)	0.144000	0.292000	0.106000	0.736111	2.520928	0.063952	2.682947
7	(PensStationery, Mobiles)	(Jewellery)	0.139333	0.304667	0.106000	0.760766	2.497042	0.063550	2.906493
13	(SportsFitness, Toys)	(BeautyPersonCare)	0.194000	0.362000	0.157333	0.810997	2.240322	0.087105	3.375600
15	(BeautyPersonCare, Toys)	(BabyCare)	0.232667	0.340667	0.163333	0.702006	2.060682	0.084072	2.212571
0	(BeautyPersonCare)	(SportsFitness)	0.362000	0.372667	0.256667	0.709024	1.902569	0.121761	2.155962
1	(SportsFitness)	(BeautyPersonCare)	0.372667	0.362000	0.256667	0.688730	1.902569	0.121761	2.049667
12	(BeautyPersonCare, Toys)	(SportsFitness)	0.232667	0.372667	0.157333	0.676218	1.814538	0.070626	1.937516
3	(Craft)	(Toys)	0.124667	0.499333	0.112000	0.898396	1.799190	0.049750	4.927614
14	(BabyCare, BeautyPersonCare)	(Toys)	0.189333	0.499333	0.163333	0.862676	1.727656	0.068793	3.645880
8	(BabyCare, BeautyPersonCare)	(SportsFitness)	0.189333	0.372667	0.119333	0.630282	1.691275	0.048775	1.696787
10	(BabyCare, SportsFitness)	(Toys)	0.125333	0.499333	0.104000	0.829787	1.661790	0.041417	2.941417
2	(BabyCare)	(Toys)	0.340667	0.499333	0.280667	0.823875	1.649949	0.110560	2.842674
4	(BeautyPersonCare)	(Toys)	0.362000	0.499333	0.232667	0.642726	1.287167	0.051908	1.401351
11	(BeautyPersonCare, SportsFitness)	(Toys)	0.256667	0.499333	0.157333	0.612987	1.227611	0.029171	1.293669

In reviewing these rules, we see that Sports-Fitness has the highest support (0.3726), followed by Beauty Personal Care (0.362), and Baby Care (0.3406). We can see purchase behavior toward items in the Toys category as a common consequent in many association rules. The last seven rules indicate items in the Toys category as a common consequent (RHS) in seven rules for several item combinations from categories- Sports Fitness, Baby Care, and Beauty Personal Care. Pairs and groups like this are easy to track down by looking for rows that share values in the support column that are closer. This does not mean that the rules are not useful. On the contrary, it can reduce the number of items to be considered for possible action from a business perspective. We can also find Toy category appears in most of the other rules in the antecedent side (LHS). It is most likely that items in Baby Care and Beauty Personal Care are part of most transactions, which may suggest that items in these categories are feasible candidates for tripwire product offers to increase the size of the customer basket. These rules also help in designing the navigation for site visitors to find their preferred basket items across categories.

14.2 | COLLABORATIVE FILTERING[3]

Recommendation systems are a critically important part of websites that offer a large variety of products or services. Examples include Amazon.com, which offers millions of different products; Netflix has thousands of movies for rental; Google searches over huge numbers of webpages; Internet radio websites such as Spotify and Pandora include a large variety of music albums by various artists; travel websites offer many destinations and hotels; social network websites have many groups. The recommender engine provides personalized recommendations to a user based on the user's information as well as on similar users' information. Information means behaviors indicative of preference, such as purchase, ratings, and clicking.

The value that recommendation systems provide to users helps online companies convert browsers into buyers, increase cross-selling, and build loyalty.

Collaborative filtering is a popular technique used by such recommendation systems. The term *collaborative filtering* is based on the notions of identifying relevant items for a specific user from the very large set of items ("filtering") by considering preferences of many users ("collaboration").

The Fortune.com article "Amazon's Recommendation Secret" (June 30, 2012) describes the company's use of collaborative filtering not only for providing personalized product recommendations, but also for customizing the entire website interface for each user:

> At root, the retail giant's recommendation system is based on a number of simple elements: what a user has bought in the past, which items they have in their

[3]This section copyright © 2019 Datastats, LLC, Galit Shmueli, and Peter Bruce.

virtual shopping cart, items they've rated and liked, and what other customers have viewed and purchased. Amazon calls this homegrown math "item-to-item collaborative filtering," and it's used this algorithm to heavily customize the browsing experience for returning customers.

Data Type and Format

Collaborative filtering requires availability of all item–user information. Specifically, for each item–user combination, we should have some measure of the user's preference for that item. Preference can be a numerical rating or a binary behavior such as a purchase, a "like," or a click.

For n users $(u_1, u_2, \dots, u_n)$ and p items $(i_1, i_2, \dots, i_p)$, we can think of the data as an $n \times p$ matrix of n rows (users) by p columns (items). Each cell includes the rating or the binary event corresponding to the user's preference of the item (see schematic in Table 14.9). Typically not every user purchases or rates every item, and therefore a purchase matrix will have many zeros (it is sparse), and a rating matrix will have many missing values. Such missing values sometimes convey "uninterested" (as opposed to non-missing values that convey interest).

TABLE 14.9 SCHEMATIC OF MATRIX FORMAT WITH RATINGS DATA

	Item ID			
User ID	I_1	I_2	⋯	I_p
U_1	$r_{1,1}$	$r_{1,2}$	⋯	$r_{1,p}$
U_2	$r_{2,1}$	$r_{2,2}$	⋯	$r_{2,p}$
⋮				
U_n	$r_{n,1}$	$r_{n,2}$	⋯	$r_{n,p}$

When both n and p are large, it is not practical to store the preferences data $(r_{u,i})$ in an $n \times p$ table. Instead, the data can be stored in many rows of triplets of the form $(U_u, I_i, r_{u,i})$, where each triplet contains the user ID, the item ID, and the preference information.

Example 3: Netflix Prize Contest

We have been considering both association rules and collaborative filtering as unsupervised techniques, but it is possible to judge how well they do by looking at holdout data to see what users purchase and how they rate items. The famous Netflix contest, mentioned in Chapter 13, did just this and provides a useful example to illustrate collaborative filtering, though the extension into training and validation is beyond the scope of this book.

In 2006, Netflix, the largest movie rental service in North America, announced a US$ 1 million contest (www.netflixprize.com) for the purpose of improving its recommendation system called *Cinematch*. Participants were provided with a number of datasets, one for each movie. Each dataset included all the customer ratings for that movie (and the timestamp). We can think of one large combined dataset of the form [customer ID, movie ID, rating, date] where each record includes the rating given by a certain customer to a certain movie on a certain date. Ratings were on a 1–5 star scale. Contestants were asked to develop a recommendation algorithm that would improve over the existing Netflix system. Table 14.10 shows a small sample from the contest data, organized in matrix format. Rows indicate customers and columns are different movies.

TABLE 14.10 SAMPLE OF RECORDS FROM THE NETFLIX PRIZE CONTEST, FOR A SUBSET OF 10 CUSTOMERS AND 9 MOVIES

	Movie ID								
Customer ID	**1**	**5**	**8**	**17**	**18**	**28**	**30**	**44**	**48**
30878	4	1			3	3	4	5	
124105	4								
822109	5								
823519	3		1	4		4	5		
885013	4	5							
893988	3						4	4	
1248029	3					2	4		3
1503895	4								
1842128	4						3		
2238063	3								

It is interesting to note that the winning team was able to improve their system by considering not just the ratings for a movie, but *whether* a movie was rated by a particular customer or not. In other words, the information on which movies a customer decided to rate turned out to be critically informative of customers' preferences, more than simply considering the 1–5 rating information[4]:

> Collaborative filtering methods address the sparse set of rating values. However, much accuracy is obtained by also looking at other features of the data. First is the information on which movies each user chose to rate, regardless of specific rating value ("the binary view"). This played a decisive role in our 2007 solution, and reflects the fact that the movies to be rated are selected deliberately by the user, and are not a random sample.

This is an example where converting the rating information into a binary matrix of rated/unrated proved to be useful.

[4]Bell, R. M., Koren, Y., and Volinsky, C., "The BellKor 2008 Solution to the Netflix Prize", www.netflixprize.com/assets/ProgressPrize2008_BellKor.pdf.

User-Based Collaborative Filtering: "People Like You"

One approach to generating personalized recommendations for a user using collaborative filtering is based on finding users with similar preferences, and recommending items that they liked but the user hasn't purchased. The algorithm has two steps:

1. Find users who are most similar to the user of interest (neighbors). This is done by comparing the preference of our user to the preferences of other users.
2. Considering only the items that the user has *not* yet purchased, recommend the ones that are most preferred by the user's neighbors.

This is the approach behind Amazon's "Customers Who Bought This Item Also Bought..." (see Figure 14.1). It is also used in a Google search for generating the "Similar pages" link shown near each search result.

Step 1 requires choosing a distance (or proximity) metric to measure the distance between our user and the other users. Once the distances are computed, we can use a threshold on the distance or on the number of required neighbors to determine the nearest neighbors to be used in Step 2. This approach is called "user-based top-N recommendation."

A nearest-neighbors approach measures the distance of our user to each of the other users in the database, similar to the k-nearest-neighbors algorithm (see Chapter 7). The Euclidean distance measure we discussed in that chapter does not perform as well for collaborative filtering as some other measures. A popular proximity measure between two users is the Pearson correlation between their ratings. We denote the ratings of items $I_1, \ldots, I_p$ by user U_1 as $r_{1,1}, r_{1,2}, \ldots, r_{1,p}$ and their average by $\bar{r}_1$. Similarly, the ratings by user U_2 are $r_{2,1}, r_{2,2}, \ldots, r_{2,p}$, with average $\bar{r}_2$. The correlation proximity between the two users is defined by

$$\text{Corr}(U_1, U_2) = \frac{\sum (r_{1,i} - \bar{r}_1)(r_{2,i} - \bar{r}_2)}{\sqrt{\sum (r_{1,i} - \bar{r}_1)^2}\sqrt{\sum (r_{2,i} - \bar{r}_2)^2}}, \tag{14.1}$$

where the summations are only over the items co-rated by both users.

To illustrate this, let us compute the correlation between customer 30878 and customer 823519 in the small Netflix sample in Table 14.10. We'll assume that the data shown in the table is the entire information. First, we compute the average rating by each of these users:

$$\bar{r}_{30878} = (4+1+3+3+4+5)/6 = 3.333,$$
$$\bar{r}_{823519} = (3+1+4+4+5)/5 = 3.4.$$

Note that the average is computed over a different number of movies for each of these customers, because they each rated a different set of movies. The average for a customer is computed over *all* the movies that a customer rated. The calculations for the correlation involve the departures from the average, but *only for the items that they co-rated*. In this case, the co-rated movie IDs are 1, 28, and 30:

$$\text{Corr}(U_{30878}, U_{823519})$$
$$= \frac{(4-3.333)(3-3.4)+(3-3.333)(4-3.4)+(4-3.333)(5-3.4)}{\sqrt{(4-3.333)^2+(3-3.333)^2+(4-3.333)^2}\sqrt{(3-3.4)^2+(4-3.4)^2+(5-3.4)^2}}$$
$$= 0.6/1.75 = 0.34.$$

The same approach can be used when the data are in the form of a binary matrix (e.g., purchased or didn't purchase.)

Another popular measure is a variant of the Pearson correlation called *cosine similarity*. It differs from the correlation formula by not subtracting the means. Subtracting the mean in the correlation formula adjusts for users' different overall approaches to rating—for example, a customer who always rates highly vs. one who tends to give low ratings.[5]

For example, the cosine similarity between the two Netflix customers is:

$$\text{Cos Sim}(U_{30878}, U_{823519}) = \frac{4\times 3+3\times 4+4\times 5}{\sqrt{4^2+3^2+4^2}\sqrt{3^2+4^2+5^2}}$$
$$= 44/45.277 = 0.972$$

Note that when the data are in the form of a binary matrix, say, for purchase or no-purchase, the cosine similarity must be calculated over all items that either user has purchased; it cannot be limited to just the items that were co-purchased.

Collaborative filtering suffers from what is called a *cold start*: it cannot be used as is to create recommendations for new users or new items. For a user who rated a single item, the correlation coefficient between this and other users (in user-generated collaborative filtering) will have a denominator of zero and the cosine proximity will be 1 regardless of the rating. In a similar vein, users with just one item, and items with just one user, do not qualify as candidates for nearby neighbors.

[5]Correlation and cosine similarity are popular in collaborative filtering because they are computationally fast for high-dimensional sparse data, and they account both for the rating values and the number of rated items.

For a user of interest, we compute his/her similarity to each of the users in our database using a correlation, cosine similarity, or another measure. Then, in Step 2, we look only at the *k* nearest users, and among all the other items that they rated/purchased, we choose the best one and recommend it to our user. What is the best one? For binary purchase data, it is the item most purchased. For rating data, it could be the highest rated, most rated, or a weighting of the two.

The nearest-neighbors approach can be computationally expensive when we have a large database of users. One solution is to use clustering methods (see Chapter 15) to group users into homogeneous clusters in terms of their preferences, and then to measure the distance of our user to each of the clusters. This approach places the computational load on the clustering step that can take place earlier and offline; it is then cheaper (and faster) to compare our user to each of the clusters in real time. The price of clustering is less accurate recommendations, because not all the members of the closest cluster are the most similar to our user.

Item-Based Collaborative Filtering

When the number of users is much larger than the number of items, it is computationally cheaper (and faster) to find similar items rather than similar users. Specifically, when a user expresses interest in a particular item, the item-based collaborative filtering algorithm has two steps:

1. Find the items that were co-rated, or co-purchased, (by any user) with the item of interest.
2. Recommend the most popular or correlated item(s) among the similar items.

Similarity is now computed between items, instead of users. For example, in our small Netflix sample (Table 14.10), the correlation between movie 1 (with average $\bar{r}_1 = 3.7$) and movie 5 (with average $\bar{r}_5 = 3$) is:

$$\text{Corr}(I_1, I_5) = \frac{(4-3.7)(1-3)+(4-3.7)(5-3)}{\sqrt{(4-3.7)^2+(4-3.7)^2}\sqrt{(1-3)^2+(5-3)^2}} = 0.$$

The zero correlation is due to the two opposite ratings of movie 5 by the users who also rated 1. One user rated it 5 stars and the other gave it a 1 star.

In a similar fashion, we can compute similarity between all the movies. This can be done offline. In real time, for a user who rates a certain movie highly, we can look up the movie correlation table and recommend the movie with the highest positive correlation to the user's newly rated movie.

According to an industry report[6] by researchers who developed the Amazon item-to-item recommendation system,

> "[The item-based] algorithm produces recommendations in real time, scales to massive data sets, and generates high-quality recommendations."

The disadvantage of item-based recommendations is that there is less diversity between items (compared to users' taste), and therefore, the recommendations are often obvious.

Tables 14.11 and 14.12 show Python code for collaborative filtering on a simulated data similar to the Netflix data using the `Surprise` package.

TABLE 14.11 COLLABORATIVE FILTERING IN PYTHON

code for collaborative filtering: dataset preparation and definition of helper function

```
import random

random.seed(0)
nratings = 5000
randomData = pd.DataFrame({
    'itemID': [random.randint(0,99) for _ in range(nratings)],
    'userID': [random.randint(0,999) for _ in range(nratings)],
    'rating': [random.randint(1,5) for _ in range(nratings)],
})

def get_top_n(predictions, n=10):
    # First map the predictions to each user.
    byUser = defaultdict(list)
    for p in predictions:
        byUser[p.uid].append(p)

    # For each user, reduce predictions to top-n
    for uid, userPredictions in byUser.items():
        byUser[uid] = heapq.nlargest(n, userPredictions, key=lambda p: p.est)
    return byUser
```

[6]"Linden, G., Smith, B., and York J., Amazon.com Recommendations: Item-to-Item Collaborative Filtering", *IEEE Internet Computing*, vol. 7, no. 1, p. 76–80, 2003.

TABLE 14.12 COLLABORATIVE FILTERING IN PYTHON

code for collaborative filtering

```
# Convert the data set into the format required by the surprise package
# The columns must correspond to user id, item id, and ratings (in that order)
reader = Reader(rating_scale=(1, 5))
data = Dataset.load_from_df(randomData[['userID', 'itemID', 'rating']], reader)

# Split into training and test set
trainset, testset = train_test_split(data, test_size=.25, random_state=1)

## User-based filtering
# compute cosine similarity between users
sim_options = {'name': 'cosine', 'user_based': True}
algo = KNNBasic(sim_options=sim_options)
algo.fit(trainset)

# predict ratings for all pairs (u, i) that are NOT in the training set.
predictions = algo.test(testset)

# Print the recommended items for each user
top_n = get_top_n(predictions, n=4)
print('Top-4 recommended items for each user')
for uid, user_ratings in list(top_n.items())[:5]:
    print('User {}'.format(uid))
    for prediction in user_ratings:
        print('  Item {0.iid} ({0.est:.2f})'.format(prediction), end='')
    print()
```

Partial output

```
Top-3 recommended items for each user
User 6
  Item 6 (5.00)  Item 77 (2.50)  Item 60 (1.00)
User 222
  Item 77 (3.50)  Item 75 (2.78)
User 424
  Item 14 (3.50)  Item 45 (3.10)  Item 54 (2.34)
User 87
  Item 27 (3.00)  Item 54 (3.00)  Item 82 (3.00)  Item 32 (1.00)
User 121
  Item 98 (3.48)  Item 32 (2.83)
```

Rebuild model using the full dataset

```
trainset = data.build_full_trainset()
sim_options = {'name': 'cosine', 'user_based': False}
algo = KNNBasic(sim_options=sim_options)
algo.fit(trainset)
```

(*Continued*)

TABLE 14.12 COLLABORATIVE FILTERING IN PYTHON (*Continued*)

```
# Predict rating for user 383 and item 7
algo.predict(383, 7)
```

Partial output

```
Prediction(uid=383, iid=7, r_ui=None, est=2.3661840936304324, ...)
```

Advantages and Weaknesses of Collaborative Filtering

Collaborative filtering relies on the availability of subjective information regarding users' preferences. It provides useful recommendations, even for "long tail" items, if our database contains sufficient similar users (not necessarily many, but at least a few per user), so that each user can find other users with similar tastes. Similarly, the data should include sufficient per-item ratings or purchases. One limitation of collaborative filtering is therefore that it cannot generate recommendations for new users, nor for new items. There are various approaches for tackling this challenge.

User-based collaborative filtering looks for similarity in terms of highly-rated or preferred items. However, it is blind to data on low-rated or unwanted items. We can therefore not expect to use it as is for detecting unwanted items.

User-based collaborative filtering helps leverage similarities between people's tastes for providing personalized recommendations. However, when the number of users becomes very large, collaborative filtering becomes computationally difficult. Solutions include item-based algorithms, clustering of users, and dimension reduction. The most popular dimension reduction method used in such cases is singular value decomposition (SVD), a computationally superior form of principal components analysis (see Chapter 4).

Although the term "prediction" is often used to describe the output of collaborative filtering, this method is unsupervised by nature. It can be used to generate predicted ratings or purchase indication for a user, but usually we do not have the true outcome value in practice. One important way to improve recommendations generated by collaborative filtering is by getting user feedback. Once a recommendation is generated, the user can indicate whether the recommendation was adequate or not. For this reason, many recommender systems entice users to provide feedback on their recommendations.

Collaborative Filtering vs. Association Rules

While collaborative filtering and association rules are both unsupervised methods used for generating recommendations, they differ in several ways:

Frequent itemsets vs. personalized recommendations: Association rules look for frequent item combinations and will provide recommendations only for those items. In contrast, collaborative filtering provides personalized recommendations for every item, thereby catering to users with unusual taste. In this sense, collaborative filtering is useful for capturing the "long tail" of user preferences, while association rules look for the "head." This difference has implications for the data needed: association rules require data on a very large number of "baskets" (transactions) in order to find a sufficient number of baskets that contain certain combinations of items. In contrast, collaborative filtering does not require many "baskets," but does require data on as many items as possible for many users. Also, association rules operate at the basket level (our database can include multiple transactions for each user), while collaborative filtering operates at the user level.

Because association rules produce generic, impersonal rules (association-based recommendations such as Amazon's "Frequently Bought Together" display the same recommendations to all users searching for a specific item), they can be used for setting common strategies such as product placement in a store or sequencing of diagnostic tests in hospitals. In contrast, collaborative filtering generates user-specific recommendations (e.g., Amazon's "Customers Who Bought This Item Also Bought…") and is therefore a tool designed for personalization.

Transactional data vs. user data: Association rules provide recommendations of items based on their co-purchase with other items in *many transactions/baskets*. In contrast, collaborative filtering provides recommendations of items based on their co-purchase or co-rating by even a small number of other *users*. Considering distinct baskets is useful when the same items are purchased over and over again (e.g., in grocery shopping). Considering distinct users is useful when each item is typically purchased/rated once (e.g., purchases of books, music, and movies).

Binary data and ratings data:Association rules treat items as binary data (1 = purchase, 0 = nonpurchase), whereas collaborative filtering can operate on either binary data or on numerical ratings.

Two or more items: In association rules, the antecedent and consequent can each include one or more items (e.g., IF milk THEN cookies and cornflakes). Hence, a recommendation might be a bundle of the item of interest with multiple items ("buy milk, cookies, and cornflakes and receive 10% discount"). In contrast, in collaborative filtering, similarity is measured between *pairs* of items or pairs of users. A recommendation will therefore be either for a single item (the most popular item purchased by people like you, which you haven't purchased), or for multiple single items which do not necessarily relate to each other (the top two most popular items purchased by people like you, which you haven't purchased).

These distinctions are sharper for purchases and recommendations of non-popular items, especially when comparing association rules to user-based collaborative filtering. When considering what to recommend to a user who purchased a popular item, then association rules and item-based collaborative filtering might yield the same recommendation for a single item. But a user-based recommendation will likely differ. Consider a customer who purchases milk every week as well as gluten-free products (which are rarely purchased by other customers). Suppose that using association rules on the transaction database we identify the rule "IF milk THEN cookies." Then, the next time our customer purchases milk, he/she will receive a recommendation (e.g., a coupon) to purchase cookies, whether or not he/she purchased cookies, and irrespective of his/her gluten-free item purchases. In item-based collaborative filtering, we would look at all items co-purchased with milk across all users and recommend the most popular item among them (which was not purchased by our customer). This might also lead to a recommendation of cookies, because this item was not purchased by our customer.[7] Now consider user-based collaborative filtering. User-based collaborative filtering searches for similar customers—those who purchased the same set of items—and then recommend the item most commonly purchased by these neighbors, which *was not purchased by our customer*. The user-based recommendation is therefore unlikely to recommend cookies and more likely to recommend popular gluten-free items that the customer has not purchased.

14.3 | SUMMARY

Association rules (also called market basket analysis) and collaborative filtering are unsupervised methods for deducing associations between purchased items from databases of transactions. Association rules search for generic rules about items that are purchased together. The main advantage of this method is that it generates clear, simple rules of the form "IF X is purchased, THEN Y is also likely to be purchased." The method is very transparent and easy to understand.

The process of creating association rules is two-staged. First, a set of candidate rules based on frequent itemsets is generated (the Apriori algorithm being the most popular rule-generating algorithm). Then from these candidate rules, the rules that indicate the strongest association between items are selected. We use the measures of support and confidence to evaluate the uncertainty in a rule. The user also specifies minimal support and confidence values to be used in the rule generation and selection process. A third

[7]If the rule is "IF milk, THEN cookies and cornflakes" then the association rules would recommend cookies and cornflakes to a milk purchaser, while item-based collaborative filtering would recommend the most popular single item purchased with milk.

measure, the lift ratio, compares the efficiency of the rule to detect a real association compared to a random combination.

One shortcoming of association rules is the profusion of rules that are generated. There is therefore a need for ways to reduce these to a small set of useful and strong rules. An important nonautomated method to condense the information involves examining the rules for uninformative and trivial rules as well as for rules that share the same support. Another issue that needs to be kept in mind is that rare combinations tend to be ignored, because they do not meet the minimum support requirement. For this reason, it is better to have items that are approximately equally frequent in the data. This can be achieved by using higher-level hierarchies as the items. An example is to use types of books rather than titles of individual books in deriving association rules from a database of bookstore transactions.

Collaborative filtering is a popular technique used in online recommendation systems. It is based on the relationship between items formed by users who acted similarly on an item, such as purchasing or rating an item highly. User-based collaborative filtering operates on data on item–user combinations, calculates the similarities between users and provides personalized recommendations to users. An important component for the success of collaborative filtering is that users provide feedback about the recommendations provided and have sufficient information on each item. One disadvantage of collaborative filtering methods is that they cannot generate recommendations for new users or new items. Also, with a huge number of users, user-based collaborative filtering becomes computationally challenging, and alternatives such as item-based methods or dimension reduction are popularly used.

PROBLEMS

14.1 Satellite Radio Customers. An analyst at a subscription-based satellite radio company has been given a sample of data from their customer database, with the goal of finding groups of customers who are associated with one another. The data consist of company data, together with purchased demographic data that are mapped to the company data (see Table 14.13). The analyst decides to apply association rules to learn more about the associations between customers. Comment on this approach.

TABLE 14.13 SAMPLE OF DATA ON SATELLITE RADIO CUSTOMERS

Row ID	zipconvert_2	zipconvert_3	zipconvert_4	zipconvert_5	homeowner dummy	NUMCHLD	INCOME	gender dummy	WEALTH
17	0	1	0	0	1	1	5	1	9
25	1	0	0	0	1	1	1	0	7
29	0	0	0	1	0	2	5	1	8
38	0	0	0	1	1	1	3	0	4
40	0	1	0	0	1	1	4	0	8
53	0	1	0	0	1	1	4	1	8
58	0	0	0	1	1	1	4	1	8
61	1	0	0	0	1	1	1	0	7
71	0	0	1	0	1	1	4	0	5
87	1	0	0	0	1	1	4	1	8
100	0	0	0	1	1	1	4	1	8
104	1	0	0	0	1	1	1	1	5
121	0	0	1	0	1	1	4	1	5
142	1	0	0	0	0	1	5	0	8

14.2 Identifying Course Combinations. The Institute for Statistics Education at Statistics.com offers online courses in statistics and analytics, and is seeking information that will help in packaging and sequencing courses. Consider the data in the file *CourseTopics.csv*, the first few rows of which are shown in Table 14.14. These data are for purchases of online statistics courses at Statistics.com. Each row represents the courses attended by a single customer. The firm wishes to assess alternative sequencings and bundling of courses. Use association rules to analyze these data, and interpret several of the resulting rules.

TABLE 14.14 DATA ON PURCHASES OF ONLINE STATISTICS COURSES

Intro	DataMining	Survey	CatData	Regression	Forecast	DOE	SW
1	1	0	0	0	0	0	0
0	0	1	0	0	0	0	0
0	1	0	1	1	0	0	1
1	0	0	0	0	0	0	0
1	1	0	0	0	0	0	0
0	1	0	0	0	0	0	0
1	0	0	0	0	0	0	0
0	0	0	1	0	1	1	1
1	0	0	0	0	0	0	0
0	0	0	1	0	0	0	0
1	0	0	0	0	0	0	0

14.3 Recommending Courses. We again consider the data in *CourseTopics.csv* describing course purchases at Statistics.com (see Problem 14.2 and data sample in Table 14.14). We want to provide a course recommendation to a student who purchased the Regression and Forecast courses. Apply user-based collaborative filtering to the data. All recommendations will be 1. Explain why this happens.

14.4 Cosmetics Purchases. The data shown in Table 14.15 and the output in Table 14.16 are based on a subset of a dataset on cosmetic purchases (*Cosmetics.csv*) at a large chain drugstore. The store wants to analyze associations among purchases of these items for purposes of point-of-sale display, guidance to sales personnel in promoting cross-sales, and guidance for piloting an eventual time-of-purchase electronic recommender system to boost cross-sales. Consider first only the data shown in Table 14.15, given in binary matrix form.

a. Select several values in the matrix and explain their meaning.

b. Consider the results of the association rules analysis shown in Table 14.16.

i. For the first row, explain the "confidence" output and how it is calculated.

ii. For the first row, explain the "support" output and how it is calculated.

iii. For the first row, explain the "lift" and how it is calculated.

iv. For the first row, explain the rule that is represented there in words.

c. Now, use the complete dataset on the cosmetics purchases (in the file *Cosmetics.csv*). Using Python, apply association rules to these data (for *apriori* use `min_support=0.1` and `use_colnames=True`, for *association_rules* use default parameters).

  i. Interpret the first three rules in the output in words.

  ii. Reviewing the first couple of dozen rules, comment on their redundancy and how you would assess their utility.

TABLE 14.15 EXCERPT FROM DATA ON COSMETICS PURCHASES IN BINARY MATRIX FORM

Trans. #	Bag	Blush	Nail polish	Brushes	Concealer	Eyebrow pencils	Bronzer
1	0	1	1	1	1	0	1
2	0	0	1	0	1	0	1
3	0	1	0	0	1	1	1
4	0	0	1	1	1	0	1
5	0	1	0	0	1	0	1
6	0	0	0	0	1	0	0
7	0	1	1	1	1	0	1
8	0	0	1	1	0	0	1
9	0	0	0	0	1	0	0
10	1	1	1	1	0	0	0
11	0	0	1	0	0	0	1
12	0	0	1	1	1	0	1

TABLE 14.16 ASSOCIATION RULES FOR COSMETICS PURCHASES DATA

```
   lhs             rhs                 support   confidence        lift
1 {Blush,
   Concealer,
   Mascara,
   Eye.shadow,
   Lipstick}    => {Eyebrow.Pencils}    0.013   0.3023255814  7.198228128
2 {Trans.,
   Blush,
   Concealer,
   Mascara,
   Eye.shadow,
   Lipstick}    => {Eyebrow.Pencils}    0.013   0.3023255814  7.198228128
3 {Blush,
   Concealer,
   Mascara,
   Lipstick}    => {Eyebrow.Pencils}    0.013   0.2888888889  6.878306878
4 {Trans.,
   Blush,
   Concealer,
   Mascara,
   Lipstick}    => {Eyebrow.Pencils}    0.013   0.2888888889  6.878306878
5 {Blush,
   Concealer,
   Eye.shadow,
   Lipstick}    => {Eyebrow.Pencils}    0.013   0.2826086957  6.728778468
```

```
6 {Trans.,
   Blush,
   Concealer,
   Eye.shadow,
   Lipstick}   => {Eyebrow.Pencils}   0.013  0.2826086957  6.728778468
```

14.5 Course Ratings. The Institute for Statistics Education at Statistics.com asks students to rate a variety of aspects of a course as soon as the student completes it. The Institute is contemplating instituting a recommendation system that would provide students with recommendations for additional courses as soon as they submit their rating for a completed course. Consider the excerpt from student ratings of online statistics courses shown in Table 14.17, and the problem of what to recommend to student E.N.

TABLE 14.17 RATINGS OF ONLINE STATISTICS COURSES: 4 = BEST, 1 = WORST, BLANK = NOT TAKEN

	SQL	Spatial	PA 1	DM in R	Python	Forecast	R Prog	Hadoop	Regression
L N	4				3	2	4		2
M H	3	4			4				
J H	2	2							
E N	**4**			**4**			**4**		**3**
D U	4	4							
F L		4							
G L		4							
A H		3							
S A			4						
R W			2					4	
B A			4						
M G			4			4			
A F			4						
K G			3						
D S	4			2			4		

a. First consider a user-based collaborative filter. This requires computing correlations between all student pairs. For which students is it possible to compute correlations with E.N.? Compute them.

b. Based on the single nearest student to E.N., which single course should we recommend to E.N.? Explain why.

c. Use `scikit-learn` function *sklearn.metrics.pairwise.cosine_similarity*() to compute the cosine similarity between users.

d. Based on the cosine similarities of the nearest students to E.N., which course should be recommended to E.N.?

e. What is the conceptual difference between using the correlation as opposed to cosine similarities? (*Hint*: How are the missing values in the matrix handled in each case?)

f. With large datasets, it is computationally difficult to compute user-based recommendations in real time, and an item-based approach is used instead. Returning to the rating data (not the binary matrix), let's now take that approach.

i. If the goal is still to find a recommendation for E.N., for which course pairs is it possible and useful to calculate correlations?

ii. Just looking at the data, and without yet calculating course pair correlations, which course would you recommend to E.N., relying on item-based filtering? Calculate two course pair correlations involving your guess and report the results.

g. Apply item-based collaborative filtering to this dataset (using Python) and based on the results, recommend a course to E.N.

CHAPTER 15

Cluster Analysis

This chapter is about the popular unsupervised learning task of clustering, where the goal is to segment the data into a set of homogeneous clusters of records for the purpose of generating insight. Separating a dataset into clusters of homogeneous records is also useful for improving performance of supervised methods, by modeling each cluster separately rather than the entire, heterogeneous dataset. Clustering is used in a vast variety of business applications, from customized marketing to industry analysis. We describe two popular clustering approaches: *hierarchical clustering* and *k-means clustering*. In hierarchical clustering, records are sequentially grouped to create clusters, based on distances between records and distances between clusters. We describe how the algorithm works in terms of the clustering process and mention several common distance metrics used. Hierarchical clustering also produces a useful graphical display of the clustering process and results, called a dendrogram. We present dendrograms and illustrate their usefulness. *k*-means clustering is widely used in large dataset applications. In *k*-means clustering, records are allocated to one of a prespecified set of clusters, according to their distance from each cluster. We describe the *k*-means clustering algorithm and its computational advantages. Finally, we present techniques that assist in generating insight from clustering results.

Python

In this chapter, we will use pandas for data handling, `scikit-learn` and `scipy` for cluster analysis, and `matplotlib` for visualization. Use the following to import statements for the code in this chapter.

We use `scipy` to demonstrate hierarchical clustering and `scikit-learn` for non-hierarchical clustering. Both packages provide methods for both types of clustering.

import required functionality for this chapter

```
import pandas as pd
from sklearn import preprocessing
from sklearn.metrics import pairwise
from scipy.cluster.hierarchy import dendrogram, linkage, fcluster
from sklearn.cluster import KMeans
import matplotlib.pylab as plt
import seaborn as sns
from pandas.plotting import parallel_coordinates
```

15.1 | INTRODUCTION

Cluster analysis is used to form groups or clusters of similar records based on several measurements made on these records. The key idea is to characterize the clusters in ways that would be useful for the aims of the analysis. This idea has been applied in many areas, including astronomy, archaeology, medicine, chemistry, education, psychology, linguistics, and sociology. Biologists, for example, have made extensive use of classes and subclasses to organize species. A spectacular success of the clustering idea in chemistry was Mendeleev's periodic table of the elements.

One popular use of cluster analysis in marketing is for *market segmentation:* customers are segmented based on demographic and transaction history information, and a marketing strategy is tailored for each segment. In countries such as India, where customer diversity is extremely location-sensitive, chain stores often perform market segmentation at the store level, rather than chain-wide (called "micro segmentation"). Another use is for *market structure analysis:* identifying groups of similar products according to competitive measures of similarity. In marketing and political forecasting, clustering of neighborhoods using US postal zip codes has been used successfully to group neighborhoods by lifestyles. Claritas, a company that pioneered this approach, grouped neighborhoods into 40 clusters using various measures of consumer expenditure and demographics. Examining the clusters enabled Claritas to come up with evocative names, such as "Bohemian Mix," "Furs and Station Wagons," and "Money and Brains," for the groups that captured the dominant lifestyles. Knowledge of lifestyles can be used to estimate the potential demand for products (such as sports utility vehicles) and services (such as pleasure cruises). Similarly, sales organizations will derive customer segments and give them names—"personas"—to focus sales efforts.

In finance, cluster analysis can be used for creating *balanced portfolios*: Given data on a variety of investment opportunities (e.g., stocks), one may find clusters based on financial performance variables such as return (daily, weekly, or monthly), volatility, beta, and other characteristics, such as industry and market capitalization. Selecting securities from different clusters can help create a balanced portfolio. Another application of cluster analysis in finance is for *industry analysis*: For a given industry, we are interested in finding groups of similar firms based on measures such as growth rate, profitability, market size, product range, and presence in various international markets. These groups can then be analyzed in order to understand industry structure and to determine, for instance, who is a competitor.

An interesting and unusual application of cluster analysis, described in Berry and Linoff (1997), is the design of a new set of sizes for army uniforms for women in the US Army. The study came up with a new clothing size system with only 20 sizes, where different sizes fit different body types. The 20 sizes are combinations of 5 measurements: chest, neck, and shoulder circumference, sleeve outseam, and neck-to-buttock length (for further details, see McCullugh et al., 1998). This example is important because it shows how a completely new insightful view can be gained by examining clusters of records.

Cluster analysis can be applied to huge amounts of data. For instance, Internet search engines use clustering techniques to cluster queries that users submit. These can then be used for improving search algorithms. The objective of this chapter is to describe the key ideas underlying the most commonly used techniques for cluster analysis and to lay out their strengths and weaknesses.

Typically, the basic data used to form clusters are a table of measurements on several variables, where each column represents a variable and a row represents a record. Our goal is to form groups of records so that similar records are in the same group. The number of clusters may be prespecified or determined from the data.

Example: State-wise Virus Recoveries

The response to covid-19 virus pandemic in India has affected almost every state. The initial lockdown (Lockdown1) started in the last week of March 2020, and in subsequent phases, states were allowed to decide on the unlocking conditions.

A dataset, *India_Cov_Jun2020.csv*, of the majority of Indian states compiled from various public sources that comprise key state profile dimensions, recovery status of people, and percentage of districts affected in each state by the pandemic towards the end of June 2020 is used here to explain the application of clustering techniques. Table 15.1 shows details of sample data and a description of variables.

Clustering recovery segments based on state or district profiles could help with the governance of virus control based on models of demographic profiles. It may bring us clarity to processes that are efficient in design and help execution of facilities, communication, and overall monitoring, apart from other necessary support based on the status of viral spread and available prevention measures.

TABLE 15.1 DATA OF VARIOUS INDIAN STATES- PROFILE AND COVID STATUS ON 26-6-2020

State	Density	SexRatio	Literacy	Lit_Rate_M	Lit_Rate_F	Conf_Cases	Recovery	Casuality	Dists_Affect
Uttar Pradesh	829	912	69.72	79.24	59.26	20943	0.65	0.0443	0.69
Maharashtra	365	929	82.91	89.82	75.48	152765	0.52	0.0818	0.89
Bihar	1106	918	63.82	73.39	53.33	8716	0.78	0.0085	0.37
West Bengal	1028	950	77.08	82.67	71.16	16190	0.65	0.0552	0.74
Andhra Pradesh	308	993	67.66	75.56	59.74	11489	0.45	0.0277	0.85
Madhya Pradesh	236	931	70.63	80.53	60.02	12798	0.77	0.0528	0.49
Tamil Nadu	555	996	80.33	86.81	73.86	74622	0.55	0.0226	0.92
Rajasthan	200	928	67.06	80.51	52.66	16660	0.78	0.0283	0.79
Karnataka	319	973	75.6	82.85	68.13	11005	0.63	0.0254	0.7
Gujarat	308	919	79.31	87.23	70.73	30095	0.73	0.0744	0.82
Orissa	270	979	73.45	82.4	64.36	6180	0.72	0.0038	0.33

Variable Descriptlon

Variable	Descriptlon
State	Name of State/Uniion Territory
Density	Population/Area of the State/UT as per census 2011
SexRatio	Females vs Males ratio (per 1000 men)
Literacy	Overall literacy ratio as per census 2011
Lit_Rate_M	Male literacy ratio as per census 2011
Lit_Rate_F	Female literacy ratio as per census 2011
Conf_Cases	Confirmed cases of Covid-19 in the state as on 26-6-2020
Recovery	Recovery % of Covld-19 in the state as on 26-6-2020
Casuality	Casuality % of Covld-19 in the state as on 26-6-2020
Dists_Affect	Percentage of districts affected at the end June 2020

(*Sources:* https://www.mohfw.gov.in/ and https://en.wikipedia.org/wiki/Demographics_of_India)

For simplicity, let us consider only two of the measurements: the literacy rate of males (Lit_Rate_M) and recovery rate (Recovery). Figure 15.1 shows a scatter plot of these two variables, with labels marking each state. At first glance, there appear to be two or three clusters of states: one with states that have high recovery rates and low male literacy rates, a second with high recovery rates and relatively low male literacy rates, and a third relatively spread-out cluster with low recovery rates and evenly distributed male literacy rates.

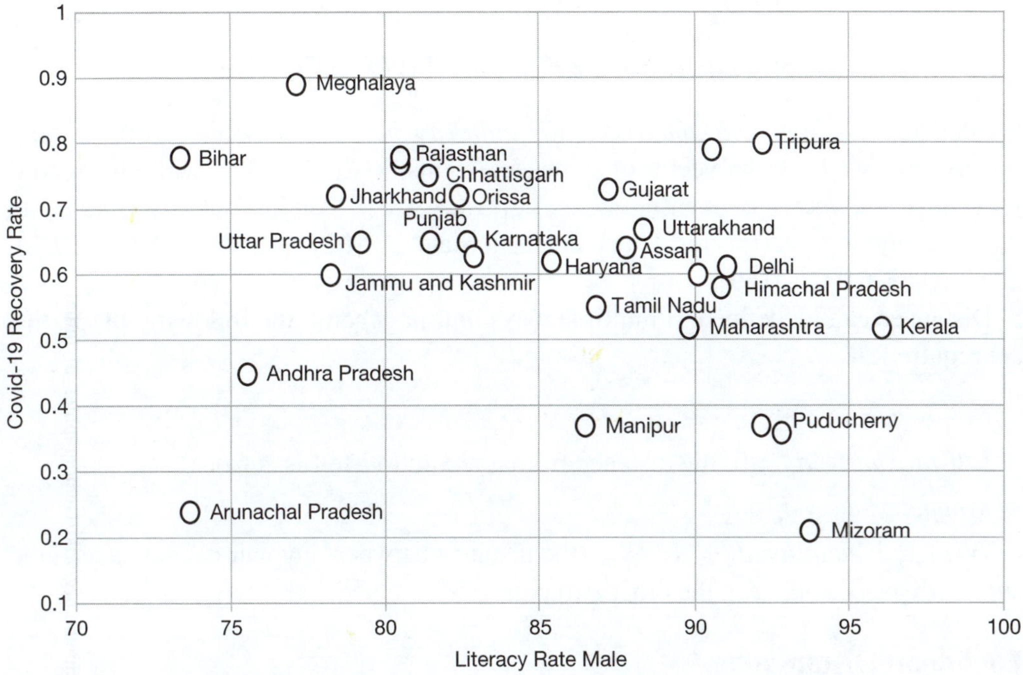

FIGURE 15.1 SCATTER PLOT OF LITERACY RATE OF MALES VERUS COVID-19 RECOVERY RATE

We can therefore think of cluster analysis as a more formal algorithm that measures the distance between records, and according to these distances (here, two-dimensional distances), forms clusters.

Two general types of clustering algorithms for a dataset of n records are hierarchical and non-hierarchical clustering:

Hierarchical methods: can be either *agglomerative* or *divisive*. Agglomerative methods begin with n clusters and sequentially merge similar clusters until a single cluster is obtained. Divisive methods work in the opposite direction, starting with one cluster that includes all records. Hierarchical methods are especially useful when the goal is to arrange the clusters into a natural hierarchy.

Non-hierarchical methods: such as *k*-means. Using a prespecified number of clusters, the method assigns records to each cluster. These methods are generally less computationally intensive and are therefore preferred with very large datasets.

We concentrate here on the two most popular methods: hierarchical agglomerative clustering and *k*-means clustering. In both cases, we need to define two types of distances: distance between two records and distance between two clusters. In both cases, there is a variety of metrics that can be used.

15.2 | MEASURING DISTANCE BETWEEN TWO RECORDS

We denote by d_{ij} a *distance metric*, or *dissimilarity measure*, between records i and j. For record i we have the vector of p measurements $(x_{i1}, x_{i2}, \ldots, x_{ip})$, while for record j we have the vector of measurements $(x_{j1}, x_{j2}, \ldots, x_{jp})$. For example, we can write the measurement vector for Uttar Pradesh State as $[829, 912, 69.72, 79.24, 59.26, 20943, 0.65, 0.0443, 0.69]$.

Distances can be defined in multiple ways, but in general, the following properties are required:

Non-negative: $d_{ij} \geq 0$

Self-proximity: $d_{ii} = 0$ (the distance from a record to itself is zero)

Symmetry: $d_{ij} = d_{ji}$

Triangle inequality: $d_{ij} \leq d_{ik} + d_{kj}$ (the distance between any pair cannot exceed the sum of distances between the other two pairs)

Euclidean Distance

The most popular distance measure is the *Euclidean distance*, d_{ij}, which between two records, i and j, is defined by

$$d_{ij} = \sqrt{(x_{i1} - x_{j1})^2 + (x_{i2} - x_{j2})^2 + \cdots + (x_{ip} - x_{jp})^2}.$$

For instance, the Euclidean distance between Uttar Pradesh and Maharashtra can be computed from the raw data by

$$\begin{aligned} d_{12} &= \sqrt{(829 - 365)^2 + (929 - 912)^2 + \cdots + (0.89 - 0.69)^2} \\ &= 131822.819. \end{aligned}$$

To compute Euclidean distance in Python, see Table 15.2.

TABLE 15.2 DISTANCE MATRIX BETWEEN PAIRS OF THE FIRST FOUR STATES

code for computing distance between records

```
#   read data from csv file
icov=pd.read_csv('India_Cov_Jun2020.csv')
#set row names to the utilities column
icov.set_index('State ', inplace= True)

# compute Euclidean distance
d = pairwise.pairwise_distances(icov, metric='euclidean')
pd.DataFrame(d, columns=icov.index, index=icov.index)
```

Partial Output

	Uttar Pradesh	Maharashtra	Bihar	West Bengal
Maharashtra	131822.81979			
Bihar	12968.69801	152787.04167		
West Bengal	5041.50207	144859.66508	7927.48794	
Andhra Pradesh	9468.69242	141276.02841	2942.29787	4986.40248
Madhya Pradesh	8166.58056	139967.06116	4329.65524	3597.84

Normalizing Numerical Measurements

The measure computed above is highly influenced by the scale of each variable, so that variables with larger scales (e.g., Conf_Cases) have a much greater influence over the total distance. It is therefore customary to *normalize* continuous measurements before computing the Euclidean distance. This converts all measurements to the same scale. Normalizing a measurement means subtracting the average and dividing by the standard deviation (normalized values are also called *z-scores*). For instance, the Conf_Cases across the 30 states is 16233.83 and the standard deviation is 32002.09. The normalized Conf_Cases for Uttar Pradesh is therefore $(20943 - 16233.83)/32002.09 = 0.147152$.

Returning to the India_Cov_Jun2020 data with only two measurements (Lit_Rate_M and Recovery), we first normalize the measurements (see Table 15.3), and then compute the Euclidean distance between each pair. Table 15.4 gives these pair-wise distances for the first five states. A similar table can be constructed for all 30 states.

Other Distance Measures for Numerical Data

It is important to note that the choice of the distance measure plays a major role in cluster analysis. The main guideline is domain dependent: What exactly is being measured? How are the different measurements related? What scale should each measurement be treated as (numerical, ordinal, or nominal)? Are there outliers? Finally, depending on the goal of the analysis, should the clusters be distinguished mostly by a

TABLE 15.3 ORIGINAL AND NORMALIZED VALUES OF MALE LITERACY RATE (LIT_RATE_M AND NORM_LIT_RATE_M) AND RECOVERY RATE (RECOVERY AND NORM_RECOVERY)

State	Lit_Rate_M	Recovery	Norm_Lit_Rate_M	Norm_Recovery
Uttar Pradesh	79.24	0.65	–0.905908286	0.253861169
Maharashtra	89.82	0.52	0.768924484	–0.519622081
Bihar	73.39	0.78	–1.831973664	1.02734442
West Bengal	82.67	0.65	–0.362933201	0.253861169
Andhra Pradesh	75.56	0.45	–1.488458814	–0.936113062
Madhya Pradesh	80.53	0.77	–0.701698997	0.967845709
Tamil Nadu	86.81	0.55	0.292436144	–0.341125946
Rajasthan	80.51	0.78	–0.704865033	1.02734442
Karnataka	82.85	0.63	–0.334438881	0.134863746
Gujarat	87.23	0.73	0.358922889	0.729850862
Orissa	82.4	0.72	–0.40567468	0.670352151
Kerala	96.02	0.52	1.750395483	–0.519622081
Jharkhand	78.45	0.72	–1.030966687	0.670352151
Assam	87.81	0.64	0.450737918	0.194362458
Punjab	81.48	0.65	–0.551312312	0.253861169
Chhattisgarh	81.45	0.75	–0.556061365	0.848848285
Haryana	85.38	0.62	0.066064607	0.075365035
Delhi	91.03	0.61	0.960469631	0.015866323
Jammu and Kashmir	78.26	0.60	–1.061044024	–0.043632389
Uttarakhand	88.33	0.67	0.533054841	0.372858593
Himachal Pradesh	90.83	0.58	0.928809276	–0.162629812
Tripura	92.18	0.80	1.142516671	1.146341843
Meghalaya	77.17	0.89	–1.233592958	1.681830248
Manipur	86.49	0.37	0.241779576	–1.412102755
Goa	92.81	0.36	1.242246788	–1.471601467
Arunachal Pradesh	73.69	0.24	–1.784483132	–2.185586006
Puducherry	92.12	0.37	1.133018564	–1.412102755
Mizoram	93.72	0.21	1.386301403	–2.364082141
Chandigarh	90.54	0.79	0.882901761	1.086843132
Andaman and Nicobar	90.11	0.60	0.814831998	–0.043632389

(*Sources:* https://www.mohw.gov.in/ and https://en.wikipedia.org/wiki/Demographics_of_Inida

small set of measurements, or should they be separated by multiple measurements that weight moderately?

Although Euclidean distance is the most widely used distance, it has three main features that need to be kept in mind. First, as mentioned earlier, it is highly scale dependent. Changing the units of one variable (e.g., from rupees to '000rupees) can have a huge influence on the results. Normalizing is therefore a common solution. But unequal weighting should be considered if we want the clusters to depend more on certain

TABLE 15.4 DISTANCE MATRIX BETWEEN PAIRS OF THE FIRST FOUR STATES POST-NORMALIZED MEASUREMENTS

code for computing distance between records

```
# scikit-learn uses population standard deviation
#icov_norm = icov.apply(preprocessing.scale, axis=0) ( not using this method in current case)

# pandas uses sample standard deviation
icov_norm = (icov - icov.mean())/icov.std()

# compute normalized distance based on normalized values obtained for Literacy rate and
Recovery rate
d_norm = pairwise.pairwise_distances(icov_norm[['Lit_Rate_M', 'Recovery']],metric='euclidean')
pd.DataFrame(d_norm, columns=icov.index, index=icov.index)
```

Partial Output

	Uttar Pradesh	Maharashtra	Bihar	West Bengal
Maharashtra	1.84481466			
Bihar	1.20659580	3.02618184		
West Bengal	0.54297509	1.37090414	1.66022776	
Andhra Pradesh	1.32491652	2.29548341	1.99328065	1.63793974

30 rows × 30 columns

measurements and less on others. The second feature of Euclidean distance is that it completely ignores the relationship between the measurements. Thus, if the measurements are in fact strongly correlated, a different distance (such as the statistical distance, described later) is likely to be a better choice. Third, Euclidean distance is sensitive to outliers. If the data are believed to contain outliers and careful removal is not a choice, the use of more robust distances (such as the Manhattan distance, described later) is preferred.

Additional popular distance metrics often used (for reasons such as the ones above) are:

Correlation-based similarity: Sometimes it is more natural or convenient to work with a similarity measure between records rather than distance, which measures dissimilarity. A popular similarity measure is the square of the Pearson correlation coefficient, r_{ij}^2, where the correlation coefficient is defined by

$$r_{ij} = \frac{\sum_{m=1}^{p}(x_{im} - \bar{x}_m)(x_{jm} - \bar{x}_m)}{\sqrt{\sum_{m=1}^{p}(x_{im} - \bar{x}_m)^2 \sum_{m=1}^{p}(x_{jm} - \bar{x}_m)^2}}. \tag{15.1}$$

Such measures can always be converted to distance measures. In the example above, we could define a distance measure $d_{ij} = 1 - r_{ij}^2$.

Statistical distance (also called Mahalanobis distance): This metric has an advantage over the other metrics mentioned in that it takes into account the correlation between measurements. With this metric, measurements that are highly correlated with other measurements do not contribute as much as those that are uncorrelated or mildly correlated. The statistical distance between records i and j is defined as

$$d_{i,j} = \sqrt{(\mathbf{x}_i - \mathbf{x}_j)' S^{-1} (\mathbf{x}_i - \mathbf{x}_j)},$$

where $\mathbf{x}_i$ and $\mathbf{x}_j$ are p-dimensional vectors of the measurements values for records i and j, respectively; and S is the covariance matrix for these vectors ($'$, a transpose operation, simply turns a column vector into a row vector). S^{-1} is the inverse matrix of S, which is the p-dimension extension to division. For further information on statistical distance, see Chapter 12.

Manhattan distance ("city block"): This distance looks at the absolute differences rather than squared differences, and is defined by

$$d_{ij} = \sum_{m=1}^{p} | x_{im} - x_{jm} | .$$

Maximum coordinate distance: This distance looks only at the measurement on which records i and j deviate most. It is defined by

$$d_{ij} = \max_{m=1,2,\ldots,p} | x_{im} - x_{jm} | .$$

Distance Measures for Categorical Data

In the case of measurements with binary values, it is more intuitively appealing to use similarity measures than distance measures. Suppose that we have binary values for all the p measurements, and for records i and j we have the following 2×2 table:

		Record *j*		
		0	1	
Record *i*	0	*a*	*b*	*a* + *b*
	1	*c*	*d*	*c* + *d*
		a + *c*	*b* + *d*	*p*

where a denotes the number of variables for which records i and j do not have that attribute (they each have value 0 on that attribute), d is the number of variables for which the two records have the attribute present, and so on. The most useful similarity measures in this situation are:

Matching coefficient: $(a + d)/p$.

Jaquard's coefficient: $d/(b + c + d)$. This coefficient ignores zero matches. This is desirable when we do not want to consider two people to be similar simply because a large number of characteristics are absent in both. For example, if *owns a Corvette* is one of the variables, a matching "yes" would be evidence of similarity, but a matching "no" tells us little about whether the two people are similar.

Distance Measures for Mixed Data

When the measurements are mixed (some continuous and some binary), a similarity coefficient suggested by Gower is very useful. *Gower's similarity measure* is a weighted average of the distances computed for each variable, after scaling each variable to a [0, 1] scale. It is defined as

$$s_{ij} = \frac{\sum_{m=1}^{p} w_{ijm} s_{ijm}}{\sum_{m=1}^{p} w_{ijm}},$$

where s_{ijm} is the similarity between records i and j on measurement m, and w_{ijm} is a binary weight given to the corresponding distance.

The similarity measures s_{ijm} and weights w_{ijm} are computed as follows:

1. For continuous measurements, $s_{ijm} = 1 - \frac{|x_{im} - x_{jm}|}{\max(x_m) - \min(x_m)}$ and $w_{ijm} = 1$ unless the value for measurement m is unknown for one or both of the records, in which case $w_{ijm} = 0$.
2. For binary measurements, $s_{ijm} = 1$ if $x_{im} = x_{jm} = 1$ and 0 otherwise. $w_{ijm} = 1$ unless $x_{im} = x_{jm} = 0$.
3. For nonbinary categorical measurements, $s_{ijm} = 1$ if both records are in the same category, and otherwise $s_{ijm} = 0$. As in continuous measurements, $w_{ijm} = 1$ unless the category for measurement m is unknown for one or both of the records, in which case $w_{ijm} = 0$.

15.3 | MEASURING DISTANCE BETWEEN TWO CLUSTERS

We define a cluster as a set of one or more records. How do we measure distance between clusters? The idea is to extend measures of *distance between records* into *distances between clusters*. Consider cluster A, which includes the m records $A_1, A_2, \ldots, A_m$ and cluster B, which includes n records $B_1, B_2, \ldots, B_n$. The most widely used measures of distance between clusters are:

Minimum Distance

The distance between the pair of records A_i and B_j that are closest:

$$\min(\text{distance}(A_i, B_j)), \quad i = 1, 2, \ldots, m; \quad j = 1, 2, \ldots, n.$$

Maximum Distance

The distance between the pair of records A_i and B_j that are farthest:

$$\max(\text{distance}(A_i, B_j)), \quad i = 1, 2, \ldots, m; \quad j = 1, 2, \ldots, n.$$

Average Distance

The average distance of all possible distances between records in one cluster and records in the other cluster:

$$\text{Average}(\text{distance}(A_i, B_j)), \quad i = 1, 2, \ldots, m; \quad j = 1, 2, \ldots, n.$$

Centroid Distance

The distance between the two cluster centroids. A *cluster centroid* is the vector of measurement averages across all the records in that cluster. For cluster A, this is the vector $\bar{x}_A = \left[(1/m \sum_{i=1}^{m} x_{1i}, \ldots, 1/m \sum_{i=1}^{m} x_{pi})\right]$. The centroid distance between clusters A and B is

$$\text{distance}(\bar{x}_{\text{A}}, \bar{x}_{\text{B}}).$$

Minimum distance, maximum distance, and centroid distance are illustrated visually for two dimensions with a map selected states of India in Figure 15.2.

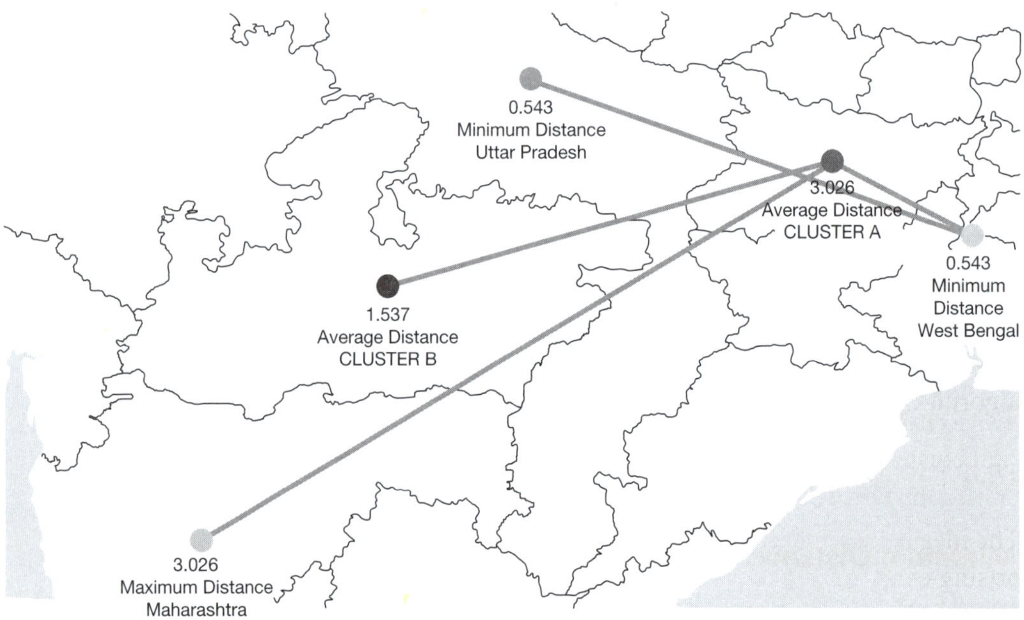

FIGURE 15.2 TWO-DIMENSIONAL REPRESENTATION OF DISTANCE MEASURES OF FOUR STATES GROUPED IN TWO CLUSTERS A AND B

For instance, consider the first two states (Uttar Pradesh and Maharashtra) as cluster *A*, and the next two states (Bihar and West Bengal) as cluster *B*. Using the normalized scores in Table 15.3 and the distance matrix in Table 15.4, we can compute each of the distances described above. Using Euclidean distance for each distance calculation, we get:

- The closest pair is Uttar Pradesh and West Bengal and therefore the minimum distance between clusters *A* and *B* is 0.543.
- The farthest pair is Maharashtra and Bihar and therefore the maximum distance between clusters *A* and *B* is 3.026.
- The average distance is (1.206 + 0.543 + 3.026 + 1.371)/4 = 1.5365
- The centroid of cluster *A* is [(−0.9059 + 0.7689)/2, (0.2538 − 0.5196)/2] = [−0.0685, −0.01329]
- The centroid of cluster *B* is [(−1.8319 − 0.3629)/2, (1.0273 + 0.2538)/2] = [−1.0974, 0.6405]
- The distance between two centroids is then

$$\sqrt{(-0.0685 + 1.0974)^2 + (-0.01329 - 0.6405)^2} = 1.2190$$

In deciding among clustering methods, domain knowledge is key. If you have good reason to believe that the clusters might be chain- or sausage-like, minimum distance would be a good choice. This method does not require that cluster members all be close to one another, only that the new members being added be close to one of the existing members. An example of an application where this might be the case would be characteristics of crops planted in long rows, or disease outbreaks along navigable waterways that are the main areas of settlement in a region. Another example is laying and finding mines (land or marine). Minimum distance is also fairly robust to small deviations in the distances. However, adding or removing data can influence it greatly.

Maximum and average distance are better choices if you know that the clusters are more likely to be spherical (e.g., customers clustered on the basis of numerous attributes). If you do not know the probable nature of the cluster, these are good default choices, since most clusters tend to be spherical in nature.

We now move to a more detailed description of the two major types of clustering algorithms: hierarchical (agglomerative) and non-hierarchical.

15.4 | HIERARCHICAL (AGGLOMERATIVE) CLUSTERING

The idea behind hierarchical agglomerative clustering is to start with each cluster comprising exactly one record and then progressively agglomerating (combining) the two nearest clusters until there is just one cluster left at the end, which consists of all the records.

Returning to the small example of four states and two measures (Lit_Rate_M and Recovery) and using the distance matrix (Table 15.4), the first step in the hierarchical clustering would join Uttar Pradesh and West Bengal, which are the closest (using normalized measurements and Euclidean distance). Next, we would recalculate a 3 × 3 distance matrix that would have the distances between these three clusters: {Uttar Pradesh and West Bengal}, {Maharashtra}, and {Bihar}. At this point, we use a measure of distance between clusters such as the ones described in Section 15.3. Each of these distances (minimum, maximum, average, and centroid distance) can be implemented in the hierarchical scheme as described below.

HIERARCHICAL AGGLOMERATIVE CLUSTERING ALGORITHM:

1. Start with n clusters (each record = cluster).
2. The two closest records are merged into one cluster.
3. At every step, the two clusters with the smallest distance are merged. This means that either single records are added to existing clusters or two existing clusters are combined.

Single Linkage

In *single linkage clustering*, the distance measure that we use is the minimum distance (the distance between the nearest pair of records in the two clusters, one record in each cluster). In our states example, we would compute the distances between each of {Uttar Pradesh and West Bengal}, {Maharashtra}, and {Bihar} to create the 3 × 3 distance matrix shown in Table 15.5. The next step would consolidate {Bihar} with {Uttar Pradesh-West Bengal} because these two clusters are closest. The distance matrix will again be recomputed (this time it will be 2 × 2), and so on.

This method has a tendency to cluster together at an early stage records that are distant from each other because of a chain of intermediate records in the same cluster. Such clusters have elongated sausage-like shapes when visualized as objects in space.

TABLE 15.5 DISTANCE MATRIX AFTER UTTAR PRADESH AND WEST BENGAL CLUSTER TOGETHER USING SINGLE LINKAGE

	Uttar Pradesh-West Bengal	Maharashtra	Bihar
Uttar Pradesh-West Bengal	0		
Maharashtra	min (1.84481466, 1.37090414)	0	
Bihar	min (1.20659580, 1.66022776)	3.026181840	0

Complete Linkage

In *complete linkage clustering*, the distance between two clusters is the maximum distance (between the farthest pair of records). If we used complete linkage with the four-states example, the recomputed distance matrix would be equivalent to Table 15.5, except that the "min" function would be replaced with a "max."

This method tends to produce clusters at the early stages with records that are within a narrow range of distances from each other. If we visualize them as objects in space, the records in such clusters would have roughly spherical shapes.

Average Linkage

Average linkage clustering is based on the average distance between clusters (between all possible pairs of records). If we used average linkage with the four-states example, the recomputed distance matrix would be equivalent to Table 15.5, except that the "min" function would be replaced with "average." This method is also called *Unweighted Pair-Group Method using Averages* (UPGMA).

Note that unlike average linkage, the results of the single and complete linkage methods depend only on the ordering of the inter-record distances. Linear transformations of the distances (and other transformations that do not change the ordering) do not affect the results.

Centroid Linkage

Centroid linkage clustering is based on centroid distance, where clusters are represented by their mean values for each variable, which forms a vector of means. The distance between two clusters is the distance between these two vectors. In average linkage, each pairwise distance is calculated, and the average of all such distances is calculated. In contrast, in centroid distance clustering, just one distance is calculated: the distance between group means. This method is also called *Unweighted Pair-Group Method using Centroids* (UPGMC).

Ward's Method

Ward's method is also agglomerative, in that it joins records and clusters together progressively to produce larger and larger clusters, but operates slightly differently from the general approach described above. Ward's method considers the "loss of information" that occurs when records are clustered together. When each cluster has one record, there is no loss of information and all individual values remain available. When records are joined together and represented in clusters, information about an individual record is replaced by the information for the cluster to which it belongs. To measure loss of information, Ward's method employs a measure "error sum of squares" (ESS) that measures the difference between individual records and a group mean.

This is easiest to see in univariate data. For example, consider the values (2, 6, 5, 6, 2, 2, 2, 2, 0, 0, 0) with a mean of 2.5. Their ESS is equal to

$$(2 - 2.5)^2 + (6 - 2.5)^2 + (5 - 2.5)^2 + \cdots + (0 - 2.5)^2 = 50.5.$$

The loss of information associated with grouping the values into a single group is therefore 50.5. Now group the records into four groups: (0, 0, 0), (2, 2, 2, 2), (5), (6, 6). The loss of information is the sum of the ESS for each group, which is 0 (each record in each group is equal to the mean for that group, so the ESS for each group is 0). Thus, clustering the 10 records into 4 clusters results in no loss of information, and this would be the first step in Ward's method. In moving to a smaller number of clusters, Ward's method would choose the configuration that results in the smallest incremental loss of information.

Ward's method tends to result in convex clusters that are of roughly equal size, which can be an important consideration in some applications (e.g., in establishing meaningful customer segments).

Dendrograms: Displaying Clustering Process and Results

A *dendrogram* is a treelike diagram that summarizes the process of clustering. On the x-axis are the records. Similar records are joined by lines whose vertical length reflects the distance between the records. Figure 15.3 shows the dendrograms that results from clustering the 30 states using the 8 normalized measurements, Euclidean distance, once with single linkage (a) and once with average linkage (b).

By choosing a cutoff distance on the y-axis, a set of clusters is created. Visually, this means drawing a horizontal line on a dendrogram. Records with connections below the horizontal line (i.e., their distance is smaller than the cutoff distance) belong to the same cluster. For example, setting the cutoff distance to 1.0 on the single linkage dendrogram in Figure 15.3(a) results in six clusters. The six clusters are (from left to right on the dendrogram):

{Andhra Pradesh, Arunachal Pradesh}, {Manipur, Mizoram, Goa, Puduchery}, {Jharkhand, Orissa, Chhattisgarh, Madhya Pradesh, Rajasthan, Punjab, West Bengal, Karnataka, Uttar Pradesh, Jammu & Kashmir}, {Bihar, Meghalaya}, {Kerala}, and {Others}. We will have four clusters if we cutoff at 1.5.

If we want six clusters using average linkage, we can choose a cutoff distance of 0.9. The resulting six clusters are slightly different. Table 15.6 shows the results for the single linkage and the average linkage clustering with six clusters. Each record is assigned a cluster number. While some records remain in the same cluster in both methods (e.g., Uttar Pradesh, West Bengal, Madhya Pradesh, Rajasthan, and Karnataka).

code for running hierarchical clustering and generating a dendrogram

```
# in linkage() set argument method =
# 'single', 'complete', 'average', 'weighted', centroid', 'median', 'ward'
from matplotlib.pyplot import figure
fig, ax = plt.subplots(1,figsize=(16, 6), dpi=80 )
Z = linkage(icov_norm, method='single')
dendrogram(Z, labels=icov_norm.index, color_threshold=2.75)
Z1 = linkage(icov_norm, method='average')
dendrogram(Z1, labels=icov_norm.index, color_threshold=3.6)
```

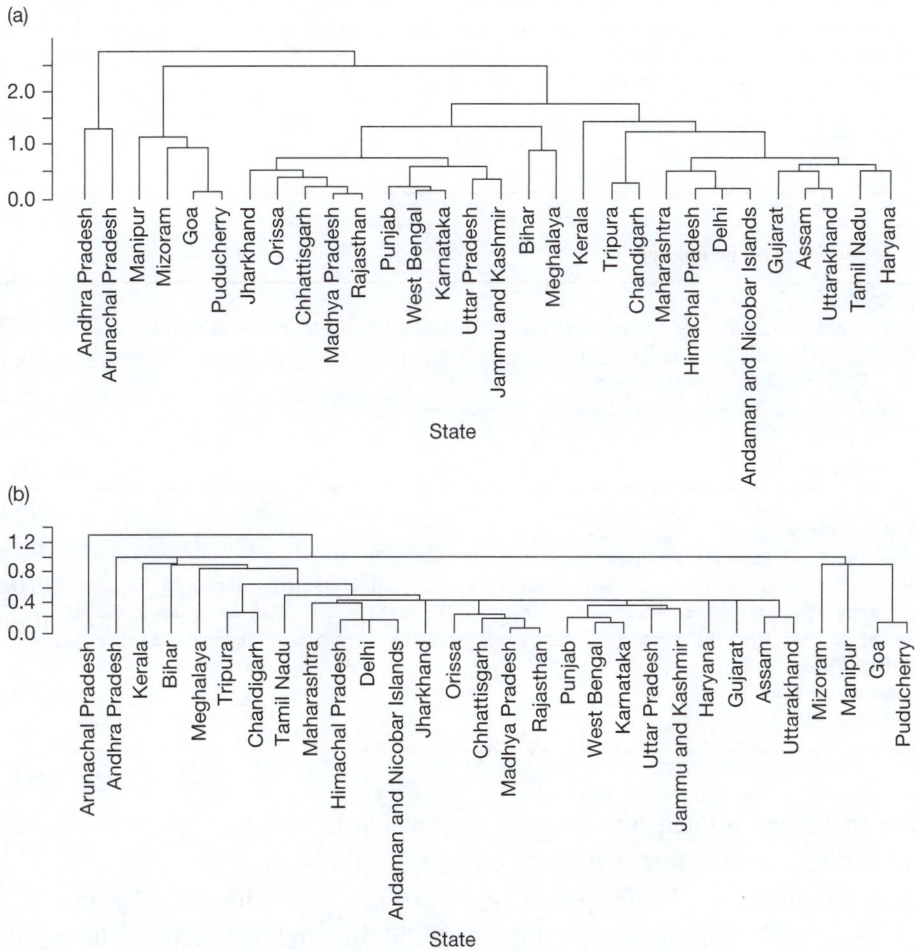

FIGURE 15.3 DENDROGRAM: SINGLE LINKAGE (a) AND AVERAGE LINKAGE (b) FOR ALL STATES, USING ALL MEASUREMENTS, SHOWS CLUSTERS WITH MULTIPLE MEMBERS

TABLE 15.6 COMPUTING CLUSTER MEMBERSHIP BY "CUTTING" THE DENDROGRAM

code for single linkage

```
memb = fcluster(linkage(icov_norm, method='single'), 6, criterion='maxclust')
memb = pd.Series(memb, index=icov_norm.index)
for key, item in memb.groupby(memb):
print(key, ': ', ', '.join(item.index))
```

Output

```
1 :  Delhi
2 :  Chandigarh
3 :  Uttar Pradesh, Bihar, West Bengal, Andhra Pradesh, Madhya Pradesh, Tamil Nadu,
     Rajasthan, Karnataka, Gujarat, Orissa, Jharkhand, Assam, Punjab, Chhattisgarh, Haryana,
     Jammu_Kashmir, Uttarakhand, Himachal Pradesh, Tripura, Meghalaya, Manipur, Goa,
     Puducherry, Mizoram, Andaman_Nicobar Islands
4 :  Kerala
5 :  Arunachal Pradesh
6 :  Maharashtra
```

code for average linkage

```
memb = fcluster(linkage(icov_norm, method='average'), 6, criterion='maxclust')
memb = pd.Series(memb, index=icov_norm.index)
for key, item in memb.groupby(memb):
print(key, ': ', ', '.join(item.index))
```

Output

```
1 :  Delhi, Chandigarh
2 :  Kerala, Goa, Puducherry, Mizoram
3 :  Uttar Pradesh, Bihar, West Bengal, Andhra Pradesh, Madhya Pradesh, Rajasthan, Karnataka,
     Gujarat, Orissa, Jharkhand, Assam, Punjab, Chhattisgarh, Haryana, Jammu_Kashmir,
     Uttarakhand, Himachal Pradesh, Tripura, Meghalaya, Manipur, Andaman_Nicobar Islands
4 :  Tamil Nadu
5 :  Arunachal Pradesh
6 :  Maharashtra
```

Note that if we wanted five clusters, they would be identical to the six given earlier, with the exception that two of the clusters would be merged into a single cluster. For example, in the single linkage case, the two right-most clusters in the dendrogram would be merged into one cluster. In general, all hierarchical methods have clusters that are nested within each other as we decrease the number of clusters. This is a valuable property for interpreting clusters and is essential in certain applications, such as taxonomy of varieties of living organisms.

Validating Clusters

One important goal of cluster analysis is to come up with *meaningful clusters*. Since there are many variations that can be chosen, it is important to make sure that the resulting clusters are valid, in the sense that they really generate some insight. To see whether the cluster analysis is useful, consider each of the following aspects:

1. *Cluster interpretability*: Is the interpretation of the resulting clusters reasonable? To interpret the clusters, explore the characteristics of each cluster by
   a. Obtaining summary statistics (e.g., average, min, max) from each cluster on each measurement that was used in the cluster analysis
   b. Examining the clusters for separation along some common feature (variable) that was not used in the cluster analysis
   c. *Labeling the clusters*: Based on the interpretation, trying to assign a name or label to each cluster
2. *Cluster stability*: Do cluster assignments change significantly if some of the inputs are altered slightly? Another way to check stability is to partition the data and see how well clusters formed based on one part apply to the other part. To do this:
   a. Cluster partition A.
   b. Use the cluster centroids from A to assign each record in partition B (each record is assigned to the cluster with the closest centroid).
   c. Assess how consistent the cluster assignments are compared to the assignments based on all the data.
3. *Cluster separation*: Examine the ratio of between-cluster variation to within-cluster variation to see whether the separation is reasonable. There exist statistical tests for this task (an F-ratio), but their usefulness is somewhat controversial.
4. *Number of clusters*: The number of resulting clusters must be useful, given the purpose of the analysis. For example, suppose the goal of the clustering is to identify categories of customers and assign labels to them for market segmentation purposes. If the marketing department can only manage to sustain three different marketing presentations, it would probably not make sense to identify more than three clusters.

One insight from dendrograms in Figure 15.3 is that clusters do not tend to group geographically. There are possibly other factors that bring states closer in the clusters. For example Punjab, West Bengal, and Karnataka cluster together. UP and J&K also cluster together. Arunachal is a standalone in one dendrogram where as clusters with Andhra Pradesh in other dendrogram.

We can further characterize each of the clusters by examining the summary statistics of their measurements, or visually looking at a heatmap of their individual measurements. Figure 15.4 shows a heatmap of the four clusters, and highlighting the different profiles that each cluster has in terms of the nine measurements. We see, for instance, that cluster 3 (Bihar and Meghalaya) is characterized by states with a high density and quite high levels of recovery rates and cluster 6 is characterized by low recovery rates, high sex ratio and high literacy rates.

code for creating heatmap

```
# set labels as cluster membership and utility name
icov_norm.index = ['{}: {}'.format(cluster, state)
for cluster, state in zip(memb, icov_norm.index)]
#plot heatmap
# the '_r' suffix reverses the color mapping to large = dark
sns.clustermap(icov_norm, method='average', col_cluster=False, cmap='mako_r') set labels as
 cluster membership and Demographic and Covid Status
row.names(icj.norm) <- paste(memb, ": ", row.names(icj), sep = "", font=3)
# plot heatmap
# rev() reverses the color mapping to large = dark
heatmap(as.matrix(icj.norm), Colv = NA,hclustfun = hclust,cexCol=.9,cexRow=.65,
col=rev(paste("gray",1:99,sep="")))
```

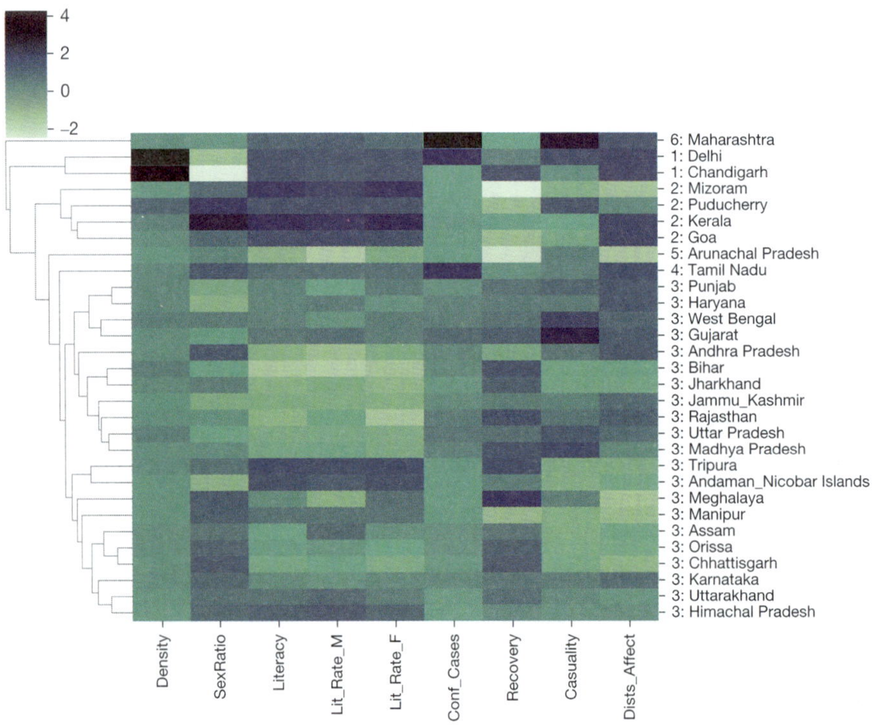

FIGURE 15.4 HEATMAP OF 30 STATES (IN ROWS). ROWS ARE SORTED BY SIX CLUSTERS FROM AVG LINKAGE CLUSTERING, DARKER CELLS DENOTE HIGHER VALUES WITHIN A COLUMN

Limitations of Hierarchical Clustering

Hierarchical clustering is very appealing in that it does not require specification of the number of clusters, and in that sense is purely data-driven. The ability to represent the clustering process and results through dendrograms is also an advantage of this method, as it is easier to understand and interpret. There are, however, a few limitations to consider:

1. Hierarchical clustering requires the computation and storage of an $n \times n$ distance matrix. For very large datasets, this can be expensive and slow.
2. The hierarchical algorithm makes only one pass through the data. This means that records that are allocated incorrectly early in the process cannot be reallocated subsequently.
3. Hierarchical clustering also tends to have low stability. Reordering data or dropping a few records can lead to a different solution.
4. With respect to the choice of distance between clusters, single and complete linkage are robust to changes in the distance metric (e.g., Euclidean, statistical distance) as long as the relative ordering is kept. In contrast, average linkage is more influenced by the choice of distance metric, and might lead to completely different clusters when the metric is changed.
5. Hierarchical clustering is sensitive to outliers.

15.5 | NON-HIERARCHICAL CLUSTERING: THE *k*-MEANS ALGORITHM

A non-hierarchical approach to forming good clusters is to pre-specify a desired number of clusters, k, and assign each case to one of the k clusters so as to minimize a measure of dispersion within the clusters. In other words, the goal is to divide the sample into a predetermined number k of non-overlapping clusters so that clusters are as homogeneous as possible with respect to the measurements used.

A common measure of within-cluster dispersion is the sum of distances (or sum of squared Euclidean distances) of records from their cluster centroid. The problem can be set up as an optimization problem involving integer programming, but because solving integer programs with a large number of variables is time-consuming, clusters are often computed using a fast, heuristic method that produces good (although not necessarily optimal) solutions. The k-means algorithm is one such method.

k-MEANS CLUSTERING ALGORITHM:

1. Start with k initial clusters (user chooses k).
2. At every step, each record is reassigned to the cluster with the "closest" centroid.
3. Recompute the centroids of clusters that lost or gained a record, and repeat Step 2.
4. Stop when moving any more records between clusters increases cluster dispersion.

The k-means algorithm starts with an initial partition of the records into k clusters. Subsequent steps modify the partition to reduce the sum of the distances of each record from its cluster centroid. The modification consists of allocating each record to the nearest of the k centroids of the previous partition. This leads to a new partition for which the sum of distances is smaller than before. The means of the new clusters are computed and the improvement step is repeated until the improvement is very small.

Returning to the example with the four states and two measurements, let us assume that $k = 2$ and that the initial clusters are A = {Uttar Pradesh and Maharashtra} and B = {Bihar and West Bengal}. The cluster centroids were computed in Section 15.3:

$$\bar{x}_A = [-0.0685, -0.01329] \quad \text{and} \quad \bar{x}_B = [-1.0974, 0.6405].$$

The distance of each record from each of these two centroids is shown in Table 15.7.

TABLE 15.7 DISTANCE OF EACH RECORD FROM EACH CENTROID

	Distance from Centroid A	Distance from Centroid B
Uttar Pradesh	0.878989415	1.558219392
Maharashtra	0.978596922	1.870737799
Biliar	2.047622852	2.579287588
West Bengal	0.39756843	1.243511024

Since all four states are closer to cluster A, and therefore move each of these records to cluster A and calculate new centroid. In case any of these states had closer distance to centroid B, and recalculated table like Table 15.7 will be prepared based on new centroid and new distances of records.

Choosing the Number of Clusters (*k*)

The choice of the number of clusters can either be driven by external considerations (e.g., previous knowledge, practical constraints, etc.), or we can try a few different values for k and compare the resulting clusters. After choosing k, the n records are partitioned into these initial clusters. If there is external reasoning that suggests a certain partitioning, this information should be used. Alternatively, if there exists external information on the centroids of the k clusters, this can be used to initially allocate the records.

In many cases, there is no information to be used for the initial partition. In these cases, the algorithm can be rerun with different randomly generated starting partitions to reduce chances of the heuristic producing a poor solution. The number of clusters in the data is generally not known, so it is a good idea to run the algorithm with different values for k that are near the number of clusters that one expects from the data, to see how the sum of distances reduces with increasing values of k. Note that the clusters obtained using different values of k will not be nested (unlike those obtained by hierarchical methods).

The results of running the k-means algorithm using class *KMeans()* for all 30 states and 9 measurements with $k = 6$ are shown in Table 15.8. We can see that this region is devoid of singleton cluster. In both hierarchical and k-means clusters, we can also see that Goa and Puducherry are in the same cluster. We can also discover other similarities.

To characterize the resulting clusters, we examine the cluster centroids (numerically in Table 15.9 and in the line chart ("profile plot") in Figure 15.5). We see, for instance, that cluster #2 is characterized by especially low sex ratio, high density (population) and lower rate of casualty. We can also see which variables do the best job of separating the clusters.

TABLE 15.8 *k*-MEANS CLUSTERING OF 30 STATES INTO *k*=6 CLUSTERS

code for *k*-means

```
kmeans = KMeans(n_clusters=6, random_state=0).fit(icov_norm)
# Cluster membership
memb = pd.Series(kmeans.labels_, index=icov_norm.index)
for key, item in memb.groupby(memb):
 print(key, ': ', ', '.join(item.index))
```

Output

```
0 :  3: Uttarakhand, 3: Himachal Pradesh, 3: Tripura, 3: Manipur, 2: Mizoram,
     3: Andaman_Nicobar Islands
1 :  4: Tamil Nadu, 2: Kerala, 2: Goa, 2: Puducherry
2 :  3: Uttar Pradesh, 3: West Bengal, 3: Andhra Pradesh, 3: Madhya Pradesh, 3: Rajasthan,
     3: Karnataka, 3: Gujarat, 3: Punjab, 3: Haryana, 3: Jammu_Kashmir
3 :  1: Delhi, 1: Chandigarh
4 :  3: Bihar, 3: Orissa, 3: Jharkhand, 3: Assam, 3: Chhattisgarh, 3: Meghalaya,
     5: Arunachal Pradesh
5 :  6: Maharashtra
```

We can also inspect the information on the within-cluster dispersion. From Table 15.9, we see that clusters #5 (with twelve records) has the largest within-cluster sum of squared distances. In comparison, cluster #3, with two records, has a smaller within-cluster sum of squared distances. This means that cluster #3 is more homogeneous than cluster #5 (although it is also has fewer records).

TABLE 15.9 CLUSTER CENTROIDS AND SQUARED DISTANCES FOR *k*-MEANS

```
centroids = pd.DataFrame(kmeans.cluster_centers_, columns=icov_norm.columns)
centroids
```

Output

```
    Density  SexRatio  Literacy  Lit_Rate_M  Lit_Rate_F  Conf_Cases   Recovery  Casuality Dists_Affect
0 -0.373750  0.144823  0.857918    0.841216    0.814247   -0.474953  -0.410541  -0.828616    -0.896981
1 -0.005877  1.397259  1.130975    1.104524    1.103975    0.117990  -0.936113  -0.159192     0.887449
2 -0.259283 -0.385365 -0.594074   -0.568567   -0.629974   -0.057982   0.271711   0.661165     0.553862
3  3.590756 -1.949823  1.050125    0.921686    1.003377    0.706162   0.551355   0.421582     1.348118
4 -0.290536  0.234504 -0.922423   -0.913145   -0.782604   -0.388724   0.415358  -0.634754    -1.057345
5 -0.288917 -0.346207  0.626048    0.768924    0.469833    4.266320  -0.519622   2.596927     0.998645
```

Within-cluster sum of squared distances and cluster count

```
# calculate the distances of each data point to the cluster centers
distances = kmeans.transform(icov_norm)
# find closest cluster for each data point
minSquaredDistances = distances.min(axis=1) ** 2
# combine with cluster labels into a data frame
df = pd.DataFrame({'squaredDistance': minSquaredDistances, 'cluster': kmeans.labels_}, index=icov_norm.index)
# group by cluster and print information
for cluster, data in df.groupby('cluster'):
    count = len(data)
    withinClustSS = data.squaredDistance.sum()
    print(f'Cluster {cluster} ({count} members): {withinClustSS:.2f} within cluster')
```

Output

```
Cluster 0 (6 members): 17.82 within cluster
Cluster 1 (4 members): 15.55 within cluster
Cluster 2 (10 members): 23.21 within cluster
Cluster 3 (2 members): 5.32 within cluster
Cluster 4 (7 members): 21.09 within cluster
Cluster 5 (1 members): 0.00 within cluster
```

When the number of clusters is not predetermined by domain requirements, we can use a graphical approach to evaluate different numbers of clusters. An "elbow chart" is a line chart depicting the decline in cluster heterogeneity as we add more clusters. Figure 15.6 shows the overall average within-cluster distance (normalized) for different choices of k. Moving from 1 to 2 tightens clusters considerably (reflected by the large reduction in within-cluster distance), and so does moving from 2 to 3 and even to 4. Adding more clusters beyond 4 brings less improvement to cluster homogeneity.

code for plotting profile plot of centroids

```
centroids['cluster'] = ['Cluster {}'.format(i) for i in centroids.index]
plt.figure(figsize=(10,6))
parallel_coordinates(centroids, class_column='cluster', colormap='Dark2', linewidth=5)
plt.legend(loc='center left', bbox_to_anchor=(1, 0.5))
```

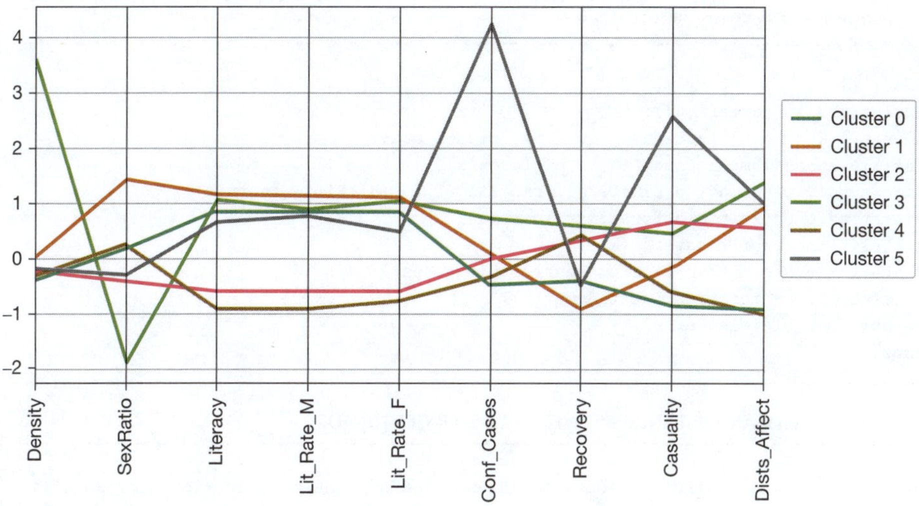

FIGURE 15.5 VISUAL PRESENTATION (PROFILE PLOT) OF CLUSTER CENTROIDS

From the distances between clusters measured by Euclidean distance between the centroids (see Table 15.10), we can learn about the separation of the different clusters. For instance, we can see that clusters #2 and #4 are the closest to one another, and clusters #4 and #5 are the most distant from one another. Clusters #3 and #5 are relatively more distant from the other clusters, overall, but there is no cluster that is a striking outlier.

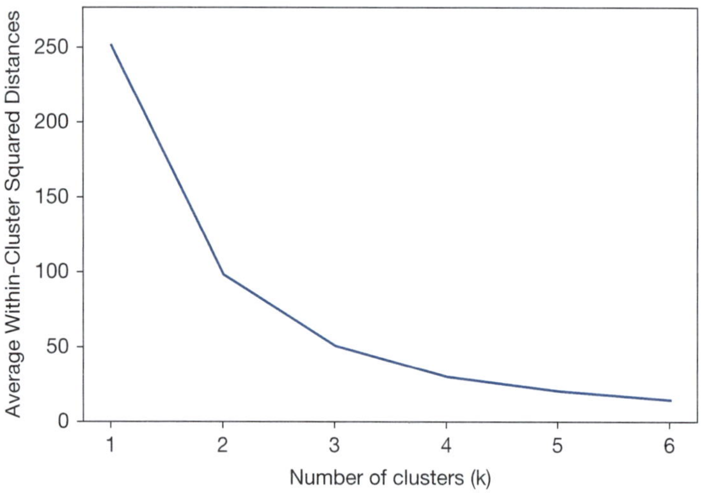

FIGURE 15.6 COMPARING DIFFERENT CHOICES OF k IN TERMS OF OVERALL AVERAGE WITHIN-CLUSTER DISTANCE

code for preparing Figure 15.6

```
inertia = []
for n_clusters in range(1, 7):
    kmeans = KMeans(n_clusters=n_clusters, random_state=0).fit(icov_norm)
    inertia.append(kmeans.inertia_ / n_clusters)
inertias = pd.DataFrame({'n_clusters': range(1, 7), 'inertia': inertia})
ax = inertias.plot(x='n_clusters', y='inertia')
plt.xlabel('Number of clusters (k)')
plt.ylabel('Average Within-Cluster Squared Distances')
plt.ylim((0, 1.1 * inertias.inertia.max()))
ax.legend().set_visible(False)
plt.show()
```

TABLE 15.10 EUCLIDEAN DISTANCE BETWEEN CLUSTER CENTROIDS

```
pd.DataFrame(pairwise.pairwise_distances(kmeans.cluster_centers_, metric='euclidean'))
```

	0	1	2	3	4	5
0	0.000000	2.488351	3.382229	5.395163	3.092755	6.184273
1	2.488351	0.000000	3.781223	5.224638	4.401279	5.374027
2	3.382229	3.781223	0.000000	5.119842	2.245100	5.268811
3	5.395163	5.224633	5.119842	0.000000	6.196964	6.065251
4	3.092755	4.401279	2.245100	6.196964	0.000000	6.659386
5	6.184273	5.374027	5.268811	6.065251	6.659386	0.000000

Finally, we can use the information on the distance between the final clusters to evaluate the cluster validity. The ratio of the sum of squared distances to cluster means for a given k to the sum of squared distances to the mean of all the records ($k = 1$) is a useful measure for the usefulness of the clustering. If the ratio is near 1.0, the clustering has not been very effective, whereas if it is small, we have well-separated groups.

PROBLEMS

15.1 University Rankings. The dataset on American College and University Rankings (available from www.dataminingbook.com) contains information on 1302 American colleges and universities offering an undergraduate program. For each university, there are 17 measurements, including continuous measurements (such as tuition and graduation rate) and categorical measurements (such as location by state and whether it is a private or public school).

Note that many records are missing some measurements. Our first goal is to estimate these missing values from "similar" records. This will be done by clustering the complete records and then finding the closest cluster for each of the partial records. The missing values will be imputed from the information in that cluster.

a. Remove all records with missing measurements from the dataset.

b. For all the continuous measurements, run hierarchical clustering using complete linkage and Euclidean distance. Make sure to normalize the measurements. From the dendrogram: How many clusters seem reasonable for describing these data?

c. Compare the summary statistics for each cluster and describe each cluster in this context (e.g., "Universities with high tuition, low acceptance rate..."). (*Hint*: To obtain cluster statistics for hierarchical clustering, use the `pandas` method *groupby(clusterlabel)* together with methods such as *mean* or *median*.)

d. Use the categorical measurements that were not used in the analysis (State and Private/Public) to characterize the different clusters. Is there any relationship between the clusters and the categorical information?

e. What other external information can explain the contents of some or all of these clusters?

f. Consider Tufts University, which is missing some information. Compute the Euclidean distance of this record from each of the clusters that you found above (using only the measurements that you have). Which cluster is it closest to? Impute the missing values for Tufts by taking the average of the cluster on those measurements.

15.2 Pharmaceutical Industry. An equities analyst is studying the pharmaceutical industry and would like your help in exploring and understanding the financial data collected by her firm. Her main objective is to understand the structure of the pharmaceutical industry using some basic financial measures.

Financial data gathered on 21 firms in the pharmaceutical industry are available in the file *Pharmaceuticals.csv*. For each firm, the following variables are recorded:

1. Market capitalization (in billions of dollars)
2. Beta

3. Price/earnings ratio
4. Return on equity
5. Return on assets
6. Asset turnover
7. Leverage
8. Estimated revenue growth
9. Net profit margin
10. Median recommendation (across major brokerages)
11. Location of firm's headquarters
12. Stock exchange on which the firm is listed

Use cluster analysis to explore and analyze the given dataset as follows:

a. Use only the numerical variables (1–9) to cluster the 21 firms. Justify the various choices made in conducting the cluster analysis, such as weights for different variables, the specific clustering algorithm(s) used, the number of clusters formed, and so on.

b. Interpret the clusters with respect to the categorical variables used in forming the clusters.

c. Is there a pattern in the clusters with respect to the numerical variables (10–12)? (those not used in forming the clusters).

d. Provide an appropriate name for each cluster using any or all of the variables in the dataset.

15.3 Customer Rating of Breakfast Cereals. The dataset *Cereals.csv* includes nutritional information, store display, and consumer ratings for 77 breakfast cereals.
Data preprocessing. Remove all cereals with missing values.

a. Apply hierarchical clustering to the data using Euclidean distance to the normalized measurements. Compare the dendrograms from single linkage and complete linkage, and look at cluster centroids. Comment on the structure of the clusters and on their stability. (*Hint*: To obtain cluster centroids for hierarchical clustering, compute the average values of each cluster members, using *groupby()* with the cluster centers followed by *mean*: `dataframe.groupby(clusterlabel).mean()`.)

b. Which method leads to the most insightful or meaningful clusters?

c. Choose one of the methods. How many clusters would you use? What distance is used for this cutoff? (Look at the dendrogram.)

d. The elementary public schools would like to choose a set of cereals to include in their daily cafeterias. Every day a different cereal is offered, but all cereals should support a healthy diet. For this goal, you are requested to find a cluster of "healthy cereals." Should the data be normalized? If not, how should they be used in the cluster analysis?

15.4 Marketing to Frequent Fliers. The file *EastWestAirlinesCluster.csv* contains information on 3999 passengers who belong to an airline's frequent flier program. For each passenger, the data include information on their mileage history and on different ways they accrued or spent miles in the last year. The goal is to try to identify clusters of passengers that have similar characteristics for the purpose of targeting different segments for different types of mileage offers.

a. Apply hierarchical clustering with Euclidean distance and Ward's method. Make sure to normalize the data first. How many clusters appear?

b. What would happen if the data were not normalized?

c. Compare the cluster centroid to characterize the different clusters, and try to give each cluster a label.

d. To check the stability of the clusters, remove a random 5% of the data (by taking a random sample of 95% of the records), and repeat the analysis. Does the same picture emerge?

e. Use *k*-means clustering with the number of clusters that you found above. Does the same picture emerge?

f. Which clusters would you target for offers, and what types of offers would you target to customers in that cluster?

PART

VI

Forecasting Time Series

CHAPTER 16

Handling Time Series

In this chapter, we describe the context of business time series forecasting and introduce the main approaches that are detailed in the next chapters, and in particular, regression-based forecasting and smoothing-based methods. Our focus is on forecasting future values of a single time series. These three chapters are meant as an introduction to the general forecasting approach and methods.

In this chapter, we discuss the difference between the predictive nature of time series forecasting vs. the descriptive or explanatory task of time series analysis. A general discussion of combining forecasting methods or results for added precision follows. Next, we present a time series in terms of four components (level, trend, seasonality, and noise) and present methods for visualizing the different components and for exploring time series data. We close with a discussion of data partitioning (creating training and validation sets), which is performed differently from cross-sectional data partitioning.

Python

In this chapter, we will use `pandas` for data handling and `matplotlib` for visualization. Models are built using `statsmodels`.

import required functionality for this chapter

```
import pandas as pd
import matplotlib.pylab as plt
import statsmodels.formula.api as sm
from statsmodels.tsa import tsatools
from dmba import regressionSummary
```

16.1 | INTRODUCTION[1]

Time series forecasting is performed in nearly every organization that works with quantifiable data. Retail stores use it to forecast sales. Energy companies use it to forecast reserves, production, demand, and prices. Educational institutions use it to forecast enrollment. Governments use it to forecast tax receipts and spending. International financial organizations like the World Bank and International Monetary Fund use it to forecast inflation and economic activity. Transportation companies use time series forecasting to forecast future travel. Banks and lending institutions use it (sometimes badly!) to forecast new home purchases. And venture capital firms use it to forecast market potential and to evaluate business plans.

Previous chapters in this book deal with classifying and predicting data where time is not a factor, in the sense that it is not treated differently from other variables, and where the sequence of measurements over time does not matter. These are typically called cross-sectional data. In contrast, this chapter deals with a different type of data: time series.

With today's technology, many time series are recorded on very frequent time scales. Stock data are available at ticker level. Purchases at online and offline stores are recorded in real time. The Internet of Things (IoT) generates huge numbers of time series, produced by sensors and other measurements devices. Although data might be available at a very frequent scale, for the purpose of forecasting, it is not always preferable to use this time scale. In considering the choice of time scale, one must consider the scale of the required forecasts and the level of noise in the data. For example, if the goal is to forecast next-day sales at a grocery store, using minute-by-minute sales data is likely to be less useful for forecasting than using daily aggregates. The minute-by-minute series will contain many sources of noise (e.g., variation by peak and non-peak shopping hours) that degrade its forecasting power, and these noise errors, when the data are aggregated to a cruder level, are likely to average out.

The focus in this part of the book is on forecasting a single time series. In some cases, multiple time series are to be forecasted (e.g., the monthly sales of multiple products). Even when multiple series are being forecasted, the most popular forecasting practice is to forecast each series individually. The advantage of single-series forecasting is its simplicity. The disadvantage is that it does not take into account possible relationships between series. The statistics literature contains models for multivariate time series which directly model the cross-correlations between series. Such methods tend to make restrictive assumptions about the data and the cross-series structure. They also require statistical expertise for estimation and maintenance. Econometric models often

[1]This and subsequent sections in this chapter, copyright ©2019 Datastats, LLC, and Galit Shmueli. Used by permission.

include information from one or more series as inputs into another series. However, such models are based on assumptions of causality that are based on theoretical models. An alternative approach is to capture the associations between the series of interest and external information more heuristically. An example is using the sales of lipstick to forecast some measure of the economy, based on the observation by Ronald Lauder, chairman of Estee Lauder, that lipstick sales tend to increase before tough economic times (a phenomenon called the "leading lipstick indicator").

16.2 | DESCRIPTIVE VS. PREDICTIVE MODELING

As with cross-sectional data, modeling time series data is done for either descriptive or predictive purposes. In descriptive modeling, or *time series analysis*, a time series is modeled to determine its components in terms of seasonal patterns, trends, relation to external factors, etc. These can then be used for decision-making and policy formulation. In contrast, *time series forecasting* uses the information in a time series (and perhaps other information) to forecast future values of that series. The difference between the goals of time series analysis and time series forecasting leads to differences in the type of methods used and in the modeling process itself. For example, in selecting a method for describing a time series, priority is given to methods that produce understandable results (rather than "blackbox" methods) and sometimes to models based on causal arguments (explanatory models). Furthermore, describing can be done in retrospect, while forecasting is *prospective* in nature. This means that descriptive models might use "future" information (e.g., averaging the values of yesterday, today, and tomorrow to obtain a smooth representation of today's value) whereas forecasting models cannot.

The focus in this chapter is on time series forecasting, where the goal is to predict future values of a time series. For information on time series analysis, see Chatfield (2003).

16.3 | POPULAR FORECASTING METHODS IN BUSINESS

In this part of the book, we focus on two main types of forecasting methods that are popular in business applications. Both are versatile and powerful, yet relatively simple to understand and deploy. One type of forecasting tool is multiple linear regression, where the user specifies a certain model and then estimates it from the time series. The other is the more data-driven tool of smoothing, where the method learns patterns from the data. Each of the two types of tools has advantages and disadvantages, as detailed in Chapters 17 and 18. We also note that data mining methods such as neural networks and others that are intended for cross-sectional data are also sometimes used for time series forecasting, especially for incorporating external information into the forecasts (see Shmueli and Lichtendahl, 2016).

Combining Methods

Before a discussion of specific forecasting methods in the following two chapters, it should be noted that a popular approach for improving predictive performance is to combine forecasting methods. This is similar to the ensembles approach described in Chapter 13. Combining forecasting methods can be done via two-level (or multi level) forecasters, where the first method uses the original time series to generate forecasts of future values, and the second method uses the residuals from the first model to generate forecasts of future forecast errors, thereby "correcting" the first level forecasts. We describe two-level forecasting in Section 17.4. Another combination approach is via "ensembles," where multiple methods are applied to the time series, and their resulting forecasts are averaged in some way to produce the final forecast. Combining methods can take advantage of the strengths of different forecasting methods to capture different aspects of the time series (also true in cross-sectional data). The averaging across multiple methods can lead to forecasts that are more robust and of higher precision.

16.4 | TIME SERIES COMPONENTS

In both types of forecasting methods, regression models and smoothing, and in general, it is customary to dissect a time series into four components: *level*, *trend*, *seasonality*, and *noise*. The first three components are assumed to be invisible, as they characterize the underlying series, which we only observe with added noise. Level describes the average value of the series, trend is the change in the series from one period to the next, and seasonality describes a short-term cyclical behavior of the series which can be observed several times within the given series. Finally, noise is the random variation that results from measurement error or other causes not accounted for. It is always present in a time series to some degree.

> Don't get confused by the standard conversational meaning of "season" (winter, spring, etc.). The statistical meaning of "season" refers to any time period that repeats itself in cycles within the larger time series. Also, note that the term "period" in forecasting means simply a span of time, and not the specific meaning that it has in physics, of the distance between two equivalent points in a cycle.

In order to identify the components of a time series, the first step is to examine a time plot. In its simplest form, a time plot is a line chart of the series values over time, with temporal labels (e.g., calendar date) on the horizontal axis. To illustrate this, consider the following example.

Example: Time Series Indices of Industrial Production of India

The data (*Timeseries Data.csv*) refers to Index of Industrial Production at two-digit industry level indices with weights, annual average indices, and growth over corresponding period of previous year. The data has been taken from the open public data site of India (data.gov.in). The contributor of this data is Ministry of Statistics and Programme Implementation. The dataset is an index, Base: 1980-81=100, of four sectors (mining, manufacturing, electrical, and general) which is based on two digital level annual production figures from April 1981 to March 1998.

A time plot for the monthly General Production series from April 1981 to March 1998 for General Index is shown in Figure 16.1a and deeper trends in 1982 and 1997 are shown in Figure 16.1b.

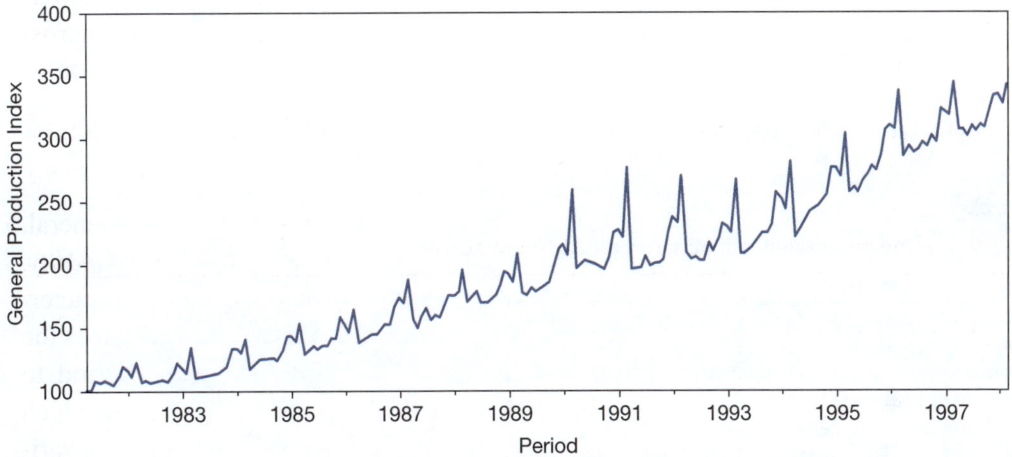

FIGURE 16.1a MONTHLY GENERAL PRODUCTION INDEX FROM APRIL 1981 TO MARCH 1998

code for creating a time series plots (Figure 16.1a)

```
# read dataset
ts=pd.read_csv('Timeseries Data.csv')

# create time series object with date variable ('Months') as the index

ts['Months'] = pd.to_datetime(ts['Months'], infer_datetime_format=True)
General_ts=pd.Series(ts.General.values, index=ts.Months, name='General_Production')
General_ts.index = pd.DatetimeIndex(General_ts.index,freq=General_ts.index.inferred_freq)

# plot the series (Fig 16.1a)
ax = General_ts.plot(figsize=(14,5))
ax.set_xlabel('Period')
ax.set_ylabel('General Production Index')
ax.set_ylim(100, 400)
```

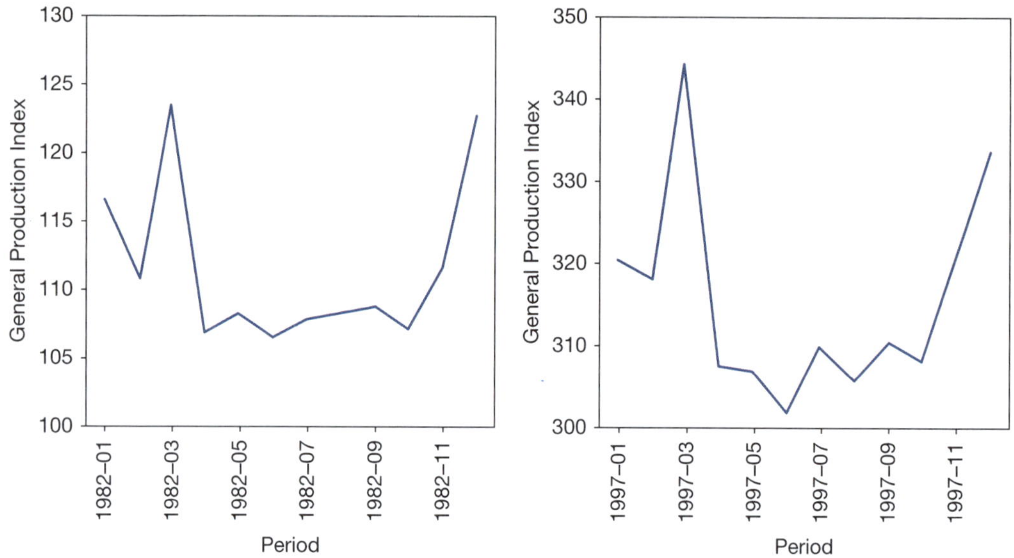

FIGURE 16.1b DEEPER INSIGHT OF SHORT PERIODS FOR GENERAL PRODUCTION INDEX 1982 AND 1997

code for creating a time series plots (Figure 16.1b)

```
fig, (ax1,ax2) =plt.subplots(1,2, figsize=(14,6))
# plot the series
General1= General_ts['1982-01-01':'1982-12-01']
ax1.plot(General1)
ax1.set_xlabel('Period')
ax1.set_ylabel('General Production Index')
ax1.set_ylim(100, 130)

# plot the series
General2= General_ts['1997-01-01':'1997-12-01']
ax2.plot(General2)
ax2.set_xlabel('Period')
ax2.set_ylabel('General Production Index')
ax2.set_ylim(300, 350)
```

Looking at the time plot reveals the nature of the series components: the General (overall) trend of Production Index per month is increasing.

A second step in visualizing a time series is to examine it more carefully. A few tools are useful:

Zoom in: Zooming in to a shorter period within the series can reveal patterns that are hidden when viewing the entire series. This is especially important when the time series is long. We can also see in Figure 16.1b that monthly trends are very close (see 1982 and 1997) but annual average index values have increased almost threefold level from approximately 100 to 300 per month. The monthly trends are U-shaped with pronounced seasonality, low index from April to October and peak values during March and December. Similarly, we can see long term trend of manufacturing sector production in Figure 16.2a and detailed trend of manufacturing sector production for period Feb 1984 to Nov 1984.

Python code for Figure 16.2

```
fig, (ax1,ax2) =plt.subplots(2,1, figsize=(14,6))
# plot the series
Manf1= Manf_ts['1981-04-01':'1998-03-01']
ax1.plot(Manf1)
ax1.set_xlabel('Period')
ax1.set_ylabel('Manufacturing Production Index')
ax1.set_ylim(100, 350)

# plot the series
Manf2= Manf_ts['1984-02-01':'1984-11-01']
ax2.plot(Manf2)
ax2.set_xlabel('Period')
ax2.set_ylabel('Manufacturing Production Index')
ax2.set_ylim(100, 150)
```

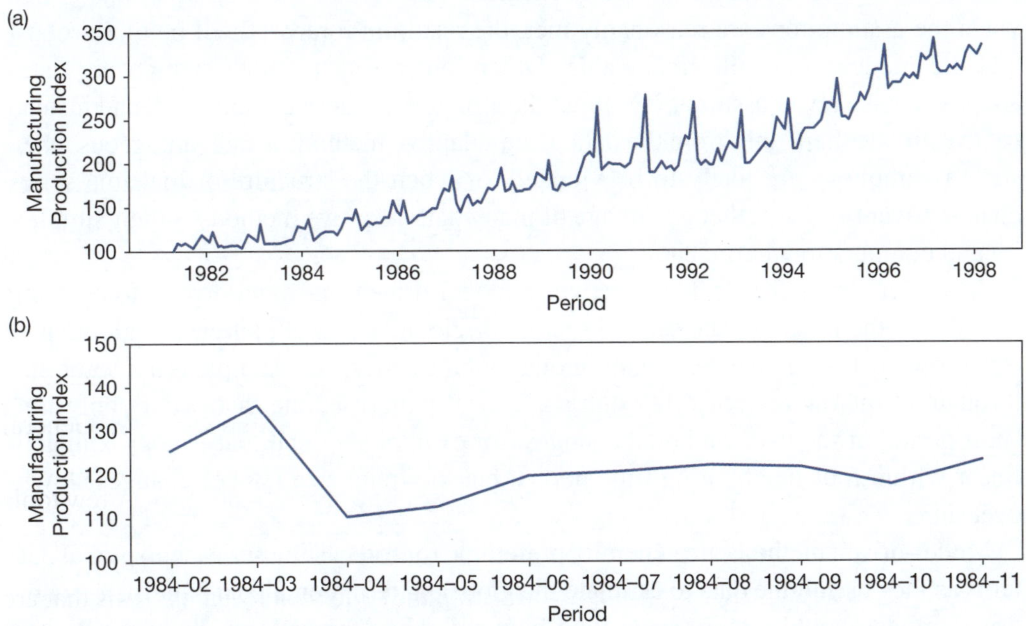

FIGURE 16.2 TIME PLOTS OF THE (a) MANUFACTURING SECTOR PRODUCTION INDEX OVERALL 1981-1998 PLOT AND (b) ZOOMED LOOK INTO SELECT MONTHS OF FEB 1984 TO NOV 1984

Change scale of series: In order to better identify the shape of a trend, it is useful to change the scale of the series. One simple option, to check for an exponential trend, is to change the vertical scale to a logarithmic scale (use `ax.set_yscale('log')`). If the trend on the new scale appears more linear, then the trend in the original series is closer to an exponential trend.

Add trend lines: Another possibility for better discerning the shape of the trend is to add a trend line. By trying different trendlines, one can see what type of trend (e.g., linear, exponential, quadratic) best approximates the data.

Suppress seasonality: It is often easier to see trends in the data when seasonality is suppressed. Suppressing seasonality patterns can be done by plotting the series at a cruder time scale (e.g., aggregating monthly data into years) or creating separate lines or time plots for each season (e.g., separate lines for each day of week). Another popular option is to use moving average charts. We will discuss these in Section 18.2.

Continuing our example of the Industrial Production Index, the charts in Figure 16.3 help make the series' components more visible.

Some forecasting methods directly model these components by making assumptions about their structure. For example, a popular assumption about trend is that it is linear or exponential over the given time period or part of it. Another common assumption is about the noise structure: many statistical methods assume that the noise follows a normal distribution. The advantage of methods that rely on such assumptions is that when the assumptions are reasonably met, the resulting forecasts will be more robust and the models more understandable. Other forecasting methods, which are data-adaptive, make fewer assumptions about the structure of these components, and instead try to estimate them only from the data. Data-adaptive methods are advantageous when such assumptions are likely to be violated, or when the structure of the time series changes over time. Another advantage of many data-adaptive methods is their simplicity and computational efficiency.

A key criterion for deciding between model-driven and data-driven forecasting methods is the nature of the series in terms of global vs. local patterns. A global pattern is one that is relatively constant throughout the series. An example is a linear trend throughout the entire series. In contrast, a local pattern is one that occurs only in a short period of the data, and then changes, for example, a trend that is approximately linear within four neighboring time points, but the trend size (slope) changes slowly over time.

Model-driven methods are generally preferable for forecasting series with global patterns as they use all the data to estimate the global pattern. For a local pattern, a model-driven model would require specifying how and when the patterns change, which is usually impractical and often unknown. Therefore, data-driven methods are preferable for local patterns. Such methods "learn" patterns from the data and their memory length can be set to best adapt to the rate of change in the series. Patterns that change quickly warrant a "short memory," whereas patterns that change slowly warrant a "long memory." In conclusion, the time plot should be used not only to identify the time series component, but also the global/local nature of the trend and seasonality.

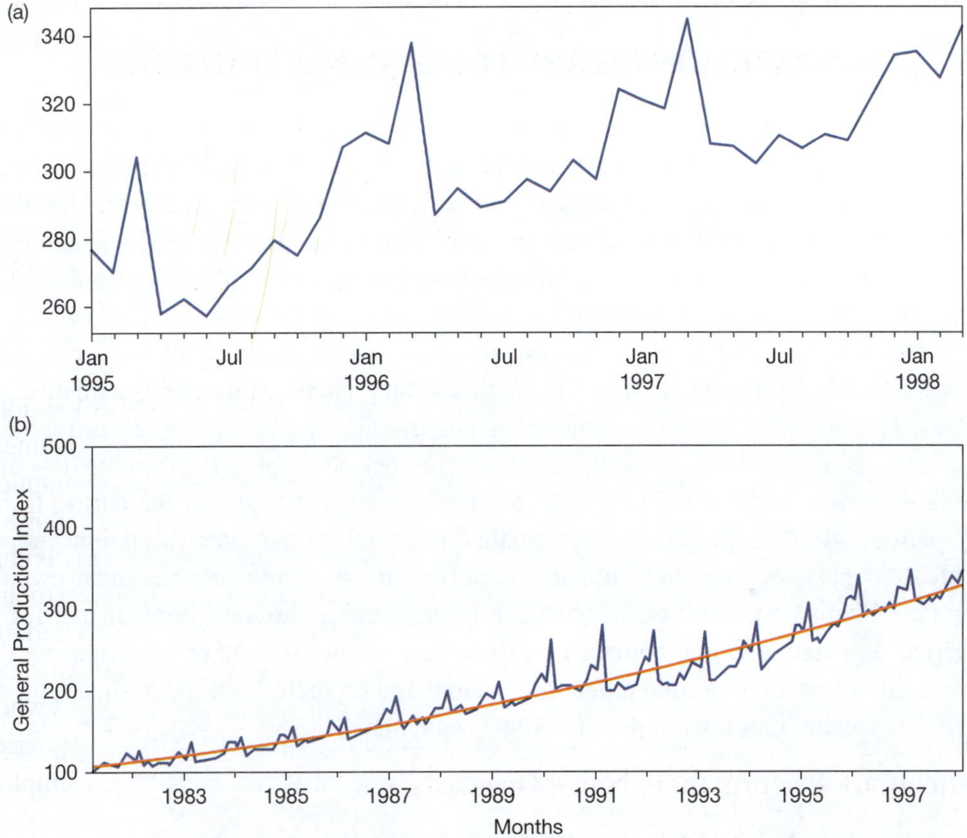

FIGURE 16.3 PLOTS THAT ENHANCE THE DIFFERENT COMPONENTS OF THE TIME SERIES.(a) ZOOM-IN TO 3 YEARS OF DATA. (b) ORIGINAL SERIES WITH OVERLAID QUADRATIC TRENDLINE

code for creating Figure 16.3

```
# create short time series from 1997 to 1999 using a slice (fig 16.3)
General_ts_3yrs = General_ts['1995':'1998']
General_df = tsatools.add_trend(General_ts, trend='ctt')
# fit a linear regression model to the time series
General_lm = sm.ols(formula='General_Production ~ trend + trend_squared', data=General_df).fit()

# shorter and longer time series
fig, axes = plt.subplots(nrows=2, ncols=1, figsize=(10,6))
```

```
General_ts_3yrs.plot(ax=axes[0])
General_ts.plot(ax=axes[1])
for ax in axes: ax.set_xlabel('Years')
ax.set_ylabel('General Production Index')
ax.set_ylim(100, 500)
General_lm.predict(General_df).plot(ax=axes[1])
plt.show()
```

16.5 | DATA-PARTITIONING AND PERFORMANCE EVALUATION

As in the case of cross-sectional data, in order to avoid overfitting and to be able to assess the predictive performance of the model on new data, we first partition the data into a training set and a validation set (and perhaps an additional test set). However, there is one important difference between data partitioning in cross-sectional and time series data. In cross-sectional data, the partitioning is usually done randomly, with a random set of records designated as training data and the remainder as validation data. However, in time series, a random partition would create two time series with "holes." Nearly all standard forecasting methods cannot handle time series with missing values. Therefore, we partition a time series into training and validation sets differently. The series is trimmed into two periods; the earlier period is set as the training data and the later period as the validation data. Methods are then trained on the earlier training period, and their predictive performance assessed on the later validation period. Evaluation measures typically use the same metrics used in cross-sectional evaluation (see Chapter 5) with *MAE*, *MAPE*, and *RMSE* being the most popular metrics in practice. In evaluating and comparing forecasting methods, another important tool is visualization: examining time plots of the actual and predicted series can shed light on performance and hint toward possible improvements.

Benchmark Performance: Naive Forecasts

While it is tempting to apply "sophisticated" forecasting methods, we must evaluate their value added compared to a very simple approach: the *naive forecast*. A naive forecast is simply the most recent value of the series. In other words, at time t, our forecast for any future period $t+k$ is simply the value of the series at time t. While simple, naive forecasts are sometimes surprisingly difficult to outperform with more sophisticated models. It is therefore important to benchmark against results from a naive-forecasting approach.

When a time series has seasonality, a seasonal naive forecast can be generated. It is simply the last similar value in the season. For example, to forecast April 1998 for any sectoral production index, we use the relevant index from the most recent April, April 1997. In Figure 16.4, we show naive (horizontal line) and seasonal naive forecasts, as well as actual values (dotted line), in a 3-year validation set from April 1995 to March 1998. Table 16.1 provides the code to generate this chart.

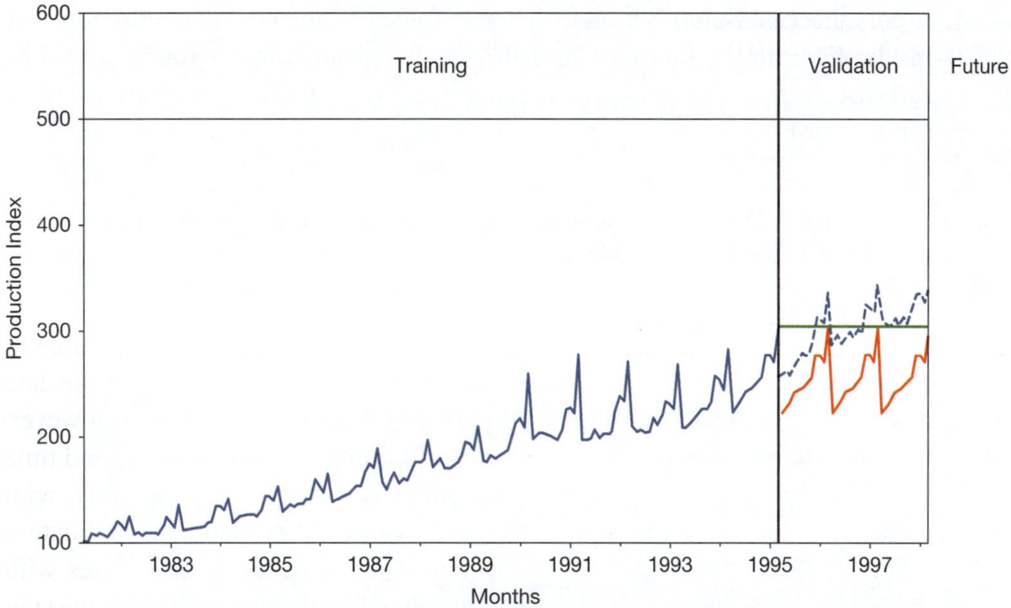

FIGURE 16.4 NAIVE AND SEASONAL NAIVE FORECASTS IN A 3-YEAR VALIDATION SET FOR PRODUCTION INDEX EXAMPLE

Table 16.2 compares the accuracies of these two naive forecasts. In case monthly seasonality would have been high, the seasonal naive forecast would have performed much better on both training and validation sets and on all popular measures. In choosing between the two models, the accuracy on the validation set is more relevant than the accuracy on the training set. Performance on the validation set is more indicative of how the models will perform in the future.

Generating Future Forecasts

Another important difference between cross-sectional and time-series partitioning occurs when creating the actual forecasts. Before attempting to forecast future values of the series, the training and validation sets are recombined into one long series, and the chosen method/model is rerun on the complete data. This final model is then used to forecast future values. The three advantages of recombining are:

1. The validation set, which is the most recent period, usually contains the most valuable information in terms of being the closest in time to the forecast period;
2. With more data (the complete time series compared to only the training set), some models can be estimated more accurately;

3. If only the training set is used to generate forecasts, then it will require forecasting farther into the future (e.g., if the validation set contains four time points, forecasting the next period will require a five-step-ahead forecast from the training set).

TABLE 16.1 CODE FOR NAIVE AND SEASONAL NAIVE FORECASTS IN A 3-YEAR VALIDATION SET FOR SECTORAL PRODUCTION INDEX

code for creating Figure 16.4

```
#  CODE FOR FIG 16.4
nValid = 48
nTrain = len(General_ts) - nValid
# partition the data
train_ts = General_ts[:nTrain]
valid_ts = General_ts[nTrain:]
# generate the naive and seasonal naive forecast
naive_pred = pd.Series(train_ts[-1], index=valid_ts.index)
last_season = train_ts[-12:]
seasonal_pred = pd.Series(pd.concat([last_season]*5)[:len(valid_ts)].values,index=valid_ts.index)
# plot forecasts and actual in the training and validation sets
ax = train_ts.plot(color='C0', linewidth=1.25, figsize=(13,7))
valid_ts.plot(ax=ax, color='C0', linestyle='dashed', linewidth= 1.75)
ax.set_xlim('1990', '2000')
ax.set_ylim(100, 600)
ax.set_xlabel('Production')
ax.set_ylabel('Production')

naive_pred.plot(ax=ax, color='green')
seasonal_pred.plot(ax=ax, color='red')

# determine coordinates for drawing the arrows and lines
one_month = pd.Timedelta('31 days')
xtrain = (min(train_ts.index), max(train_ts.index) - one_month)
xvalid = (min(valid_ts.index) + one_month, max(valid_ts.index) - one_month)
xfuture = (max(valid_ts.index) + one_month, '2006')
xtv = xtrain[1] + 0.5 * (xvalid[0] - xtrain[1])
xvf = xvalid[1] + 0.5 * (xfuture[0] - xvalid[1])

ax.add_line(plt.Line2D(xtrain, (500,500), color='black', linewidth=1))
ax.add_line(plt.Line2D(xvalid,(500,500), color='black', linewidth=1))
ax.add_line(plt.Line2D(xfuture, (500,500), color='black', linewidth=1))
ax.text('1989', 550, 'Training')
ax.text('1996', 550, 'Validation')
ax.text('2001', 550, 'Future')
ax.axvline(x=xtv, ymin=0, ymax=1, color='black', linewidth=2)
ax.axvline(x=xvf, ymin=0, ymax=1, color='black', linewidth=2)
plt.show()
```

TABLE 16.2 PREDICTIVE ACCURACY OF NAIVE AND SEASONAL NAIVE FORECASTS IN THE VALIDATION SET FOR GENERAL PRODUCTION INDEX EXAMPLE

code for naive metrics in training and validation data

```
# CODE FOR TABLE 16.1
print('NAIVE METRICS FOR VALIDATION DATA')
regressionSummary(valid_ts, naive_pred)
print('SEASONAL NAIVE METRICS FOR VALIDATION DATA')
regressionSummary(valid_ts, seasonal_pred)
# calculate naive metrics for training set (shifted by 1 month)
print('NAIVE METRICS FOR TRAINING DATA')
regressionSummary(train_ts[1:], train_ts[:-1])
# calculate seasonal naive metrics for training set (shifted by 12 months)
print('SEASONAL NAIVE METRICS FOR TRAINING DATA')
regressionSummary(train_ts[12:], train_ts[:-12])
```

```
NAIVE METRICS FOR VALIDATION DATA

Regression statistics

                      Mean Error (ME) : 8.7229
       Root Mean Squared Error (RMSE) : 32.3778
            Mean Absolute Error (MAE) : 27.7354
          Mean percentage Error (MPE) : 1.8120
Mean Absolute Percentage Error (MAPE) : 9.6270

SEASONAL NAIVE METRICS FOR VALIDATION DATA

Regression statistics

                      Mean Error (ME) : 58.0229
       Root Mean Squared Error (RMSE) : 63.1361
            Mean Absolute Error (MAE) : 58.0229
          Mean percentage Error (MPE) : 19.5096
Mean Absolute Percentage Error (MAPE) : 19.5096

NAVIE METRICS FOR TRAINING DATA

Regression statistics

                      Mean Error (ME) : 1.1684
       Root Mean Squared Error (RMSE) : 16.3502
            Mean Absolute Error (MAE) : 9.3916
          Mean percentage Error (MPE) : 0.3232
Mean Absolute Percentage Error (MAPE) : 5.2661
```

(Continued)

TABLE 16.2 PREDICTIVE ACCURACY OF NAIVE AND SEASONAL NAIVE FORECASTS IN THE VALIDATION SET FOR GENERAL PRODUCTION INDEX EXAMPLE (*Continued*)

```
SEASONAL NAIVE METRICS FOR TRAINING DATA

Regression statistics

                      Mean Error (ME) : 10.2243
       Root Mean Squared Error (RMSE) : 12.8583
            Mean Absolute Error (MAE) : 10.8299
          Mean percentage Error (MPE) : 5.9787
Mean Absolute Percentage Error (MAPE) : 6.2611
```

PROBLEMS

16.1 Impact of September 11 on Air Travel in the United States. The Research and Innovative Technology Administration's Bureau of Transportation Statistics conducted a study to evaluate the impact of the September 11, 2001 terrorist attack on US transportation. The 2006 study report and the data can be found at https://www.bts.gov/archive/publications/estimated_impacts_of_9_11_on_us_travel/index. The goal of the study was stated as follows:

> The purpose of this study is to provide a greater understanding of the passenger travel behavior patterns of persons making long distance trips before and after 9/11.

The report analyzes monthly passenger movement data between January 1990 and May 2004. Data on three monthly time series are given in file *Sept11Travel.csv* for this period:

1. Actual airline revenue passenger miles (Air),
2. Rail passenger miles (Rail), and
3. Vehicle miles traveled (Car).

In order to assess the impact of September 11, BTS took the following approach: using data before September 11, they forecasted future data (under the assumption of no terrorist attack). Then, they compared the forecasted series with the actual data to assess the impact of the event. Our first step, therefore, is to split each of the time series into two parts: pre- and post September 11. We now concentrate only on the earlier time series.

a. Is the goal of this study descriptive or predictive?

b. Plot each of the three pre-event time series (Air, Rail, Car).

  i. What time series components appear from the plot?

  ii. What type of trend appears? Change the scale of the series, add trendlines and suppress seasonality to better visualize the trend pattern.

16.2 Performance on Training and Validation Data. Two different models were fit to the same time series. The first 100 time periods were used for the training set and the last 12 periods were treated as a hold-out set. Assume that both models make sense practically and fit the data pretty well. Below are the RMSE values for each of the models:

	Training set	Validation set
Model A	543	690
Model B	669	675

a. Which model appears more useful for explaining the different components of this time series? Why?

b. Which model appears to be more useful for forecasting purposes? Why?

16.3 Forecasting Department Store Sales. The file *DepartmentStoreSales.csv* contains data on the quarterly sales for a department store over a 6-year period (data courtesy of Chris Albright).

a. Create a well-formatted time plot of the data.

b. Which of the four components (level, trend, seasonality, noise) seem to be present in this series?

16.4 Shipments of Household Appliances. The file *ApplianceShipments.csv* contains the series of quarterly shipments (in million dollars) of US household appliances between 1985 and 1989 (data courtesy of Ken Black).

a. Create a well-formatted time plot of the data.

b. Which of the four components (level, trend, seasonality, noise) seem to be present in this series?

16.5 Canadian Manufacturing Workers Workhours. The time plot in Figure 16.5 describes the average annual number of weekly hours spent by Canadian manufacturing workers (data are available in *CanadianWorkHours.csv*—thanks to Ken Black for the data).

a. Reproduce the time plot.

b. Which of the four components (level, trend, seasonality, noise) seem to be present in this series?

16.6 Souvenir Sales. The file *SouvenirSales.csv* contains monthly sales for a souvenir shop at a beach resort town in Queensland, Australia, between 1995 and 2001. [Source: Hyndman and Yang (2018).]

Back in 2001, the store wanted to use the data to forecast sales for the next 12 months (year 2002). They hired an analyst to generate forecasts. The analyst first partitioned the data into training and validation sets, with the validation set containing the last 12 months of data (year 2001). She then fit a regression model to sales, using the training set.

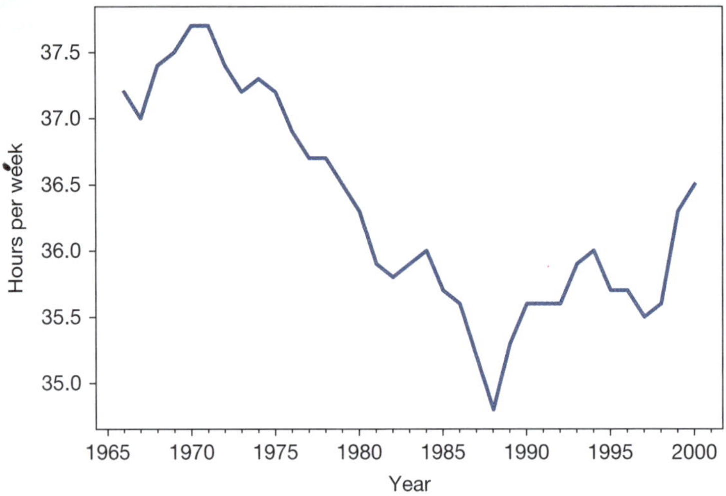

FIGURE 16.5 AVERAGE ANNUAL WEEKLY HOURS SPENT BY CANADIAN MANUFACTURING WORKERS

a. Create a well-formatted time plot of the data.

b. Change the scale on the *x*-axis, or on the *y*-axis, or on both to log-scale in order to achieve a linear relationship. Select the time plot that seems most linear.

c. Comparing the two time plots, what can be said about the type of trend in the data?

d. Why were the data partitioned? Partition the data into the training and validation set as explained above.

16.7 Shampoo Sales. The file *ShampooSales.csv* contains data on the monthly sales of a certain shampoo over a 3-year period. [Source: Hyndman and Yang (2018).]

a. Create a well-formatted time plot of the data.

b. Which of the four components (level, trend, seasonality, noise) seem to be present in this series?

c. Do you expect to see seasonality in sales of shampoo? Why?

d. If the goal is forecasting sales in future months, which of the following steps should be taken?

- Partition the data into training and validation sets
- Tweak the model parameters to obtain good fit to the validation data
- Look at MAPE and RMSE values for the training set
- Look at MAPE and RMSE values for the validation set

CHAPTER 17

Regression-Based Forecasting

A popular forecasting tool is based on multiple linear regression models, using suitable predictors to capture trend and/or seasonality. In this chapter, we show how a linear regression model can be set up to capture a time series with a trend and/or seasonality. The model, which is estimated from the data, can then produce future forecasts by inserting the relevant predictor information into the estimated regression equation. We describe different types of common trends (linear, exponential, polynomial), as well as two types of seasonality (additive and multiplicative). Next, we show how a regression model can be used to quantify the correlation between neighboring values in a time series (called autocorrelation). This type of model, called an autoregressive model, is useful for improving forecast precision by making use of the information contained in the autocorrelation (beyond trend and seasonality). It is also useful for evaluating the predictability of a series, by evaluating whether the series is a "random walk." The various steps of fitting linear regression and autoregressive models, using them to generate forecasts, and assessing their predictive accuracy, are illustrated using the Amtrak ridership series.

Python

In this chapter, we will use `numpy` and `pandas` for data handling and `matplotlib` for visualization. Models are built using `statsmodels`.

import required functionality for this chapter

```
import math
import numpy as np
import pandas as pd
import matplotlib.pylab as plt
import statsmodels.formula.api as sm
from statsmodels.tsa import tsatools, stattools
from statsmodels.tsa.arima_model import ARIMA
from statsmodels.graphics import tsaplots
```

17.1 | A MODEL WITH TREND[1]

Linear Trend

To create a linear regression model that captures a time series with a global linear trend, the outcome variable (Y) is set as the time series values or some function of it, and the predictor (X) is set as a time index. Let us consider a simple example: fitting a linear trend to the Amtrak ridership data. This type of trend is shown in Figure 17.1.

From the time plot, it is obvious that the global trend is not linear. However, we use this example to illustrate how a linear trend is fitted, and later we consider more appropriate models for this series.

code for creating Figure 17.1

```
# load data and convert to time series
Amtrak_df = pd.read_csv('Amtrak.csv')
Amtrak_df['Date'] = pd.to_datetime(Amtrak_df.Month, format='%d/%m/%Y')
ridership_ts = pd.Series(Amtrak_df.Ridership.values, index=Amtrak_df.Date)

# fit a linear trend model to the time series
ridership_df = tsatools.add_trend(ridership_ts, trend='ct')
ridership_lm = sm.ols(formula='Ridership ~ trend', data=ridership_df).fit()

# plot the time series
ax = ridership_ts.plot()
ax.set_xlabel('Time')
ax.set_ylabel('Ridership (in 000s)')
ax.set_ylim(1300, 2300)
ridership_lm.predict(ridership_df).plot(ax=ax)
plt.show()
```

[1]This and subsequent sections in this chapter copyright © 2019 Datastats, LLC, and Galit Shmueli. Used by permission.

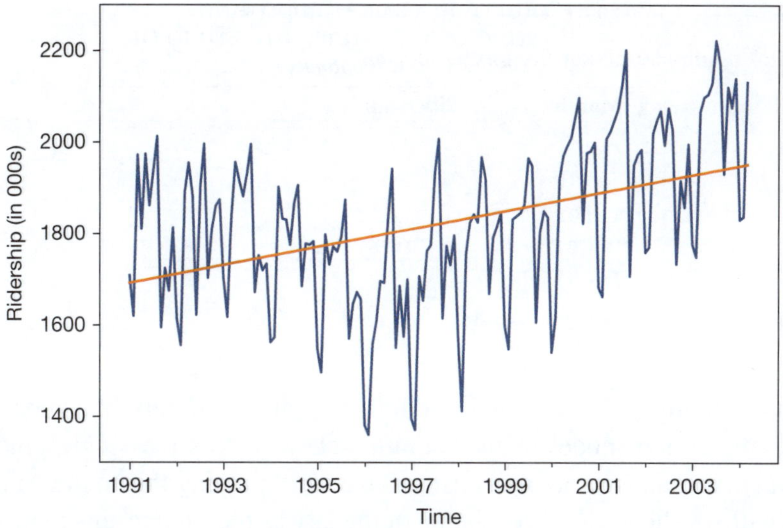

FIGURE 17.1 A LINEAR TREND FIT TO AMTRAK RIDERSHIP

To obtain a linear relationship between Ridership and Time, we set the output variable Y as the Amtrak Ridership and create a new variable that is a time index $t = 1, 2, 3, \ldots$. This time index is then used as a single predictor in the regression model:

$$Y_t = \beta_0 + \beta_1 t + \epsilon,$$

where Y_t is the Ridership at period t and ϵ is the standard noise term in a linear regression. Thus, we are modeling three of the four time series components: level (β_0), trend (β_1), and noise (ϵ). Seasonality is not modeled. A snapshot of the two corresponding columns (Y_t and t) are shown in Table 17.1.

TABLE 17.1 OUTCOME VARIABLE (MIDDLE) AND PREDICTOR VARIABLE (RIGHT) USED TO FIT A LINEAR TREND

Month	Ridership (Y_t)	t
Jan 91	1709	1
Feb 91	1621	2
Mar 91	1973	3
Apr 91	1812	4
May 91	1975	5
Jun 91	1862	6
Jul 91	1940	7

(Continued)

TABLE 17.1 OUTCOME VARIABLE (MIDDLE) AND PREDICTOR VARIABLE (RIGHT) USED TO FIT A LINEAR TREND (*Continued*)

Month	Ridership (Y_t)	t
Aug 91	2013	8
Sep 91	1596	9
Oct 91	1725	10
Nov 91	1676	11
Dec 91	1814	12
Jan 92	1615	13
Feb 92	1557	14

After partitioning the data into training and validation sets, the next step is to fit a linear regression model to the training set, with t as the single predictor (the *tsatools.add_trend* adds variables *const* and *trend*). Applying this to the Amtrak ridership data (with a validation set consisting of the last 12 months) results in the estimated model shown in Figure 17.2 and Table 17.2. The actual and fitted values and the residuals (or forecast errors) are shown in the two time plots.

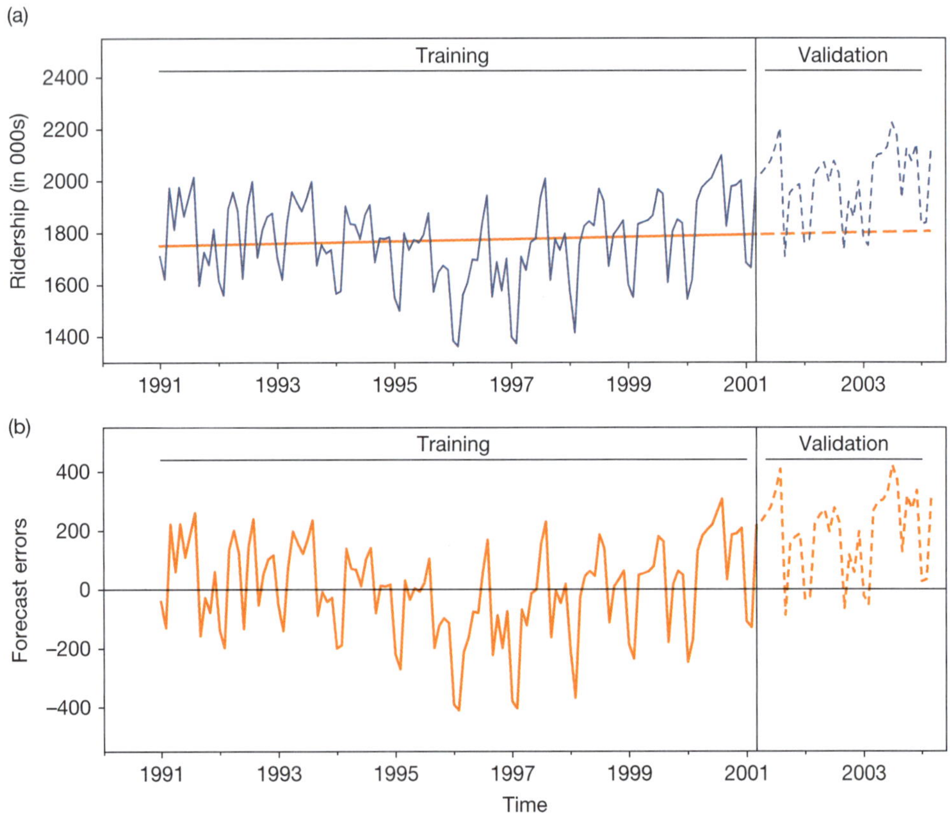

FIGURE 17.2 A LINEAR TREND FIT TO AMTRAK RIDERSHIP IN THE TRAINING PERIOD (a) AND FORECASTED IN THE VALIDATION PERIOD (b)

TABLE 17.2 A LINEAR TREND FIT TO AMTRAK RIDERSHIP IN THE TRAINING PERIOD AND FORECASTED IN THE VALIDATION PERIOD

code for creating Figure 17.2

```
# fit linear model using training set and predict on validation set
ridership_lm = sm.ols(formula='Ridership ~ trend', data=train_df).fit()
predict_df = ridership_lm.predict(valid_df)

# create the plot
def singleGraphLayout(ax, ylim, train_df, valid_df):
    ax.set_xlim('1990', '2004-6')
    ax.set_ylim(*ylim)
    ax.set_xlabel('Time')
    one_month = pd.Timedelta('31 days')
    xtrain = (min(train_df.index), max(train_df.index) - one_month)
    xvalid = (min(valid_df.index) + one_month, max(valid_df.index) - one_month)
    xtv = xtrain[1] + 0.5 * (xvalid[0] - xtrain[1])

    ypos = 0.9 * ylim[1] + 0.1 * ylim[0]
    ax.add_line(plt.Line2D(xtrain, (ypos, ypos), color='black', linewidth=0.5))
    ax.add_line(plt.Line2D(xvalid, (ypos, ypos), color='black', linewidth=0.5))
    ax.axvline(x=xtv, ymin=0, ymax=1, color='black', linewidth=0.5)

    ypos = 0.925 * ylim[1] + 0.075 * ylim[0]
    ax.text('1995', ypos, 'Training')
    ax.text('2002-3', ypos, 'Validation')

def graphLayout(axes, train_df, valid_df):
    singleGraphLayout(axes[0], [1300, 2550], train_df, valid_df)
    singleGraphLayout(axes[1], [-550, 550], train_df, valid_df)
    train_df.plot(y='Ridership', ax=axes[0], color='C0', linewidth=0.75)
    valid_df.plot(y='Ridership', ax=axes[0], color='C0', linestyle='dashed',
                  linewidth=0.75)
    axes[1].axhline(y=0, xmin=0, xmax=1, color='black', linewidth=0.5)
    axes[0].set_xlabel('')
    axes[0].set_ylabel('Ridership (in 000s)')
    axes[1].set_ylabel('Forecast Errors')
    if axes[0].get_legend():
        axes[0].get_legend().remove()

fig, axes = plt.subplots(nrows=2, ncols=1, figsize=(9, 7.5))
ridership_lm.predict(train_df).plot(ax=axes[0], color='C1')
ridership_lm.predict(valid_df).plot(ax=axes[0], color='C1', linestyle='dashed')

residual = train_df.Ridership - ridership_lm.predict(train_df)
residual.plot(ax=axes[1], color='C1')
residual = valid_df.Ridership - ridership_lm.predict(valid_df)
residual.plot(ax=axes[1], color='C1', linestyle='dashed')
graphLayout(axes, train_df, valid_df)
plt.tight_layout()
plt.show()
```

Table 17.3 contains a report of the estimated coefficients. Note that examining only the estimated coefficients and their statistical significance can be misleading! In this example, they would indicate that the linear fit is reasonable, although it is obvious from the time plots that the trend is not linear. An inadequate trend shape is easiest to detect by examining the time plot of the residuals.

TABLE 17.3 SUMMARY OF OUTPUT FROM A LINEAR REGRESSION MODEL APPLIED TO THE AMTRAK RIDERSHIP DATA IN THE TRAINING PEROID

```
> ridership_lm.summary()
```

Partial output

```
                 coef    std err          t      P>|t|      [0.025      0.975]
------------------------------------------------------------------------------
Intercept   1750.3595     29.073     60.206      0.000    1692.802    1807.917
trend          0.3514      0.407      0.864      0.390      -0.454       1.157
```

Exponential Trend

Several alternative trend shapes are useful and easy to fit via a linear regression model. One such shape is an exponential trend. An exponential trend implies a multiplicative increase/decrease of the series over time ($Y_t = ce^{\beta_1 t+\epsilon}$). To fit an exponential trend, simply replace the outcome variable Y with log Y (where log is the natural logarithm), and fit a linear regression ($\log Y_t = \beta_0 + \beta_1 t + \epsilon$). In the Amtrak example, for instance, we would fit a linear regression of log(Ridership) on the index variable t. Exponential trends are popular in sales data, where they reflect percentage growth. In *statsmodels*, we modify the formula to `np.log(Ridership) ~ trend`.

Note: As in the general case of linear regression, when comparing the predictive accuracy of models that have a different output variable, such as a linear trend model (with Y) and an exponential trend model (with log Y), it is essential to compare forecasts or forecast errors on the same scale. Therefore, when using an exponential trend model, the forecasts of log Y are made and then need to be converted back to the original scale. An example is shown in Figure 17.3, where an exponential trend is fit to the Amtrak ridership data.

code for creating Figure 17.3

```
ridership_lm_linear = sm.ols(formula='Ridership ~ trend', data=train_df).fit()
predict_df_linear = ridership_lm_linear.predict(valid_df)

ridership_lm_expo = sm.ols(formula='np.log(Ridership) ~ trend', data=train_df).fit()
predict_df_expo = ridership_lm_expo.predict(valid_df)
```

```
fig, ax = plt.subplots(nrows=1, ncols=1, figsize=(9,3.75))
train_df.plot(y='Ridership', ax=ax, color='C0', linewidth=0.75)
valid_df.plot(y='Ridership', ax=ax, color='C0', linestyle='dashed', linewidth=0.75)
singleGraphLayout(ax, [1300, 2600], train_df, valid_df)
ridership_lm_linear.predict(train_df).plot(color='C1')
ridership_lm_linear.predict(valid_df).plot(color='C1', linestyle='dashed')
ridership_lm_expo.predict(train_df).apply(lambda row: math.exp(row)).plot(color='C2')
ridership_lm_expo.predict(valid_df).apply(lambda row: math.exp(row)).plot(color='C2',
                                                        linestyle='dashed')

ax.get_legend().remove()
plt.show()
```

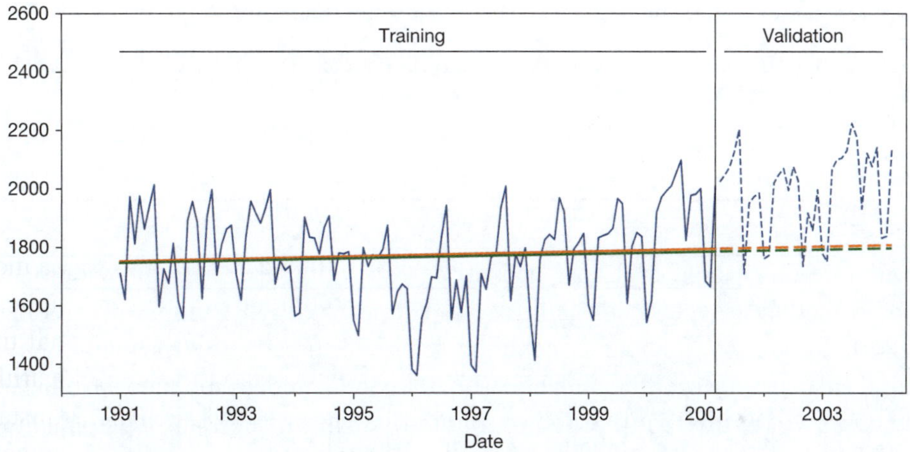

FIGURE 17.3 EXPONENTIAL (GREEN) AND LINEAR (ORANGE) TREND USED TO FORECAST AMTRAK RIDERSHIP

Polynomial Trend

Another non-linear trend shape that is easy to fit via linear regression is a polynomial trend, and in particular, a quadratic relationship of the form $Y_t = \beta_0 + \beta_1 t + \beta_2 t^2 + \epsilon$. This is done by creating an additional predictor t^2 (the square of t), and fitting a multiple linear regression with the two predictors t and t^2. In *statsmodels*, we can either add linear and quadratic trend terms using the method *add_trend('ctt')* or define the quadratic trend in the formula using *np.square(trend)* (Figure 17.4). For the Amtrak ridership data, we have already seen a U-shaped trend in the data. We therefore fit a quadratic model. The fitted and residual charts are shown in Figure 17.4. We conclude from these plots that this shape adequately captures the trend. The forecast errors are now devoid of trend and exhibit only seasonality.

In general, any type of trend shape can be fit as long as it has a mathematical representation. However, the underlying assumption is that this shape is applicable throughout the period of data that we have and also during the period that we are going to forecast. Do not choose an overly complex shape. Although it will fit the training data well, it will in fact be overfitting them. To avoid overfitting, always examine the validation performance and refrain from choosing overly complex trend patterns.

code for creating Figure 17.4

```
ridership_lm_poly = sm.ols(formula='Ridership ~ trend + np.square(trend)',
                           data=train_df).fit()

fig, axes = plt.subplots(nrows=2, ncols=1, figsize=(9, 7.5))

ridership_lm_poly.predict(train_df).plot(ax=axes[0], color='C1')
ridership_lm_poly.predict(valid_df).plot(ax=axes[0], color='C1', linestyle='dashed')
residual = train_df.Ridership - ridership_lm_poly.predict(train_df)
residual.plot(ax=axes[1], color='C1')
residual = valid_df.Ridership - ridership_lm_poly.predict(valid_df)
residual.plot(ax=axes[1], color='C1', linestyle='dashed')

graphLayout(axes, train_df, valid_df)
plt.show()
```

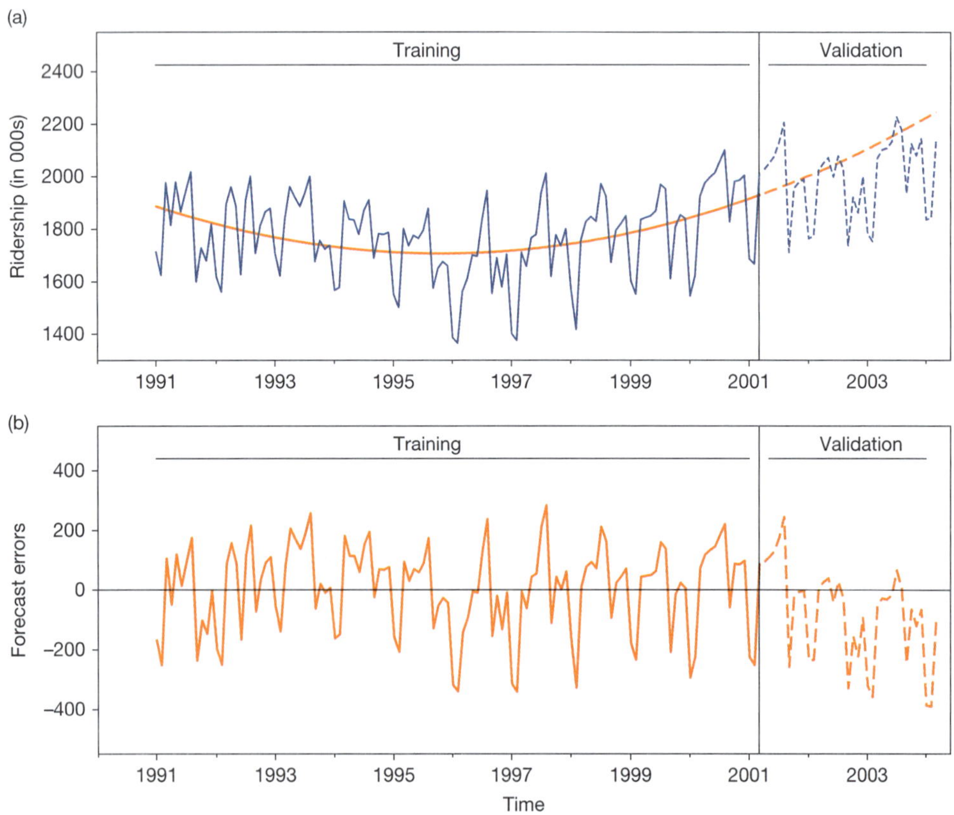

FIGURE 17.4 QUADRATIC TREND MODEL USED TO FORECAST AMTRAK RIDERSHIP. PLOTS OF FITTED, FORECASTED, AND ACTUAL VALUES (a) AND FORECAST ERRORS (b)

17.2 | A MODEL WITH SEASONALITY

A seasonal pattern in a time series means that periods that fall in some seasons have consistently higher or lower values than those that fall in other seasons. Examples are day-of-week patterns, monthly patterns, and quarterly patterns. The Amtrak ridership monthly time series, as can be seen in the time plot, exhibits strong monthly seasonality (with highest traffic during summer months).

Seasonality is captured in a regression model by creating a new categorical variable that denotes the season for each value. This categorical variable is then turned into dummies, which in turn are included as predictors in the regression model. To illustrate this, we created a new "Month" column for the Amtrak data, as shown in Table 17.4. Then, to include the Month categorical variable as a predictor in a regression model for Y (Ridership), we turn it into dummies (for $m = 12$ seasons we create 11 dummies that take on the value 1 if the record falls in that particular season, and 0 otherwise[2]).

TABLE 17.4 NEW CATEGORICAL VARIABLE (RIGHT) TO BE USED AS PREDICTOR(S) IN A LINEAR REGRESSION MODEL

Month	Ridership	Season
Jan 91	1709	Jan
Feb 91	1621	Feb
Mar 91	1973	Mar
Apr 91	1812	Apr
May 91	1975	May
Jun 91	1862	Jun
Jul 91	1940	Jul
Aug 91	2013	Aug
Sep 91	1596	Sep
Oct 91	1725	Oct
Nov 91	1676	Nov
Dec 91	1814	Dec
Jan 92	1615	Jan
Feb 92	1557	Feb
Mar 92	1891	Mar
Apr 92	1956	Apr
May 92	1885	May

With *statsmodels*, we add a variable for month and include it as a categorical variable in the linear regression formula `Ridership ~ C(Month)`. This will automatically create and use the dummies correctly for the regression.

[2]Using only $m-1$ dummies is sufficient. If all $m-1$ dummies are zero, then the season must be the mth season. Including all m dummies causes multicollinearity.

After partitioning the data into training and validation sets (see Section 16.5), we fit the regression model to the training data. The fitted series and the residuals from this model are shown in Figure 17.5. The model appears to capture the seasonality in the data. However, since we have not included a trend component in the model (as shown in Section 17.1), the fitted values do not capture the existing trend. Therefore, the residuals, which are the difference between the actual and the fitted values, clearly display the remaining U-shaped trend.

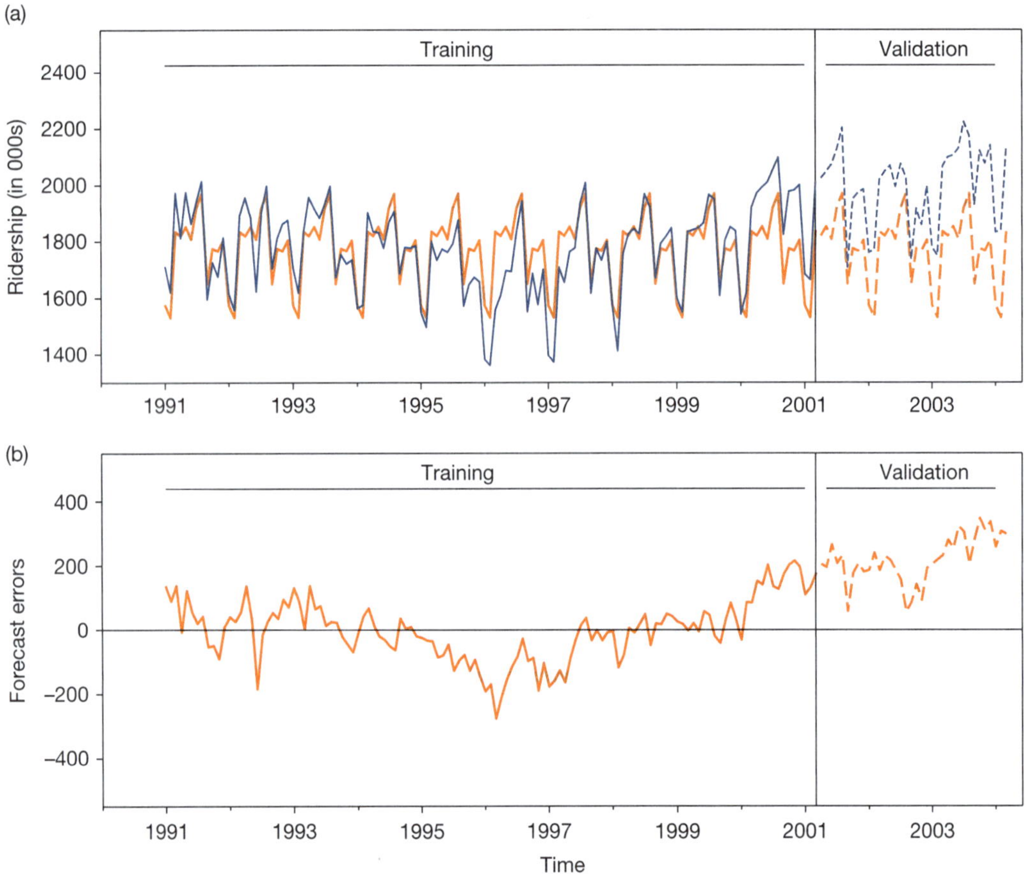

FIGURE 17.5 REGRESSION MODEL WITH SEASONALITY APPLIED TO THE AMTRAK RIDERSHIP (a) AND ITS FORECAST ERRORS (b)

When seasonality is added as described above (create categorical seasonal variable, then create dummies from it, then regress on Y), it captures *additive seasonality*. This means that the average value of Y in a certain season is a fixed amount more or less than that in another season. Table 17.5 shows the output of a linear regression fit to Ridership (Y) with seasonality. For example, in the Amtrak ridership, the coefficient for *C(Month)[T.8]* (396.66) indicates that the average number of passengers in August is higher by 396,660 passengers than the average in January (the reference category). Using regression models, we can also capture *multiplicative seasonality*, where values in a certain season are on average, higher or lower by a percentage amount compared to another season. To fit multiplicative seasonality, we use the same model as above, except that we use log(Y) as the outcome variable as described above for *Exponential trend*.

TABLE 17.5 SUMMARY OF OUTPUT FROM FITTING ADDITIVE SEASONALITY TO THE AMTRAK RIDERSHIP DATA IN THE TRAINING PERIOD

```
ridership_df = tsatools.add_trend(ridership_ts, trend='c')
ridership_df['Month'] = ridership_df.index.month
# partition the data
train_df = ridership_df[:nTrain]
valid_df = ridership_df[nTrain:]
ridership_lm_season = sm.ols(formula='Ridership ~ C(Month)', data=train_df).fit()
ridership_lm_season.summary()
```

Partial output

	coef	std err	t	P>|t|	[0.025	0.975]
Intercept	1573.9722	30.578	51.475	0.000	1513.381	1634.564
C(Month)[T.2]	-42.9302	43.243	-0.993	0.323	-128.620	42.759
C(Month)[T.3]	260.7677	43.243	6.030	0.000	175.078	346.457
C(Month)[T.4]	245.0919	44.311	5.531	0.000	157.286	332.897
C(Month)[T.5]	278.2222	44.311	6.279	0.000	190.417	366.028
C(Month)[T.6]	233.4598	44.311	5.269	0.000	145.654	321.265
C(Month)[T.7]	345.3265	44.311	7.793	0.000	257.521	433.132
C(Month)[T.8]	396.6595	44.311	8.952	0.000	308.854	484.465
C(Month)[T.9]	75.7615	44.311	1.710	0.090	-12.044	163.567
C(Month)[T.10]	200.6076	44.311	4.527	0.000	112.802	288.413
C(Month)[T.11]	192.3552	44.311	4.341	0.000	104.550	280.161
C(Month)[T.12]	230.4151	44.311	5.200	0.000	142.610	318.221

17.3 | A MODEL WITH TREND AND SEASONALITY

Finally, we can create models that capture both trend and seasonality by including predictors of both types. For example, from our exploration of the Amtrak Ridership data, it appears that a quadratic trend and monthly seasonality are both warranted. We therefore fit a model to the training data with 13 predictors: 11 dummies for month, and t and t^2 for trend. The fit and output from this final model are shown in Figure 17.6 and Table 17.6. If we are satisfied with this model after evaluating its predictive performance on the validation data and comparing it against alternatives, we would re-fit it to the entire un-partitioned series. This re-fitted model can then be used to generate k-step-ahead forecasts (denoted by F_{t+k}) by plugging in the appropriate month and index terms.

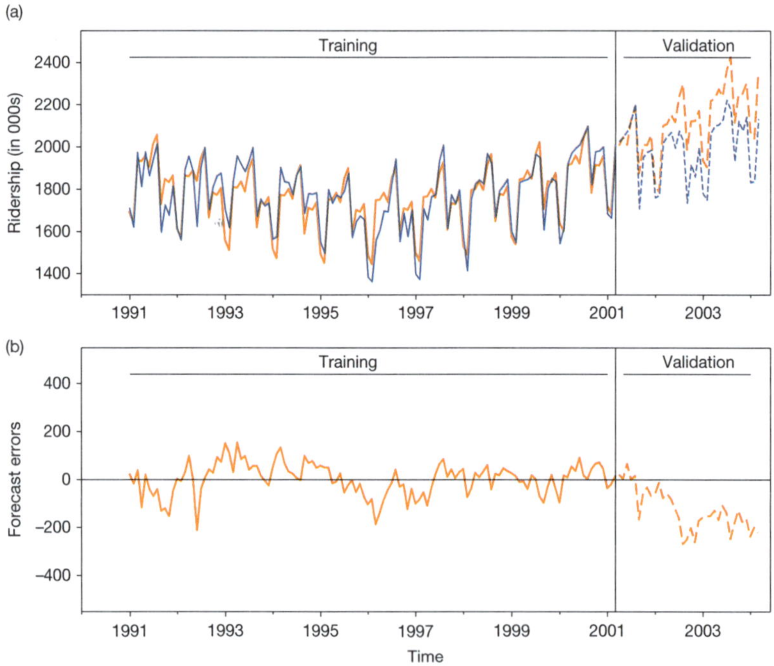

FIGURE 17.6 REGRESSION MODEL WITH TREND AND SEASONALITY APPLIED TO AMTRAK RIDERSHIP (a) AND ITS FORECAST ERRORS (b)

TABLE 17.6 SUMMARY OF OUTPUT FROM FITTING TREND AND SEASONALITY TO AMTRAK RIDERSHIP IN THE TRAINING PERIOD

```
> formula = 'Ridership ~ trend + np.square(trend) + C(Month)'
> ridership_lm_trendseason = sm.ols(formula=formula, data=train_df).fit()
                          OLS Regression Results
=====================================================================================
                       coef    std err          t      P>|t|      [0.025      0.975]
-------------------------------------------------------------------------------------
Intercept         1696.9794     27.675     61.318      0.000    1642.128    1751.831
C(Month)[T.2]      -43.2458     30.241     -1.430      0.156    -103.182      16.690
C(Month)[T.3]      260.0149     30.242      8.598      0.000     200.076     319.954
C(Month)[T.4]      260.6175     31.021      8.401      0.000     199.135     322.100
C(Month)[T.5]      293.7966     31.020      9.471      0.000     232.316     355.278
C(Month)[T.6]      248.9615     31.020      8.026      0.000     187.481     310.442
C(Month)[T.7]      360.6340     31.020     11.626      0.000     299.153     422.115
C(Month)[T.8]      411.6513     31.021     13.270      0.000     350.169     473.134
C(Month)[T.9]       90.3162     31.022      2.911      0.004      28.831     151.801
C(Month)[T.10]     214.6037     31.024      6.917      0.000     153.115     276.092
C(Month)[T.11]     205.6711     31.026      6.629      0.000     144.178     267.165
C(Month)[T.12]     242.9294     31.029      7.829      0.000     181.430     304.429
trend               -7.1559      0.729     -9.812      0.000      -8.601      -5.710
np.square(trend)     0.0607      0.006     10.660      0.000       0.049       0.072
```

17.4 | AUTOCORRELATION AND ARIMA MODELS

When we use linear regression for time series forecasting, we are able to account for patterns such as trend and seasonality. However, ordinary regression models do not account for dependence between values in different periods, which in cross-sectional data is assumed to be absent. Yet, in the time series context, values in neighboring periods tend to be correlated. Such correlation, called *autocorrelation*, is informative and can help in improving forecasts. If we know that a high value tends to be followed by high values (positive autocorrelation), then we can use that to adjust forecasts. We will now discuss how to compute the autocorrelation of a series, and how best to utilize the information for improving forecasts.

Computing Autocorrelation

Correlation between values of a time series in neighboring periods is called *autocorrelation*, because it describes a relationship between the series and itself. To compute autocorrelation, we compute the correlation between the series and a lagged version of the series. A *lagged series* is a "copy" of the original series which is moved forward one or more time periods. A lagged series with lag-1 is the original series moved forward one time period; a lagged series with lag-2 is the original series moved forward two time periods, etc. Table 17.7 shows the first 24 months of the Amtrak ridership series, the lag-1 series and the lag-2 series.

TABLE 17.7 FIRST 24 MONTHS OF AMTRAK RIDERSHIP SERIES WITH LAG-1 AND LAG-2 SERIES

Month	Ridership	Lag-1 series	Lag-2 series
Jan 91	1709		
Feb 91	1621	1709	
Mar 91	1973	1621	1709
Apr 91	1812	1973	1621
May 91	1975	1812	1973
Jun 91	1862	1975	1812
Jul 91	1940	1862	1975
Aug 91	2013	1940	1862
Sep 91	1596	2013	1940
Oct 91	1725	1596	2013
Nov 91	1676	1725	1596
Dec 91	1814	1676	1725
Jan 92	1615	1814	1676
Feb 92	1557	1615	1814
Mar 92	1891	1557	1615
Apr 92	1956	1891	1557

(Continued)

TABLE 17.7 FIRST 24 MONTHS OF AMTRAK RIDERSHIP SERIES WITH LAG-1 AND LAG-2 SERIES (*Continued*)

Month	Ridership	Lag-1 series	Lag-2 series
May 92	1885	1956	1891
Jun 92	1623	1885	1956
Jul 92	1903	1623	1885
Aug 92	1997	1903	1623
Sep 92	1704	1997	1903
Oct 92	1810	1704	1997
Nov 92	1862	1810	1704
Dec 92	1875	1862	1810

Next, to compute the lag-1 autocorrelation, which measures the linear relationship between values in consecutive time periods, we compute the correlation between the original series and the lag-1 series (e.g., via the function *np.corrcoef*) to be 0.063. Note that although the original series in Table 17.7 has 24 time periods, the lag-1 autocorrelation will only be based on 23 pairs (because the lag-1 series does not have a value for January 1991). Similarly, the lag-2 autocorrelation, measuring the relationship between values that are two time periods apart, is the correlation between the original series and the lag-2 series (yielding −0.15).

We can use `statsmodel`'s function *acf* to compute the autocorrelation function (ACF) of a series and the function *plot_acf* to directly create a plot. For example, the output for the 24-month ridership is shown in Figure 17.7.

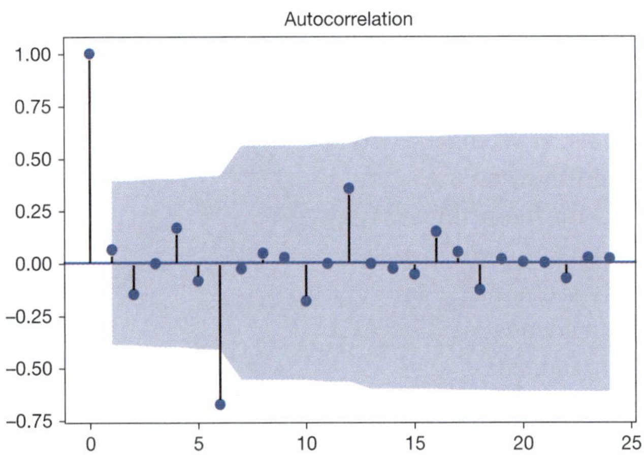

FIGURE 17.7 AUTOCORRELATION PLOT FOR LAGS 1–12 (FOR FIRST 24 MONTHS OF AMTRAK RIDERSHIP, 95% CONFIDENCE REGION IS BLUE SHADED)

code for creating Figure 17.7

```
tsaplots.plot_acf(train_df['1991-01-01':'1993-01-01'].Ridership)
plt.show()
```

A few typical autocorrelation behaviors that are useful to explore are:

Strong autocorrelation (positive or negative) at a lag k larger than 1 and its multiples ($2k, 3k, \ldots$) typically reflects a cyclical pattern. For example, strong positive lag-12 autocorrelation in monthly data will reflect an annual seasonality (where values during a given month each year are positively correlated).

Positive lag-1 autocorrelation (called "stickiness") describes a series where consecutive values move generally in the same direction. In the presence of a strong linear trend, we would expect to see a strong and positive lag-1 autocorrelation.

Negative lag-1 autocorrelation reflects swings in the series, where high values are immediately followed by low values and vice versa.

Examining the autocorrelation of a series can therefore help to detect seasonality patterns. In Figure 17.7, for example, we see that the strongest autocorrelation at lag 6 and is negative (exceeding the 95% confidence interval). Autocorrelations that fall outside the confidence interval point to possible model improvement. This indicates a bi-annual pattern in ridership, with 6-month switches from high to low ridership. A look at the time plot confirms the high-summer low-winter pattern.

In addition to looking at the autocorrelation of the raw series, it is very useful to look at the autocorrelation of the *residual series*. For example, after fitting a regression model (or using any other forecasting method), we can examine the autocorrelation of the series of residuals. If we have adequately modeled the seasonal pattern, then the residual series should show no autocorrelation at the season's lag. Figure 17.8 displays the autocorrelations for the residuals from the regression model with seasonality and quadratic trend shown in Figure 17.6. It is clear that the 6-month (and 12-month) cyclical behavior no longer dominates the series of residuals, indicating that the regression model captured them adequately. However, we can also see a strong positive autocorrelation from lag 1 on, indicating a positive relationship between neighboring residuals. This is valuable information, which can be used to improve forecasts.

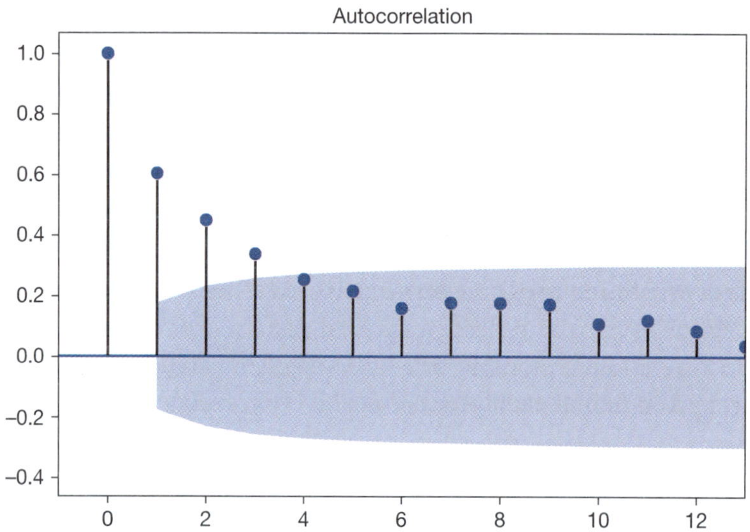

FIGURE 17.8 AUTOCORRELATION PLOT OF FORECAST ERRORS SERIES FROM FIGURE 17.6

Improving Forecasts by Integrating Autocorrelation Information

In general, there are two approaches to taking advantage of autocorrelation. One is by directly building the autocorrelation into the regression model, and the other is by constructing a second-level forecasting model on the residual series.

Among regression-type models that directly account for autocorrelation are *autoregressive* (AR) models, or the more general class of models called ARIMA (Autoregressive Integrated Moving Average) models. AR models are similar to linear regression models, except that the predictors are the past values of the series. For example, an autoregressive model of order 2, denoted AR(2), can be written as

$$Y_t = \beta_0 + \beta_1 Y_{t-1} + \beta_2 Y_{t-2} + \epsilon. \tag{17.1}$$

Estimating such models is roughly equivalent to fitting a linear regression model with the series as the outcome variable, and the two lagged series (at lag 1 and 2 in this example) as the predictors. However, it is better to use designated ARIMA estimation methods (e.g., those available in the `statsmodel` package) over ordinary linear regression estimation, to produce more accurate results.[3] Although moving from AR to ARIMA models creates a larger set of more flexible forecasting models, it also requires much more statistical expertise. Even with the simpler AR models, fitting them to raw time series that contain patterns such as trends and seasonality requires the user to perform several initial data transformations and to choose the order of the model. These are not straightforward tasks. Because ARIMA modeling is less robust and requires

[3]ARIMA model estimation differs from ordinary regression estimation by accounting for the dependence between records.

more experience and statistical expertise than other methods, the use of such models for forecasting raw series is generally less popular in practical forecasting. We therefore direct the interested reader to classic time series textbooks (e.g., see Chapter 4 in Chatfield, 2003).

However, we do discuss one particular use of AR models that is straightforward to apply in the context of forecasting, which can provide a significant improvement to short-term forecasts. This relates to the second approach for utilizing autocorrelation, which requires constructing a second-level forecasting model for the residuals, as follows:

1. Generate a k-step-ahead forecast of the series (F_{t+k}), using any forecasting method
2. Generate a k-step-ahead forecast of the forecast error (residual) (E_{t+k}), using an AR (or other) model
3. Improve the initial k-step-ahead forecast of the series by adjusting it according to its forecasted error: *Improved* $F^*_{t+k} = F_{t+k} + E_{t+k}$.

In particular, we can fit low-order AR models to series of residuals (or *forecast errors*) which can then be used to forecast future forecast errors. By fitting the series of residuals, rather than the raw series, we avoid the need for initial data transformations (because the residual series is not expected to contain any trends or cyclical behavior besides autocorrelation).

To fit an AR model to the series of residuals, we first examine the autocorrelations of the residual series. We then choose the order of the AR model according to the lags in which autocorrelation appears. Often, when autocorrelation exists at lag-1 and higher, it is sufficient to fit an AR(1) model of the form

$$E_t = \beta_0 + \beta_1 E_{t-1} + \epsilon, \tag{17.2}$$

where E_t denotes the residual (or *forecast error*) at time t. For example, although the autocorrelations in Figure 17.8 appear large from lags 1 to 10 or so, it is likely that an AR(1) would capture all of these relationships. The reason is that if immediate neighboring values are correlated, then the relationship propagates to values that are two periods away, then three periods away, etc.[4]

Assuming that the residuals (forecast errors) have mean zero, we can fit an AR model with no intercept ($\beta_0 = 0$). The result of fitting such an AR(1) model to the Amtrak

[4] *Partial autocorrelations* (function *pacf()*) measure the contribution of each lag series *over and above* smaller lags. For example, the lag-2 partial autocorrelation is the contribution of lag-2 beyond that of lag-1.

ridership residual series is shown in Table 17.8. The AR(1) coefficient (0.5998) is close to the lag-1 autocorrelation (0.6041) that we found earlier (Figure 17.8). The forecasted residual for April 2001 is computed by plugging in the most recent residual from March 2001 (equal to 12.108) into the AR(1) model:

$$(0.5998)(12.108) = 7.262.$$

You can obtain this number directly by using the *forecast()* method (see output in Table 17.8). The positive value tells us that the regression model will produce a ridership forecast for April 2001 that is too low and that we should adjust it up by adding 7262 riders. In this particular example, the regression model (with quadratic trend and seasonality) produced a forecast of 2,004,271 riders, and the improved two-stage model [regression + AR(1) correction] corrected it by increasing it to 2,011,533 riders. The actual value for April 2001 turned out to be 2,023,792 riders—much closer to the improved forecast.

TABLE 17.8 OUTPUT FOR AR(1) MODEL ON RIDERSHIP RESIDUALS

code for running AR(1) model on residuals

```
formula = 'Ridership ~ trend + np.square(trend) + C(Month)'
train_lm_trendseason = sm.ols(formula=formula, data=train_df).fit()
train_res_arima = ARIMA(train_lm_trendseason.resid, order=(1, 0, 0),
                        freq='MS').fit(trend='nc')
forecast, _, conf_int = train_res_arima.forecast(1)
```

Output

```
> print(pd.DataFrame({'coef': train_res_arima.params, 'std err': train_res_arima.bse}))
              coef    std err
ar.L1.y   0.599789   0.071268

> print('Forecast {0:.3f} [{1[0][0]:.3f}, {1[0][1]:.3f}]'.format(forecast, conf_int))
 Forecast 7.262 [-96.992, 111.516]
```

From the plot of the actual vs. forecasted residual series (Figure 17.9), we can see that the AR(1) model fits the residual series quite well. Note, however, that the plot is based on the training data (until March 2001). To evaluate predictive performance of the two-level model [regression + AR(1)], we would have to examine performance (e.g., via MAPE or RMSE metrics) on the validation data, in a fashion similar to the calculation that we performed for April 2001.

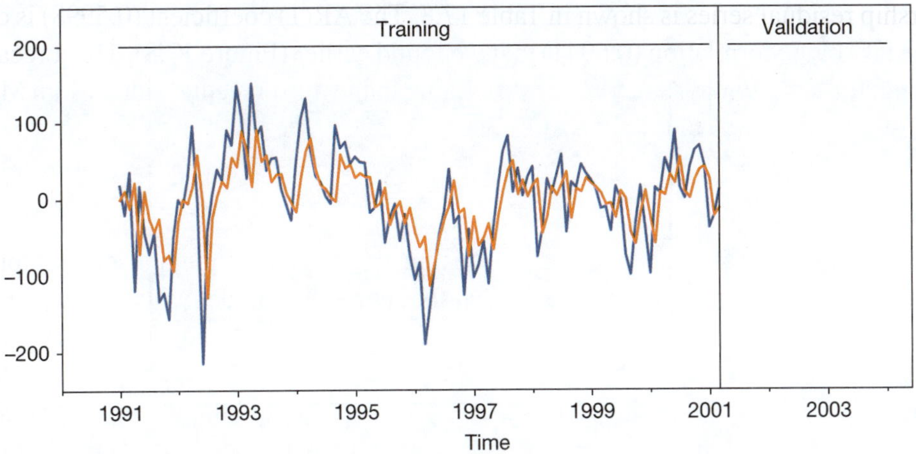

FIGURE 17.9 FITTING AN AR(1) MODEL TO THE RESIDUAL SERIES FROM FIGURE 17.6

code for creating Figure 17.9

```
ax = train_lm_trendseason.resid.plot(figsize=(9,4))
train_res_arima.fittedvalues.plot(ax=ax)
singleGraphLayout(ax, [-250, 250], train_df, valid_df)
plt.show()
```

Finally, to examine whether we have indeed accounted for the autocorrelation in the series and that no more information remains in the series, we examine the autocorrelations of the series of residuals-of-residuals (the residuals obtained after the AR(1), which was applied to the regression residuals). This is seen in Figure 17.10. It is clear that no more autocorrelation remains, and that the addition of the AR(1) has adequately captured the autocorrelation information.

We mentioned earlier that improving forecasts via an additional AR layer is useful for short-term forecasting. The reason is that an AR model of order k will usually only provide useful forecasts for the next k periods, and after that forecasts will rely on earlier forecasts rather than on actual data. For example, to forecast the residual of May 2001 when the time of prediction is March 2001, we would need the residual for April 2001. However, because that value is not available, it would be replaced by its forecast. Hence, the forecast for May 2001 would be based on the forecast for April 2001.

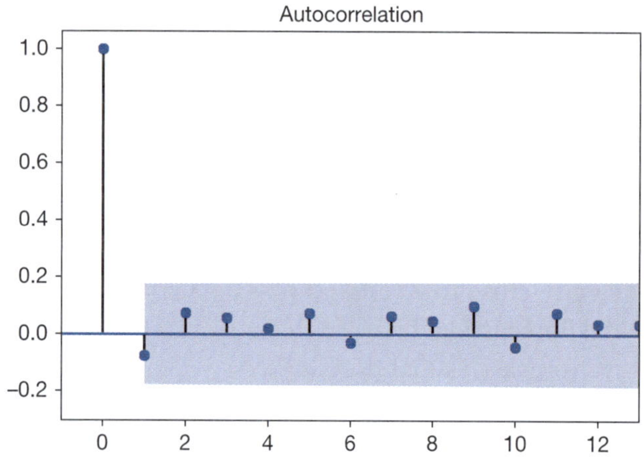

FIGURE 17.10 AUTOCORRELATIONS OF RESIDUALS-OF-RESIDUALS SERIES

Evaluating Predictability

Before attempting to forecast a time series, it is important to determine whether it is predictable, in the sense that its past can be used to predict its future beyond the naive forecast. One useful way to assess predictability is to test whether the series is a *random walk*. A random walk is a series in which changes from one time period to the next are random. According to the efficient market hypothesis in economics, asset prices are random walks and therefore predicting stock prices is a game of chance.[5]

A random walk is a special case of an AR(1) model, where the slope coefficient is equal to 1:

$$Y_t = \beta_0 + Y_{t-1} + \epsilon_t. \tag{17.3}$$

We can also write this as

$$Y_t - Y_{t-1} = \beta_0 + \epsilon_t. \tag{17.4}$$

We see from the last equation that the difference between the values at periods $t - 1$ and t is random, hence the term "random walk." Forecasts from such a model are basically equal to the most recent observed value (the naive forecast), reflecting the lack of any other information.

To test whether a series is a random walk, we fit an AR(1) model and test the hypothesis that the slope coefficient is equal to 1 ($H_0\colon \beta_1 = 1$ vs. $H_1\colon \beta_1 \neq 1$). If the

[5]There is some controversy surrounding the efficient market hypothesis, with claims that there is slight autocorrelation in asset prices, which does make them predictable to some extent. However, transaction costs and bid-ask spreads tend to offset any prediction benefits.

null hypothesis is rejected (reflected by a small p-value), then the series is not a random walk and we can attempt to predict it.

As an example, consider the AR(1) model shown in Figure 17.6. The slope coefficient (0.5998) is more than 5 standard errors away from 1, indicating that this is not a random walk. In contrast, consider the AR(1) model fitted to the series of S&P500 monthly closing prices between May 1995 and August 2003 (in *SP500.csv*, shown in Table 17.9). Here the slope coefficient is 0.9833, with a standard error of 0.0145. The coefficient is sufficiently close to 1 (around one standard error away), indicating that this is a random walk. Forecasting this series using any of the methods described earlier (aside from the naive forecast) is therefore futile.

TABLE 17.9 OUTPUT FOR AR(1) MODEL ON S&P500 MONTHLY CLOSING PRICES

```
sp500_df = pd.read_csv('SP500.csv')
# convert date to first of each month
sp500_df['Date'] = pd.to_datetime(sp500_df.Date, format='%d-%b-%y').dt.to_period('M')
sp500_ts = pd.Series(sp500_df.Close.values, index=sp500_df.Date, name='sp500')
sp500_arima = ARIMA(sp500_ts, order=(1, 0, 0)).fit(disp=0)
print(pd.DataFrame({'coef': sp500_arima.params, 'std err': sp500_arima.bse}))
```

Output

```
                  coef     std err
const        888.11275  221.980066
ar.L1.sp500    0.98338    0.014523
```

PROBLEMS

17.1 Impact of September 11 on Air Travel in the United States. The Research and Innovative Technology Administration's Bureau of Transportation Statistics conducted a study to evaluate the impact of the September 11, 2001 terrorist attack on US transportation. The 2006 study report and the data can be found at https://www.bts.gov/archive/publications/estimated_impacts_of_9_11_on_us_travel/index. The goal of the study was stated as follows:

> The purpose of this study is to provide a greater understanding of the passenger travel behavior patterns of persons making long distance trips before and after 9/11.

The report analyzes monthly passenger movement data between January 1990 and May 2004. Data on three monthly time series are given in file *Sept11Travel.csv* for this period: (1) Actual airline revenue passenger miles (Air), (2) rail passenger miles (Rail), and (3) vehicle miles traveled (Car).

In order to assess the impact of September 11, BTS took the following approach: using data before September 11, they forecasted future data (under the assumption of no terrorist attack). Then, they compared the forecasted series with the actual data to assess the impact of the event. Our first step, therefore, is to split each of the time series into two parts: pre- and post September 11. We now concentrate only on the earlier time series.

a. Plot the pre-event AIR time series. What time series components appear?

b. Figure 17.11 shows a time plot of the **seasonally adjusted** pre-September-11 AIR series. Which of the following methods would be adequate for forecasting the series shown in the figure?

- Linear regression model seasonality
- Linear regression model with trend
- Linear regression model with trend and seasonality

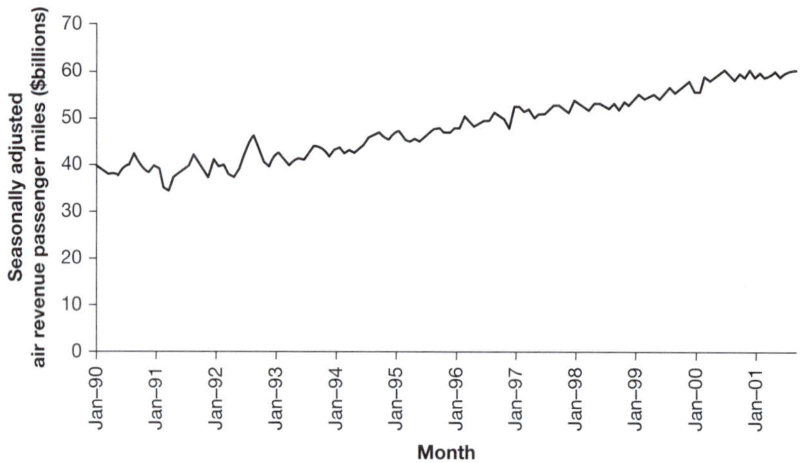

FIGURE 17.11 SEASONALLY ADJUSTED PRE-SEPTEMBER-11 AIR SERIES

c. Specify a linear regression model for the AIR series that would produce a seasonally adjusted series similar to the one shown in Figure 17.11, with multiplicative seasonality. What is the outcome variable? What are the predictors?

d. Run the regression model from (c). Remember to use only pre-event data.

  i. What can we learn from the statistical insignificance of the coefficients for October and September?

  ii. The actual value of AIR (air revenue passenger miles) in January 1990 was 35.153577 billion. What is the residual for this month, using the regression model? Report the residual in terms of air revenue passenger miles.

e. Create an ACF (autocorrelation) plot of the regression residuals.

  i. What does the ACF plot tell us about the regression model's forecasts?

  ii. How can this information be used to improve the model?

f. Fit linear regression models to Air, Rail, and to Auto with additive seasonality and an appropriate trend. For Air and Rail, fit a linear trend. For Rail, use a quadratic trend.

Remember to use only pre-event data. Once the models are estimated, use them to forecast each of the three post-event series.

i. For each series (Air, Rail, Auto), plot the complete pre-event and post-event actual series overlayed with the predicted series.

ii. What can be said about the effect of the September 11 terrorist attack on the three modes of transportation? Discuss the magnitude of the effect, its time span, and any other relevant aspects.

17.2 Milk Purchase Trends in North Delhi. The time plot in Figure 17.12 describes the monthly trends in the average purchase of milk (in liters) by households in select housing societies of Delhi city for the period July 2017 to May 2020. The figures were derived based on digital transactions carried out by sample households at outlets of popular milk-selling organizations (data are available in *AvgMilkPurchase.csv*).

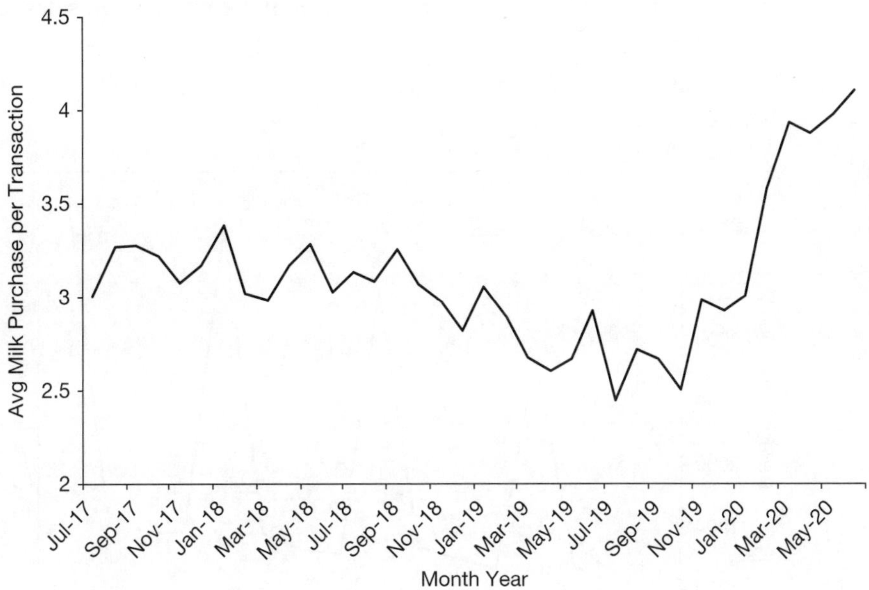

FIGURE 17.12 AVERAGE PURCHASE OF MILK (IN LITERS) BY HOUSEHOLDS IN NORTH DELHI

a. Which of the following regression models would fit the series best? (Choose one.)

- Linear trend model
- Linear trend model with seasonality
- Quadratic trend model
- Quadratic trend model with seasonality

b. If we computed the autocorrelation of this series, would the lag-1 autocorrelation exhibit negative, positive, or no autocorrelation? How can you see this from the plot?

c. Compute the autocorrelation of the series and produce an ACF plot. Verify your answer to the previous question.

17.3 Toys "R" US Revenues. Figure 17.13 is a time plot of the quarterly revenues of Toys "R" US between 1992 and 1995 (thanks to Chris Albright for suggesting the use of these data, which are available in *ToysRUsRevenues.csv*).

a. Fit a regression model with a linear trend and additive seasonality. Use the entire series (excluding the last two quarters) as the training set.

b. A partial output of the regression model is shown in Table 17.10 (where *C(Quarter)[T.2]* is the Quarter 2 dummy). Use this output to answer the following questions:

i. Which two statistics (and their values) measure how well this model fits the training data?

ii. Which two statistics (and their values) measure the predictive accuracy of this model?

iii. After adjusting for trend, what is the average difference between sales in Q3 and sales in Q1?

iv. After adjusting for seasonality, which quarter (Q1, Q2, Q3, or Q4) has the highest average sales?

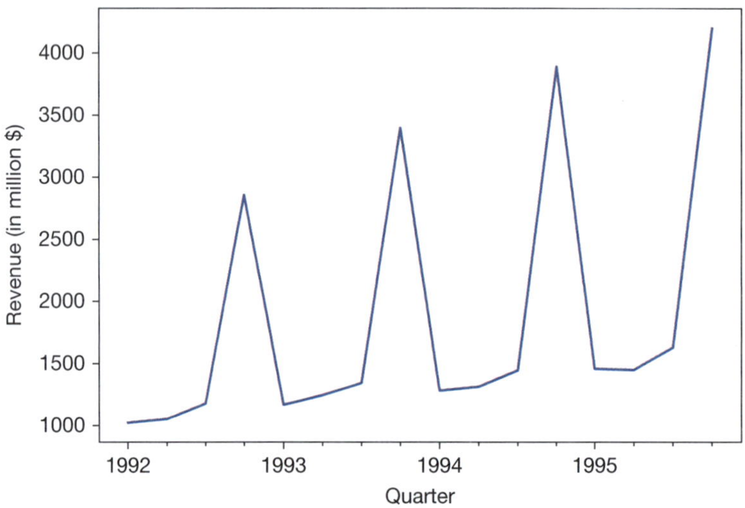

FIGURE 17.13 QUARTERLY REVENUES OF TOYS "R" US, 1992–1995

TABLE 17.10 REGRESSION MODEL FITTED TO TOYS "R" US TIME SERIES AND ITS PREDICTIVE PERFORMANCE IN TRAINING AND VALIDATION PERIODS

	coef	std err
Intercept	906.750000	115.346119
C(Quarter)[T.2]	-15.107143	119.659603
C(Quarter)[T.3]	89.166667	128.673983
C(Quarter)[T.4]	2101.726190	129.165419
trend	47.107143	11.256629

17.4 Reliance Industries Limited (RIL) Stock. Figure 17.14 shows the series of RIL daily closing prices between July 2019 and June 2020 in BSE.
Source: (www.bseindia.com/markets/equity/EQReports/StockPrcHistori.aspx?expandable=7&scripcode=500325&flag=sp&Submit=G)

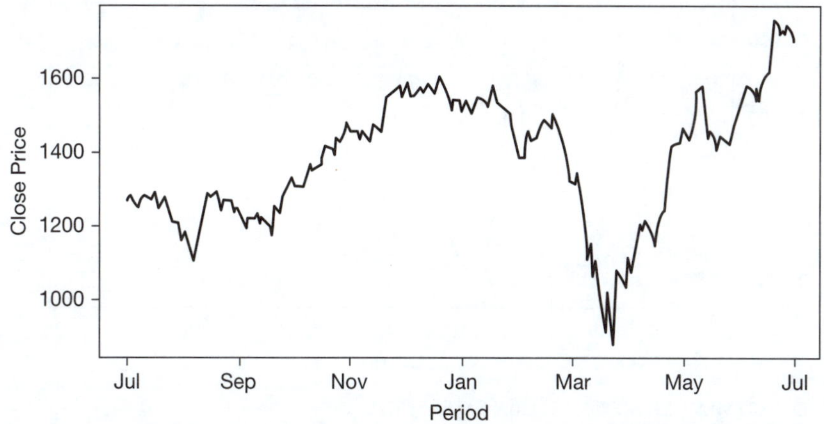

FIGURE 17.14 DAILY CLOSE PRICE OF RELIANCE INDIA LTD. IN BSE JULY 2019–JUNE 2020

a. Fit an AR(1) model to the close price series. Report the coefficient table.

b. Which of the following is/are relevant for testing whether this stock is a random walk?
- The autocorrelations of the close prices series
- The AR(1) slope coefficient
- The AR(1) constant coefficient

c. Does the AR model indicate that this is a random walk? Explain how you reached your conclusion.

d. What are the implications of finding that a time-series is a random walk? Choose the correct statement(s) below.
- It is impossible to obtain forecasts that are more accurate than naive forecasts for the series
- The series is random
- The changes in the series from one period to the next are random

17.5 Department Store Sales. The time plot in Figure 17.15 describes actual quarterly sales for a department store over a 6-year period (data are available in *DepartmentStoreSales.csv*, data courtesy of Chris Albright).

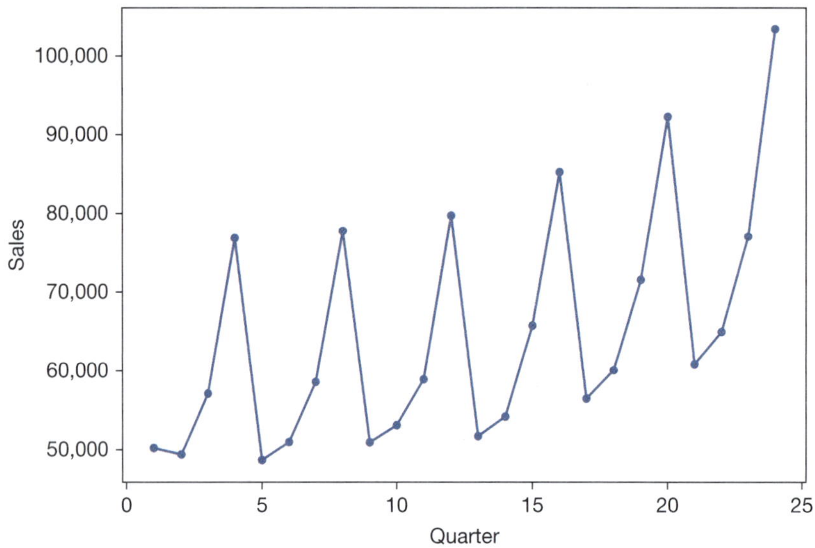

FIGURE 17.15 DEPARTMENT STORE QUARTERLY SALES SERIES

a. The forecaster decided that there is an exponential trend in the series. In order to fit a regression-based model that accounts for this trend, which of the following operations must be performed?

- Take log of quarter index
- Take log of sales
- Take an exponent of sales
- Take an exponent of quarter index

b. Fit a regression model with an exponential trend and seasonality, using the first 20 quarters as the training data (remember to first partition the series into training and validation series).

c. A partial output is shown in Table 17.11. From the output, after adjusting for trend, are Q2 average sales higher, lower, or approximately equal to the average Q1 sales?

TABLE 17.11 OUTPUT FROM REGRESSION MODEL FIT TO DEPARTMENT STORE SALES IN THE TRAINING PERIOD

	coef	std err
Intercept	10.748945	0.018725
Quarter[T.Q2]	0.024956	0.020764
Quarter[T.Q3]	0.165343	0.020884
Quarter[T.Q4]	0.433746	0.021084
trend	0.011088	0.001295

d. Use this model to forecast sales in Q21 and Q22.

e. The plots in Figure 17.16 describe the fit (a) and forecast errors (b) from this regression model.

  i. Recreate these plots.

  ii. Based on these plots, what can you say about your forecasts for Q21 and Q22? Are they likely to over-forecast, under-forecast, or be reasonably close to the real sales values?

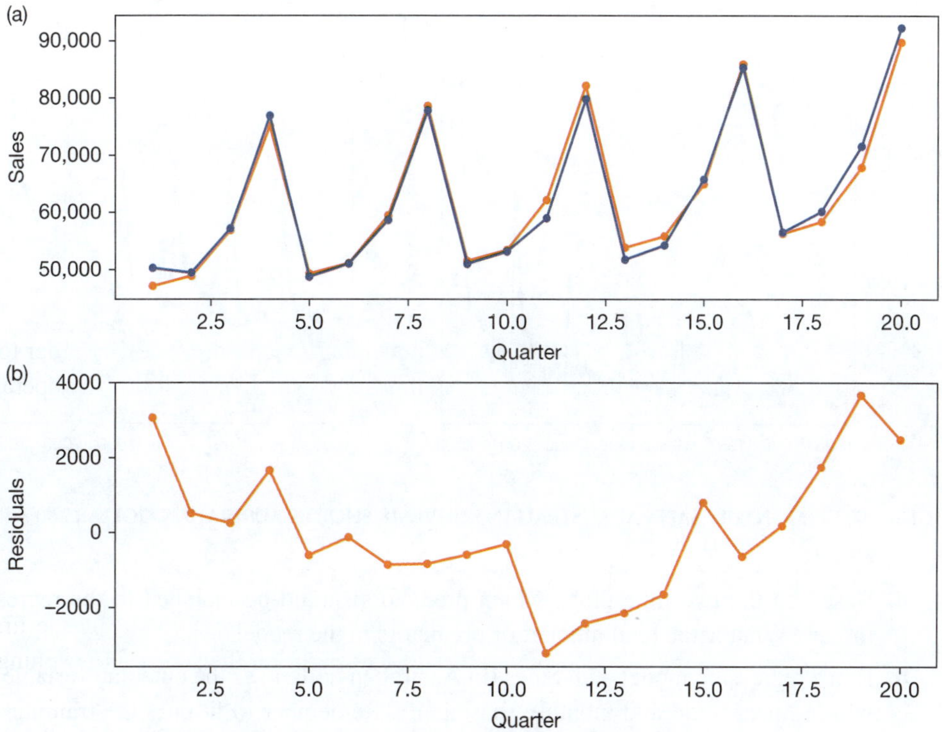

FIGURE 17.16 FIT OF REGRESSION MODEL FOR DEPARTMENT STORE SALES

f. From the forecast errors plot, which of the following statements appear true?

- Seasonality is not captured well.
- The regression model fits the data well.
- The trend in the data is not captured well by the model.

g. Which of the following solutions is adequate *and* a parsimonious solution for improving model fit?

- Fit a quadratic trend model to the residuals (with Quarter and Quarter^2)[6]
- Fit an AR model to the residuals
- Fit a quadratic trend model to Sales (with Quarter and Quarter^2)

[6]Note that the variable "Quarter" in the dataset is equivalent to the usual "trend" variable.

17.6 Souvenir Sales. The file *SouvenirSales.csv* contains monthly sales for a souvenir shop at a beach resort town in Queensland, Australia, between 1995 and 2001. [Source: Hyndman and Yang (2018)]. Figure 17.17 displays the sales time plot. The series is presented twice, in Australian dollars and in log-scale. Back in 2001, the store wanted to use the data to forecast sales for the next 12 months (year 2002). They hired an analyst to generate forecasts. The analyst first partitioned the data into training and validation sets, with the validation set containing the last 12 months of data (year 2001). She then fit a regression model to sales, using the training set.

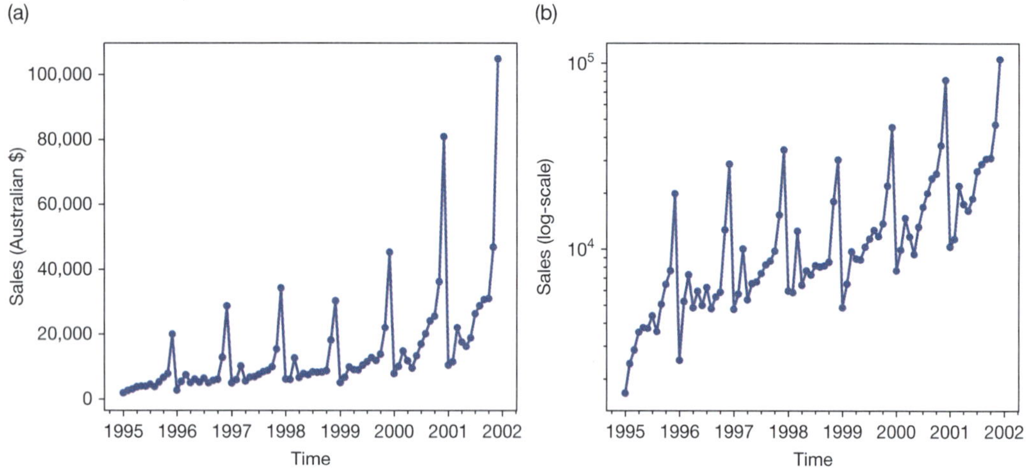

FIGURE 17.17 MONTHLY SALES AT AUSTRALIAN SOUVENIR SHOP IN AUSTRALIAN DOLLARS (a) AND IN LOG-SCALE (b)

a. Based on the two time plots, which predictors should be included in the regression model? What is the total number of predictors in the model?

b. Run a regression model with Sales (in Australian dollars) as the outcome variable, and with a linear trend and monthly seasonality. Remember to fit only the training data. Call this model A.

  i. Examine the estimated coefficients: which month tends to have the highest average sales during the year? Why is this reasonable?

  ii. The estimated trend coefficient in model A is 245.36. What does this mean?

c. Run a regression model with an exponential trend and multiplicative seasonality. Remember to fit only the training data. Call this model B.

  i. Fitting a model to log(Sales) with a linear trend is equivalent to fitting a model to Sales (in dollars) with what type of trend?

  ii. The estimated trend coefficient in model B is 0.02. What does this mean?

  iii. Use this model to forecast the sales in February 2002.

d. Compare the two regression models (A and B) in terms of forecast performance. Which model is preferable for forecasting? Mention at least two reasons based on the information in the outputs.

e. Continuing with model B, create an ACF plot until lag-15 for the forecast errors. Now fit an AR model with lag 2 [ARIMA(2,0,0)] to the forecast errors.

i. Examining the ACF plot and the estimated coefficients of the AR(2) model (and their statistical significance), what can we learn about the forecasts that result from model B?

ii. Use the autocorrelation information to compute an improved forecast for January 2002, using model B and the AR(2) model above.

f. How would you model these data differently if the goal was to understand the different components of sales in the souvenir shop between 1995–2001? Mention two differences.

17.7 Shipments of Household Appliances. The time plot in Figure 17.18 shows the series of quarterly shipments (in million dollars) of US household appliances between 1985 and 1989 (data are available in *ApplianceShipments.csv*, data courtesy of Ken Black). If we compute the autocorrelation of the series, which lag (>0) is most likely to have the largest coefficient (in absolute value)? Create an ACF plot and compare with your answer.

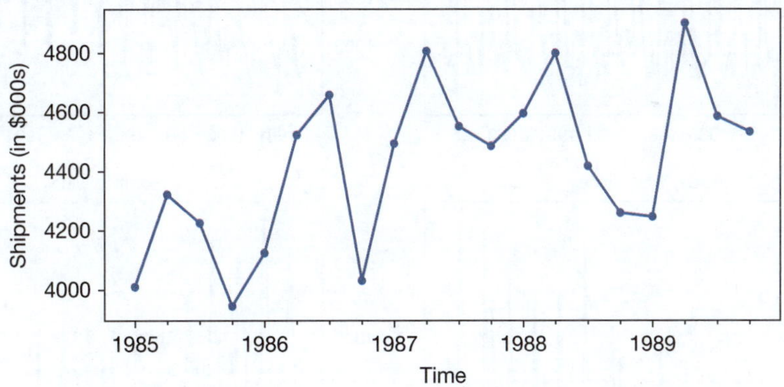

FIGURE 17.18 QUARTERLY SHIPMENTS OF US HOUSEHOLD APPLIANCES OVER 5 YEARS

17.8 Australian Wine Sales. Figure 17.19 shows time plots of monthly sales of six types of Australian wines (red, rose, sweet white, dry white, sparkling, and fortified) for 1980–1994 [Data are available in *AustralianWines.csv*, Source: Hyndman and Yang (2018)]. The units are thousands of liters. You are hired to obtain short-term forecasts (2–3 months ahead) for each of the six series, and this task will be repeated every month.

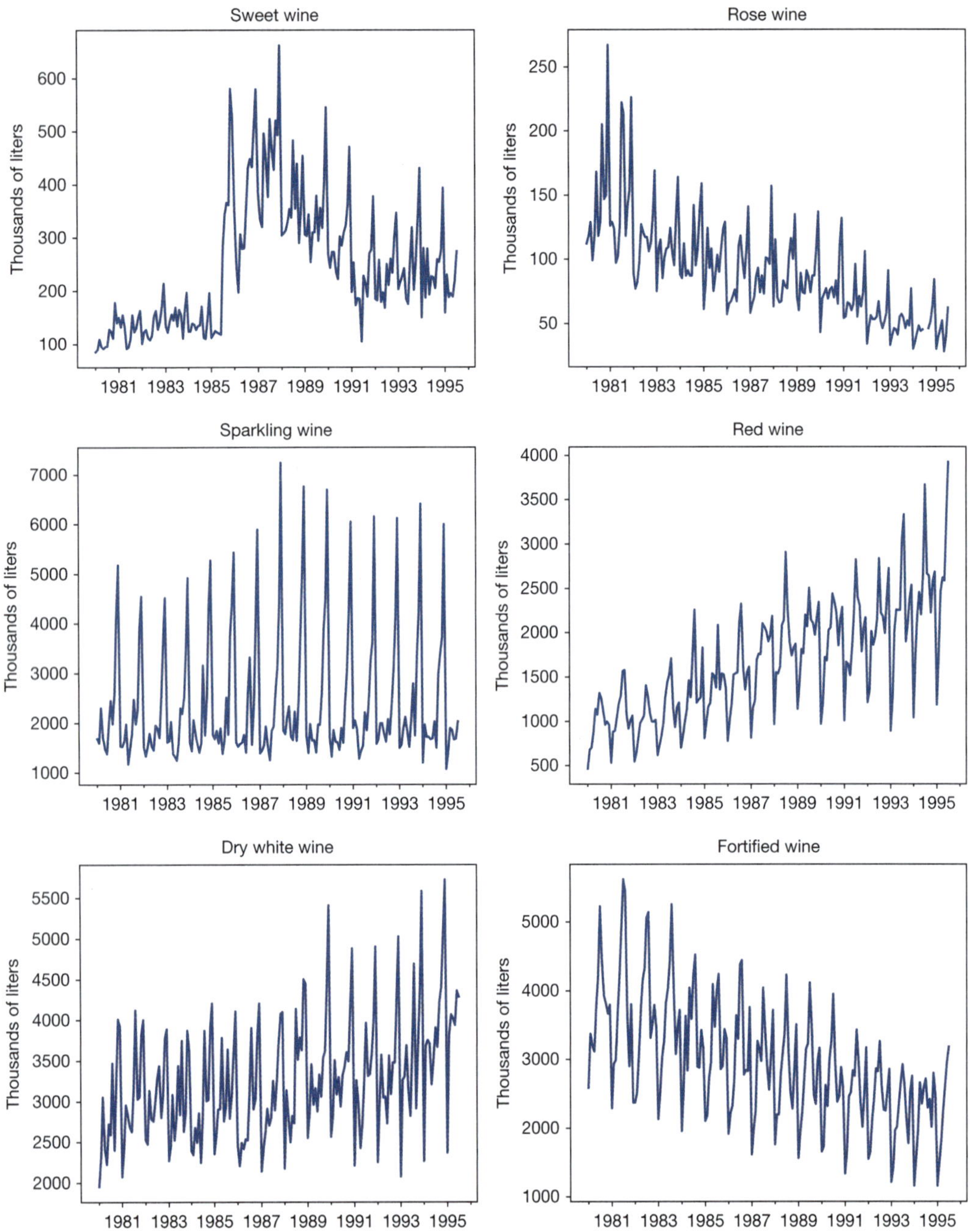

FIGURE 17.19 MONTHLY SALES OF SIX TYPES OF AUSTRALIAN WINES BETWEEN 1980 AND 1994

a. Comment on the suitability of a regression-based forecaster for each wine type.

b. Fortified wine has the largest market share of the above six types of wine. You are asked to focus on fortified wine sales alone, and produce as accurate as possible forecasts for the next 2 months.

- Start by partitioning the data: use the period until December 1993 as the training set.
- Fit a regression model to sales with a linear trend and additive seasonality.

i. Create the "actual vs. forecast" plot. What can you say about the model fit?

ii. Use the regression model to forecast sales in January and February 1994.

c. Create an ACF plot for the residuals from the above model until lag-12. Examining this plot (only), which of the following statements are reasonable conclusions?

- Decembers (month 12) are not captured well by the model.
- There is a strong correlation between sales on the same calendar month.
- The model does not capture the seasonality well.
- We should try to fit an autoregressive model with lag-12 to the residuals.

CHAPTER 18

Smoothing Methods

In this chapter, we describe a set of popular and flexible methods for forecasting time series that rely on *smoothing*. Smoothing is based on averaging over multiple periods in order to reduce the noise. We start with two simple smoothers, the *moving average* and *simple exponential smoother*, which are suitable for forecasting series that contain no trend or seasonality. In both cases, forecasts are averages of previous values of the series (the length of the series history considered and the weights used in the averaging differ between the methods). We also show how a moving average can be used, with a slight adaptation, for data visualization. We then proceed to describe smoothing methods suitable for forecasting series with a trend and/or seasonality. Smoothing methods are data-driven, and are able to adapt to changes in the series over time. Although highly automated, the user must specify *smoothing constants* that determine how fast the method adapts to new data. We discuss the choice of such constants, and their meaning. The different methods are illustrated using the Amtrak ridership series.

Python

In this chapter, we will use `numpy` and `pandas` for data handling and `matplotlib` for visualization. Models are built using `statsmodels`. We also make use of functions *singleGraphLayout()* and *graphLayout()* defined in Table 17.2. Use the following import statements to run the Python code in this chapter.

import required functionality for this chapter

```
import numpy as np
import pandas as pd
import matplotlib.pylab as plt
import statsmodels.formula.api as sm
from statsmodels.tsa import tsatools
from statsmodels.tsa.holtwinters import ExponentialSmoothing
```

18.1 | INTRODUCTION[1]

A second class of methods for time series forecasting is *smoothing methods*. Unlike regression models, which rely on an underlying theoretical model for the components of a time series (e.g., linear trend or multiplicative seasonality), smoothing methods are data-driven, in the sense that they estimate time series components directly from the data without assuming a predetermined structure. Data-driven methods are especially useful in series where patterns change over time. Smoothing methods "smooth" out the noise in a series in an attempt to uncover the patterns. Smoothing is done by averaging the series over multiple periods, where different smoothers differ by the number of periods averaged, how the average is computed, how many times averaging is performed, and so on. We now describe two types of smoothing methods that are popular in business applications due to their simplicity and adaptability. These are the moving average method and exponential smoothing.

18.2 | MOVING AVERAGE

The moving average is a simple smoother: it consists of averaging values across a window of consecutive periods, thereby generating a series of averages. A moving average with window width w means averaging across each set of w consecutive values, where w is determined by the user.

In general, there are two types of moving averages: a *centered moving average* and a *trailing moving average*. Centered moving averages are powerful for visualizing trends, because the averaging operation can suppress seasonality and noise, thereby making the trend more visible. In contrast, trailing moving averages are useful for forecasting. The difference between the two is in terms of the window's location on the time series.

[1]This and subsequent sections in this chapter copyright © 2019 Datastats, LLC, and Galit Shmueli.Used by permission.

Centered Moving Average for Visualization

In a centered moving average, the value of the moving average at time t (MA_t) is computed by centering the window around time t and averaging across the w values within the window:

$$MA_t = (Y_{t-(w-1)/2} + \cdots + Y_{t-1} + Y_t + Y_{t+1} + \cdots + Y_{t+(w-1)/2})/w. \tag{18.1}$$

For example, with a window of width $w = 5$, the moving average at time point $t = 3$ means averaging the values of the series at time points $1, 2, 3, 4, 5$; at time point $t = 4$, the moving average is the average of the series at time points $2, 3, 4, 5, 6$, and so on.[2] This is illustrated in Figure 18.1a.

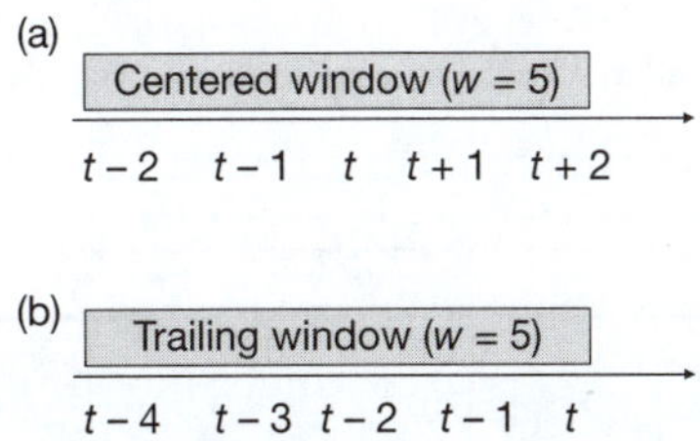

FIGURE 18.1 SCHEMATIC OF CENTERED MOVING AVERAGE (a) AND TRAILING MOVING AVERAGE (b), BOTH WITH WINDOW WIDTH $W = 5$

Choosing the window width in a seasonal series is straightforward: because the goal is to suppress seasonality for better visualizing the trend, the default choice should be the length of a seasonal cycle. Returning to the Amtrak ridership data, the annual seasonality indicates a choice of $w = 12$. Figure 18.2 (smooth blue line) shows a centered moving average line overlaid on the original series. We can see a global U-shape, but unlike the regression model that fits a strict U-shape, the moving average shows some deviation, such as the slight dip during the last year.

code for creating Figure 18.2

```
# Load data and convert to time series
Amtrak_df = pd.read_csv('Amtrak.csv')
Amtrak_df['Date'] = pd.to_datetime(Amtrak_df.Month, format='%d/%m/%Y')
ridership_ts = pd.Series(Amtrak_df.Ridership.values, index=Amtrak_df.Date,
                         name='Ridership')
ridership_ts.index = pd.DatetimeIndex(ridership_ts.index,
                                      freq=ridership_ts.index.inferred_freq)
```

[2]For an even window width, for example, $w = 4$, obtaining the moving average at time point $t = 3$ requires averaging across two windows: across time points $1, 2, 3, 4$; across time points $2, 3, 4, 5$; and finally the average of the two averages is the final moving average.

```
# centered moving average with window size = 12
ma_centered = ridership_ts.rolling(12, center=True).mean()

# trailing moving average with window size = 12
ma_trailing = ridership_ts.rolling(12).mean()

# shift the average by one time unit to get the next day predictions
ma_centered = pd.Series(ma_centered[:-1].values, index=ma_centered.index[1:])
ma_trailing = pd.Series(ma_trailing[:-1].values, index=ma_trailing.index[1:])


fig, ax = plt.subplots(figsize=(8, 7))
ax = ridership_ts.plot(ax=ax, color='black', linewidth=0.25)
ma_centered.plot(ax=ax, linewidth=2)
ma_trailing.plot(ax=ax, style='--', linewidth=2)
ax.set_xlabel('Time')
ax.set_ylabel('Ridership')
ax.legend(['Ridership', 'Centered Moving Average', 'Trailing Moving Average'])

plt.show()
```

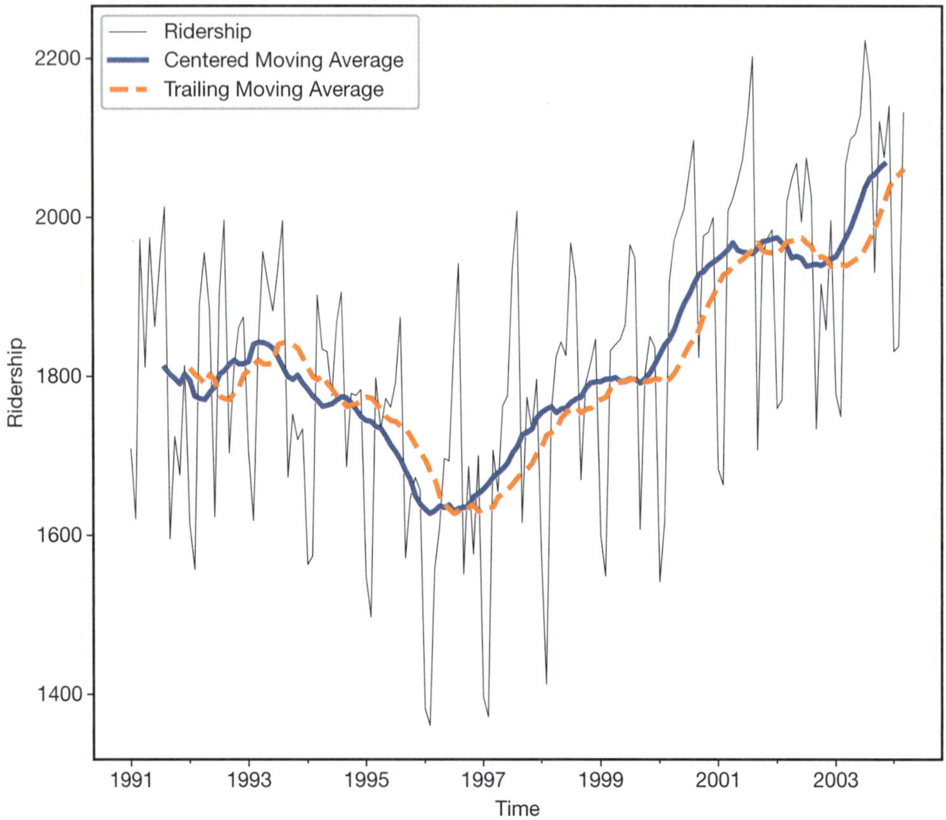

FIGURE 18.2 CENTERED MOVING AVERAGE (SMOOTH BLUE LINE) AND TRAILING MOVING AVERAGE (BROKEN ORANGE LINE) WITH WINDOW $W = 12$, OVERLAID ON AMTRAK RIDERSHIP SERIES

Trailing Moving Average for Forecasting

Centered moving averages are computed by averaging across data in the past and the future of a given time point. In that sense, they cannot be used for forecasting because at the time of forecasting, the future is typically unknown. Hence, for purposes of forecasting, we use *trailing moving averages*, where the window of width w is set on the most recent available w values of the series. The k-step ahead forecast F_{t+k} $(k = 1, 2, 3, \ldots)$ is then the average of these w values (see also bottom plot in Figure 18.1):

$$F_{t+k} = (Y_t + Y_{t-1} + \cdots + Y_{t-w+1})/w.$$

For example, in the Amtrak ridership series, to forecast ridership in February 1992 or later months, given information until January 1992 and using a moving average with window width $w = 12$, we would take the average ridership during the most recent 12 months (February 1991 to January 1992). Figure 18.2 (broken blue line) shows a trailing moving average line overlaid on the original series.

Next, we illustrate a 12-month moving average forecaster for the Amtrak ridership. We partition the Amtrak ridership time series, leaving the last 36 months as the validation period. Applying a moving average forecaster with window $w = 12$, we obtained the output shown in Figure 18.3. Note that for the first 12 records of the training period, there is no forecast (because there are less than 12 past values to average). Also, note that the forecasts for all months in the validation period are identical (1938.481) because the method assumes that information is known only until March 2001.

code for creating Figure 18.3

```
# partition the data
nValid = 36
nTrain = len(ridership_ts) - nValid

train_ts = ridership_ts[:nTrain]
valid_ts = ridership_ts[nTrain:]

# moving average on training
ma_trailing = train_ts.rolling(12).mean()
last_ma = ma_trailing[-1]

# create forecast based on last moving average in the training period
ma_trailing_pred = pd.Series(last_ma, index=valid_ts.index)

fig, axes = plt.subplots(nrows=2, ncols=1, figsize=(9, 7.5))
ma_trailing.plot(ax=axes[0], linewidth=2, color='C1')
ma_trailing_pred.plot(ax=axes[0], linewidth=2, color='C1', linestyle='dashed')
residual = train_ts - ma_trailing
residual.plot(ax=axes[1], color='C1')
```

```
residual = valid_ts - ma_trailing_pred
residual.plot(ax=axes[1], color='C1', linestyle='dashed')
graphLayout(axes, train_ts, valid_ts)
```

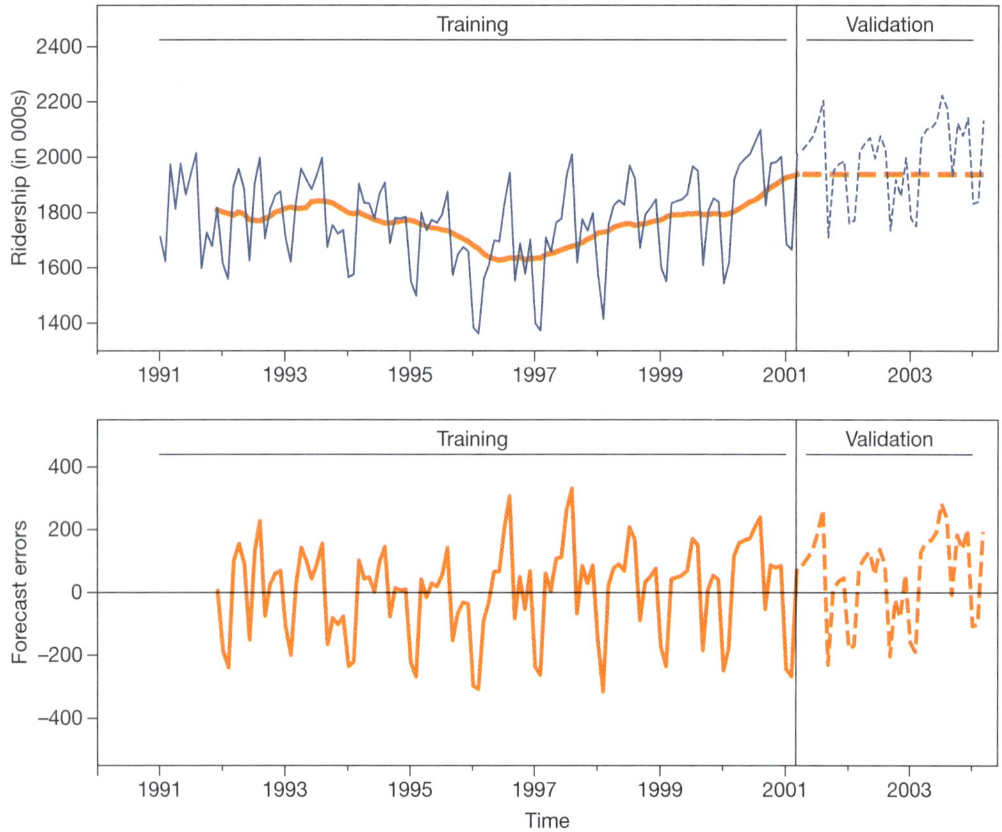

FIGURE 18.3 TRAILING MOVING AVERAGE FORECASTER WITH $W = 12$ APPLIED TO AMTRAK RIDERSHIP SERIES

In this example, it is clear that the moving average forecaster is inadequate for generating monthly forecasts because it does not capture the seasonality in the data. Seasons with high ridership are under-forecasted, and seasons with low ridership are over-forecasted. A similar issue arises when forecasting a series with a trend: the moving average "lags behind," thereby under-forecasting in the presence of an increasing trend and over-forecasting in the presence of a decreasing trend. This "lagging behind" of the trailing moving average can also be seen in Figure 18.2.

In general, the moving average should be used for forecasting *only in series that lack seasonality and trend*. Such a limitation might seem impractical. However, there are a few popular methods for removing trends (de-trending) and removing seasonality (de-seasonalizing) from a series, such as regression models. The moving average can then be used to forecast such de-trended and de-seasonalized series, and then the trend and seasonality can be added back to the forecast. For example, consider the regression model shown in Figure 17.6 in Chapter 17, which yields residuals devoid of seasonality and trend (see bottom chart). We can apply a moving average forecaster to that series of residuals (also called forecast errors), thereby creating a forecast for the next *forecast error*. For example, to forecast ridership in April 2001 (the first period in the validation set), assuming that we have information until March 2001, we use the regression model in Table 17.6 to generate a forecast for April 2001 [which yields 2004.271 thousand (=2,004,271) riders]. We then use a 12-month moving average (using the period April 2000 to March 2001) to forecast the *forecast error* for April 2001, which yields 30.78068 (manually, or using Python, as shown in Table 18.1). The positive value implies that the regression model's forecast for April 2001 is too low, and therefore we should adjust it by adding approximately 31 thousand riders to the regression model's forecast of 2004.271 thousand riders.

TABLE 18.1 APPLYING MA TO THE RESIDUALS FROM THE REGRESSION MODEL (WHICH LACK TREND AND SEASONALITY), TO FORECAST THE APRIL 2001 RESIDUAL

code for applying moving average to residuals

```
# Build a model with seasonality, trend, and quadratic trend
ridership_df = tsatools.add_trend(ridership_ts, trend='ct')
ridership_df['Month'] = ridership_df.index.month

# partition the data
train_df = ridership_df[:nTrain]
valid_df = ridership_df[nTrain:]

formula = 'Ridership ~ trend + np.square(trend) + C(Month)'
ridership_lm_trendseason = sm.ols(formula=formula, data=train_df).fit()

# create single-point forecast
ridership_prediction = ridership_lm_trendseason.predict(valid_df.iloc[0, :])

# apply MA to residuals
ma_trailing = ridership_lm_trendseason.resid.rolling(12).mean()

print('Prediction', ridership_prediction[0])
print('ma_trailing', ma_trailing[-1])
```

Output

```
Prediction 2004.2708927644996
ma_trailing 30.78068462405899
```

Choosing Window Width (w)

With moving average forecasting or visualization, the only choice that the user must make is the width of the window (w). As with other methods such as k-nearest neighbors, the choice of the smoothing parameter is a balance between under-smoothing and over-smoothing. For visualization (using a centered window), wider windows will expose more global trends, while narrow windows will reveal local trends. Hence, examining several window widths is useful for exploring trends of differing local/global nature. For forecasting (using a trailing window), the choice should incorporate domain knowledge in terms of relevance of past values and how fast the series changes. Empirical predictive evaluation can also be done by experimenting with different values of w and comparing performance. However, care should be taken not to overfit!

18.3 | SIMPLE EXPONENTIAL SMOOTHING

A popular forecasting method in business is exponential smoothing. Its popularity derives from its flexibility, ease of automation, cheap computation, and good performance. Simple exponential smoothing is similar to forecasting with a moving average, except that instead of taking a simple average over the w most recent values, we take a *weighted average* of *all* past values, such that the weights decrease exponentially into the past. The idea is to give more weight to recent information, yet not to completely ignore older information.

Like the moving average, simple exponential smoothing should only be used for forecasting *series that have no trend or seasonality*. As mentioned earlier, such series can be obtained by removing trend and/or seasonality from raw series, and then applying exponential smoothing to the series of residuals (which are assumed to contain no trend or seasonality).

The exponential smoother generates a forecast at time $t + 1$ (F_{t+1}) as follows:

$$F_{t+1} = \alpha Y_t + \alpha(1 - \alpha)Y_{t-1} + \alpha(1 - \alpha)^2 Y_{t-2} + \cdots , \tag{18.2}$$

where α is a constant between 0 and 1 called the *smoothing parameter*. The above formulation displays the exponential smoother as a weighted average of all past observations, with exponentially decaying weights.

It turns out that we can write the exponential forecaster in another way, which is very useful in practice:

$$F_{t+1} = F_t + \alpha E_t, \tag{18.3}$$

where E_t is the forecast error at time t. This formulation presents the exponential forecaster as an "active learner": It looks at the previous forecast (F_t) and how far it was from the actual value (E_t), and then corrects the next forecast based on that information. If in one period the forecast was too high, the next period is adjusted down. The amount of correction depends on the value of the smoothing parameter α. The formulation in (18.3) is also advantageous in terms of data storage and computation time: it means that we need to store and use only the forecast and forecast error from the most recent period, rather than the entire series. In applications where real-time forecasting is done, or many series are being forecasted in parallel and continuously, such savings are critical.

Note that forecasting further into the future yields the same forecast as a one-step-ahead forecast. Because the series is assumed to lack trend and seasonality, forecasts into the future rely only on information until the time of prediction. Hence, the k-step ahead forecast is equal to

$$F_{t+k} = F_{t+1}.$$

Choosing Smoothing Parameter α

The smoothing parameter α, which is set by the user, determines the rate of learning. A value close to 1 indicates fast learning (that is, only the most recent values have influence on forecasts) whereas a value close to 0 indicates slow learning (past values have a large influence on forecasts). This can be seen by plugging 0 or 1 into equation (18.2) or (18.3). Hence, the choice of α depends on the required amount of smoothing, and on how relevant the history is for generating forecasts. Default values that have been shown to work well are around 0.1–0.2. Some trial and error can also help in the choice of α: examine the time plot of the actual and predicted series, as well as the predictive accuracy (e.g., MAPE or RMSE of the validation set). Finding the α value that optimizes predictive accuracy on the validation set can be used to determine the degree of local vs. global nature of the trend. However, beware of choosing the "best α" for forecasting purposes, as this will most likely lead to model overfitting and low predictive accuracy on future data.

To use exponential smoothing in Python, we use the *ExponentialSmoothing* method in `statmodels`. Argument *smoothing_level* sets the value of α.

To illustrate forecasting with simple exponential smoothing, we return to the residuals from the regression model, which are assumed to contain no trend or seasonality. To forecast the residual on April 2001, we apply exponential smoothing to the entire period until March 2001, and use $\alpha = 0.2$. The forecasts of this model are shown in Figure 18.4. The forecast for the residual (the horizontal broken line) is 14.143 (in thousands of riders), implying that we should adjust the regression's forecast by adding 14,143 riders to that forecast.

code for creating Figure 18.4

```
residuals_ts = ridership_lm_trendseason.resid
residuals_pred = valid_df.Ridership - ridership_lm_trendseason.predict(valid_df)

fig, ax = plt.subplots(figsize=(9,4))

ridership_lm_trendseason.resid.plot(ax=ax, color='black', linewidth=0.5)
residuals_pred.plot(ax=ax, color='black', linewidth=0.5)
ax.set_ylabel('Ridership')
ax.set_xlabel('Time')
ax.axhline(y=0, xmin=0, xmax=1, color='grey', linewidth=0.5)

# run exponential smoothing
# with smoothing level alpha = 0.2
expSmooth = ExponentialSmoothing(residuals_ts, freq='MS')
expSmoothFit = expSmooth.fit(smoothing_level=0.2)

expSmoothFit.fittedvalues.plot(ax=ax)
expSmoothFit.forecast(len(valid_ts)).plot(ax=ax, style='--', linewidth=2, color='C0')

singleGraphLayout(ax, [-550, 550], train_df, valid_df)
```

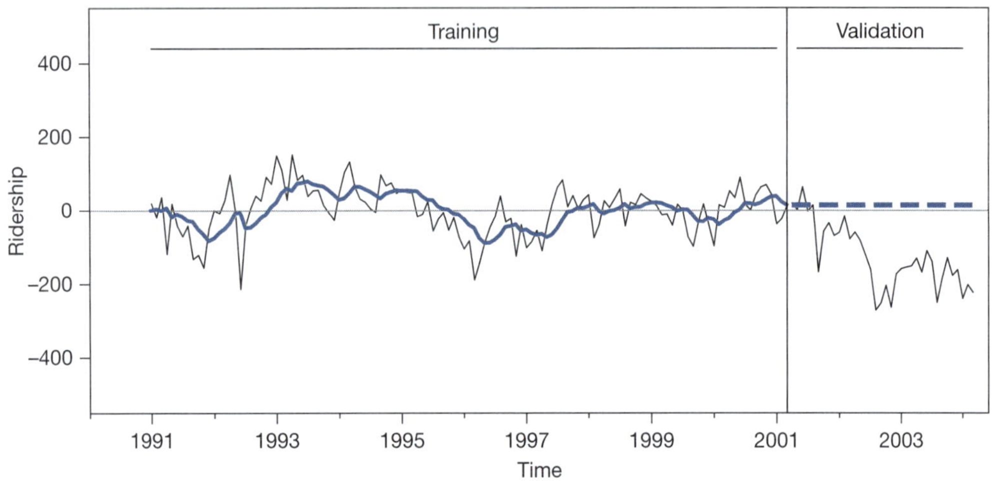

FIGURE 18.4 OUTPUT FOR SIMPLE EXPONENTIAL SMOOTHING FORECASTER WITH α = 0.2, APPLIED TO THE SERIES OF RESIDUALS FROM THE REGRESSION MODEL (WHICH LACK TREND AND SEASONALITY). THE FORECAST VALUE IS 14.143

Relation Between Moving Average and Simple Exponential Smoothing

In both smoothing methods, the user must specify a single parameter: In moving averages, the window width (w) must be set; in exponential smoothing, the smoothing parameter (α) must be set. In both cases, the parameter determines the importance of fresh information over older information. In fact, the two smoothers are approximately equal if the window width of the moving average is equal to $w = 2/\alpha - 1$.

18.4 | ADVANCED EXPONENTIAL SMOOTHING

As mentioned earlier, both the moving average and simple exponential smoothing should only be used for forecasting series with no trend or seasonality; series that have only a level and noise. One solution for forecasting series with trend and/or seasonality is first to remove those components (e.g., via regression models). Another solution is to use a more sophisticated version of exponential smoothing, which can capture trend and/or seasonality.

Series with a Trend

For series that contain a trend, we can use "double exponential smoothing." Unlike in regression models, the trend shape is not assumed to be global, but rather, it can change over time. In double exponential smoothing, the local trend is estimated from the data and is updated as more data arrive. Similar to simple exponential smoothing, the level of the series is also estimated from the data, and is updated as more data arrive. The k-step-ahead forecast is given by combining the level estimate at time t (L_t) and the trend estimate at time t (T_t):

$$F_{t+k} = L_t + kT_t. \tag{18.4}$$

Note that in the presence of a trend, one-, two-, three-step-ahead (etc.), forecasts are no longer identical. The level and trend are updated through a pair of updating equations:

$$L_t = \alpha Y_t + (1 - \alpha)(L_{t-1} + T_{t-1}), \tag{18.5}$$

$$T_t = \beta(L_t - L_{t-1}) + (1 - \beta)T_{t-1}. \tag{18.6}$$

The first equation means that the level at time t is a weighted average of the actual value at time t and the level in the previous period, adjusted for trend (in the presence of a trend, moving from one period to the next requires factoring in the trend). The second equation means that the trend at time t is a weighted average of the trend in the previous period and the more recent information on the change in level.[3] Here there are two smoothing parameters, α and β, which determine the rate of learning. As in simple exponential smoothing, they are both constants in the range [0,1], set by the user, with higher values leading to faster learning (more weight to most recent information).

[3]There are various ways to estimate the initial values L_1 and T_1, but the differences among these ways usually disappear after a few periods.

Series with a Trend and Seasonality

For series that contain both trend and seasonality, the "Holt-Winter's Exponential Smoothing" method can be used. This is a further extension of double exponential smoothing, where the k-step-ahead forecast also takes into account the seasonality at period $t + k$. Assuming seasonality with M seasons (e.g., for weekly seasonality $M = 7$), the forecast is given by

$$F_{t+k} = (L_t + kT_t)S_{t+k-M}. \tag{18.7}$$

(Note that by the time of forecasting t, the series must have included at least one full cycle of seasons in order to produce forecasts using this formula, that is, $t > M$.)

Being an adaptive method, Holt-Winter's exponential smoothing allows the level, trend, and seasonality patterns to change over time. These three components are estimated and updated as more information arrives. The three updating equations are given by

$$L_t = \alpha Y_t/S_{t-M} + (1 - \alpha)(L_{t-1} + T_{t-1}), \tag{18.8}$$

$$T_t = \beta(L_t - L_{t-1}) + (1 - \beta)T_{t-1}, \tag{18.9}$$

$$S_t = \gamma Y_t/L_t + (1 - \gamma)S_{t-M}. \tag{18.10}$$

The first equation is similar to that in double exponential smoothing, except that it uses the seasonally-adjusted value at time t rather than the raw value. This is done by dividing Y_t by its seasonal index, as estimated in the last cycle. The second equation is identical to double exponential smoothing. The third equation means that the seasonal index is updated by taking a weighted average of the seasonal index from the previous cycle and the current trend-adjusted value. Note that this formulation describes a multiplicative seasonal relationship, where values on different seasons differ by percentage amounts. There is also an additive seasonality version of Holt-Winter's exponential smoothing, where seasons differ by a constant amount (for more detail, see Shmueli and Lichtendahl, 2016).

code for creating Figure 18.5

```
# run exponential smoothing with additive trend and additive seasonal
expSmooth = ExponentialSmoothing(train_ts, trend='additive', seasonal='additive',
  seasonal_periods=12, freq='MS')
expSmoothFit = expSmooth.fit()

fig, axes = plt.subplots(nrows=2, ncols=1, figsize=(9, 7.5))
expSmoothFit.fittedvalues.plot(ax=axes[0], linewidth=2, color='C1')
```

```
expSmoothFit.forecast(len(valid_ts)).plot(ax=axes[0], linewidth=2, color='C1',
                                          linestyle='dashed')
residual = train_ts - expSmoothFit.fittedvalues
residual.plot(ax=axes[1], color='C1')
residual = valid_ts - expSmoothFit.forecast(len(valid_ts))
residual.plot(ax=axes[1], color='C1', linestyle='dashed')
graphLayout(axes, train_ts, valid_ts)
```

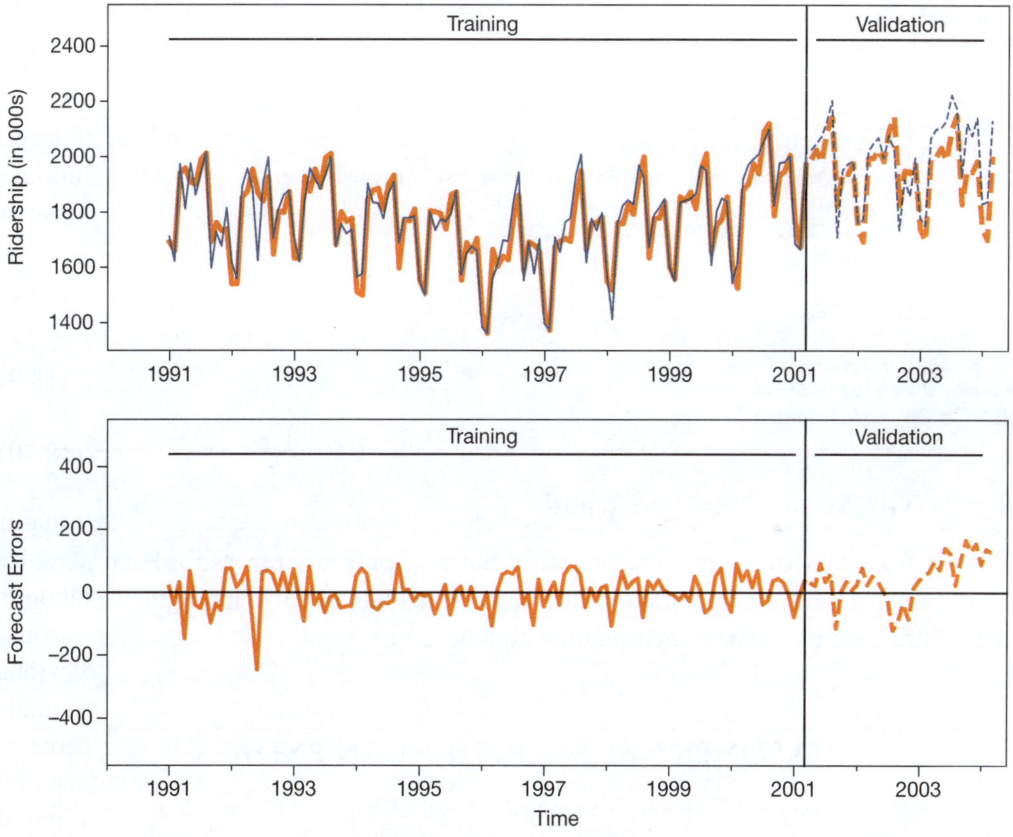

FIGURE 18.5 HOLT-WINTERS EXPONENTIAL SMOOTHING APPLIED TO AMTRAK RIDERSHIP SERIES

To illustrate forecasting a series with the Holt-Winter's method, consider the raw Amtrak ridership data. As we observed earlier, the data contain both a trend and monthly seasonality. Figure 18.5 depicts the fitted and forecasted values. Table 18.2 presents a summary of the model.

TABLE 18.2 SUMMARY OF A HOLT-WINTER'S EXPONENTIAL SMOOTHING MODEL APPLIED TO THE AMTRAK RIDERSHIP DATA. INCLUDED ARE THE INITIAL AND FINAL STATES

```
> print(expSmoothFit.params)
> print('AIC: ', expSmoothFit.aic)
> print('AICc: ', expSmoothFit.aicc)
> print('BIC: ', expSmoothFit.bic)
```

Output

```
{'smoothing_level': 0.5739301428618576,
 'smoothing_slope': 4.427106197126462e-78,
 'smoothing_seasonal': 8.604237951641415e-64,
 'damping_slope': nan,
 'initial_level': 1659.4023614918137,
 'initial_slope': 0.3287888147245162,
 'initial_seasons': array([ 31.35240029, -11.35543731, 291.69040179, 291.41159861,
        324.22688177, 279.21976391, 390.31153542, 441.32947772,
        119.95805216, 244.32751369, 235.62891276, 273.93418743]),
 'use_boxcox': False,
 'lamda': None,
 'remove_bias': False}

AIC:  1021.662594988854
AICc:  1028.239518065777
BIC:  1066.6575446748127
```

Series with Seasonality (No Trend)

Finally, for series that contain seasonality but no trend, we can use a Holt-Winter's exponential smoothing formulation that lacks a trend term, by deleting the trend term in the forecasting equation and updating equations.

EXPONENTIAL SMOOTHING IN PYTHON

In Python, forecasting using exponential smoothing can be done via the `ExponentialSmoothing` method in the `statsmodels` class. This can be used for simple exponential smoothing as well as advanced exponential smoothing.

Applying this method to a time series and using *forecast()* or *predict()* will yield forecasts. To include an additive or multiplicative trend and/or seasonality, use arguments *trend* and *seasonal*, such as *trend='additive'* and *seasonal='multiplicative'*. The default is *None*. The number of seasons is specified by *seasonal_periods*. You can set the smoothing parameters to specific values using arguments *smoothing_level* (α), *smoothing_slope* (β), and *smoothing_seasonal* (γ). Leaving them unspecified will lead to optimized values (*optimized=True*).

PROBLEMS

18.1 Impact of September 11 on Air Travel in the United States. The Research and Innovative Technology Administration's Bureau of Transportation Statistics conducted a study to evaluate the impact of the September 11, 2001 terrorist attack on US transportation. The 2006 study report and the data can be found at https://www.bts.gov/archive/publications/estimated_impacts_of_9_11_on_us_travel/index. The goal of the study was stated as follows:

> The purpose of this study is to provide a greater understanding of the passenger travel behavior patterns of persons making long distance trips before and after 9/11.

The report analyzes monthly passenger movement data between January 1990 and May 2004. Data on three monthly time series are given in file *Sept11Travel.csv* for this period: (1) Actual airline revenue passenger miles (Air), (2) Rail passenger miles (Rail), and (3) Vehicle miles traveled (Car).

In order to assess the impact of September 11, BTS took the following approach: using data before September 11, they forecasted future data (under the assumption of no terrorist attack). Then, they compared the forecasted series with the actual data to assess the impact of the event. Our first step, therefore, is to split each of the time series into two parts: pre- and post-September 11. We now concentrate only on the earlier time series.

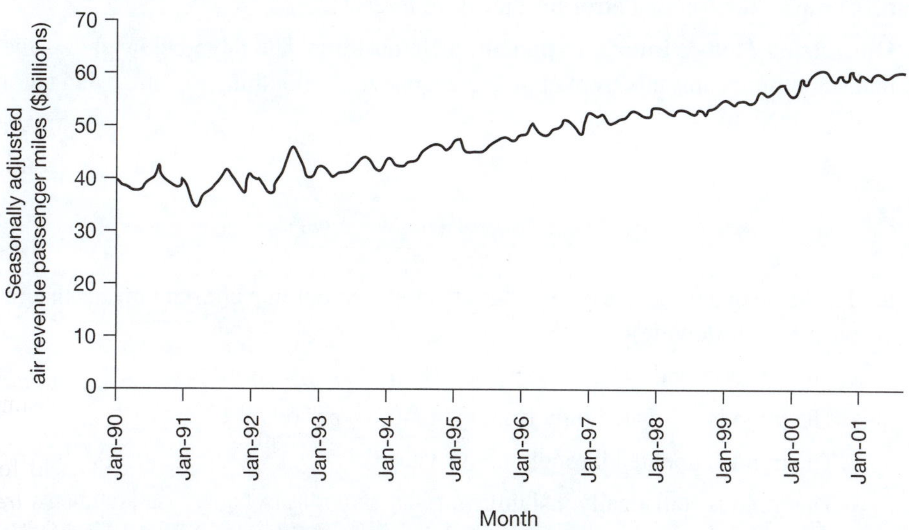

FIGURE 18.6 SEASONALLY ADJUSTED PRE-SEPTEMBER-11 AIR SERIES

a. Create a time plot for the pre-event AIR time series. What time series components appear from the plot?

b. Figure 18.6 shows a time plot of the **seasonally adjusted** pre-September-11 AIR series. Which of the following smoothing methods would be adequate for forecasting this series?

- Moving average (with what window width?)
- Simple exponential smoothing
- Holt exponential smoothing
- Holt-Winter's exponential smoothing

18.2 Relation Between Moving Average and Exponential Smoothing. Assume that we apply a moving average to a series, using a very short window span. If we wanted to achieve an equivalent result using simple exponential smoothing, what value should the smoothing coefficient take?

18.3 Forecasting with a Moving Average. For a given time series of sales, the training set consists of 50 months. The first 5 months' data are shown below:

Month	Sales
Sept 98	27
Oct 98	31
Nov 98	58
Dec 98	63
Jan 99	59

a. Compute the sales forecast for January 1999 based on a moving average with $w = 4$.

b. Compute the forecast error for the above forecast.

18.4 Optimizing Holt-Winter's Exponential Smoothing. The table below shows the optimal smoothing constants from applying exponential smoothing to data, using automated model selection:

Level	1.000
Trend	0.000
Seasonality	0.246

a. The value of zero that is obtained for the trend smoothing constant means that (choose one of the following):

- There is no trend.
- The trend is estimated only from the first two periods.
- The trend is updated throughout the data.
- The trend is statistically insignificant.

b. What is the danger of using the optimal smoothing constant values?

18.5 Department Store Sales. The time plot in Figure 18.7 describes actual quarterly sales for a department store over a 6-year period (data are available in *DepartmentStoreSales.csv*, data courtesy of Chris Albright).

a. Which of the following methods would **not** be suitable for forecasting this series?

- Moving average of raw series
- Moving average of deseasonalized series

- Simple exponential smoothing of the raw series
- Double exponential smoothing of the raw series
- Holt-Winter's exponential smoothing of the raw series

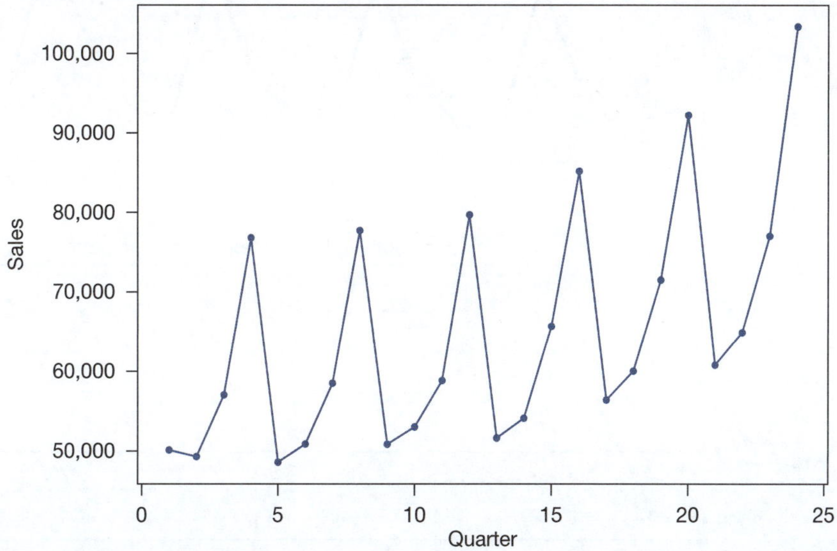

FIGURE 18.7 DEPARTMENT STORE QUARTERLY SALES SERIES

b. The forecaster was tasked to generate forecasts for four quarters ahead. He therefore partitioned the data such that the last four quarters were designated as the validation period. The forecaster approached the forecasting task by using multiplicative Holt-Winter's exponential smoothing. The smoothing parameters used were $\alpha = 0.2$, $\beta = 0.15, \gamma = 0.05$.

i. Run this method on the data.

ii. The forecasts for the validation set are given in Table 18.3. Compute the MAPE values for the forecasts of Q21 and Q22.

TABLE 18.3 FORECASTS FOR VALIDATION SERIES USING EXPONENTIAL SMOOTHING

Quarter	Actual	Forecast	Error
21	60,800	59,384.56586	1415.434145
22	64,900	61,656.49426	3243.505741
23	76,997	71,853.01442	5143.985579
24	103,337	95,074.69842	8262.301585

c. The fit and residuals from the exponential smoothing are shown in Figure 18.8. Using all the information thus far, is this model suitable for forecasting Q21 and Q22?

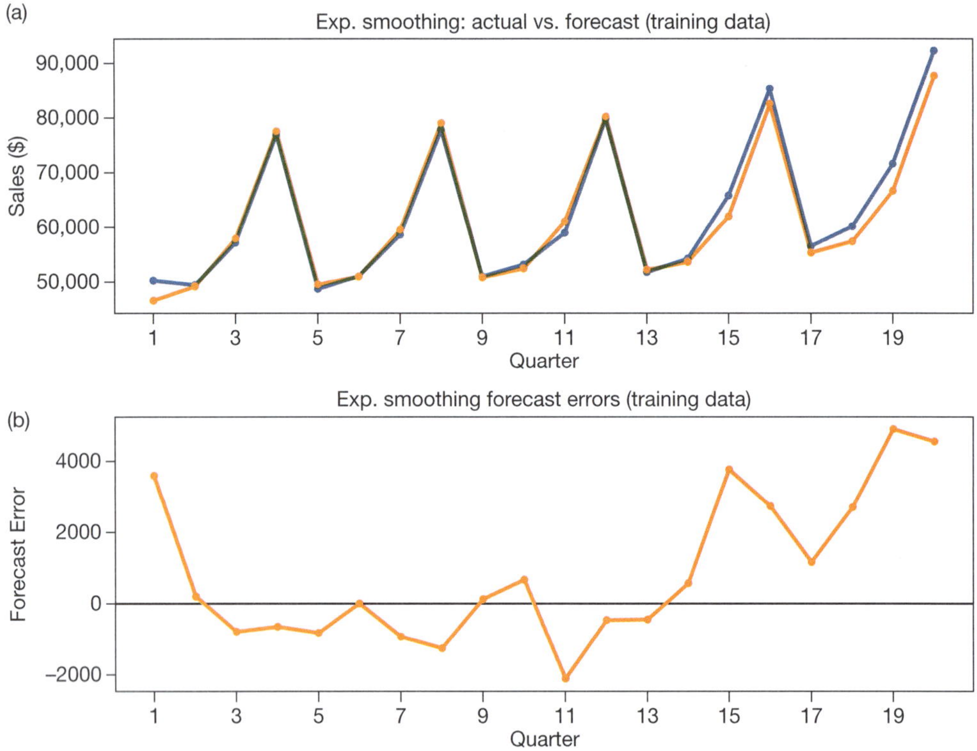

FIGURE 18.8 FORECASTS AND ACTUALS (a) AND FORECAST ERRORS (b) USING EXPONENTIAL SMOOTHING

18.6 Shipments of Household Appliances. The time plot in Figure 18.9 shows the series of quarterly shipments (in million dollars) of US household appliances between 1985 and 1989 (data are available in *ApplianceShipments.csv*, data courtesy of Ken Black).

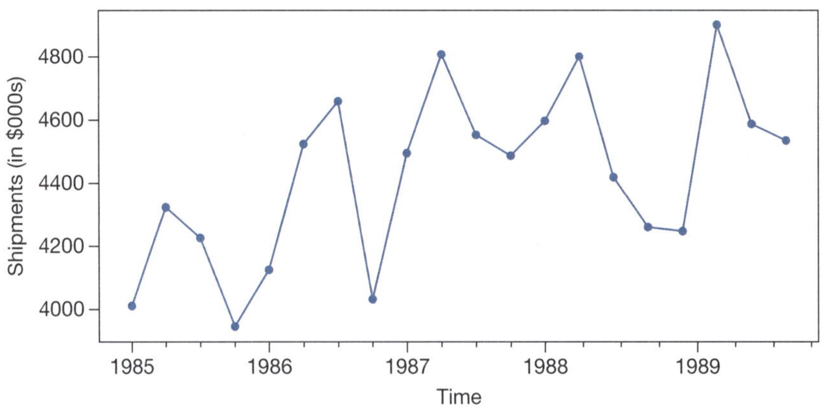

FIGURE 18.9 QUARTELY SHIPMENTS OF US HOUSEHOLD APPLIANCES OVER 5 YEARS

a. Which of the following methods would be suitable for forecasting this series if applied to the raw data?
   - Moving average
   - Simple exponential smoothing
   - Double exponential smoothing
   - Holt-Winter's exponential smoothing

b. Apply a moving average with window span $w = 4$ to the data. Use all but the last year as the training set. Create a time plot of the moving average series.
   i. What does the MA(4) chart reveal?
   ii. Use the MA(4) model to forecast appliance sales in Q1-1990.
   iii. Use the MA(4) model to forecast appliance sales in Q1-1991.
   iv. Is the forecast for Q1-1990 most likely to under-estimate, over-estimate or accurately estimate the actual sales on Q1-1990? Explain.
   v. Management feels most comfortable with moving averages. The analyst therefore plans to use this method for forecasting future quarters. What else should be considered before using the MA(4) to forecast future quarterly shipments of household appliances?

c. We now focus on forecasting beyond 1989. In the following, continue to use all but the last year as the training set, and the last four quarters as the validation set. First, fit a regression model to sales with a linear trend and quarterly seasonality to the training data. Next, apply Holt-Winter's exponential smoothing with smoothing parameters $\alpha = 0.2, \beta = 0.15, \gamma = 0.05$ to the training data. Choose an adequate "season length."
   i. Compute the MAPE for the validation data using the regression model.
   ii. Compute the MAPE for the validation data using Holt-Winter's exponential smoothing.
   iii. Which model would you prefer to use for forecasting Q1-1990? Give three reasons.
   iv. If we optimize the smoothing parameters in the Holt-Winter's method, is it likely to get values that are close to zero? Why or why not?

18.7 Shampoo Sales. The time plot in Figure 18.10 describes monthly sales of a certain shampoo over a 3-year period. [Data are available in *ShampooSales.csv*, Source: Hyndman and Yang (2018).]

Which of the following methods would be suitable for forecasting this series if applied to the raw data?

- Moving average
- Simple exponential smoothing
- Double exponential smoothing
- Holt-Winter's exponential smoothing

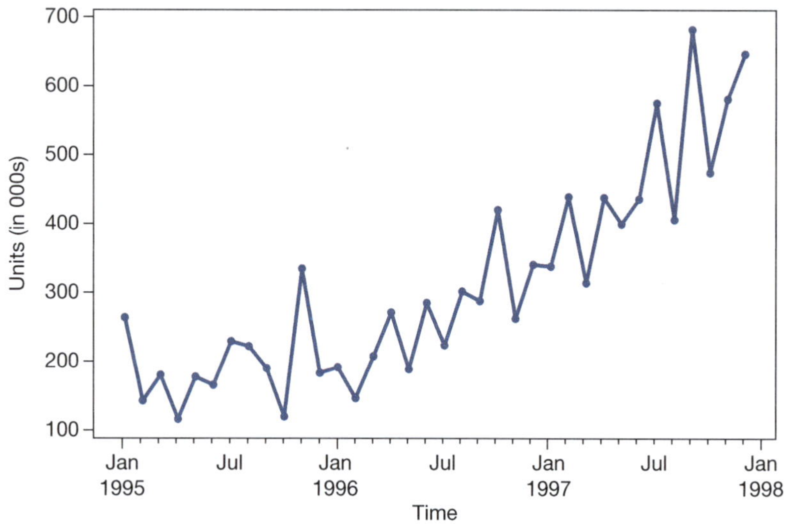

FIGURE 18.10 MONTHLY SALES OF A CERTAIN SHAMPOO

18.8 Annual Average Rainfall in Delhi, Haryana, and Chandigarh. Figure 18.11 is a time plot for the period 2002 to 2015 of annual average rainfall (in millimetres) measures in combined Haryana, Chandigarh, and Delhi. Use moving average method to forecast next 2 years.

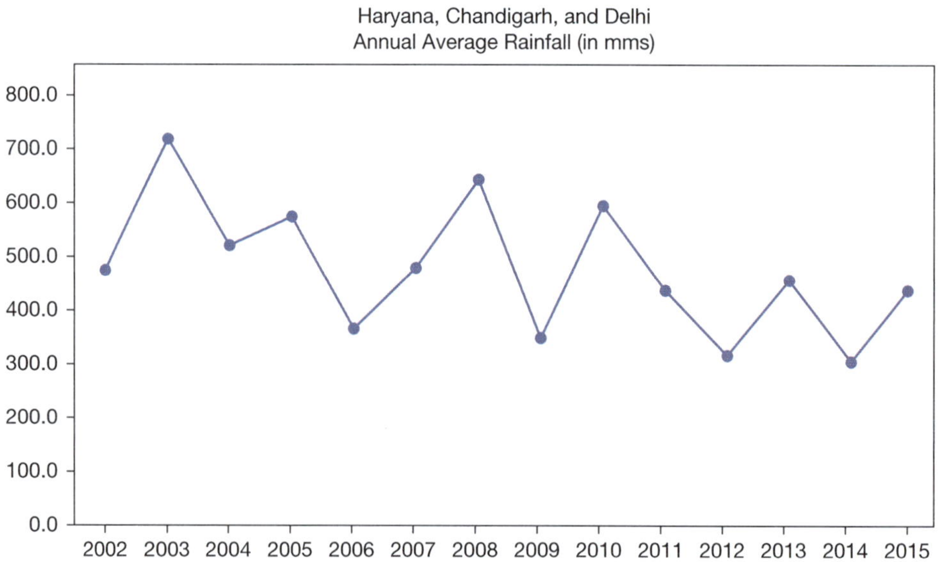

FIGURE 18.11 ANNUAL AVERAGE RAINFALL IN DELHI, HARYANA, AND CHANDIGARH (2002–2015)

Year	2002	2003	2004	2005	2006	2007	2008	2009	2010	2011	2012	2013	2014	2015
Haryana, Chandigarh, and Delhi	471.8	720.7	524.0	586.9	377.1	479.9	633.0	350.4	598.1	433.0	313.6	461.3	305.5	437.8

18.9 Australian Wine Sales. Figure 18.12 shows time plots of monthly sales of six types of Australian wines (red, rose, sweet white, dry white, sparkling, and fortified) for 1980–1994. [Data are available in *AustralianWines.csv*, Source: Hyndman and Yang (2018).] The units are thousands of litres. You are hired to obtain short-term forecasts (2–3 months ahead) for each of the six series, and this task will be repeated every month.

a. Which forecasting method would you choose if you had to choose the same method for all series? Why?

b. Fortified wine has the largest market share of the above six types of wine. You are asked to focus on fortified wine sales alone, and produce as accurate as possible forecasts for the next 2 months.

- Start by partitioning the data using the period until December 1993 as the training set.
- Apply Holt-Winter's exponential smoothing to sales with an appropriate season length (use smoothing parameters $\alpha = 0.2, \beta = 0.15, \gamma = 0.05$).

c. Create an ACF plot for the residuals from the Holt-Winter's exponential smoothing until lag-12.

i. Examining this plot, which of the following statements are reasonable conclusions?

- Decembers (month 12) are not captured well by the model.
- There is a strong correlation between sales on the same calendar month.
- The model does not capture the seasonality well.
- We should try to fit an autoregressive model with lag-12 to the residuals.
- We should first deseasonalize the data and then apply Holt-Winter's exponential smoothing.

ii. How can you handle the above effect without adding another layer to your model?

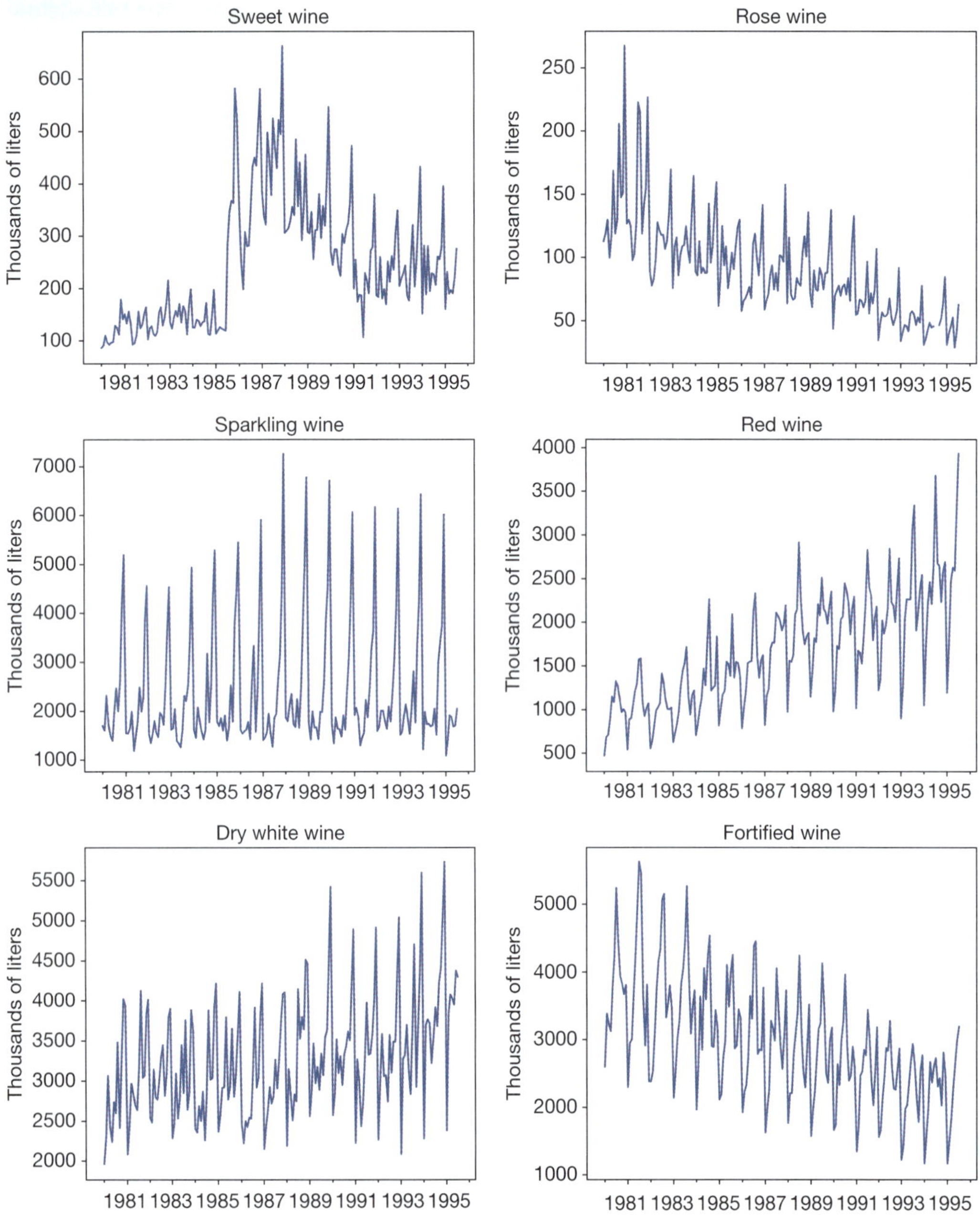

FIGURE 18.12 MONTHLY SALES OF SIX TYPES OF AUSTRALIAN WINES BETWEEN 1980 AND 1994

PART VII

Data Analytics

CHAPTER 19

Social Network Analytics[1]

In this chapter, we examine the basic ways to visualize and describe social networks, measure linkages, and analyze the network with both supervised and unsupervised techniques. The methods we use long predate the Internet, but gained widespread use with the explosion in social media data. Twitter, for example, makes its feed available for public analysis, and some other social media firms make some of their data available to programmers and developers via an application programming interface (API).

Python

In this chapter, we will use `pandas` and `numpy` for data handling. The `networkx` library specializes in manipulating and analyzing networks. It makes use of `matplotlib` to visualize network plots.

import required functionality for this chapter

```
import collections
import pandas as pd
import networkx as nx
import matplotlib.pyplot as plt
```

[1]The organization of ideas in this chapter owes much to Jennifer Golbeck and her book *Analyzing the Social Web* (Golbeck, 2013).

19.1 | INTRODUCTION[2]

The use of social media began its rapid growth in the early 2000s with the advent of Friendster and MySpace, and, in 2004, Facebook. LinkedIn, catering to professionals, soon followed, as did Twitter, Tumblr, Instagram, Yelp, TripAdvisor, and others. These information-based companies quickly began generating a deluge of data—especially data concerning links among people (friends, followers, connections, etc.).

For some companies, like Facebook, Twitter, and LinkedIn, nearly the entire value of the company lies in the analytic and predictive value of this data from their social networks. As of this writing (March 2017), Facebook was worth more than double General Motors and Ford combined. Other companies, like Amazon and Pandora, use social network data as important components of predictive engines aimed at selling products and services.

Social networks are basically entities (e.g., people) and the connections among them. Let's look at the building blocks for describing, depicting, and analyzing networks. The basic elements of a network are:

- Nodes (also called vertices or vertexes)
- Edges (connections or links between nodes)

A very simple LinkedIn network might be depicted as shown in Figure 19.1. This network has six nodes depicting members, with edges connecting some, but not all, of the pairs of nodes.

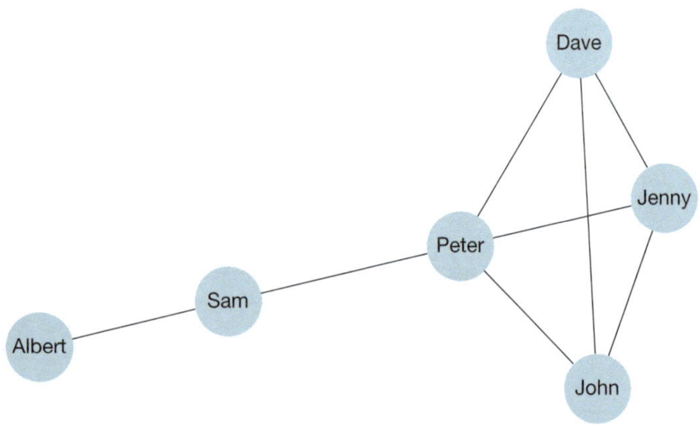

FIGURE 19.1 TINY HYPOTHETICAL LINKEDIN NETWORK; THE EDGES REPRESENT CONNECTIONS AMONG THE MEMBERS

---

[2]This and subsequent sections in this chapter copyright © 2019 Datastats, LLC, and Galit Shmueli. Used by permission.

code for plotting hypothetical LinkedIn network

```
df = pd.DataFrame([
    ("Dave", "Jenny"), ("Peter", "Jenny"), ("John", "Jenny"),
    ("Dave", "Peter"), ("Dave", "John"), ("Peter", "Sam"),
    ("Sam", "Albert"), ("Peter", "John")
], columns=['from', 'to'])
G = nx.from_pandas_edgelist(df, 'from', 'to')
nx.draw(G, with_labels=True, node_color='skyblue')
plt.show()
```

19.2 | DIRECTED VS. UNDIRECTED NETWORKS

In the plot shown in Figure 19.1, edges are bidirectional or undirected, meaning that if John is connected to Peter, then Peter must also be connected to John, and there is no difference in the nature of these connections. You can see from this plot that there is a group of well-connected members (Peter, John, Dave and Jenny), plus two less-connected members (Sam and Albert).

Connections might also be directional, or directed. For example, in Twitter, Dave might follow Peter, but Peter might not follow Dave. A simple Twitter network (using the same members and connections) might be depicted using edges with arrows as shown in Figure 19.2.

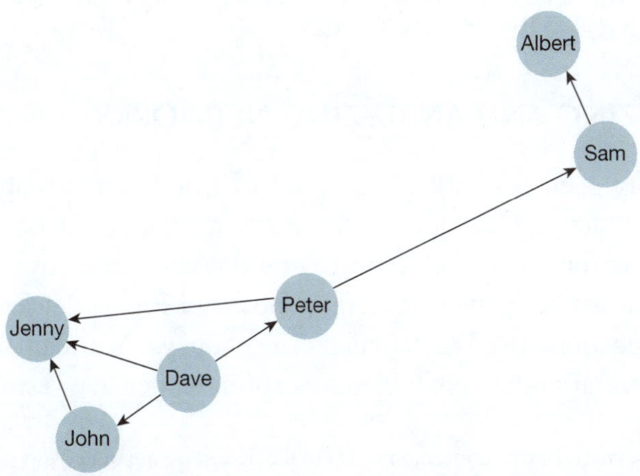

FIGURE 19.2 TINY HYPOTHETICAL TWITTER NETWORK WITH DIRECTED EDGES (ARROWS) SHOWING WHO FOLLOWS WHOM

code for tiny Twitter network

```
# use nx.DiGraph to create a directed network
G = nx.from_pandas_edgelist(df, 'from', 'to', create_using=nx.DiGraph())
nx.draw(G, with_labels=True, node_color='skyblue')
plt.show()
```

Edges can also be weighted to reflect attributes of the connection. For example, the thickness of the edge might represent the level of e-mail traffic between two members in a network, or the bandwidth capacity between two nodes in a digital network (as illustrated in Figure 19.3). Edge length can also be used to represent attributes such as physical distance between two points on a map.

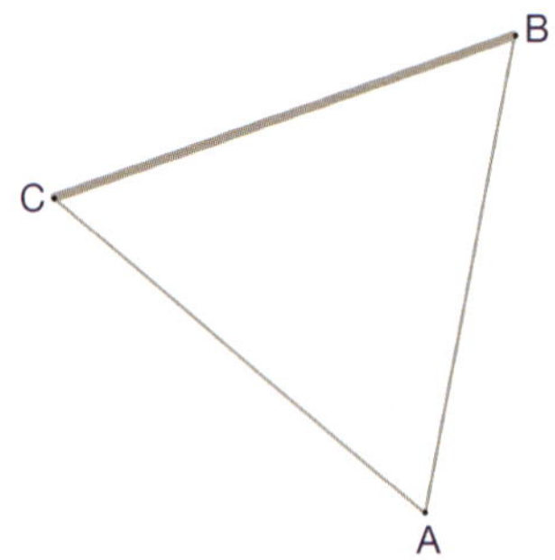

FIGURE 19.3 EDGE WEIGHTS REPRESENTED BY LINE THICKNESS, FOR EXAMPLE, BANDWIDTH CAPACITY BETWEEN NODES IN A DIGITAL NETWORK

19.3 | VISUALIZING AND ANALYZING NETWORKS

You have probably seen network plots[3] used as a tool for visualizing and exploring networks; they are used widely in the news media. Jason Buch and Guillermo Contreras, reporters for the *San Antonio Express News*,[4] pored over law enforcement records and produced the network diagram shown in Figure 19.4 to understand and illustrate the connections used to launder drug money.[5] You can see that there is a well-connected central node; it is the address of an expensive residence in the gated

[3]In the field of network analysis, the term *graph* refers to the data structure of networks (i.e., lists of edges and nodes). In a more general sense, and in other areas of statistics, the term is used synonymously with "chart" or "plot." Here, to avoid confusion, we will will use the term *plot* or *network plot* to refer to the visualization, and *network data* to refer to the data itself.

[4] *San Antonio Express News*, May 23, 2012, accessed June 16, 2014.

[5]The original visualization can be seen at www.google.com/fusiontables/DataSource?snapid=S457047pVkn, accessed October 14, 2018.

Dominion community in San Antonio, owned by accused launderers Mauricio and Alejandro Sanchez Garza. There are several entities in the lower left connected only to themselves, and one singleton. Nodes are sized according to how central they are to the network (specifically, in proportion to their *eigenvector centrality*, which is discussed in Section 19.4).

code for plotting the drug money laundries network

```
drug_df = pd.read_csv('drug.csv')

G = nx.from_pandas_edgelist(drug_df, 'Entity', 'Related Entity')

centrality = nx.eigenvector_centrality(G)
node_size = [400*centrality[n] for n in G.nodes()]
nx.draw(G, with_labels=False, node_color='skyblue', node_size=node_size)
plt.show()
```

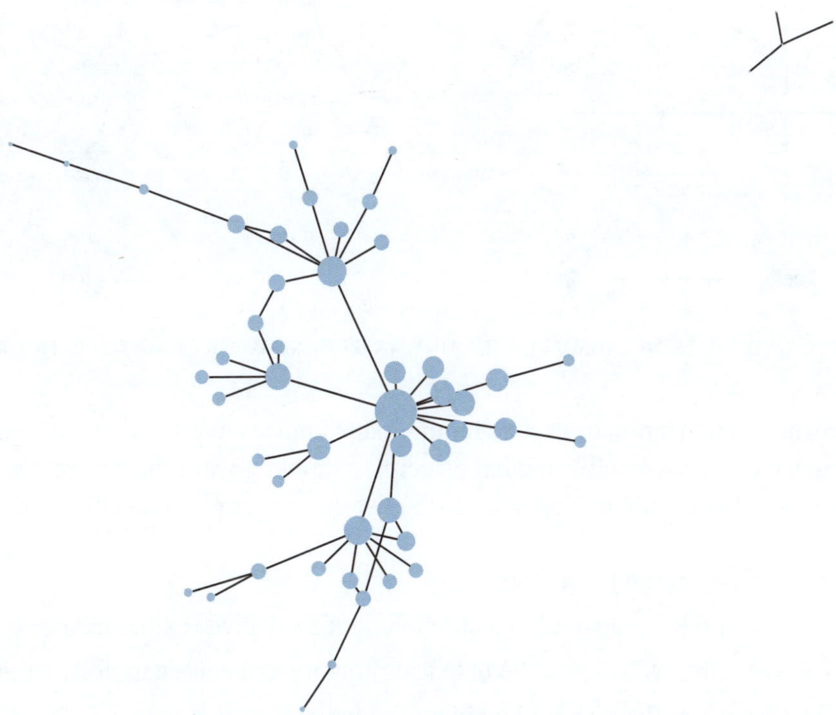

FIGURE 19.4 DRUG LAUNDRY NETWORK IN SAN ANTONIO, TX

Plot Layout

It is important to note that *x*, *y* coordinates usually carry no meaning in network plots; the meaning is conveyed in other elements such as node size, edge width, labels, and directional arrows. Consequently, the same network may be depicted by two very different looking plots. For example, Figure 19.5 presents two different layouts of the hypothetical LinkedIn network.

code for plotting the different layouts

```
G = nx.from_pandas_edgelist(df, 'from', 'to')

plt.subplot(121)
nx.draw_circular(G, with_labels=True, node_color='skyblue', node_size=1000)
plt.subplot(122)
nx.draw_kamada_kawai(G, with_labels=True, node_color='skyblue', node_size=1000)
plt.show()
```

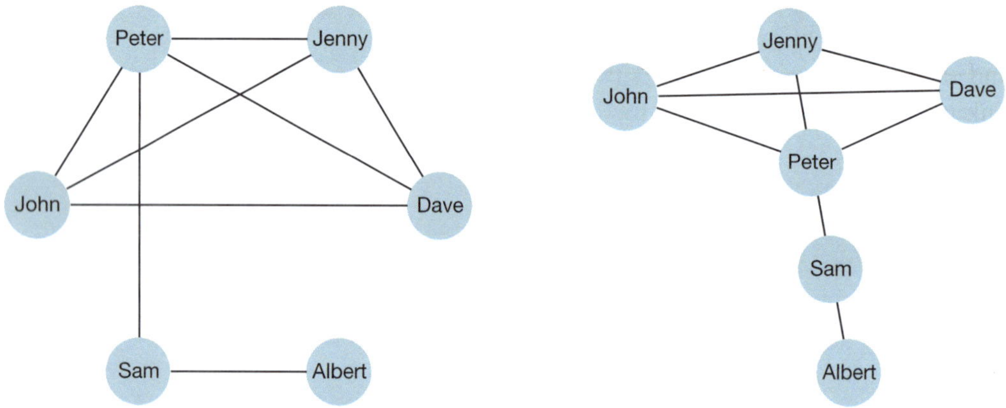

FIGURE 19.5 TWO DIFFERENT LAYOUTS OF THE TINY LINKEDIN NETWORK PRESENTED IN FIGURE 19.1

As a result, visualization tools face innumerable choices in plot layout. The first step in making a choice is to establish what principles should govern the layout. Dunne and Shneiderman (2009, cited in Golbeck, 2013) list these four plot readability principles:

1. Every node should be visible.
2. For every node, you should be able to count its degree (explained below).
3. For every link, you should be able to follow it from source to destination.
4. Clusters and outliers should be identifiable.

These general principles are then translated into readability metrics by which plots can be judged. One simple layouts is *circular* (all nodes lie in a circle) and *grid* (all nodes lie at the intersection of grid lines in a rectangular grid).

You can probably think of alternate layouts that more clearly reveal structures such as clusters and singletons, and so can computers using a variety of algorithms. These algorithms typically use a combination of fixed arbitrary starting structures, random tweaking, analogs to physical properties (e.g., springs connecting nodes), and a sequence of iteration and measurement against the readability principles. The Kamada–Kawai force-directed layout available in `networkx` is an example of such an algorithm. A detailed discussion of layout algorithms is beyond the scope of this chapter; see Golbeck (2013, chapter 4) for an introduction to layout issues, including algorithms, the use of size, shape and color, scaling issues, and labeling.

Edge List

A network plot such as the one in Figure 19.4 (drug laundry network) is always tied to a data table called an *edge list*, or an *adjacency list*. Table 19.1 shows an excerpt from the data table used to generate Figure 19.4. All the entities in both columns are nodes, and each row represents a link between the two nodes. If the network is directional, the link is usually structured from the left column to the right column.

TABLE 19.1 EDGE LIST EXCERPT CORRESPONDING TO THE DRUG-LAUNDERING NETWORK IN FIGURE 19.4

6451 Babcock Road	Q & M LLC
Q & M LLC	10 Kings Heath
Maurico Sanchez	Q & M LLC
Hilda Riebeling	Q & M LLC
Ponte Vedra Apartments	Q & M LLC
O S F STEAK HOUSE, LLC	Mauricio Sanchez
Arturo Madrigal	O S F STEAK HOUSE
HARBARD BAR, LLC	Arturo Madrigal
10223 Sahara Street	O S F STEAK HOUSE
HARBARD BAR, LLC	Maurico Sanchez
9510 Tioga Drive, Suite 206	Mauricio Sanchez
FDA FIBER, INC	Arturo Madrigal
10223 Sahara Street	O S F STEAK HOUSE
A G Q FULL SERVICE, LLC	Alvaro Garcia de Quevedo
19510 Gran Roble	Arturo Madrigal
Lorenza Madrigal Cristan	19519 Gran Roble
Laredo National Bank	19519 Gran Roble

In a typical network visualization tool, you can select a row from the data table and see its node and connections highlighted in the network plot. Likewise, in the plot, you can click on a node and see it highlighted in the data table.

Adjacency Matrix

The same relationships can be presented in a matrix. The adjacency matrix for the small directed network for Twitter in Figure 19.2 is shown in Table 19.2.

Each cell in the matrix indicates an edge, with the originating node in the left header column and the destination node in the top row of headers. Reading the first row, we see that Dave is following three people—Peter, Jenny, and John.

TABLE 19.2 ADJACENCY MATRIX EXCERPT CORRESPONDING TO THE TWITTER DATA IN FIGURE 19.2

	Dave	Peter	Jenny	Sam	John	Albert
Dave	0	1	1	0	1	0
Peter	0	0	1	1	1	0
Jenny	0	0	0	0	0	0
Sam	0	0	0	0	0	1
John	0	1	1	0	0	0
Albert	0	0	0	0	0	0

Using Network Data in Classification and Prediction

In our discussion of classification and prediction, as well as clustering and data reduction, we were dealing mostly with highly structured data in the form of a data frame—columns were variables (features), and rows were records. We saw how to use Python to sample from relational databases to bring data into the form of a data frame.

Highly structured data can be used for network analysis, but network data often start out in a more unstructured or semi-structured format. Twitter provides a public feed of a portion of its voluminous stream of tweets, which has captured researchers' attention and accelerated interest in the application of network analytics to social media data. Network analysis can take this unstructured data and turn it into structured data with usable metrics.

We now turn our attention to those metrics. These metrics can be used not only to describe the attributes of networks, but as inputs to more traditional data mining methods.

19.4 | SOCIAL DATA METRICS AND TAXONOMY

Several popular network metrics are used in network analysis. Before introducing them, we introduce some basic network terminology used for constructing the metrics.

Edge weight measures the strength of the relationship between the two connected nodes. For example, in an e-mail network, there might be an edge weight that reflects the number of e-mails exchanged between two individuals linked by that edge.

Path and **path length** are important for measuring distance between nodes. A path is the route of nodes needed to go from node A to node B; path length is the number of edges in that route. Typically these terms refer to the shortest route. In a weighted network, the shortest path does not necessarily reflect the path with the fewest edges, but rather the path with the least weight. For example, if the weights reflect a cost factor, the shortest path would reflect the minimal cost.

A connected network is a network where each node in the network has a path, of any length, to all other nodes. A network may be unconnected in its entirety, but consist of segments that are connected within themselves. In the money laundering visualization (Figure 19.4), the network as a whole is unconnected—the nodes are not all connected to one another. You can see two independent sub-networks, one large and a small one with four nodes.

A clique is a network in which each node is directly connected by an edge to every other node. The connections must all be single edges—a connection via a multi-node path does not count.

A singleton is an unconnected node. It might arise when an individual signs up for a social network service (e.g., to read reviews) and does not participate in any networking activities.

Node-Level Centrality Metrics

Often we may be interested in the importance or influence of a particular individual or node, which is reflected in how central that node is in the network.

The most common way to calculate this is by degree—how many edges are connected to the node. Nodes with many connections are more central. In Figure 19.1, the Albert node is of degree 1, Sam of degree 2, and Jenny of degree 3. In a directed network, we are interested in both indegree and outdegree—the number of incoming and outgoing connections of a node. In Figure 19.2, Peter has indegree of 2, and outdegree of 1.

Another metric for a node's centrality is *closeness*—how close the node is to the other nodes in the network. This is measured by finding the shortest path from that node to all the other nodes, then taking the reciprocal of the average of these path lengths. In Figure 19.1 example, Albert's closeness centrality is $5/(1 + 2 + 3 + 3 + 3) = 0.417$.

Still another metric is *betweenness*—the extent to which a given node lies on the shortest path between pairs of nodes. The calculation starts with the given node, say, node A, and two other nodes, say B and C, out of perhaps many nodes in a network. The shortest paths between B and C are listed, and the proportion of paths that include A is recorded. The betweenness of a node is the sum of this proportion over all pairs of nodes. In Figure 19.1 example, Peter's node is on all the shortest paths between one of the nodes Dave, Jenny, and John with either Albert or Sam. Because in this example we have only one shortest path between pairs of nodes, this gives an unnormalized betweenness for Peter of 6. To normalize, this number is divided by the number of all possible shortest paths between the other nodes $\binom{n-1}{2} = \frac{(n-1)(n-2)}{2}$. In our example, this is 10, so the normalized betweenness of Peter is 0.6. This proportion is recorded also for all other nodal pairs, and betweenness is the average proportion.

An aphorism relevant for social media networks is "it's not what you know, but who you know." A more accurate rendition would qualify it further—"it's who you know and who they know." A link to a member that has many other connections can be more valuable than a link to a member with few connections. A metric that measures this connectivity aspect is *eigenvector centrality*, which factors in both the number of links from a node and the number of onward connections from those links. The details of the calculation is not discussed here, but the result always lies between 0 (not central) and 1 (maximum centrality). The larger the value for a given node, the more central it is.

Centrality can be depicted on a network plot by the size of a node—the more central the node, the larger it is.

Code for computing centrality measures in Python for the small undirected LinkedIn data is given in Table 19.3.

TABLE 19.3 COMPUTING CENTRALITY IN PYTHON

```
>>> G = nx.from_pandas_edgelist(df, 'from', 'to')
>>> G.degree()
[('Dave', 3), ('Jenny', 3), ('Peter', 4), ('John', 3), ('Sam', 2), ('Albert', 1)]
>>> nx.closeness_centrality(G)
{'Dave': 0.625, 'Jenny': 0.625, 'Peter': 0.833, 'John': 0.625,
 'Sam': 0.625, 'Albert': 0.417}
 >>> nx.betweenness_centrality(G)
{'Dave': 0.0, 'Jenny': 0.0, 'Peter': 0.6, 'John': 0.0, 'Sam': 0.4, 'Albert': 0.0}
>>> nx.eigenvector_centrality(G, tol=1e-2)
{'Dave': 0.47, 'Jenny': 0.47, 'Peter': 0.53, 'John': 0.47,
 'Sam': 0.21, 'Albert': 0.08}
```

Egocentric Network

It is often important to gain information that comes only from the analysis of individuals and their connections. For example, an executive recruiting firm may be interested in individuals with certain job titles and the people those individuals are connected to.

An egocentric network is the network of connections centered around an individual node. A degree 1 egocentric network consists of all the edges connected to the individual node, plus their connections. A degree 2 egocentric network is the network of all those nodes and edges, plus the edges and nodes connected to them. The degree 1 and degree 2 egocentric network for Peter in the LinkedIn network are shown in Figure 19.6. Note that the degree 2 egocentric network for Peter is the entire network shown in Figure 19.1.

code for computing egocentric network

```
# nx.ego_graph get Peter's 1-level ego network
% # for a 2-level ego network set argument order = 2 in make_ego_graph().
plt.subplot(121)
# get 1-level ego network for 'Peter'
G_ego = nx.ego_graph(G, 'Peter')
nx.draw(G_ego, with_labels=True, node_color='skyblue')
plt.subplot(122)
# set radius=2 to get 2-level ego network
G_ego = nx.ego_graph(G, 'Peter', radius=2)
nx.draw(G_ego, with_labels=True, node_color='skyblue')
```

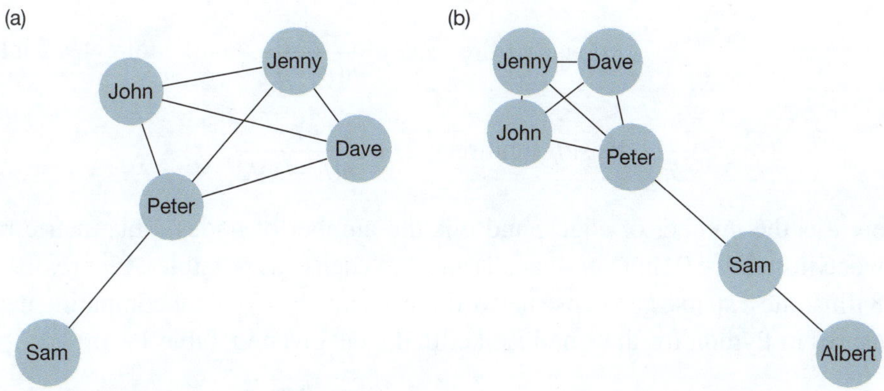

FIGURE 19.6 THE DEGREE 1 (a) AND DEGREE 2 (b) EGOCENTRIC NETWORKS FOR PETER, FROM THE LINKEDIN NETWORK IN FIGURE 19.1

Network Metrics

To this point, we have discussed metrics and terms that apply to nodes and edges. We can also measure attributes of the network as a whole. Two main network metrics are *degree distribution* and *density*.

Degree distribution describes the range of *connectedness* of the nodes—how many nodes have, for example, five connections, how many have four connections, how many have three, etc. In the tiny LinkedIn network (Figure 19.1), we see that Peter, Jenny, and Dave have three connections, John and Sam have two connections, and Albert has one. A table of this degree distribution is shown in Table 19.4.

TABLE 19.4 DEGREE DISTRIBUTION OF THE TINY LINKEDIN NETWORK

Degree	Frequency
Degree 0	0
Degree 1	1
Degree 2	1
Degree 3	3
Degree 4	1

Density is another way to describe the overall connectedness of network data which focuses on the edges, not the nodes. The metric looks at the ratio of the actual number of edges to the maximum number of potential edges (i.e., if every node were connected to every other node) in a network with a fixed number of nodes. For a directed network with n nodes, there can be a maximum of $n(n-1)$ edges. For an undirected network, the number is $n(n-1)/2$. More formally, density calculations for directed and undirected networks are as follows:

$$\text{density (directed)} = \frac{e}{n(n-1)}, \tag{19.1}$$

$$\text{density (undirected)} = \frac{e}{n(n-1)/2}, \tag{19.2}$$

where e is the number of edges, and n is the number of nodes. This metric ranges between just above 0 (not dense at all) and 1 (as dense as possible). Figures 19.7 and 19.8 illustrate a sparse and dense network, respectively. Code for computing network measures in Python for the small LinkedIn data is given in Table 19.5.

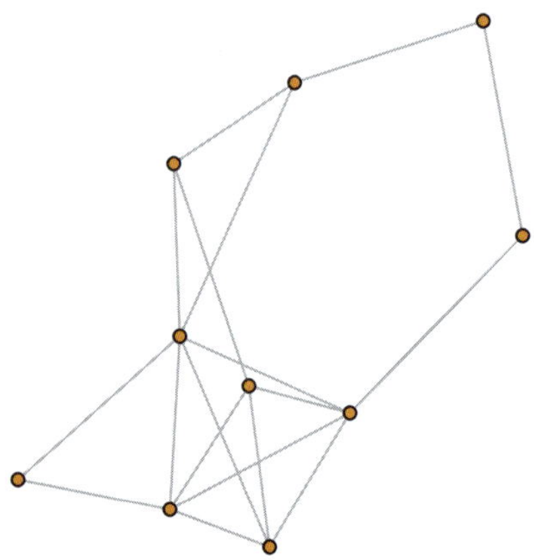

FIGURE 19.7 A RELATIVELY SPARSE NETWORK

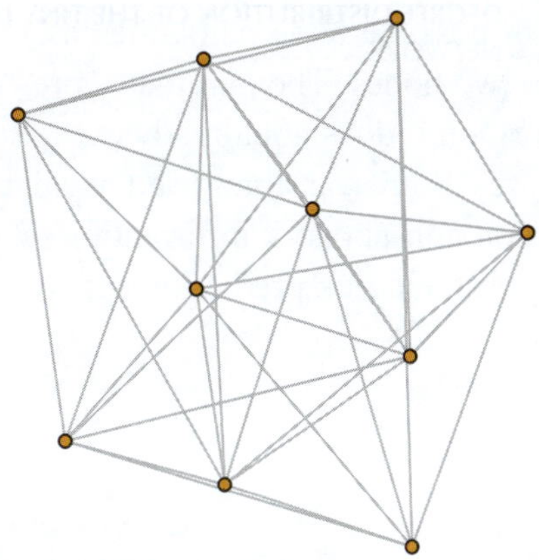

FIGURE 19.8 A RELATIVELY DENSE NETWORK

TABLE 19.5 COMPUTING NETWORK MEASURES IN PYTHON

```
> degreeCount = collections.Counter(d for node, d in G.degree())
> degreeDistribution = [0] * (1 + max(degreeCount))
> for degree, count in degreeCount.items():
>     degreeDistribution[degree] = count
> degreeDistribution
[0, 1, 1, 3, 1]

> nx.density(G)
0.26666666666666666
```

19.5 USING NETWORK METRICS IN PREDICTION AND CLASSIFICATION

Network attributes can be used along with other predictors in standard classification and prediction procedures. The most common applications involve the concept of *matching*. Online dating services, for example, will predict for their members which other members might be potentially compatible. Their algorithms typically involve calculation of a distance measure between a member seeking a relationship and candidate matches. It might also go beyond the members' self-reported features and incorporate information about links between the member and candidate matches. A link might represent the action "viewed candidate profile."

Link Prediction

Social networks such as Facebook and LinkedIn use network information to recommend new connections. The translation of this goal into an analytics problem is:

> "If presented with a network, can you predict the next link to form?"

Prediction algorithms list all possible node pairs, then assign a score to each pair that reflects the similarity of the two nodes. The pair that scores as most similar (closest) is the next link predicted to form, if it does not already exist. See Chapter 15 for a discussion of such distance measures. Some variables used in calculating similarity measures are the same as those based on non-network information (e.g., years of education, age, sex, location). Other metrics used in link prediction apply specifically to network data:

- shortest path
- number of common neighbors
- edge weight

Link prediction is also used in targeting intelligence surveillance. "Collecting everything" may be technically, politically, or legally unfeasible, and an agency must therefore identify apriori a smaller set of individuals requiring surveillance. The agency will often start with known targets, then use link prediction to identify additional targets and prioritize collection efforts.

Entity Resolution

Governments use network analysis to track terrorist networks, and a key part of that effort is identification of individuals. The same individual may appear multiple times from different data sources, and the agencies want to know, for example, whether individual A identified by French surveillance in Tunisia is the same as individual AA identified by Israeli intelligence in Lebanon and individual AAA identified by US intelligence in Pakistan.

One way to evaluate whether an individual appears in multiple databases is to measure distances and use them in a similar fashion to nearest neighbors or clustering. In Chapter 15, we looked in particular at Euclidean distance, and discussed this metric not in terms of the network an individual belongs to, but rather in terms of the profile (predictor values) of the individual. When basing entity resolution on these variables, it is useful to bring domain knowledge into the picture to weight the importance of each variable. For example, two variables in an individual's record might be street address and zip code. A match on street address is more definitive than a match on zip code, so we would probably want to give street address more weight in the scoring algorithm. For a more detailed discussion of automated weight calculation and assignment, see p. 137 in Golbeck (2013).

In addition to measuring distance based on individual profiles, we can bring network attributes into the picture. Consider the simple networks for each individual in Figure 19.9, showing connections to known individuals: Based on network connections, you would conclude that A and AA are likely the same person, while AAA is

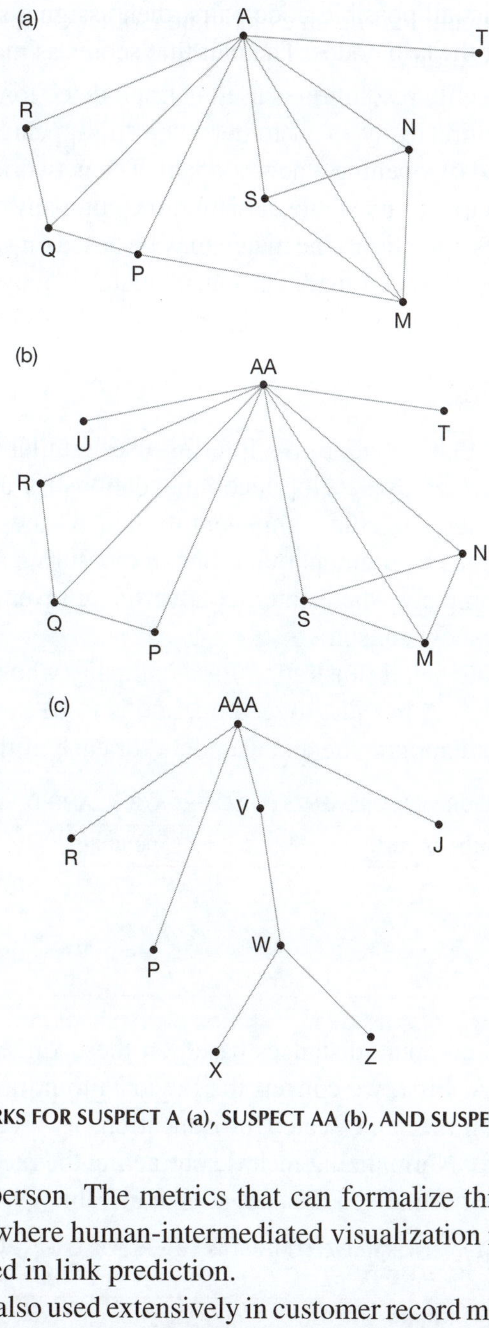

FIGURE 19.9 THE NETWORKS FOR SUSPECT A (a), SUSPECT AA (b), AND SUSPECT AAA (c)

probably a different person. The metrics that can formalize this search, and be used in automated fashion where human-intermediated visualization is not practical, are the same ones that are used in link prediction.

Entity resolution is also used extensively in customer record management and search. For example, a customer might contact a company inquiring about a product or service, triggering the creation of a customer record. The same customer might later inquire again, or purchase something. The customer database system should flag the second interaction as belonging to the first customer. Ideally, the customer will enter his or her information exactly the same way in each interaction, facilitating the match, but this does not necessarily happen. Failing an exact match, other customers may be proposed as matches based on proximity.

Another area where entity resolution is used is fraud detection. For example, a large telecom used link resolution to detect customers who "disappeared" after accumulating debt but then reappeared by opening a new account. The network of phone calls to and from such people tends to remain stable, assisting the company to identify them.

In traditional business operations, the match may be based on variables such as name, address and postal code. In social media products, matches may also be calculated on the basis of network similarity.

Collaborative Filtering

We saw in Chapter 14 that collaborative filtering uses similarity metrics to identify similar individuals, and thereby develop recommendations for a particular individual. Companies that have a social media component to their business can use information about network connections to augment other data in measuring similarity.

For example, in a company where Internet advertising revenue is important, a key question is what ads to show consumers.

Consider the following small illustration for a company whose business is centered around online users: User A has just logged on, and is to be compared to users B–D. Table 19.6 shows some demographic and user data for each of the users.

TABLE 19.6 FOUR MEASUREMENTS FOR USERS A, B, C, AND D

User	Months as cust.	Age	Spending	Education
A	7	23	0	3
B	3	45	0	2
C	5	29	100	3
D	11	59	0	3

Our initial step is to compute distances based on these values, to determine which user is closest to user A. First, we convert the raw data to normalized values to place all the measurements on the same scale (for Education, 1 = high school, 2 = college, 3 = post college degree). Normalizing means subtracting the mean and dividing by the standard deviation. The normalized data are shown in Table 19.7.

TABLE 19.7 NORMALIZED MEASUREMENTS FOR USERS A, B, C, AND D

User	Months as cust.	Age	Spending	Education
A	0.17	−1.14	−0.58	0.58
B	−1.18	0.43	−0.58	−1.73
C	−0.51	−0.71	1.73	0.58
D	1.52	1.42	−0.58	0.58

Next, we calculate the Euclidean distance between A and each of the other users (see Table 19.8). Based on these calculations, which only take into account the demographic and user data, user C is the closest one to the new user A.

TABLE 19.8 EUCLIDEAN DISTANCE BETWEEN EACH PAIR OF USERS

Pair	Months as cust.	Age	Spending	Education	Euclidean dist.
A–B	1.83	2.44	0	5.33	3.1
A–C	0.46	0.18	5.33	0	2.44
A–D	1.83	6.55	0	0	2.89

Let's now bring in network metrics, and suppose that the inter-user distances in terms of shortest path are A–B = 2, A–C = 4, and A–D = 3 (Table 19.9).

TABLE 19.9 NETWORK METRICS

Pair	Shortest path
A–B	2
A–C	4
A–D	3

Finally, we can combine this network metric with the other user measurement distances calculated earlier. There is no need to calculate and normalize differences, as we did with the other user measurements, since the shortest-path metric itself already measures distance between records. We therefore take a weighted average of the network and non-network metrics, using weights that reflect the relative importance we want to attach to each. Using equal weights (Table 19.10), user B is scored as the closest to A, and could be recommended as a link for user A (in a social environment), or could be used as a source for product and service recommendations. With different weights, it is possible to obtain different results. Choosing weights is not a scientific process; rather, it depends on the business judgment about the relative importance of the network metrics vs. the non-network user measurements.

TABLE 19.10 COMBINING THE NETWORK AND NON-NETWORK METRICS

Pair	Shortest path	Weight	Non-network	Weight	Mean
A–B	2	0.5	3.1	0.5	2.55
A–C	4	0.5	2.44	0.5	3.22
A–D	3	0.5	2.89	0.5	2.95

In addition to recommending social media connections and providing data for recommendations, network analysis has been used for identifying clusters of similar individuals based on network data (e.g., for marketing purposes), identifying influential individuals (e.g., to target with promotions or outreach), and understanding—in some cases, controlling—the propagation of disease and information.

USING SOCIAL NETWORK DATA

The primary users of social network data are the social networks themselves, those who develop applications (apps) for the networks, and their advertisers. Facebook, Twitter, other networks and associated app developers use the network data to customize each user's individual experience and increase engagement (i.e., encourage more and longer use). Social network data are also a powerful advertising tool. Facebook generates roughly $50 billion in advertising revenue annually, Twitter $2 billion, and LinkedIn about $5 billion, at this writing. Unlike traditional media, Internet social media platforms offer highly specific microtargeting of ads, the ability to experiment with different ads on a continuous basis to optimize performance, and the ability to measure response and charge advertisers only for the ads that people click on. Facebook gains its advantage from its large user base and the rich information portfolio it has on its regular users (including the identity of a user's connection, as well as information on those connected users).

Perhaps the most well-known example of this advantage was Donald Trump's 2016 campaign for President. Although Trump is most often associated with Twitter, Brad Parscale, Digital Director of the 2016 campaign, gives credit for the victory to Facebook, due to its ability to microtarget ads. He put it this way in a 2018 *60 Minutes* television interview:

> "Facebook now lets you get to places ... that you would never go with TV ads. Now, I can find, you know, 15 people in the Florida Panhandle that I would never buy a TV commercial for."

Parscale explained that he was able to generate 50,000–60,000 different ads per day, combining both microtargeting and continuous massive experimentation to see what ads worked best with what individuals. Although Trump lost the popular vote by 2.8 million votes overall, he was able to win the Electoral College by a razor thin margin of 77,744 votes in 3 key states—Pennsylvania, Wisconsin and Michigan. The ability to surgically target voters where they would be most effective was crucial, and Facebook was instrumental in this effort. Facebook experts were embedded with the Trump campaign to implement the complex job, and Parscale credited the company with a key role in Trump's victory: "Donald Trump won, but I think Facebook was the method."

Facebook and Twitter have in the past made data publicly available via Application Programming Interfaces (APIs). Controversial use of Facebook data via third-party apps has resulted in changes to Facebook procedures and significant limitations. Twitter requires that you register as an app developer to gain access to its API. Twitter data is especially popular with researchers for more than just its network data—it is used for analysis of social trends, political opinions and consumer sentiment. Social media APIs are updated on a regular basis, as are the limits on what you can do with the data. See www.dataminingbook.com for updated references on social media API documentation, and useful references on using Python in conjunction with this data.

19.6 | COLLECTING SOCIAL NETWORK DATA WITH PYTHON

In this section, we briefly show how to collect data from one of the most used social networks: Twitter. There are several packages available in Python to interface with this and other social networks.

Here we show code using the package `twython`. It requires pre-registration as a developer, to obtain an application authorization code. Before crawling for Twitter data, create a new Twitter application and obtain a consumer key and consumer secret code from https://developer.twitter.com. For more information on the `twython` package, see https://twython.readthedocs.io/en/latest.

Table 19.11 provides a simple example for the `twython` package. The code collects data on 25 recent tweets that contain the words "text mining." The output shows the text content of the resulting first two tweets.

TABLE 19.11 TWITTER INTERFACE IN PYTHON

code for Twitter interface

```
import os
from twython import Twython

credentials = {}
credentials['CONSUMER_KEY'] = os.environ['TWITTER_CONSUMER_KEY']
credentials['CONSUMER_SECRET'] = os.environ['TWITTER_CONSUMER_SECRET']

python_tweets = Twython(credentials['CONSUMER_KEY'], credentials['CONSUMER_SECRET'])

# Create our query
query = {'q': 'text mining', 'result_type': 'recent',
        'count': 25, 'lang': 'en'}

recentTweets = python_tweets.search(**query)
for tweet in recentTweets['statuses'][:2]:
    print(tweet['text'])
```

Output

```
Text Mining and Analysis: Practical Methods, Examples, and Case Studies Using
   SAS https://t.co/jFjmmSgjtO
RT @scilib: Canada - House of Commons - Standing Committee on Industry, Science
   and Technology #INDU - Statutory Review of the Copyright Ac…
```

19.7 | ADVANTAGES AND DISADVANTAGES

The key value of social network data to businesses is the information it provides about individuals and their needs, desires, and tastes. This information can be used to improve target advertising—and perfectly targeted advertising is the holy grail of the advertising business. People often disdain or ignore traditional "broad spectrum" advertising, whereas they pay close attention when presented with information about something specific that they are interested in. The power of network data is that they allow capturing information on individual needs and tastes without measuring or collecting such data directly. Moreover, network data are often user-provided rather than actively collected.

To see the power of social network data, one need look no further than the data-based social media giants of the 21st century—Facebook, LinkedIn, Twitter, Yelp, and others. They have built enormous value based almost exclusively on the information contained in their social data—they manufacture no products and sell no services (in the traditional sense) to their users. The main value they generate is the ability to generate real-time information at the level of the individual to better target ads.

It is important to distinguish between social network *engagement* and the use of social network *analytics*. Many organizations have social media policies and use social media as part of their communications and advertising strategies; however, this does not mean they have access to detailed social network data that they can use for analysis. Abrams Research, an Internet marketing agency, cited the edgy online retailer Zappos in 2009 for the best use of social media, but Zappos' orientation was engagement—use of social media for product support and customer service—rather than analytics.

Reliance on social network analytics comes with hazards and challenges. One major hazard is the dynamic, faddish, and somewhat ephemeral nature of social media use. In part this is because social media involvement is relatively new, and the landscape is changing with the arrival of new players and new technologies. It also stems from the essential nature of social media. People use social media not to provide essential needs like food and shelter, but as a voluntary avocation to provide entertainment and interaction with others. Tastes change, and what's in and out of fashion shifts rapidly in these spheres.

Facebook was a pioneer, and its initial appeal was to the college crowd and later to young adults. Eight years later, nearly half its users were of age 45 years or older, significantly higher than in the rest of the social media industry. These users spend more time per visit and are wealthier than college students, so Facebook may be benefiting from this demographic trend. However, this rapid shift shows how fast the essentials of their business model can shift.

Other challenges lie in the public and personal nature of the data involved. Although individuals nearly always engage with social media voluntarily, this does not mean they do so responsibly or with knowledge of the potential consequences. Information posted on Facebook became evidence in 33% of US divorce cases, and numerous cases have been cited of individuals being fired because of information they posted on Facebook.

One enterprising programmer created the website pleaserobme.com (since removed) that listed the real-time location of people who had "checked in" via FourSquare to a cafe or restaurant, thus letting the world know that they were not at home. FourSquare was not making this information easily available to hackers, but the check-ins were auto-posted to Twitter, where they could be harvested via an API. Thus, information collected for the purpose of enriching the "targetability" of advertising to users ended up creating a liability for both FourSquare and Twitter. Twitter's liability came about indirectly, and it would have been easy for Twitter to overlook this risk in setting up their connection with FourSquare.

In summary, despite the potential for abuse and exposure to risk, the value provided by social network analytics seems large enough to ensure that the analytics methods outlined in this chapter will continue to be in demand.

PROBLEMS

19.1 Describing a Network. Consider an undirected network for individuals A, B, C, D, and E. A is connected to B and C. B is connected to A and C. C is connected to A, B, and D. D is connected to C and E. E is connected to D.

- **a.** Produce a network plot for this network.
- **b.** What node(s) would need to be removed from the network for the remaining nodes to constitute a clique?
- **c.** What is the degree for node A?
- **d.** Which node(s) have the lowest degree?
- **e.** Tabulate the degree distribution for this network.
- **f.** Is this network connected?
- **g.** Calculate the betweenness centrality for nodes A and C.
- **h.** Calculate the density of the network.

19.2 Network Density and Size. Imagine that two new nodes are added to the undirected network in the previous exercise.

- **a.** By what percent has the number of nodes increased?
- **b.** By what percent has the number of possible edges increased?
- **c.** Suppose the new node has a typical (median) number of connections. What will happen to network density?
- **d.** Comment on comparing densities in networks of different sizes.
- **e.** Tabulate the degree distribution for this network.

19.3 Link Prediction. Consider the network shown in Figure 19.10.

a. Using the number of common neighbors score, predict the next link to form (that is, suggest which new link has the best chance of success).

b. Using the shortest path score, identify the link that is least likely to form.

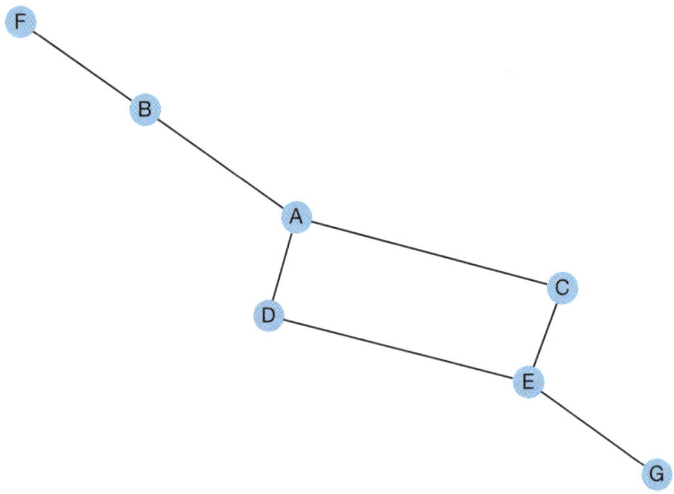

FIGURE 19.10 NETWORK FOR LINK PREDICTION EXERCISE

CHAPTER 20

Text Mining

In this chapter, we introduce text as a form of data. First, we discuss a tabular representation of text data in which each column is a word, each row is a document, and each cell is a 0 or 1, indicating whether that column's word is present in that row's document. Then we consider how to move from unstructured documents to this structured matrix. Finally, we illustrate how to integrate this process into the standard data mining procedures covered in earlier parts of the book.

Python

In this chapter, we will use pandas for data handling and `scikit-learn` for the feature creation and model building. The Natural Language Toolkit will be used for more advanced text processing (nltk: https://www.nltk.org).

import required functionality for this chapter

```
from zipfile import ZipFile
import pandas as pd
from sklearn.model_selection import train_test_split
from sklearn.feature_extraction.text import CountVectorizer
from sklearn.feature_extraction.text import TfidfTransformer
from sklearn.feature_extraction.stop_words import ENGLISH_STOP_WORDS
from sklearn.decomposition import TruncatedSVD
from sklearn.preprocessing import Normalizer
from sklearn.pipeline import make_pipeline
from sklearn.linear_model import LogisticRegression
import nltk
from nltk import word_tokenize
from nltk.stem.snowball import EnglishStemmer
import matplotlib.pylab as plt
from dmba import printTermDocumentMatrix, classificationSummary, liftChart

# download data required for NLTK
nltk.download('punkt')
```

20.1 | INTRODUCTION[1]

Up to this point, and in data mining in general, we have been dealing with three types of data:

- numerical
- binary (yes/no)
- multicategory

In some common predictive analytics applications, though, data come in text form. An Internet service provider, for example, might want to use an automated algorithm to classify support tickets as urgent or routine, so that the urgent ones can receive immediate human review. A law firm facing a massive discovery process (review of large numbers of documents) would benefit from a document review algorithm that could classify documents as relevant or irrelevant. In both of these cases, the predictor variables (features) are embedded as text in documents.

Text mining methods have gotten a boost from the availability of social media data—the Twitter feed, for example, as well as blogs, online forums, review sites, and news articles. According to the Rexer Analytics 2013 Data Mining Survey, between 25% and 40% of data miners responding to the survey use data mining with text from these sources. Their public availability and high profile has provided a huge repository of data on which researchers can hone text mining methods. One area of growth has been the application of text mining methods to notes and transcripts from contact centers and service centers.

20.2 | THE TABULAR REPRESENTATION OF TEXT: TERM-DOCUMENT MATRIX AND "BAG-OF-WORDS"

Consider the following three sentences:

```
S1. this is the first sentence.
S2. this is a second sentence.
S3. the third sentence is here.
```

We can represent the words (called *terms*) in these three sentences (called *documents*) in a *term-document matrix*, where each row is a word and each column is a sentence. In `scikit-learn`, converting a set of documents into a term-document matrix can be done by first collecting the documents into a list and then using the `CountVectorizer` from `scikit-learn`. Table 20.1 illustrates this process for the three-sentence example.

[1]This and subsequent sections in this chapter copyright © 2019 Datastats, LLC, and Galit Shmueli. Used by permission.

TABLE 20.1 TERM-DOCUMENT MATRIX REPRESENTATION OF WORDS IN SENTENCES S1–S3

code for term frequency

```
text = ['this is the first sentence.',
        'this is a second sentence.',
        'the third sentence is here.']

# learn features based on text
count_vect = CountVectorizer()
counts = count_vect.fit_transform(text)

printTermDocumentMatrix(count_vect, counts)
```

Output

```
          S1  S2  S3
first      1   0   0
here       0   0   1
is         1   1   1
second     0   1   0
sentence   1   1   1
the        1   0   1
third      0   0   1
this       1   1   0
```

Note that all the words in all three sentences are represented in the matrix and each word has exactly one row. Order is not important, and the number in the cell indicates the frequency of that term in that sentence. This is the *bag-of-words* approach, where the document is treated simply as a collection of words in which order, grammar, and syntax do not matter.

The three sentences have now been transformed into a tabular data format just like those we have seen to this point. In a simple world, this binary matrix could be used in clustering, or, with the appending of an outcome variable, for classification or prediction. However, the text mining world is not a simple one. Even confining our analysis to the bag-of-words approach, considerable thinking and preprocessing may be required. Some human review of the documents, beyond simply classifying them for training purposes, may be indispensable.

20.3 BAG-OF-WORDS VS. MEANING EXTRACTION AT DOCUMENT LEVEL

We can distinguish between two undertakings in text mining:

- Labeling a document as belonging to a class, or clustering similar documents
- Extracting more detailed meaning from a document

The first goal requires a sizable collection of documents, or a *corpus*,[2] the ability to extract predictor variables from documents, and for the classification task, lots of prelabeled documents to train a model. The models that are used, though, are the standard statistical and machine learning predictive models that we have already dealt with for numerical and categorical data.

The second goal might involve a single document, and is much more ambitious. The computer must learn at least some version of the complex "algorithms" that make up human language comprehension: grammar, syntax, punctuation, etc. In other words, it must undertake the processing of a natural (i.e., noncomputer) language to *understand* documents in that language. Understanding the meaning of one document on its own is a far more formidable task than probabilistically assigning a class to a document based on rules derived from hundreds or thousands of similar documents.

For one thing, text comprehension requires maintenance and consideration of word order. "San Francisco beat Boston in last night's baseball game" is very different from "Boston beat San Francisco in last night's baseball game."

Even identical words in the same order can carry different meanings, depending on the cultural and social context: "Hitchcock shot The Birds in Bodega Bay," to an avid outdoors person indifferent to capitalization and unfamiliar with Alfred Hitchcock's films, might be about bird hunting. Ambiguity resolution is a major challenge in text comprehension—does "bot" mean "bought," or does it refer to robots?

Our focus will remain with the overall focus of the book and the easier goal—probabilistically assigning a class to a document, or clustering similar documents. The second goal—deriving understanding from a single document—is the subject of the field of natural language processing (NLP).

20.4 | PREPROCESSING THE TEXT

The simple example we presented had ordinary words separated by spaces, and a period to denote the end of the each sentence. A fairly simple algorithm could break the sentences up into the word matrix with a few rules about spaces and periods. It should be evident that the rules required to parse data from real-world sources will need to be more complex. It should also be evident that the preparation of data for text mining is a more involved undertaking than the preparation of numerical or categorical data for predictive models. For example, consider the modified example in Table 20.2, based on the following sentences:

---

[2]The term "corpus" is often used to refer to a large, fixed standard set of documents that can be used by text preprocessing algorithms, often to train algorithms for a specific type of text, or to compare the results of different algorithms. A specific text mining setting may rely on algorithms trained on a corpus specially suited to that task. One early general-purpose standard corpus was the Brown corpus of 500 English language documents of varying types (named Brown because it was compiled at Brown University in the early 1960s).

```
S1.  this is the first    sentence!!
S2.  this is a second Sentence :)
S3.  the third sentence, is here
S4.  forth of all sentences
```

This set of sentences has extra spaces, non-alpha characters, incorrect capitalization, and a misspelling of "fourth."

Tokenization

Our first simple dataset was composed entirely of words found in the dictionary. A real set of documents will have more variety—it will contain numbers, alphanumeric strings like date stamps or part numbers, web and e-mail addresses, abbreviations, slang, proper nouns, misspellings, and more.

TABLE 20.2 TERM-DOCUMENT MATRIX REPRESENTATION OF WORDS IN SENTENCES S1–S4 (EXAMPLE 2)

code for term frequency of second example

```
text = ['this is the first     sentence!!',
        'this is a second Sentence :)',
        'the third sentence, is here ',
        'forth of all sentences']

# Learn features based on text. Special characters are excluded in the analysis
count_vect = CountVectorizer()
counts = count_vect.fit_transform(text)

printTermDocumentMatrix(count_vect, counts)
```

Output

	S1	S2	S3	S4
all	0	0	0	1
first	1	0	0	0
forth	0	0	0	1
here	0	0	1	0
is	1	1	1	0
of	0	0	0	1
second	0	1	0	0
sentence	1	1	1	0
sentences	0	0	0	1
the	1	0	1	0
third	0	0	1	0
this	1	1	0	0

Tokenization is the process of taking a text and, in an automated fashion, dividing it into separate "tokens" or terms. A token (term) is the basic unit of analysis. A word separated by spaces is a token. 2+3 would need to be separated into three tokens, while 23 would remain as one token. Punctuation might also stand as its own token (e.g., the @ symbol). These tokens become the row headers in the data matrix. Each text mining software program will have its own list of delimiters (spaces, commas, colons, etc.) that it uses to divide up the text into tokens. By default, the tokenizer in `CountVectorizer` ignores numbers and punctuation marks as shown in Table 20.2. In Table 20.3, we modify the default tokenizer to consider punctuation marks. This captures the emoji and the emphasis of the first sentence.

For a sizeable corpus, tokenization will result in a huge number of variables—the English language has over a million words, let alone the non-word terms that will be

TABLE 20.3 TOKENIZATION OF S1–S4 EXAMPLE

code for term frequency of second example

```
text = ['this is the first      sentence!!',
        'this is a second Sentence :)',
        'the third sentence, is here ',
        'forth of all sentences']

# Learn features based on text. Include special characters that are part of a word
# in the analysis
count_vect = CountVectorizer(token_pattern='[a-zA-Z!:)]+')
counts = count_vect.fit_transform(text)

printTermDocumentMatrix(count_vect, counts)
```

Output

```
           S1  S2  S3  S4
:)          0   1   0   0
a           0   1   0   0
all         0   0   0   1
first       1   0   0   0
forth       0   0   0   1
here        0   0   1   0
is          1   1   1   0
of          0   0   0   1
second      0   1   0   0
sentence    0   1   1   0
sentence!!  1   0   0   0
sentences   0   0   0   1
the         1   0   1   0
third       0   0   1   0
this        1   1   0   0
```

encountered in typical documents. Anything that can be done in the preprocessing stage to reduce the number of terms will aid in the analysis. The initial focus is on eliminating terms that simply add bulk and noise.

Some of the terms that result from the initial parsing of the corpus might not be useful in further analyses and can be eliminated in the preprocessing stage. For example, in a legal discovery case, one corpus of documents might be e-mails, all of which have company information and some boilerplate as part of the signature. These terms might be added to a *stopword list* of terms that are to be automatically eliminated in the preprocessing stage.

Text Reduction

Most text-processing software (the `CountVectorizer` class in `scitkit-learn` included) come with a generic *stopword* list of frequently occurring terms to be removed. If you review `scikit-learn`'s stopword list during preprocessing stages, you will see that it contains a large number of terms to be removed (Table 20.4 shows the first 180 stopwords). You can provide your own list of stopwords using the `stop_words` keyword argument to `CountVectorizer`.

Additional techniques to reduce the volume of text ("vocabulary reduction") and to focus on the most meaningful text include:

- *Stemming*, a linguistic method that reduces different variants of words to a common core.
- Frequency filters can be used to eliminate either terms that occur in a great majority of documents or very rare terms. Frequency filters can also be used to limit the vocabulary to the *n* most frequent terms.
- Synonyms or synonymous phrases may be consolidated.
- Letter case (uppercase/lowercase) can be ignored.
- A variety of specific terms in a category can be replaced with the category name. This is called *normalization*. For example, different e-mail addresses or different numbers might all be replaced with "emailtoken" or "numbertoken."

Table 20.5 presents the text reduction step applied to the four sentences example, after tokenization. We can see the number of terms has been reduced to five.

Presence/Absence vs. Frequency

The bag-of-words approach can be implemented either in terms of *frequency* of terms, or *presence/absence* of terms. The latter might be appropriate in some circumstances—in a forensic accounting classification model, for example, the

TABLE 20.4 STOPWORDS IN SCIKIT-LEARN

```
from sklearn.feature_extraction.stop_words import ENGLISH_STOP_WORDS
stopWords = list(sorted(ENGLISH_STOP_WORDS))
ncolumns = 6; nrows= 30

print('First {} of {} stopwords'.format(ncolumns * nrows, len(stopWords)))
for i in range(0, len(stopWords[:(ncolumns * nrows)]), ncolumns):
    print(''.join(word.ljust(13) for word in stopWords[i:(i+ncolumns)]))
```

```
First 180 of 318 stopwords
a            about        above        across       after        afterwards
again        against      all          almost       alone        along
already      also         although     always       am           among
amongst      amoungst     amount       an           and          another
any          anyhow       anyone       anything     anyway       anywhere
are          around       as           at           back         be
became       because      become       becomes      becoming     been
before       beforehand   behind       being        below        beside
besides      between      beyond       bill         both         bottom
but          by           call         can          cannot       cant
co           con          could        couldnt      cry          de
describe     detail       do           done         down         due
during       each         eg           eight        either       eleven
else         elsewhere    empty        enough       etc          even
ever         every        everyone     everything   everywhere   except
few          fifteen      fifty        fill         find         fire
first        five         for          former       formerly     forty
found        four         from         front        full         further
get          give         go           had          has          hasnt
have         he           hence        her          here         hereafter
hereby       herein       hereupon     hers         herself      him
himself      his          how          however      hundred      i
ie           if           in           inc          indeed       interest
into         is           it           its          itself       keep
last         latter       latterly     least        less         ltd
made         many         may          me           meanwhile    might
mill         mine         more         moreover     most         mostly
move         much         must         my           myself       name
namely       neither      never        nevertheless next         nine
no           nobody       none         noone        nor          not
```

presence or absence of a particular vendor name might be a key predictor variable, without regard to how often it appears in a given document. *Frequency* can be important in other circumstances, however. For example, in processing support tickets, a single mention of "IP address" might be non-meaningful—all support tickets might involve a user's IP address as part of the submission. Repetition of the phrase multiple times, however, might provide useful information that IP address is part of the problem (e.g.,

TABLE 20.5 TEXT REDUCTION OF S1–S4 (AFTER TOKENIZATION)

code for text reduction using stemming

```
text = ['this is the first      sentence!! ',
        'this is a second Sentence :)',
        'the third sentence, is here ',
        'forth of all sentences']

# Create a custom tokenizer that will use NLTK for tokenizing and lemmatizing
# (removes interpunctuation and stop words)
class LemmaTokenizer(object):
    def __init__(self):
        self.stemmer = EnglishStemmer()
        self.stopWords = set(ENGLISH_STOP_WORDS)

    def __call__(self, doc):
        return [self.stemmer.stem(t) for t in word_tokenize(doc)
                if t.isalpha() and t not in self.stopWords]

# Learn features based on text
count_vect = CountVectorizer(tokenizer=LemmaTokenizer())
counts = count_vect.fit_transform(text)

printTermDocumentMatrix(count_vect, counts)
```

Output

```
        S1  S2  S3  S4
forth    0   0   0   1
second   0   1   0   0
sentenc  1   1   1   1
```

DNS resolution). *Note*: The `CountVectorizer` by default returns the frequency option. To implement the presence/absence option, you need to use the argument `binary=True` so that the vectorizer returns a binary matrix (i.e., convert all non-zero counts to 1's).

Term Frequency–Inverse Document Frequency (TF-IDF)

There are additional popular options that factor in both the frequency of a term in a document and the frequency of documents with that term. One such popular option, which measures the importance of a term to a document, is *Term Frequency–Inverse Document Frequency* (TF-IDF). For a given document d and term t, the term frequency (TF) is the number of times term t appears in document d:

$$\text{TF}(t, d) = \#\text{times term } t \text{ appears in document } d.$$

To account for terms that appear frequently in the domain of interest, we compute the *Inverse Document Frequency* (IDF) of term t, calculated over the entire corpus and defined as[3]

$$\text{IDF}(t) = 1 + \log\left(\frac{\text{total number of documents}}{\text{\# documents containing term } t}\right).$$

The addition of 1 makes sure that terms for which the logarithm is zero are not ignored in the analysis

TF-IDF(t, d) for a specific term–document pair is the product of TF(t, d) and IDF(t):

$$\text{TF-IDF}(t, d) = \text{TF}(t, d) \times \text{IDF}(t). \quad (20.1)$$

The TF-IDF matrix contains the value for each term-document combination. The above definition of TF-IDF is a common one, however, there are multiple ways to define and weight both TF and IDF, so there are a variety of possible definitions of TF-IDF. For example, Table 20.6 shows the TF-IDF matrix for the four-sentence example (after tokenization and text reduction). The function `TfidfTransformer` class uses the natural logarithm for the computation of IDF. For example, the TF-IDF value for the term "first" in document 1 is computed by

$$\text{TF-IDF(first, 1)} = 1 \times \left[1 + \log\left(\frac{4}{1}\right)\right] \approx 2.386.$$

The general idea of TF-IDF is that it identifies documents with frequent occurrences of rare terms. TF-IDF yields high values for documents with a relatively high frequency for terms that are relatively rare overall, and near-zero values for terms that are absent from a document, or present in most documents.

From Terms to Concepts: Latent Semantic Indexing

In Chapter 4, we showed how numerous numeric variables can be reduced to a small number of "principal components" that explain most of the variation in a set of variables. The principal components are linear combinations of the original (typically correlated) variables, and a subset of them serve as new variables to replace the numerous original variables.

---

[3]IDF(t) is actually just the fraction, without the logarithm, although using a logarithm is very common.

TABLE 20.6 TF-IDF MATRIX FOR S1–S4 EXAMPLE (AFTER TOKENIZATION AND TEXT REDUCTION)

tf-idf transformation of term-document matrix

```
text = ['this is the first     sentence!!',
        'this is a second Sentence :)',
        'the third sentence, is here ',
        'forth of all sentences']

# Apply CountVectorizer and TfidfTransformer sequentially
count_vect = CountVectorizer()
tfidfTransformer = TfidfTransformer(smooth_idf=False, norm=None)
counts = count_vect.fit_transform(text)
tfidf = tfidfTransformer.fit_transform(counts)

printTermDocumentMatrix(count_vect, tfidf)
```

Output

```
                S1        S2        S3        S4
all       0.000000  0.000000  0.000000  2.386294
first     2.386294  0.000000  0.000000  0.000000
forth     0.000000  0.000000  0.000000  2.386294
here      0.000000  0.000000  2.386294  0.000000
is        1.287682  1.287682  1.287682  0.000000
of        0.000000  0.000000  0.000000  2.386294
second    0.000000  2.386294  0.000000  0.000000
sentence  1.287682  1.287682  1.287682  0.000000
sentences 0.000000  0.000000  0.000000  2.386294
the       1.693147  0.000000  1.693147  0.000000
third     0.000000  0.000000  2.386294  0.000000
this      1.693147  1.693147  0.000000  0.000000
```

An analogous dimension reduction method—*latent semantic indexing* [or *latent semantic analysis*, (LSA)]—can be applied to text data. The mathematics of the algorithm are beyond the scope of this chapter,[4] but a good intuitive explanation comes from the user guide for XLMiner software[5]:

> For example, if we inspected our document collection, we might find that each time the term "alternator" appeared in an automobile document, the document also included the terms "battery" and "headlights." Or each time the term "brake" appeared in an automobile document, the terms "pads" and "squeaky" also appeared. However, there is no

[4]Generally, in PCA, the dimension is reduced by replacing the covariance matrix by a smaller one; in LSA, dimension is reduced by replacing the term-document matrix by a smaller one.

[5]Analytic Solver Platform, XLMiner Platform, Data Mining User Guide, 2014, Frontline Systems, p. 245.

detectable pattern regarding the use of the terms "alternator" and "brake" together. Documents including "alternator" might or might not include "brake" and documents including "brake" might or might not include "alternator." Our four terms, battery, headlights, pads, and squeaky describe two different automobile repair issues: failing brakes and a bad alternator.

So, in this case, latent semantic indexing would reduce the four terms to two concepts:

- brake failure
- alternator failure

We illustrate latent semantic indexing using Python in the example in Section 20.6.

Extracting Meaning

In the simple latent semantic indexing example, the concepts to which the terms map (failing brakes, bad alternator) are clear and understandable. In many cases, unfortunately, this will not be true—the concepts to which the terms map will not be obvious. In such cases, latent semantic indexing will greatly enhance the manageability of the text for purposes of building predictive models, and sharpen predictive power by reducing noise, but it will turn the model into a blackbox device for prediction, not so useful for understanding the roles that terms and concepts play. This is OK for our purposes—as noted earlier, we are focusing on text mining to classify or cluster new documents, not to extract meaning.

Example: Important Factors in Online Purchase Decisions (Text Analysis)

Here, we will use the dataset (*Ecom_Service_Factors.csv*) as an example, which carries details of important considerations in the column "Comments" for satisfactory online e-commerce services among the Indian audiences in metro cities. The data is a portion of a larger dataset captured during a primary survey of a marketing research study carried out in New Delhi. The dataset has five variables/columns ("Age," "Education," "Occupation," "Gender," and "Comments"). These details, in text form, were provided by the respondents in column "Comments" in an open-ended question asking important factors in online service satisfaction. The view of sample five responses out of 240 responses collected is shown in Table 20.7.

Next, we will do necessary imports of libraries, as already mentioned at the beginning of this chapter, for necessary vectorization, and generate TDF and TF-IDF values. We will read the file and extract the comments column to create our document source. In Table 20.8, "Comments" column is used as vector source to create corpus for the creation of the TDF in the process of text analysis.

TABLE 20.7 FIRST 5 RECORDS OF ECOM_SERVICE_FACTORS DATASET

	Age	Education	Occupation	Gender	Comments
0	30-40	Post Graduate	Professional/Service	Male	Product range, Ease of return, Quality, mod...
1	15-30	Graduate	Professional/Service	Male	Maximum Options, Security, Easy to choose,...
2	above 51	Graduate	Professional/Service	Female	Product Description, Reviews, Known Website...
3	40-50	Graduate	Professional/Service	Female	Customer review on site, Clear product descr...
4	30-40	Graduate	Professional/Service	Male	Choice and preference

TABLE 20.8 TERM DOCUMENT MATRIX REPRESENTATION OF WORDS

code for generating TDM

```
# Activate CountVectorizer
from sklearn.feature_extraction.text import CountVectorizer
# Count Vectorizer
vect = CountVectorizer()
vects = vect.fit_transform(ecs.Comments)
# Select the first five rows from the data set
td = pd.DataFrame(vects.todense()).iloc[:5]
td.columns = vect.get_feature_names()
term_document_matrix = td.T
term_document_matrix.columns = ['Doc '+str(i) for i in range(1, 6)]
term_document_matrix['total_count'] = term_document_matrix.sum(axis=1)
# Top 25 words
term_document_matrix = term_document_matrix.sort_values (by ='total_count',
    ascending=False)[:25]
# Print the first 10 rows
print(term_document_matrix.head(10))
```

Output

```
             Doc 1  Doc 2  Doc 3  Doc 4  Doc 5  total_count
product          1      0      1      1      0            3
review           0      0      0      2      0            2
of               2      0      0      0      0            2
description      0      0      1      1      0            2
return           1      0      1      0      0            2
payments         1      0      0      0      0            1
reviews          0      0      1      0      0            1
discounts        0      1      0      0      0            1
options          0      1      0      0      0            1
range            1      0      0      0      0            1
```

We can also plot the term-document matrix with the help of the plot function. We see in Figure 20.1, the term "Product" has the highest frequency of 3 followed by the terms "Review," "Description," and "Returns."

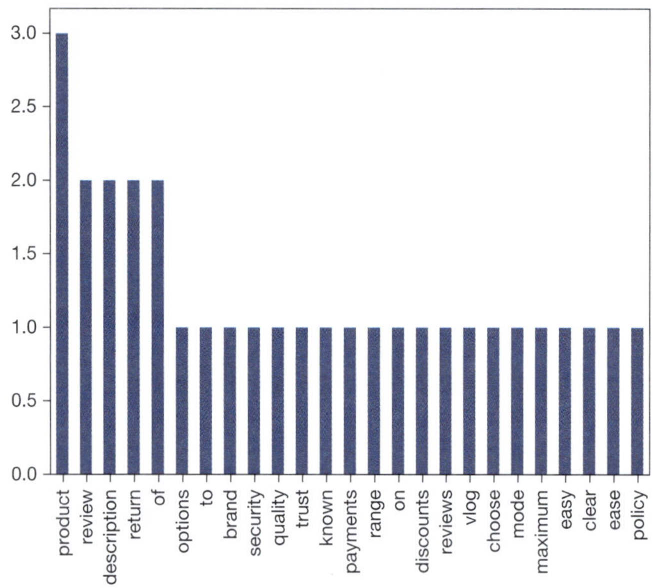

FIGURE 20.1 **TERM FREQUENCY PLOT**

code for generating Term Frequency Plot

```
term_document_matrix['total_count'].plot.bar()
```

Now let us generate TF-IDF, which is a numerical statistic that is intended to reflect how important a word is to a document.

We can see this from the order of the TF-IDF values and corresponding terms in the Table 20.9, "payments" term has the highest value, indicating its highest relevance. However, we are not using cleaned data, therefore, all other terms are appearing in the list. In a real situation, we need to clean the corpus or document vector before we generate these values.

20.5 | IMPLEMENTING DATA MINING METHODS

After the text has gone through the preprocessing stage, it is then in a numeric matrix format and you can apply the various data mining methods discussed earlier in this book. Clustering methods can be used to identify clusters of documents—for example, large numbers of medical reports can be mined to identify clusters of symptoms. Prediction methods can be used with tech support tickets to predict how long it will

TABLE 20.9 GENERATING TF-IDF VALUES

code for generating TF-IDF

```
from sklearn.feature_extraction.text import TfidfVectorizer
ecs=pd.read_csv('Ecom_Service_Factors.csv')
corpus=ecs['Comments']
tfidf = TfidfVectorizer()
transformed = tfidf.fit_transform(corpus)
df = pd.DataFrame(transformed[0].T.todense(),
    index=tfidf.get_feature_names(), columns=["TF-IDF"])
df = df.sort_values('TF-IDF', ascending=False)
df.head(10)
```

Output

```
           TF-IDF
  payments 0.474346
        of 0.435088
      mode 0.417576
     range 0.417576
    return 0.274314
      ease 0.270828
   product 0.233192
   quality 0.184336
       200 0.000000
     price 0.000000
```

take to resolve an issue. Perhaps the most popular application of text mining is for classification—also termed *labeling*—of documents.

20.6 | EXAMPLE: ONLINE DISCUSSIONS ON AUTOS AND ELECTRONICS

This example[6] illustrates a classification task—to classify Internet discussion posts as either auto-related or electronics-related. One post looks like this:

> From: smith@logos.asd.sgi.com (Tom Smith) Subject: Ford Explorer 4WD - do I need performance axle?
>
> We're considering getting a Ford Explorer XLT with 4WD and we have the following questions (All we would do is go skiing - no off-roading):

[6]The dataset is taken from www.cs.cmu.edu/afs/cs/project/theo-20/www/data/news20.html, with minor modifications.

1. With 4WD, do we need the "performance axle" - (limited slip axle). Its purpose is to allow the tires to act independently when the tires are on different terrain.
2. Do we need the all-terrain tires (P235/75X15) or will the all-season (P225/70X15) be good enough for us at Lake Tahoe?

Thanks,

Tom

–

==

Tom Smith Silicon Graphics smith@asd.sgi.com 2011 N. Shoreline Rd. MS 8U-815 415-962-0494 (fax) Mountain View, CA 94043

==

The posts are taken from Internet groups devoted to autos and electronics, so are pre-labeled. This one, clearly, is auto-related. A related organizational scenario might involve messages received by a medical office that must be classified as medical or non-medical (the messages in such a real scenario would probably have to be labeled by humans as part of the preprocessing).

The posts are in the form a zipped file that contains two folders: *auto posts* and *electronics posts*, each contains a set of 1000 posts organized in small files. In the following, we describe the main steps from preprocessing to building a classification model on the data. Table 20.10 provides Python code for the text processing step for this example. We describe each step separately next.

Importing and Labeling the Records

The `ZipFile` module in the standard library of Python is used to read the individual documents in the zipped datafile. We additionally create a label array that corresponds to the order of the documents—we will use "1" for autos and "0" for electronics. The assignment is based on the file path (see Step 1 in Table 20.10).

Text Preprocessing in Python

The text preprocessing step does *tokenization* into words followed by stemming and removal of stopwords. These two operations are shown in Step 2 in Table 20.10.

Producing a Concept Matrix

The preprocessing step will produce a "clean" corpus and term-document matrix that can be used to compute the TF-IDF term-document matrix described earlier. The TF-IDF matrix incorporates both the frequency of a term and the frequency with which

TABLE 20.10 IMPORTING AND LABELING THE RECORDS, PREPROCESSING TEXT, AND PRODUCING CONCEPT MATRIX

code for importing and labeling records, preprocessing text, and producing concept matrix

```
# Step 1: import and label records
corpus = []
label = []
with ZipFile('AutoAndElectronics.zip') as rawData:
    for info in rawData.infolist():
        if info.is_dir():
            continue
        label.append(1 if 'rec.autos' in info.filename else 0)
        corpus.append(rawData.read(info))

# Step 2: preprocessing (tokenization, stemming, and stopwords)
class LemmaTokenizer(object):
    def __init__(self):
        self.stemmer = EnglishStemmer()
        self.stopWords = set(ENGLISH_STOP_WORDS)
    def __call__(self, doc):
        return [self.stemmer.stem(t) for t in word_tokenize(doc)
                if t.isalpha() and t not in self.stopWords]

preprocessor = CountVectorizer(tokenizer=LemmaTokenizer(), encoding='latin1')
preprocessedText = preprocessor.fit_transform(corpus)

# Step 3: TF-IDF and latent semantic analysis
tfidfTransformer = TfidfTransformer()
tfidf = tfidfTransformer.fit_transform(preprocessedText)

# Extract 20 concepts using LSA ()
svd = TruncatedSVD(20)
normalizer = Normalizer(copy=False)
lsa = make_pipeline(svd, normalizer)

lsa_tfidf = lsa.fit_transform(tfidf)
```

documents containing that term appear in the overall corpus. We use here the default settings for the `TfidfTransformer`.

The resulting matrix is probably too large to efficiently analyze in a predictive model (specifically, the number of predictors in the example is 13,466, so we use latent semantic indexing to extract a reduced space, termed "concepts." For manageability, we will limit the number of concepts to 20. In `scikit-learn`, latent semantic indexing can be implemented by `TruncatedSVD` followed by normalization using `Normalizer`. Table 20.10 shows the Python code for applying these two operations—creating a TF-IDF matrix and latent semantic indexing—to the example.

Finally, we can use this reduced set of concepts to facilitate the building of a predictive model. We will not attempt to interpret the concepts for meaning.

Fitting a Predictive Model

At this point, we have transformed the original text data into a familiar form needed for predictive modeling—a single target variable (1 = autos, 0 = electronics), and 20 predictor variables (the concepts).

We can now partition the data (60% training, 40% validation), and try applying several classification models. Table 20.11 shows the performance of a logistic regression, with "class" as the outcome variable and the 20 concept variables as the predictors.

The confusion matrix (Table 20.11) shows reasonably high accuracy in separating the two classes of documents—an accuracy of 0.96. The decile-wise lift chart (Figure 20.2) confirms the high separability of the classes and the usefulness of this model for a ranking goal. For a two class dataset with a nearly 50/50 split between the classes, the maximum lift per decile is 2, and the lift shown here is just under 2 for the first 50% of the cases, and close to 0 for the last 40%.

Next, we would also try other models to see how they compare; this is left as an exercise.

TABLE 20.11 FITTING A PREDICTIVE MODEL TO THE AUTOS AND ELECTRONICS DISCUSSION DATA

code for fitting and evaluating a logistic regression predictive model

```
# split dataset into 60% training and 40% test set
Xtrain, Xtest, ytrain, ytest = train_test_split(lsa_tfidf, label, test_size=0.4,
                                                random_state=42)

# run logistic regression model on training
logit_reg = LogisticRegression(solver='lbfgs')
logit_reg.fit(Xtrain, ytrain)

# print confusion matrix and accuracty
classificationSummary(ytest, logit_reg.predict(Xtest))
```

Output

```
Confusion Matrix (Accuracy 0.9563)

       Prediction
Actual   0   1
     0 389   8
     1  27 376
```

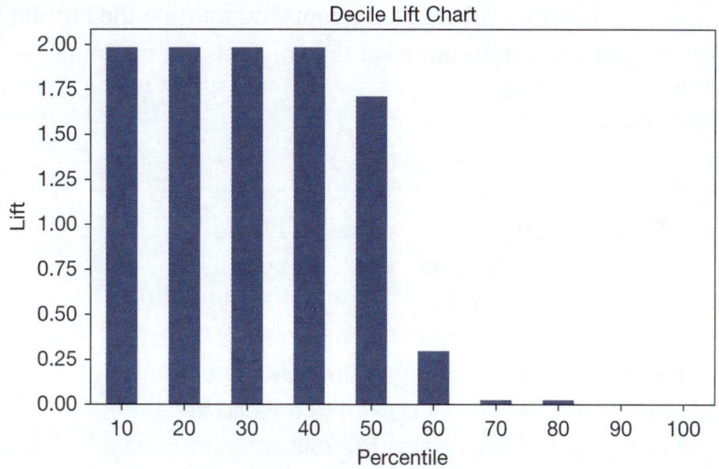

FIGURE 20.2 DECILE-WISE LIFT CHART FOR AUTOS-ELECTRONICS DOCUMENT CLASSIFICATION

Prediction

The most prevalent application of text mining is classification ("labeling"), but it can also be used for prediction of numerical values. For example, maintenance or support tickets could be used to predict length or cost of repair. The only step that would be different in the above process is the label that is applied after the preprocessing, which would be a numeric value rather than a class.

20.7 | SUMMARY

In this chapter, we drew a distinction between text processing for the purpose of extracting meaning from a single document (natural language processing—NLP) and classifying or labeling numerous documents in probabilistic fashion (text mining). We concentrated on the latter, and examined the preprocessing steps that need to occur before text can be mined. Those steps are more varied and involved than those involved in preparing numerical data. The ultimate goal is to produce a matrix in which rows are terms and columns are documents. The nature of language is such that the number of terms is excessive for effective model-building, so the preprocessing steps include vocabulary reduction. A final major reduction takes place if we use, instead of the terms, a limited set of concepts that represents most of the variation in the documents, in the same way that principal components capture most of the variation in numerical data. Finally, we end up with a quantitative matrix in which the cells represent the frequency or presence of terms and the columns represent documents. To this we append document labels (classes), and then we are ready to use this matrix for classifying documents using classification methods.

PROBLEMS

20.1 Tokenization. Consider the following text version of a post to an online learning forum in a statistics course:

```
Thanks John!<br /><br /><font size="3">
&quot;Illustrations and demos will be
provided for students to work through on
their own&quot;</font>.
Do we need that to finish project? If yes,
where to find the illustration and demos?
Thanks for your help.\<img title="smile"
alt="smile" src="\url{http://lms.statistics.
com/pix/smartpix.php/statistics_com_1/s/smil
ey.gif}" \><br /> <br />
```

a. Identify 10 non-word tokens in the passage.

b. Suppose this passage constitutes a document to be classified, but you are not certain of the business goal of the classification task. Identify material (at least 20% of the terms) that, in your judgment, could be discarded fairly safely without knowing that goal.

c. Suppose the classification task is to predict whether this post requires the attention of the instructor, or whether a teaching assistant might suffice. Identify the 20% of the terms that you think might be most helpful in that task.

d. What aspect of the passage is most problematic from the standpoint of simply using a bag-of-words approach, as opposed to an approach in which meaning is extracted?

20.2 Classifying Internet Discussion Posts. In this problem, you will use the data and scenario described in this chapter's example, in which the task is to develop a model to classify documents as either auto-related or electronics-related.

a. Load the zipped file into Python and create a label vector.

b. Following the example in this chapter, preprocess the documents. Explain what would be different if you did not perform the "stemming" step.

c. Use the LSA to create 10 concepts. Explain what is different about the concept matrix, as opposed to the TF-IDF matrix.

d. Using this matrix, fit a predictive model (different from the model presented in the chapter illustration) to classify documents as autos or electronics. Compare its performance to that of the model presented in the chapter illustration.

20.3 Classifying Classified Ads Submitted Online. Consider the case of a website that caters to the needs of a specific farming community, and carries classified ads intended for that community. Anyone, including robots, can post an ad via a web interface, and the site owners have problems with ads that are fraudulent, spam, or simply not relevant to the community. They have provided a file with 4143 ads, each ad in a row, and each ad labeled as either −1 (not relevant) or 1 (relevant). The goal is to develop a predictive model that can classify ads automatically.

- Open the file *farm-ads.csv*, and briefly review some of the relevant and non-relevant ads to get a flavor for their contents.
- Following the example in the chapter, preprocess the data in Python, and create a term-document matrix, and a concept matrix. Limit the number of concepts to 20.

a. Examine the term-document matrix.

i. Is it sparse or dense?

ii. Find two non-zero entries and briefly interpret their meaning, in words (you do not need to derive their calculation).

b. Briefly explain the difference between the term-document matrix and the concept-document matrix. Relate the latter to what you learned in the principal components chapter (Chapter 4).

c. Using logistic regression, partition the data (60% training, 40% validation), and develop a model to classify the documents as "relevant" or "non-relevant." Comment on its efficacy.

d. Why use the concept-document matrix, and not the term-document matrix, to provide the predictor variables?

20.4 Clustering Auto Posts. In this problem, you will use the data and scenario described in this chapter's example. The task is to cluster the auto posts.

a. Following the example in this chapter, preprocess the documents, except do not create a label vector.

b. Use the LSA to create 10 concepts.

c. Before doing the clustering, state how many natural clusters you expect to find.

d. Perform hierarchical clustering and inspect the dendrogram.

i. From the dendrogram, how many natural clusters appear?

ii. Examining the dendrogram as it branches beyond the number of main clusters, select a sub-cluster and assess its characteristics.

e. Perform *k*-means clustering for two clusters and report how distant and separated they are (using between-cluster distance and within cluster dispersion).

PART

VIII

Cases

CHAPTER 21

Cases

21.1 | CHARLES BOOK CLUB[1]

CharlesBookClub.csv is the dataset for this case study.

The Book Industry

Approximately 50,000 new titles, including new editions, are published each year in the United States, giving rise to a $25 billion industry in 2001. In terms of percentage of sales, this industry may be segmented as follows:

16%	Textbooks
16%	Trade books sold in bookstores
21%	Technical, scientific, and professional books
10%	Book clubs and other mail-order books
17%	Mass-market paperbound books
20%	All other books

Book retailing in the United States in the 1970s was characterized by the growth of bookstore chains located in shopping malls. The 1980s saw increased purchases in bookstores stimulated through the widespread practice of discounting. By the 1990s, the superstore concept of book retailing gained acceptance and contributed to double-digit growth of the book industry. Conveniently situated near large shopping centers, superstores maintain large inventories of 30,000–80,000 titles and employ well-informed sales personnel.

[1]The Charles Book Club case was derived, with the assistance of Ms. Vinni Bhandari, from *The Bookbinders Club, a Case Study in Database Marketing*, prepared by Nissan Levin and Jacob Zahavi, Tel Aviv University; used with permission.

Book retailing changed fundamentally with the arrival of Amazon, which started out as an online bookseller and, as of 2015, was the world's largest online retailer of any kind. Amazon's margins were small and the convenience factor high, putting intense competitive pressure on all other book retailers. Borders, one of the two major superstore chains, discontinued operations in 2011.

Subscription-based book clubs offer an alternative model that has persisted, though it too has suffered from the dominance of Amazon.

Historically, book clubs offered their readers different types of membership programs. Two common membership programs are the continuity and negative option programs, which are both extended contractual relationships between the club and its members. Under a *continuity program*, a reader signs up by accepting an offer of several books for just a few dollars (plus shipping and handling) and an agreement to receive a shipment of one or two books each month thereafter at more-standard pricing. The continuity program is most common in the children's book market, where parents are willing to delegate the rights to the book club to make a selection, and much of the club's prestige depends on the quality of its selections.

In a *negative option program*, readers get to select how many and which additional books they would like to receive. However, the club's selection of the month is delivered to them automatically unless they specifically mark "no" on their order form by a deadline date. Negative option programs sometimes result in customer dissatisfaction and always give rise to significant mailing and processing costs.

In an attempt to combat these trends, some book clubs have begun to offer books on a *positive option basis*, but only to specific segments of their customer base that are likely to be receptive to specific offers. Rather than expanding the volume and coverage of mailings, some book clubs are beginning to use database-marketing techniques to target customers more accurately. Information contained in their databases is used to identify who is most likely to be interested in a specific offer. This information enables clubs to design special programs carefully tailored to meet their customer segments' varying needs.

Database Marketing at Charles

The Club The Charles Book Club (CBC) was established in December 1986 on the premise that a book club could differentiate itself through a deep understanding of its customer base and by delivering uniquely tailored offerings. CBC focused on selling specialty books by direct marketing through a variety of channels, including media advertising (TV, magazines, and newspapers) and mailing. CBC is strictly a distributor and does not publish any of the books that it sells. In line with its commitment to understanding its customer base, CBC built and maintained a detailed database about its club members. Upon enrollment, readers were required to fill out an insert and mail it to CBC. Through this process, CBC created an active database of 500,000 readers; most were acquired through advertising in specialty magazines.

The Problem CBC sent mailings to its club members each month containing the latest offerings. On the surface, CBC appeared very successful: mailing volume was increasing, book selection was diversifying and growing, and their customer database was increasing. However, their bottom-line profits were falling. The decreasing profits led CBC to revisit their original plan of using database marketing to improve mailing yields and to stay profitable.

A Possible Solution CBC embraced the idea of deriving intelligence from their data to allow them to know their customers better and enable multiple targeted campaigns where each target audience would receive appropriate mailings. CBC's management decided to focus its efforts on the most profitable customers and prospects, and to design targeted marketing strategies to best reach them. The two processes they had in place were:

1. Customer acquisition:
   - **a.** New members would be acquired by advertising in specialty magazines, newspapers, and on TV.
   - **b.** Direct mailing and telemarketing would contact existing club members.
   - **c.** Every new book would be offered to club members before general advertising.
2. Data collection:
   - **a.** All customer responses would be recorded and maintained in the database.
   - **b.** Any information not being collected that is critical would be requested from the customer.

For each new title, they decided to use a two-step approach:

1. Conduct a market test involving a random sample of 4000 customers from the database to enable analysis of customer responses. The analysis would create and calibrate response models for the current book offering.
2. Based on the response models, compute a score for each customer in the database. Use this score and a cutoff value to extract a target customer list for direct-mail promotion.

Targeting promotions was considered to be of prime importance. Other opportunities to create successful marketing campaigns based on customer behavior data (returns, inactivity, complaints, compliments, etc.) would be addressed by CBC at a later stage.

Art History of Florence A new title, *The Art History of Florence*, is ready for release. CBC sent a test mailing to a random sample of 4000 customers from its customer base. The customer responses have been collated with past purchase data. The dataset was randomly partitioned into three parts: *Training Data* (1800 customers): initial data to be used to fit models, *Validation Data* (1400 customers): holdout data used to compare the performance of different models, and *Test Data* (800 customers): data to be used only after a final model has been selected to estimate the probable performance of the model when it is deployed. Each row (or case) in the spreadsheet (other than the header) corresponds to one market test customer. Each column is a variable, with the header row giving the name of the variable. The variable names and descriptions are given in Table 21.1.

TABLE 21.1 LIST OF VARIABLES IN CHARLES BOOK CLUB DATASET

Variable name	Description
Seq#	Sequence number in the partition
ID#	Identification number in the full (unpartitioned) market test dataset
Gender	0 = Male, 1 = Female
M	Monetary—Total money spent on books
R	Recency—Months since last purchase
F	Frequency—Total number of purchases
FirstPurch	Months since first purchase
ChildBks	Number of purchases from the category child books
YouthBks	Number of purchases from the category youth books
CookBks	Number of purchases from the category cookbooks
DoItYBks	Number of purchases from the category do-it-yourself books
RefBks	Number of purchases from the category reference books (atlases, encyclopedias, dictionaries)
ArtBks	Number of purchases from the category art books
GeoBks	Number of purchases from the category geography books
ItalCook	Number of purchases of book title *Secrets of Italian Cooking*
ItalAtlas	Number of purchases of book title *Historical Atlas of Italy*
ItalArt	Number of purchases of book title *Italian Art*
Florence	= 1 if *The Art History of Florence* was bought; = 0 if not
Related Purchase	Number of related books purchased

(*Source:* Reproduced with permission of Jacob Zahavi)

Data Mining Techniques

Various data mining techniques can be used to mine the data collected from the market test. No one technique is universally better than another. The particular context and the particular characteristics of the data are the major factors in determining which techniques perform better in an application. For this assignment, we focus on two fundamental techniques: *k*-nearest neighbors (*k*-NN) and logistic regression. We compare them with each other as well as with a standard industry practice known as *RFM (recency, frequency, monetary) segmentation*.

RFM Segmentation The segmentation process in database marketing aims to partition customers in a list of prospects into homogeneous groups (segments) that are similar with respect to buying behavior. The homogeneity criterion we need for segmentation is the propensity to purchase the offering. However, since we cannot measure this attribute, we use variables that are plausible indicators of this propensity.

In the direct marketing business, the most commonly used variables are the *RFM variables*:

R = *recency*, time since last purchase

F = *frequency*, number of previous purchases from the company over a period

M = *monetary*, amount of money spent on the company's products over a period

The assumption is that the more recent the last purchase, the more products bought from the company in the past, and the more money spent in the past buying the company's products, the more likely the customer is to purchase the product offered.

The 1800 observations in the dataset were divided into recency, frequency, and monetary categories as follows:

Recency:

0–2 months (Rcode = 1)
3–6 months (Rcode = 2)
7–12 months (Rcode = 3)
13 months and up (Rcode = 4)

Frequency:

1 book (Fcode = l)
2 books (Fcode = 2)
3 books and up (Fcode = 3)

Monetary:

\$0–\$25 (Mcode = 1)
\$26–\$50 (Mcode = 2)
\$51–\$100 (Mcode = 3)
\$101–\$200 (Mcode = 4)
\$201 and up (Mcode = 5)

Assignment

Partition the data into training (60%) and validation (40%). Use seed = 1.

1. What is the response rate for the training data customers taken as a whole? What is the response rate for each of the $4 \times 5 \times 3 = 60$ combinations of RFM categories? Which combinations have response rates in the training data that are above the overall response in the training data?
2. Suppose that we decide to send promotional mail only to the "above-average" RFM combinations identified in part 1. Compute the response rate in the validation data using these combinations.
3. Rework parts 1 and 2 with three segments:

   Segment 1: RFM combinations that have response rates that exceed twice the overall response rate

   Segment 2: RFM combinations that exceed the overall response rate but do not exceed twice that rate

   Segment 3: the remaining RFM combinations

   Draw the lift curve (consisting of three points for these three segments) showing the number of customers in the validation dataset on the x-axis and cumulative number of buyers in the validation dataset on the y-axis.

***k*-Nearest Neighbors** The *k*-NN technique can be used to create segments based on product proximity to similar products of the products offered as well as the propensity to purchase (as measured by the RFM variables). For *The Art History of Florence*, a possible segmentation by product proximity could be created using the following variables:

R: recency—months since last purchase

F: frequency—total number of past purchases

M: monetary—total money (in dollars) spent on books

FirstPurch: months since first purchase

RelatedPurch: total number of past purchases of related books (i.e., sum of purchases from the art and geography categories and of titles *Secrets of Italian Cooking*, *Historical Atlas of Italy*, and *Italian Art*)

4. Use the *k*-NN approach to classify cases with $k = 1, 2, ..., 11$, using Florence as the outcome variable. Based on the validation set, find the best *k*. Remember to

normalize all five variables. Create a lift curve for the best *k* model, and report the expected lift for an equal number of customers from the validation dataset.

5. The *k*-NN prediction algorithm gives a numerical value, which is a weighted average of the values of the Florence variable for the *k*-NN with weights that are inversely proportional to distance. Using the best *k* that you calculated above with *k*-NN classification, now run a model with *k*-NN prediction and compute a lift curve for the validation data. Use all 5 predictors and normalized data. What is the range within which a prediction will fall? How does this result compare to the output you get with the *k*-NN classification?

Logistic Regression The logistic regression model offers a powerful method for modeling response because it yields well-defined purchase probabilities. The model is especially attractive in consumer-choice settings because it can be derived from the random utility theory of consumer behavior.

Use the training set data of 1800 records to construct three logistic regression models with Florence as the outcome variable and each of the following sets of predictors:

- The full set of 15 predictors in the dataset
- A subset of predictors that you judge to be the best
- Only the *R*, *F*, and *M* variables

6. Create a cumulative gains chart summarizing the results from the three logistic regression models created above, along with the expected cumulative gains for a random selection of an equal number of customers from the validation dataset.
7. If the cutoff criterion for a campaign is a 30% likelihood of a purchase, find the customers in the validation data that would be targeted and count the number of buyers in this set.

21.2 | GERMAN CREDIT

GermanCredit.csv is the dataset for this case study.

Background

Money-lending has been around since the advent of money; it is perhaps the world's second-oldest profession. The systematic evaluation of credit risk, though, is a relatively recent arrival, and lending was largely based on reputation and very incomplete data. Thomas Jefferson, the third President of the United States, was in debt throughout his life and unreliable in his debt payments, yet people continued to lend him money.

It wasn't until the beginning of the 20th century that the Retail Credit Company was founded to share information about credit. That company is now Equifax, one of the big three credit scoring agencies (the other two are Transunion and Experion).

Individual and local human judgment are now largely irrelevant to the credit reporting process. Credit agencies and other big financial institutions extending credit at the retail level collect huge amounts of data to predict whether defaults or other adverse events will occur, based on numerous customer and transaction information.

Data

This case deals with an early stage of the historical transition to predictive modeling, in which humans were employed to label records as either good or poor credit. The German Credit dataset[2] has 30 variables and 1000 records, each record being a prior applicant for credit. Each applicant was rated as "good credit" (700 cases) or "bad credit" (300 cases). Table 21.2 shows the values of these variables for the first four records. All the variables are explained in Table 21.3. New applicants for credit can also be evaluated on these 30 predictor variables and classified as a good or a bad credit risk based on the predictor values.

TABLE 21.2 FIRST FOUR RECORDS FROM GERMAN CREDIT DATASET

OBS#	CHK_ACCT	DURATION	HISTORY	NEW_CAR	USED_CAR	FURNITURE	RADIO/TV	EDUCATION	RETRAINING	AMOUNT	SAV_ACCT	EMPLOYMENT	INSTALL_RATE	MALE_DIV	MALE_SINGLE	MALE_MAR_WID	CO-APPLICANT	GUARANTOR
1	0	6	4	0	0	0	1	0	0	1169	4	4	4	0	1	0	0	0
2	1	48	2	0	0	0	1	0	0	5951	0	2	2	0	0	0	0	0
3	3	12	4	0	0	0	0	1	0	2096	0	3	2	0	1	0	0	0
4	0	42	2	0	0	1	0	0	0	7882	0	3	2	0	1	0	0	1

PRESENT_RESIDENT	REAL_ESTATE	PROP_UNKN_NONE	AGE	OTHER_INSTALL	RENT	OWN_RES	NUM_CREDITS	JOB	NUM_DEPENDENTS	TELEPHONE	FOREIGN	RESPONSE
4	1	0	67	0	0	1	2	2	1	1	0	1
2	1	0	22	0	0	1	1	2	1	0	0	0
3	1	0	49	0	0	1	1	1	2	0	0	1
4	0	0	45	0	0	0	1	2	2	0	0	1

(Data adapted from German Credit)

[2]This dataset is available from ftp.ics.uci.edu/pub/machine-learning-databases/statlog.

TABLE 21.3 VARIABLES FOR THE GERMAN CREDIT DATASET

Variable number	Variable name	Description	Variable type	Code description
1	OBS#	Observation numbers	Categorical	Sequence number in dataset
2	CHK_ACCT	Checking account status	Categorical	0: <0 DM 1: 0–200 DM 2 : >200 DM 3: No checking account
3	DURATION	Duration of credit in months	Numerical	
4	HISTORY	Credit history	Categorical	0: No credits taken 1: All credits at this bank paid back duly 2: Existing credits paid back duly until now 3: Delay in paying off in the past 4: Critical account
5	NEW_CAR	Purpose of credit	Binary	Car (new), 0: no, 1: yes
6	USED_CAR	Purpose of credit	Binary	Car (used), 0: no, 1: yes
7	FURNITURE	Purpose of credit	Binary	Furniture/equipment, 0: no, 1: yes
8	RADIO/TV	Purpose of credit	Binary	Radio/television, 0: no, 1: yes
9	EDUCATION	Purpose of credit	Binary	Education, 0: no, 1: yes
10	RETRAINING	Purpose of credit	Binary	Retraining, 0: no, 1: yes
11	AMOUNT	Credit amount	Numerical	
12	SAV_ACCT	Average balance in savings account	Categorical	0: <100 DM 1: 101–500 DM 2: 501–1000 DM 3: >1000 DM 4: Unknown/no savings account
13	EMPLOYMENT	Present employment since	Categorical	0: Unemployed 1: <1 year 2: 1–3 years 3: 4–6 years 4: ≥7 years
14	INSTALL_RATE	Installment rate as % of disposable income	Numerical	
15	MALE_DIV	Applicant is male and divorced	Binary	0: no, 1: yes

(*Continued*)

TABLE 21.3 VARIABLES FOR THE GERMAN CREDIT DATASET (*Continued*)

Variable number	Variable name	Description	Variable type	Code description
16	MALE_SINGLE	Applicant is male and single	Binary	0: No, 1: Yes
17	MALE_MAR_WID	Applicant is male and married or a widower	Binary	0: No, 1: Yes
18	CO-APPLICANT	Application has a coapplicant	Binary	0: No, 1: Yes
19	GUARANTOR	Applicant has a guarantor	Binary	0: No, 1: Yes
20	PRESENT_RESIDENT	Present resident since (years)	Categorical	0: ≤1 year 1: 1–2 years 2: 2–3 years 3: ≥3 years
21	REAL_ESTATE	Applicant owns real estate	Binary	0: No, 1: Yes
22	PROP_UNKN_NONE	Applicant owns no property (or unknown)	Binary	0: No, 1: Yes
23	AGE	Age in years	Numerical	
24	OTHER_INSTALL	Applicant has other installment plan credit	Binary	0: No, 1: Yes
25	RENT	Applicant rents	Binary	0: No, 1: Yes
26	OWN_RES	Applicant owns residence	Binary	0: No, 1: Yes
27	NUM_CREDITS	Number of existing credits at this bank	Numerical	
28	JOB	Nature of job	Categorical	0: Unemployed/ unskilled—non-resident 1: Unskilled—resident 2: Skilled employee/ official 3: Management/ self-employed/highly qualified employee/ officer
29	NUM_DEPENDENTS	Number of people for whom liable to provide maintenance	Numerical	
30	TELEPHONE	Applicant has phone in his or her name	Binary	0: No, 1: Yes
31	FOREIGN	Foreign worker	Binary	0: No, 1: Yes
32	RESPONSE	Credit rating is good	Binary	0: No, 1: Yes

The original dataset had a number of categorical variables, some of which were transformed into a series of binary variables and some ordered categorical variables were left as is, to be treated as numerical. (Data adapted from German Credit)

The consequences of misclassification have been assessed as follows: The costs of a false positive (incorrectly saying that an applicant is a good credit risk) outweigh the benefits of a true positive (correctly saying that an applicant is a good credit risk) by a factor of 5. This is summarized in Table 21.4. The opportunity cost table was derived from the average net profit per loan as shown in Table 21.5. Because decision makers are used to thinking of their decision in terms of net profits, we use these tables in assessing the performance of the various models.

TABLE 21.4 OPPORTUNITY COST TABLE (DEUTSCHE MARKS)

	Predicted (decision)	
Actual	**Good (accept)**	**Bad (reject)**
Good	0	100
Bad	500	0

(Data adapted from Deutsche Marks)

TABLE 21.5 AVERAGE NET PROFIT (DEUTSCHE MARKS)

	Predicted (decision)	
Actual	**Good (accept)**	**Bad (reject)**
Good	100	0
Bad	−500	0

(Data adapted from Deutsche Marks)

Assignment

1. Review the predictor variables and guess what their role in a credit decision might be. Are there any surprises in the data?
2. Divide the data into training and validation partitions, and develop classification models using the following data mining techniques: logistic regression, classification trees, and neural networks.
3. Choose one model from each technique and report the confusion matrix and the cost/gain matrix for the validation data. Which technique has the highest net profit?
4. Let us try and improve our performance. Rather than accept the default classification of all applicants' credit status, use the estimated probabilities (propensities) from the logistic regression (where *success* means 1) as a basis for selecting the best credit risks first, followed by poorer-risk applicants. Create a vector containing the net profit for each record in the validation set. Use this vector to create a cumulative gains chart for the validation set that incorporates the net profit.

a. How far into the validation data should you go to get maximum net profit? (Often, this is specified as a percentile or rounded to deciles.)

b. If this logistic regression model is used to score to future applicants, what "probability of success" cutoff should be used in extending credit?

21.3 | TAYKO SOFTWARE CATALOGER[3]

Tayko.csv is the dataset for this case study.

Background

Tayko is a software catalog firm that sells games and educational software. It started out as a software manufacturer and later added third-party titles to its offerings. It has recently put together a revised collection of items in a new catalog, which it is preparing to roll out in a mailing.

In addition to its own software titles, Tayko's customer list is a key asset. In an attempt to expand its customer base, it has recently joined a consortium of catalog firms that specialize in computer and software products. The consortium affords members the opportunity to mail catalogs to names drawn from a pooled list of customers. Members supply their own customer lists to the pool, and can "withdraw" an equivalent number of names each quarter. Members are allowed to do predictive modeling on the records in the pool so they can do a better job of selecting names from the pool.

The Mailing Experiment

Tayko has supplied its customer list of 200,000 names to the pool, which totals over 5,000,000 names, so it is now entitled to draw 200,000 names for a mailing. Tayko would like to select the names that have the best chance of performing well, so it conducts a test—it draws 20,000 names from the pool and does a test mailing of the new catalog.

This mailing yielded 1065 purchasers, a response rate of 0.053. To optimize the performance of the data mining techniques, it was decided to work with a stratified sample that contained equal numbers of purchasers and nonpurchasers. For ease of presentation, the dataset for this case includes just 1000 purchasers and 1000 nonpurchasers, an apparent response rate of 0.5. Therefore, after using the dataset to predict who will be a purchaser, we must adjust the purchase rate back down by multiplying each case's "probability of purchase" by 0.053/0.5, or 0.107.

---

[3]Copyright © Datastats, LLC 2019 used with permission.

Data

There are two outcome variables in this case. Purchase indicates whether or not a prospect responded to the test mailing and purchased something. Spending indicates, for those who made a purchase, how much they spent. The overall procedure in this case will be to develop two models. One will be used to classify records as *purchase* or *no purchase*. The second will be used for those cases that are classified as *purchase* and will predict the amount they will spend.

Table 21.6 shows the first few rows of data. Table 21.7 provides a description of the variables available in this case.

TABLE 21.6 FIRST 10 RECORDS FROM TAYKO DATASET

sequence_number	US	source_a	source_c	source_b	source_d	source_e	source_m	source_o	source_h	source_r	source_s	source_t	source_u	source_p	source_x	source_w	Freq	last_update_days_ago	1st_update_days_ago	Web order	Gender=male	Address_is_res	Purchase	Spending
1	1	0	0	1	0	0	0	0	0	0	0	0	0	0	0	0	2	3662	3662	1	0	1	1	127.87
2	1	0	0	0	0	1	0	0	0	0	0	0	0	0	0	0	0	2900	2900	1	1	0	0	0
3	1	0	0	0	0	0	0	0	0	0	0	1	0	0	0	0	2	3883	3914	0	0	0	1	127.48
4	1	0	1	0	0	0	0	0	0	0	0	0	0	0	0	0	1	829	829	0	1	0	0	0
5	1	0	1	0	0	0	0	0	0	0	0	0	0	0	0	0	1	869	869	0	0	0	0	0
6	1	0	0	0	0	0	0	0	0	1	0	0	0	0	0	0	1	1995	2002	0	0	1	0	0.06
7	1	0	0	0	0	0	0	0	0	0	0	0	0	0	0	1	2	1498	1529	0	0	1	0	0.06
8	1	0	0	1	0	0	0	0	0	0	0	0	0	0	0	0	1	3397	3397	0	1	0	0	0.08
9	1	1	0	0	0	0	0	0	0	0	0	0	0	0	0	0	4	525	2914	1	1	0	1	488.5
10	1	1	0	0	0	0	0	0	0	0	0	0	0	0	0	0	1	3215	3215	0	0	0	1	173.5

(*Source:* Reproduced with permission from Datastats, LLC, ©2020 and Cytel Corp)

TABLE 21.7 DESCRIPTION OF VARIABLES FOR TAYKO DATASET

Variable number	Variable name	Description	Variable type	Code description
1	US	Is it a US address?	Binary	1: Yes 0: No
2–16	Source_*	Source catalog for the record (15 possible sources)	Binary	1: Yes 0: No
17	Freq.	Number of transactions in last year at source catalog	Numerical	
18	last_update_days_ago	How many days ago last update was made to customer record	Numerical	

(*Continued*)

TABLE 21.7 DESCRIPTION OF VARIABLES FOR TAYKO DATASET (*Continued*)

Variable number	Variable name	Description	Variable type	Code description
19	1st_update_days_ago	How many days ago first update to customer record was made	Numerical	
20	RFM%	Recency–frequency–monetary percentile, as reported by source catalog (see Section 21.1)	Numerical	
21	Web_order	Customer placed at least one order via web	Binary	1: Yes 0: No
22	Gender=mal	Customer is male	Binary	1: Yes 0: No
23	Address_is_res	Address is a residence	Binary	1: Yes 0: No
24	Purchase	Person made purchase in test mailing	Binary	1: Yes 0: No
25	Spending	Amount (dollars) spent by customer in test mailing	Numerical	

Assignment

1. Each catalog costs approximately $2 to mail (including printing, postage, and mailing costs). Estimate the gross profit that the firm could expect from the remaining 180,000 names if it selects them randomly from the pool.
2. Develop a model for classifying a customer as a purchaser or nonpurchaser.
   a. Partition the data randomly into a training set (800 records), validation set (700 records), and test set (500 records).
   b. Run logistic regression with L2 penalty, using method *LogisticRegressionCV*, to select the best subset of variables, then use this model to classify the data into purchasers and nonpurchasers. Use only the training set for running the model. (Logistic regression is used because it yields an estimated "probability of purchase," which is required later in the analysis.)
3. Develop a model for predicting spending among the purchasers.
   a. Create subsets of the training and validation sets for only purchasers' records by filtering for *Purchase = 1*.
   b. Develop models for predicting spending with the filtered datasets, using:
      i. Multiple linear regression (use stepwise regression)
      ii. Regression trees
   c. Choose one model on the basis of its performance on the validation data.

4. Return to the original test data partition. Note that this test data partition includes both purchasers and nonpurchasers. Create a new data frame called *Score Analysis* that contains the test data portion of this dataset.

   a. Add a column to the data frame with the predicted scores from the logistic regression.

   b. Add another column with the predicted spending amount from the prediction model chosen.

   c. Add a column for "adjusted probability of purchase" by multiplying "predicted probability of purchase" by 0.107. *This is to adjust for oversampling the purchasers* (see earlier description).

   d. Add a column for expected spending: adjusted probability of purchase × predicted spending.

   e. Plot the cumulative gains chart of the expected spending (cumulative expected spending as a function of number of records targeted).

   f. Using this cumulative gains curve, estimate the gross profit that would result from mailing to the 180,000 names on the basis of your data mining models.

Note: Although Tayko is a hypothetical company, the data in this case (modified slightly for illustrative purposes) were supplied by a real company that sells software through direct sales. The concept of a catalog consortium is based on the Abacus Catalog Alliance.

21.4 | POLITICAL PERSUASION[4]

Voter-Persuasion.csv is the dataset for this case study.
Note: Our thanks to Ken Strasma, President of HaystaqDNA and director of targeting for the 2004 Kerry campaign and the 2008 Obama campaign, for the data used in this case, and for sharing the information in the following writeup.

Background

When you think of political persuasion, you may think of the efforts that political campaigns undertake to persuade you that their candidate is better than the other candidate. In truth, campaigns are less about persuading people to change their minds, and more about persuading those who agree with you to actually go out and vote. Predictive analytics now plays a big role in this effort, but in 2004, it was a new arrival in the political toolbox.

Predictive Analytics Arrives in US Politics

In January of 2004, candidates in the US presidential campaign were competing in the Iowa caucuses, part of a lengthy state-by-state primary campaign that culminates in the selection of the Republican and Democratic candidates for president. Among the Democrats, Howard Dean was leading in national polls. The Iowa caucuses, however, are a complex and intensive process attracting only the most committed and interested voters. Those participating are not a representative sample of voters nationwide. Surveys of those planning to take part showed a close race between Dean and three other candidates, including John Kerry.

Kerry ended up winning by a surprisingly large margin, and the better than expected performance was due to his campaign's innovative and successful use of predictive analytics to learn more about the likely actions of individual voters. This allowed the campaign to target voters in such a way as to optimize performance in the caucuses. For example, once the model showed sufficient support in a precinct to win that precinct's delegate to the caucus, money and time could be redirected to other precincts where the race was closer.

Political Targeting

Targeting of voters is not new in politics. It has traditionally taken three forms:

- Geographic
- Demographic
- Individual

In geographic targeting, resources are directed to a geographic unit—state, city, county, etc.—on the basis of prior voting patterns or surveys that reveal the political tendency in that geographic unit. It has significant limitations, though. If a county is only, say, 52% in your favor, it may be in the greatest need of attention, but if messaging is directed to everyone in the county, nearly half of it is reaching the wrong people.

In demographic targeting, the messaging is intended for demographic groups—for example, older voters, younger women voters, Hispanic voters, etc. The limitation of this method is that it is often not easy to implement—messaging is hard to deliver just to single demographic groups.

Traditional individual targeting, the most effective form of targeting, was done on the basis of surveys asking voters how they plan to vote. The big limitation of this method is, of course, the cost. The expense of reaching all voters in a phone or door-to-door survey can be prohibitive.

The use of predictive analytics adds power to the individual targeting method, and reduces cost. A model allows prediction to be rolled out to the entire voter base, not just those surveyed, and brings to bear a wealth of information. Geographic and demographic data remain part of the picture, but they are used at an individual level.

Uplift

In a classical predictive modeling application for marketing, a sample of data is selected and an offer is made (e.g., on the web) or a message is sent (e.g., by mail), and a predictive model is developed to classify individuals as responding or not-responding. The model is then applied to new data, propensities to respond are calculated, individuals are ranked by their propensity to respond, and the marketer can then select those most likely to respond to mailings or offers.

Some key information is missing from this classical approach: how would the individual respond in the absence of the offer or mailing? Might a high-propensity customer be inclined to purchase irrespective of the offer? Might a person's propensity to buy actually be diminished by the offer? Uplift modeling (see Chapter 13) allows us to estimate the effect of "offer vs. no offer" or "mailing vs. no mailing" at the individual level.

In this case, we will apply uplift modeling to actual voter data that were augmented with the results of a hypothetical experiment. The experiment consisted of the following steps:

1. Conduct a pre-survey of the voters to determine their inclination to vote Democratic.
2. Randomly split the voters into two samples—control and treatment.
3. Send a flyer promoting the Democratic candidate to the treatment group.
4. Conduct another survey of the voters to determine their inclination to vote Democratic.

Data

The data in this case are in the file *Voter-Persuasion.csv*. The target variable is MOVED_AD, where a 1 = "opinion moved in favor of the Democratic candidate" and 0 = "opinion did not move in favor of the Democratic candidate." This variable encapsulates the information from the pre- and post-surveys. The important predictor variable is *Flyer*, a binary variable that indicates whether or not a voter received the flyer. In addition, there are numerous other predictor variables from these sources:

1. Government voter files
2. Political party data
3. Commercial consumer and demographic data
4. Census neighborhood data

Government voter files are maintained, and made public, to assure the integrity of the voting process. They contain essential data for identification purposes such as name, address and date of birth. The file used in this case also contains party identification (needed if a state limits participation in party primaries to voters in that party). Parties also staff elections with their own poll-watchers, who record whether an individual votes in an election. These data (termed "derived" in the case data) are maintained and curated by each party, and can be readily matched to the voter data by name. Demographic data at the neighborhood level are available from the census, and can be appended to the voter data by address matching. Consumer and additional demographic data (buying habits, education) can be purchased from marketing firms and appended to the voter data (matching by name and address).

Assignment

The task in this case is to develop an uplift model that predicts the uplift for each voter. Uplift is defined as the increase in propensity to move one's opinion in a Democratic direction. First, review the variables in *Voter-Persuasion.csv* and understand which data source they are probably coming from. Then, answer the following questions and perform the tasks indicated:

1. Overall, how well did the flyer do in moving voters in a Democratic direction? (Look at the target variable among those who got the flyer, compared to those who did not.)
2. Explore the data to learn more about the relationships between the predictor variables and MOVED_AD (visualization can be helpful). Which of the predictors seem to have good predictive potential? Show supporting charts and/or tables.
3. Partition the data using the partition variable that is in the dataset, make decisions about predictor inclusion, and fit three predictive models accordingly. For each model, give sufficient detail about the method used, its parameters, and the predictors used, so that your results can be replicated.
4. Among your three models, choose the best one in terms of predictive power. Which one is it? Why did you choose it?
5. Using your chosen model, report the propensities for the first three records in the validation set.
6. Create a derived variable that is the opposite of *Flyer*. Call it *Flyer-reversed*. Using your chosen model, re-score the validation data using the *Flyer-reversed* variable as a predictor, instead of *Flyer*. Report the propensities for the first three records in the validation set.

7. For each record, uplift is computed based on the following difference:

$$P(\text{success}|\text{Flyer} = 1) - P(\text{success}|\text{Flyer} = 0)$$

   Compute the uplift for each of the voters in the validation set, and report the uplift for the first three records.

8. If a campaign has the resources to mail the flyer only to 10% of the voters, what uplift cutoff should be used?

21.5 | TAXI CANCELLATIONS[5]

Taxi-cancellation-case.csv is the dataset for this case study.

Business Situation

In late 2013, the taxi company Yourcabs.com in Bangalore, India was facing a problem with the drivers using their platform—not all drivers were showing up for their scheduled calls. Drivers would cancel their acceptance of a call, and, if the cancellation did not occur with adequate notice, the customer would be delayed or even left high and dry.

Bangalore is a key tech center in India, and technology was transforming the taxi industry. Yourcabs.com featured an online booking system (though customers could phone in as well), and presented itself as a taxi booking portal. The Uber ride sharing service started its Bangalore operations in mid-2014.

Yourcabs.com had collected data on its bookings from 2011 to 2013, and posted a contest on Kaggle, in coordination with the Indian School of Business, to see what it could learn about the problem of cab cancellations.

The data presented for this case are a randomly selected subset of the original data, with 10,000 rows, one row for each booking. There are 17 input variables, including user (customer) ID, vehicle model, whether the booking was made online or via a mobile app, type of travel, type of booking package, geographic information, and the date and time of the scheduled trip. The target variable of interest is the binary indicator of whether a ride was canceled. The overall cancellation rate is between 7% and 8%.

Assignment

1. How can a predictive model based on these data be used by Yourcabs.com?
2. How can a profiling model (identifying predictors that distinguish canceled/uncanceled trips) be used by Yourcabs.com?

[5]Copyright © Datastats, LLC and Galit Shmueli 2019; used with permission.

3. Explore, prepare, and transform the data to facilitate predictive modeling. Here are some hints:
   - In exploratory modeling, it is useful to move fairly soon to at least an initial model without solving *all* data preparation issues. One example is the GPS information—other geographic information is available so you could defer the challenge of how to interpret/use the GPS information.
   - How will you deal with missing data, such as cases where NaN is indicated?
   - Think about what useful information might be held within the date and time fields (the booking timestamp and the trip timestamp). The data file contains a worksheet with some hints on how to extract features from the date/time field.
   - Think also about the categorical variables, and how to deal with them. Should we turn them all into dummies? Use only some?
4. Fit several predictive models of your choice. Do they provide information on how the predictor variables relate to cancellations?
5. Report the predictive performance of your model in terms of error rates (the confusion matrix). How well does the model perform? Can the model be used in practice?
6. Examine the predictive performance of your model in terms of ranking (lift). How well does the model perform? Can the model be used in practice?

21.6 | SEGMENTING CONSUMERS OF BATH SOAP[6]

BathSoapHousehold.csv is the dataset for this case study.

Business Situation

CRISA is an Asian market research agency that specializes in tracking consumer purchase behavior in consumer goods (both durable and nondurable). In one major research project, CRISA tracks numerous consumer product categories (e.g., "detergents"), and, within each category, perhaps dozens of brands. To track purchase behavior, CRISA constituted household panels in over 100 cities and towns in India, covering most of the Indian urban market. The households were carefully selected using stratified sampling to ensure a representative sample; a subset of 600 records is analyzed here. The strata were defined on the basis of socioeconomic status and the market (a collection of cities).

[6]Copyright © Cytel, Inc. and Datastats, LLC 2019; used with permission.

CRISA has both transaction data (each row is a transaction) and household data (each row is a household), and for the household data it maintains the following information:

- Demographics of the households (updated annually)
- Possession of durable goods (car, washing machine, etc., updated annually; an "affluence index" is computed from this information)
- Purchase data of product categories and brands (updated monthly)

CRISA has two categories of clients: (1) advertising agencies that subscribe to the database services, obtain updated data every month, and use the data to advise their clients on advertising and promotion strategies; (2) consumer goods manufacturers, which monitor their market share using the CRISA database.

Key Problems

CRISA has traditionally segmented markets on the basis of purchaser demographics. They would now like to segment the market based on two key sets of variables more directly related to the purchase process and to brand loyalty:

1. Purchase behavior (volume, frequency, susceptibility to discounts, and brand loyalty)
2. Basis of purchase (price, selling proposition)

Doing so would allow CRISA to gain information about what demographic attributes are associated with different purchase behaviors and degrees of brand loyalty, and thus deploy promotion budgets more effectively. More effective market segmentation would enable CRISA's clients (in this case, a firm called IMRB) to design more cost-effective promotions targeted at appropriate segments. Thus, multiple promotions could be launched, each targeted at different market segments at different times of the year. This would result in a more cost-effective allocation of the promotion budget to different market segments. It would also enable IMRB to design more effective customer reward systems and thereby increase brand loyalty.

Data

The data in Table 21.8 profile each household, each row containing the data for one household.

TABLE 21.8 DESCRIPTION OF VARIABLES FOR EACH HOUSEHOLD

Variable type	Variable name	Description
Member ID	Member id	Unique identifier for each household
Demographics	SEC	Socioeconomic class (1 = high, 5 = low)
	FEH	Eating habits(1 = vegetarian, 2 = vegetarian but eat eggs, 3 = nonvegetarian, 0 = not specified)
	MT	Native language (see table in worksheet)
	SEX	Gender of homemaker (1 = male, 2 = female)
	AGE	Age of homemaker
	EDU	Education of homemaker (1 = minimum, 9 = maximum)
	HS	Number of members in household
	CHILD	Presence of children in household (4 categories)
	CS	Television availability (1 = available, 2 = unavailable)
	Affluence Index	Weighted value of durables possessed
Purchase summary over the period	No. of Brands	Number of brands purchased
	Brand Runs	Number of instances of consecutive purchase of brands
	Total Volume	Sum of volume
	No. of Trans	Number of purchase transactions (multiple brands purchased in a month are counted as separate transactions)
	Value	Sum of value
	Trans/Brand Runs	Average transactions per brand run
	Vol/Trans	Average volume per transaction
	Avg. Price	Average price of purchase
Purchase within promotion	Pur Vol	Percent of volume purchased
	No Promo - %	Percent of volume purchased under no promotion
	Pur Vol Promo 6%	Percent of volume purchased under promotion code 6
	Pur Vol Other Promo %	Percent of volume purchased under other promotions
Brandwise purchase	Br. Cd. (57, 144), 55, 272, 286, 24, 481, 352, 5, and 999 (others)	Percent of volume purchased of the brand
Price categorywise purchase	Price Cat 1 to 4	Percent of volume purchased under the price category
Selling propositionwise purchase	Proposition Cat 5 to 15	Percent of volume purchased under the product proposition category

(*Source:* © Cytel, Inc. and Datastats, LLC 2019)

Measuring Brand Loyalty

Several variables in this case measure aspects of brand loyalty. The number of different brands purchased by the customer is one measure of loyalty. However, a consumer who purchases one or two brands in quick succession, then settles on a third for a long streak, is different from a consumer who constantly switches back and forth among three brands. Therefore, how often customers switch from one brand to another is another measure of loyalty. Yet a third perspective on the same issue is the proportion of purchases that go to different brands—a consumer who spends 90% of his or her purchase money on one brand is more loyal than a consumer who spends more equally among several brands.

All three of these components can be measured with the data in the purchase summary worksheet.

Assignment

1. Use *k*-means clustering to identify clusters of households based on:
   - **a.** The variables that describe purchase behavior (including brand loyalty)
   - **b.** The variables that describe the basis for purchase
   - **c.** The variables that describe both purchase behavior and basis of purchase

   Note 1: How should *k* be chosen? Think about how the clusters would be used. It is likely that the marketing efforts would support two to five different promotional approaches.

   Note 2: How should the percentages of total purchases comprised by various brands be treated? Isn't a customer who buys all brand A just as loyal as a customer who buys all brand B? What will be the effect on any distance measure of using the brand share variables as is? Consider using a single derived variable.
2. Select what you think is the best segmentation and comment on the characteristics (demographic, brand loyalty, and basis for purchase) of these clusters. (This information would be used to guide the development of advertising and promotional campaigns.)
3. Develop a model that classifies the data into these segments. Since this information would most likely be used in targeting direct-mail promotions, it would be useful to select a market segment that would be defined as a *success* in the classification model.

21.7 | DIRECT-MAIL FUNDRAISING

Fundraising.csv and *FutureFundraising.csv* are the datasets used for this case study.

Background

Note: Be sure to read the information about oversampling and adjustment in Chapter 5 before starting to work on this case.

A national veterans' organization wishes to develop a predictive model to improve the cost-effectiveness of their direct marketing campaign. The organization, with its in-house database of over 13 million donors, is one of the largest direct-mail fundraisers in the United States. According to their recent mailing records, the overall response rate is 5.1%. Out of those who responded (donated), the average donation is $13.00. Each mailing, which includes a gift of personalized address labels and assortments of cards and envelopes, costs $0.68 to produce and send. Using these facts, we take a sample of this dataset to develop a classification model that can effectively capture donors so that the expected net profit is maximized. Weighted sampling is used, under-representing the non-responders so that the sample has equal numbers of donors and non-donors.

Data

The file *Fundraising.csv* contains 3120 records with 50% donors (TARGET_B = 1) and 50% non-donors (TARGET_B = 0). The amount of donation (TARGET_D) is also included but is not used in this case. The descriptions for the 22 variables (including two target variables) are listed in Table 21.9.

TABLE 21.9 DESCRIPTION OF VARIABLES FOR THE FUNDRAISING DATASET

Variable	Description
ZIP	Zip code group (zip codes were grouped into five groups; 1 = the potential donor belongs to this zip group.) 00000–19999 ⇒ zipconvert_1 20000–39999 ⇒ zipconvert_2 40000–59999 ⇒ zipconvert_3 60000–79999 ⇒ zipconvert_4 80000–99999 ⇒ zipconvert_5
HOMEOWNER	1 = homeowner, 0 = not a homeowner
NUMCHLD	Number of children
INCOME	Household income
GENDER	0 = male, 1 = female
WEALTH	Wealth rating uses median family income and population statistics from each area to index relative wealth within each state. The segments are denoted 0 to 9, with 9 being the highest-wealth group and zero the lowest. Each rating has a different meaning within each state.
HV	Average home value in potential donor's neighborhood in hundreds of dollars
ICmed	Median family income in potential donor's neighborhood in hundreds of dollars
ICavg	Average family income in potential donor's neighborhood in hundreds
IC15	Percent earning less than $15K in potential donor's neighborhood
NUMPROM	Lifetime number of promotions received to date
RAMNTALL	Dollar amount of lifetime gifts to date
MAXRAMNT	Dollar amount of largest gift to date
LASTGIFT	Dollar amount of most recent gift

TABLE 21.9 **DESCRIPTION OF VARIABLES FOR THE FUNDRAISING DATASET** (*Continued*)

Variable	Description
TOTALMONTHS	Number of months from last donation to July 1998 (the last time the case was updated)
TIMELAG	Number of months between first and second gift
AVGGIFT	Average dollar amount of gifts to date
TARGET_*B*	Outcome variable: binary indicator for response 1 = donor, 0 = non-donor
TARGET_*D*	Outcome variable: donation amount (in dollars). We will NOT be using this variable for this case.

Assignment

Step 1—Partitioning: Partition the dataset into 60% training and 40% validation (set the seed to 12345).

Step 2—Model Building: Follow the following steps to build, evaluate, and choose a model.

1. *Select classification tool and parameters*: Run at least two classification models of your choosing. Be sure NOT to use TARGET_D in your analysis. Describe the two models that you chose, with sufficient detail (method, parameters, variables, etc.) so that it can be replicated.
2. *Classification under asymmetric response and cost*: What is the reasoning behind using weighted sampling to produce a training set with equal numbers of donors and non-donors? Why not use a simple random sample from the original dataset?
3. *Calculate net profit*: For each method, calculate the cumulative gains of net profit for both the training and validation sets based on the actual response rate (5.1%.) Again, the expected donation, given that they are donors, is $13.00, and the total cost of each mailing is $0.68. (*Hint*: To calculate estimated net profit, we will need to undo the effects of the weighted sampling and calculate the net profit that would reflect the actual response distribution of 5.1% donors and 94.9% non-donors. To do this, divide each row's net profit by the oversampling weights applicable to the actual status of that row. The oversampling weight for actual donors is 50%/5.1% = 9.8. The oversampling weight for actual non-donors is 50%/94.9% = 0.53.)
4. *Draw cumulative gains curves*: Draw the different models' net profit cumulative gains curves for the validation set in a single plot (net profit on the *y*-axis, proportion of list or number mailed on the *x*-axis). Is there a model that dominates?
5. *Select best model*: From your answer in (4), what do you think is the "best" model?

Step 3—TestingFutureFundraising.csv contains the attributes for future mailing candidates.

6. Using your "best" model from Step 2 (number 5), which of these candidates do you predict as donors and non-donors? List them in descending order of the probability of being a donor. Starting at the top of this sorted list, roughly how far down would you go in a mailing campaign?

21.8 | PREDICTING TOURIST TRAVEL PACKAGES

Travel_Desti_India.csv is the dataset for this case study.

Background

Travel companies offer individuals, families, and interested groups various travel packages across various tourist locations in their scope of operations. Their growth and sustainability depend on several factors, including how well they are able to target potential customers and understand their preferences for sites, logistics arrangements, complementary facilities, etc. Based on such insights, these firms can accordingly plan and execute the necessary mobilization of resources and facilitation. It helps with the acquisition and retention of clients to sustain themselves in a highly competitive ecosystem.

Data

You will use a dataset named *Travel_Desti_India.csv* with 4511 records and 25 variables. The first five variables are ID (client identifier), Category (Friend, Family, Single, and Others), TouristCountry (NA, AS, AF, A, SA, EU), Stay_period (Long, Short, and Medium), and Repeat Visitor (Yes, No), followed by twenty fields that comprise a visit to any of the twenty tourist destinations (Jaipur, Udaipur, Goa, Mumbai, Srinagar, Mysore, Varanasi, Kolkata, Leh, Rishikesh, Jodhpur, Amritsar, Bodh Gaya, Sikkim, Bhopal, Kochi, Darjeeling, Kovalam, Konark, and Agra) in their latest travel to India. TouristCountry has been aggregated at the continent level (NA- North America, AS-Asia, EU–Europe, and so on). The dataset is in tabular form to ease further analysis. The dataset has been developed based on the patterns of an earlier field survey of foreign tourists where tourists expressed satisfaction about the entire trip and the places they visited.

Assignment

You will carry out analytical modeling in two phases. In the first phase, analyze 20 destination-based variables. Explore interesting combinations through relevant visualization and develop association rules to identify destinations visited together. Determine support, confidence, and lift of various combinations. Interpret these measures to decide interesting combinations which could be promoted together as a package trip.

1. Create new features for these combinations.
2. Assign a target role for these new features and use tourist profile variables as predictors.
3. Develop classification rules, if any, with decision tree methods.
4. Check the model accuracy with classification accuracy measures like Precision, Recall, CA, F1, and confusion matrix.

21.9 TIME SERIES CASE: FORECASTING PUBLIC TRANSPORTATION DEMAND

bicup2006.csv is the dataset for this case study.

Background

Forecasting transportation demand is important for multiple purposes such as staffing, planning, and inventory control. The public transportation system in Santiago de Chile has gone through a major effort of reconstruction. In this context, a business intelligence competition took place in October 2006, which focused on forecasting demand for public transportation. This case is based on the competition, with some modifications.

Problem Description

A public transportation company is expecting an increase in demand for its services and is planning to acquire new buses and to extend its terminals. These investments require a reliable forecast of future demand. To create such forecasts, one can use data on historic demand. The company's data warehouse has data on each 15-minute interval between 6:30 and 22:00, on the number of passengers arriving at the terminal. As a forecasting consultant, you have been asked to create a forecasting method that can generate forecasts for the number of passengers arriving at the terminal.

Available Data

Part of the historic information is available in the file *bicup2006.csv*. The file contains the historic information with known demand for a 3-week period, separated into 15-minute intervals, and dates and times for a future 3-day period (DEMAND = NaN), for which forecasts should be generated (as part of the 2006 competition).

Assignment Goal

Your goal is to create a model/method that produces accurate forecasts. To evaluate your accuracy, partition the given historic data into two periods: a training period (the first two weeks), and a validation period (the last week). Models should be fitted only to the training data and evaluated on the validation data.

Although the competition winning criterion was the lowest Mean Absolute Error (MAE) on the future 3-day data, this is *not* the goal for this assignment. Instead, if we consider a more realistic business context, our goal is to create a model that generates reasonably good forecasts on any time/day of the week. Consider not only predictive metrics such as MAE, MAPE (mean absolute percentage error), and RMSE (root-mean-squared error), but also look at actual and forecasted values, overlaid on a time plot, as well as a time plot of the forecast errors.

Assignment

For your final model, present the following summary:

1. Name of the method/combination of methods.
2. A brief description of the method/combination.
3. All estimated equations associated with constructing forecasts from this method.
4. The MAPE and MAE for the training period and the validation period.
5. Forecasts for the future period (March 22–24), in 15-minute bins.
6. A single chart showing the fit of the final version of the model to the entire period (including training, validation, and future). Note that this model should be fitted using the combined training plus validation data.

Tips and Suggested Steps

1. Use exploratory analysis to identify the components of this time series. Is there a trend? Is there seasonality? If so, how many "seasons" are there? Are there any other visible patterns? Are the patterns global (the same throughout the series) or local?
2. Consider the frequency of the data from a practical and technical point of view. What are some options?
3. Compare the weekdays and weekends. How do they differ? Consider how these differences can be captured by different methods.
4. Examine the series for missing values or unusual values. Think of solutions.

5. Based on the patterns that you found in the data, which models or methods should be considered?
6. Consider how to handle actual counts of zero within the computation of MAPE.

21.10 | PREDICTING ATTRITION

EmpRatingAttrition.csv is the dataset for this case study.

Talent Attrition in Automobile Firm

Organizations globally face the challenge of identifying, recruiting, developing, and managing the retention of competent talent. One of the common analytical assignments concerning human resource management is identifying determinants of employee retention specifically those who are high contributors across departments or functions. This is a case of an automobile accessory manufacturing firm where its HR function is concerned about the higher attrition rates in general compared to the sector average and more specifically for those employees who are high contributors in various functions. The firm supplies parts to vehicle manufacturers.

Data

The file *EmpRatingAttrition.csv* contains records of 856 employees of an automobile accessory manufacturing firm including their performance rating in the last three years whether they are still working or left the organization. The data captured in early 2020, carries a few profile variables, performance rating during the period 2012 to 2019, and status of whether they are still working in the organization or left. The dataset has records of only those employees who have at least served three or more than three years during the said period. These employees are either working in the organization in early 2020 or leaving in any year 2015 to 2019. There are 11 variables in this curated dataset. The description of variables in the dataset is as follows:

Emp_ID: Employee Identifier

Gender

Pre_Exp: Previous professional work experience in years

Event_Participation: Number of corporate events participated. The organization organizes two major social events every year. The field captures the participation by the employee in a number of events during the last three reference years.

Age_Joining: Age (in years) at the time of joining the organization.

Depart: Departments or functions like Procurement (PROC), Marketing (MKT), Operations (OPR), Finance (FIN), R&D (RD), and Human Resources (HR).

Last_Position: Responsibility level in the function from L2 to L5. L2 is a lower level, whereas L5 is a higher level.
Active: "Yes" means an active status in the organization, whereas "No" means left.
RATE-L-2: Performance rating for the year, 2 years before the last year. For example, if an employee is working in the organization since the beginning of 2013, but left in early 2016. Hence, we have three years of annual performance ratings for this employee, that is, 2013, 2014, and 2015. The rating of 2013 is put under RATE-L-2, 2014 under RATE-L-1, and 2015 under RATE-L. In another example, if an employee is working in the organization since 2010 and still working in the year 2020. In this case, the rating of 2017 is under RATE-L-2, 2018 under RATE-L-1, and 2019 under RATE-L.
RATE-L-1: Performance rating for the year, 1 year before the last year. Already explained above.
RATE-L: Performance rating for the last year. Already explained above.

Assignment

You need to develop a suitable model to predict attrition/retention based on the available employee profile and performance variables. Start with necessary descriptive analysis and visualization, which can guide the next stage of model building. Compare alternate approaches. Substantiate your choice of the model/s for deployment purposes. Carry out systematic assessment and validation process of the model suggested.

21.11 | ATTITUDE TOWARD THERAPY SUGGESTIONS IN COVID-19 TIMES

SentimentTweets.csv is the dataset for this case study.

Sentiment Analysis of Alternate Treatment Suggestions on Twitter

Sentiment analysis has been widely used by research professionals to gauge the attitude of the target population toward brands, new initiatives, investments, collaborations, new products, services, offers, etc. The scope has widened across domains including entertainment, politics, public policy, and events of public interest. The Covid-19 pandemic led to a variety of therapies attempting to treat and contain the virus spread. There have been debates of all sorts in various forums including Twitter, about the efficacy of various treatment approaches, which could be indicative of public trust and attitude towards such treatment methods. These debates include the efficacy of various forms of alternative medicine including homeopathy. Homeopathy is one of the popular forms of alternative medicine. It originated in Germany in the 18th century.

Homeopathy is based on the philosophy that both the cure and the ailment come from the same situation. We are taking a specific case of debate on Twitter about homeopathic treatment for virus infection.

Data

You will use 571 tweets in the dataset *SentimentTweets.csv* sourced from Twitter site for hashtag # Homeopath on 12th June 2020. The dataset has been curated and the sample set has 10 variables. The description of various fields is as follows:

Author ID: Author ID has been replaced by a serial number to indicate unique identification.

Content: Tweet content written or posted.

Date: Date and time of posting content.

Number of Likes: Number of likes for the user's tweet.

Number of Retweets: Number of retweets for the user's tweet.

Author Statuses Count: The number of Tweets (including retweets) issued by the user.

Author Favorites Count: The number of Tweets this user has liked in the account's lifetime.

Author Friends Count: Accounts following.

Author Followers Count: Number of followers.

Author Listed Count: The number of public lists that this user is a member of.

Assignment

Preprocess and develop a frequency plot of key terms and expressions by the authors in the provided tweets. Generate sentiment score of the content around the topic "Homeopathy". Plot the histogram of the scores. Discuss the output and explore possibilities of additional insights with these scores as targets in combination with other potential predictor variables given in the dataset. Discuss ways in which these insights can be helpful in governance and decision-making of public healthcare facilitation during healthcare emergency times like the Covid-19 pandemic.

References

Agrawal, R., Imielinski, T., and Swami, A. (1993). Mining associations between sets of items in massive databases. In: *Proceedings of the 1993 ACM-SIGMOD International Conference on Management of Data*, pp. 207–216. New York: ACM Press.

Berry, M. J. A., and Linoff, G. S. (1997). *Data Mining Techniques*. New York: Wiley.

Berry, M. J. A., and Linoff, G. S. (2000). *Mastering Data Mining*. New York: Wiley.

Breiman, L., Friedman, J., Olshen, R., and Stone, C. (1984). *Classification and Regression Trees*. Boca Raton, FL: Chapman Hall/CRC (orig. published by Wadsworth).

Chatfield, C. (2003). *The Analysis of Time Series: An Introduction*, 6th ed. Boca Raton, FL: Chapman Hall/CRC.

Delmaster, R., and Hancock, M. (2001). *Data Mining Explained*. Boston, MA: Digital Press.

Efron, B. (1975). The efficiency of logistic regression compared to normal discriminant analysis. *Journal of the American Statistical Association*, vol. 70, number 352, pp. 892–898.

Few, S. (2009). *Now You See It*. Oakland, CA: Analytics Press.

Few, S. (2012). *Show Me the Numbers*, 2nd ed. Oakland, CA: Analytics Press.

Golbeck, J. (2013). *Analyzing the Social Web*. Waltham, MA: Morgan Kaufmann.

Han, J., and Kamber, M. (2001). *Data Mining: Concepts and Techniques*. San Diego, CA: Academic Press.

Hand, D., Mannila, H., and Smyth, P. (2001). *Principles of Data Mining*. Cambridge, MA: MIT Press.

Harris, H., Murphy, S., and Vaisman, M. (2013). *Analyzing the Analyzers: An Introspective Survey of Data Scientists and Their Work*. Cambridge, MA: O'Reilly Media.

Hastie, T., Tibshirani, R., and Friedman, J. (2001). *The Elements of Statistical Learning*. New York: Springer.

Hosmer, D. W., and Lemeshow, S. (2000). *Applied Logistic Regression*, 2nd ed. New York: Wiley-Interscience.

Hothorn, T., Hornik K., and Zeileis, A. (2006). Unbiased recursive partitioning: a conditional inference framework. *Journal of Computational and Graphical Statistics*, vol. 15, number 3, pp. 651–674.

Hyndman, R., and Yang, Y. Z. (2018). tsdl: Time Series Data Library. v0.1.0. https://pkg.yangzhuoranyang.com/tsdl/.

Jank, W., and Yahav, I. (2010). E-Loyalty networks in online auctions. *Annal of Applied Statistics*, vol. 4, number 1, pp. 151–178.

Johnson, W., and Wichern, D. (2002). *Applied Multivariate Statistics*. Upper Saddle River, NJ: Prentice Hall.

Larsen, K. (2005). Generalized naive Bayes classifiers. *SIGKDD Explorations*, vol. 7, number 1, pp. 76–81.

Le, Q. V., Ranzato, M. A., Monga, R., Devin, M., Chen, K., Corrado, G. S., Dean, J., and Ng, A.Y. (2012). Building high-level features using large scale unsupervised learning. In: *Proceedings of the Twenty-Ninth International Conference on Machine Learning*. Editors: J. Langford and J. Pineau. Edinburgh: Omnipress.

Loh, W.-Y., and Shih, Y.-S. (1997). Split selection methods for classification trees. *Statistica Sinica*, vol. 7, pp. 815–840.

McCullugh, C. E., Paal, B., and Ashdown, S. P. (1998). An optimisation approach to apparel sizing. *Journal of the Operational Research Society*, vol. 49, number 5, pp. 492–499.

Matz, S. C., Kosinski, S. C., Nave, G., and Stillwell, D. J. (2017). Psychological targeting in digital mass persuasion. *Proceedings of the National Academy of Sciences*, vol. 114, number 48, pp. 12714–12719. DOI: 10.1073/pnas.1710966114.

O'Neil, C. (2016) *Weapons of Math Destruction*. New York: Crown Publishers.

Pregibon, D. (1999). 2001: A statistical odyssey. Invited talk at *The Fifth ACM SIGKDD International Conference on Knowledge Discovery and Data Mining*. New York: ACM Press, p. 4.

Saddiqi, N. (2017). *Intelligent Credit Scoring: Building and Implementing Better Credit Risk Scorecards*, 2nd ed. Hoboken, NJ: Wiley.

Shmueli, G., and Lichtendahl, K. C. (2016). *Practical Time Series Forecasting with R: A Hands-On Guide*, 2nd ed. Axelrod-Schnall Publishers.

Siegel, E. (2013). *Predictive Analytics*. New York: Wiley.

Trippi, R., and Turban, E. (eds.) (1996). *Neural Networks in Finance and Investing*. New York: McGraw-Hill.

Veenhoven, R., World Database of Happiness, Erasmus University Rotterdam. Available at http://worlddatabaseofhappiness.eur.nl.

Data Files Used in the Book

1. accidents.csv
2. accidentsFull.csv
3. accidentsnn.csv
4. Airfares.csv
5. Amtrak.csv
6. Allwin Summer-19 I.csv
7. Allwin Summer-19 II.csv
8. ApplianceShipments.csv
9. AustralianWines.csv
10. AutoAndElectronics.zip
11. AvgMilkPurchase.csv
12. Bankruptcy.csv
13. banks.csv
14. BareggTunnel.csv
15. BathSoapHousehold.csv
16. bicup2006.csv
17. BostonHousing.csv
18. CanadianWorkHours.csv
19. Cereals.csv
20. CharlesBookClub.csv
21. Cosmetics.csv
22. courserating.csv
23. CourseTopics.csv
24. CrossCatBuying.csv
25. DepartmentStoreSales.csv
26. drug.csv
27. EastWestAirlinesCluster.csv

28. EastWestAirlinesNN.csv
29. eBayAuctions.csv
30. ebayNetwork.csv
31. EbayTreemap.csv
32. Ecommerce_Example.csv
33. Ecommerce_Sample.csv
34. Ecom_Service_Factors.csv
35. EmpRatingAttrition.csv
36. Ent_Test.csv
37. Faceplate.csv
38. farm-ads.csv
39. FlightDelays.csv
40. Fruit Variety Classification Example.csv
41. Fruit_Variety.csv
42. Fruit_Variety_Sample.csv
43. Fundraising.csv
44. FutureFundraising.csv
45. gdp.csv
46. GermanCredit.csv
47. Hair-Care-Product.csv
48. India_Cov_Jun2020.csv
49. LaptopSales.csv
50. LaptopSalesJanuary2008.csv
51. liftExample.csv
52. NaturalGasSales.csv
53. NYPD_Motor_Vehicle_Collisions_1000.csv
54. OQFS.csv
55. ownerExample.csv
56. Pharmaceuticals.csv
57. RidingMowers.csv
58. SC-US-students-GPS-data-2016.csv
59. SentimentTweets.csv
60. ShampooSales.csv

61. Sept11Travel.csv
62. Service_Rcommend.csv
63. Service_Usage.csv
64. SouvenirSales.csv
65. SP500.csv
66. Spambase.csv
67. SystemAdministrators.csv
68. Taxi-cancellation-case.csv
69. Tayko.csv
70. Timeseries Data.csv
71. ToyotaCorolla.csv
72. ToysRUsRevenues.csv
73. Transformation_Example.csv
74. Travel_Desti_India.csv
75. UniversalBank.csv
76. Universities.csv
77. Utilities.csv
78. Veerhoven.csv
79. Voter-Persuasion.csv
80. WestRoxbury.csv
81. Wine.csv

Python Utilities Functions

This appendix includes several Python utilities that are used throughout the book. The utilities were designed to simplify the use and improve the display of several often-used data mining methods. They are combined in the dmba package, that is available from the Python Package Index at https://pypi.org/project/dmba. Install the package using:

```
pip install dmba
```

The source code is available and maintained on https://github.com/gedeck/dmba.

regressionSummary

```
import math
import numpy as np
from sklearn.metrics import regression

def regressionSummary(y_true, y_pred):
    """ print regression performance metrics

    Input:
        y_true: actual values
        y_pred: predicted values
    """
    y_true = np.asarray(y_true)
    y_pred = np.asarray(y_pred)
    y_res = y_true - y_pred
    metrics = [
        ('Mean Error (ME)', sum(y_res) / len(y_res)),
        ('Root Mean Squared Error (RMSE)', math.sqrt(regression.
          mean_squared_error(y_true, y_pred))),
        ('Mean Absolute Error (MAE)', sum(abs(y_res)) / len(y_res)),
        ('Mean Percentage Error (MPE)', 100 * sum(y_res / y_true) /
          len(y_res)),
        ('Mean Absolute Percentage Error (MAPE)', 100 * sum(abs(y_res /
          y_true) / len(y_res))),
    ]
    fmt1 = '{{:>{}}} : {{:.4f}}'.format(max(len(m[0]) for m in metrics))
    print('\nRegression statistics\n')
    for metric, value in metrics:
        print(fmt1.format(metric, value))
```

classificationSummary

```
from sklearn.metrics import classification

def classificationSummary(y_true, y_pred, class_names=None):
    """ Print a summary of classification performance

    Input:
        y_true: actual values
        y_pred: predicted values
        class_names (optional): list of class names
    """
    confusionMatrix = classification.confusion_matrix(y_true, y_pred)
    accuracy = classification.accuracy_score(y_true, y_pred)

    print('Confusion Matrix (Accuracy {:.4f})\n'.format(accuracy))

    # Pretty-print confusion matrix
    cm = confusionMatrix

    labels = class_names
    if labels is None:
        labels = [str(i) for i in range(len(cm))]

    # Convert the confusion matrix and labels to strings
    cm = [[str(i) for i in row] for row in cm]
    labels = [str(i) for i in labels]

    # Determine the width for the first label column and the individual cells
    prediction = 'Prediction'
    actual = 'Actual'
    labelWidth = max(len(s) for s in labels)
    cmWidth = max(max(len(s) for row in cm for s in row), labelWidth) + 1
    labelWidth = max(labelWidth, len(actual))

    # Construct the format statements
    fmt1 = '{{:>{}}}'.format(labelWidth)
    fmt2 = '{{:>{}}}'.format(cmWidth) * len(labels)

    # And print the confusion matrix
    print(fmt1.format(' ') + ' ' + prediction)
    print(fmt1.format(actual), end='')
    print(fmt2.format(*labels))

    for cls, row in zip(labels, cm):
        print(fmt1.format(cls), end='')
        print(fmt2.format(*row))
```

liftChart, gainsChart

```
import pandas as pd

def liftChart(predicted, title='Decile Lift Chart', labelBars=True, ax=None, figsize=None):
    """ Create a lift chart using predicted values

    Input:
        predictions: must be sorted by probability
        ax (optional): axis for matplotlib graph
        title (optional): set to None to suppress title
        labelBars (optional): set to False to avoid mean response labels on bar chart
    """
    # group the sorted predictions into 10 roughly equal groups and calculate the mean
    groups = [int(10 * i / len(predicted)) for i in range(len(predicted))]
    meanPercentile = predicted.groupby(groups).mean()
    # divide by the mean prediction to get the mean response
    meanResponse = meanPercentile / predicted.mean()
    meanResponse.index = (meanResponse.index + 1) * 10

    ax = meanResponse.plot.bar(color='C0', ax=ax, figsize=figsize)
    ax.set_ylim(0, 1.12 * meanResponse.max() if labelBars else None)
    ax.set_xlabel('Percentile')
    ax.set_ylabel('Lift')
    if title:
        ax.set_title(title)

    if labelBars:
        for p in ax.patches:
            ax.annotate('{:.1f}'.format(p.get_height()), (p.get_x(), p.get_height() + 0.1))
    return ax

def gainsChart(gains, color=None, label=None, ax=None, figsize=None):
    """ Create a gains chart using predicted values

    Input:
        gains: must be sorted by probability
        color (optional): color of graph
        ax (optional): axis for matplotlib graph
        figsize (optional): size of matplotlib graph
    """
    nTotal = len(gains)  # number of records
    nActual = gains.sum()  # number of desired records

    # get cumulative sum of gains and convert to percentage
    cumGains = pd.concat([pd.Series([0]), gains.cumsum()])  # Note the additional 0 at the
                                                                front
    gains_df = pd.DataFrame({'records': list(range(len(gains) + 1)), 'cumGains': cumGains})

    ax = gains_df.plot(x='records', y='cumGains', color=color, label=label, legend=False,
                       ax=ax, figsize=figsize)
```

```
# Add line for random gain
    ax.plot([0, nTotal], [0, nActual], linestyle='--', color='k')
    ax.set_xlabel('# records')
    ax.set_ylabel('# cumulative gains')
    return ax
```

plotDecisionTree

```
import io
# import pandas as pd
from sklearn.tree import export_graphviz
try:
  from IPython.display import Image
except ImportError:
  Image = None
try:
  import pydotplus
except ImportError:
  pydotplus = None


def plotDecisionTree(decisionTree, feature_names=None, class_names=None, impurity=False,
                      label='root', max_depth=None, rotate=False, pdfFile=None):
    """ Create a plot of the scikit-learn decision tree and show in the Jupyter notebooke
    Input:
        decisionTree: scikit-learn decision tree
        feature_names (optional): variable names
        class_names (optional): class names, only relevant for classification trees
        impurity (optional): show node impurity
        label (optional): only show labels at the root
        max_depth (optional): limit
        rotate (optional): rotate the layout of the graph
        pdfFile (optional): provide pathname to create a PDF file of the graph
    """
    if pydotplus is None:
        return 'You need to install pydotplus to visualize decision trees'
    if Image is None:
        return 'You need to install ipython to visualize decision trees'
    if class_names is not None:
        class_names = [str(s) for s in class_names]  # convert to strings
    dot_data = io.StringIO()
    export_graphviz(decisionTree, feature_names=feature_names, class_names=class_names,
                    impurity=impurity, label=label, out_file=dot_data, filled=True,
                    rounded=True, special_characters=True, max_depth=max_depth,
                    rotate=rotate)
    graph = pydotplus.graph_from_dot_data(dot_data.getvalue())
    if pdfFile is not None:
        graph.write_pdf(str(pdfFile))
    return Image(graph.create_png())
```

exhaustive_search

```
import itertools

def exhaustive_search(variables, train_model, score_model):
    """ Variable selection using backward elimination

    Input:
        variables: complete list of variables to consider in model building
        train_model: function that returns a fitted model for a given set of variables
        score_model: function that returns the score of a model; better models have lower
                     scores

    Returns:
        List of best subset models for increasing number of variables
    """
    # create models of increasing size and determine the best models in each case
    result = []
    for nvariables in range(1, len(variables) + 1):
        best_subset = None
        best_score = None
        best_model = None
        for subset in itertools.combinations(variables, nvariables):
            subset = list(subset)
            subset_model = train_model(subset)
            subset_score = score_model(subset_model, subset)
            if best_subset is None or best_score > subset_score:
                best_subset = subset
                best_score = subset_score
                best_model = subset_model
        result.append({
            'n': nvariables,
            'variables': best_subset,
            'score': best_score,
            'model': best_model,
        })
    return result
```

Example use

```
def train_model(variables):
    if len(variables) == 0:
        formula = 'y ~ 1'
    else:
        formula = 'y ~ ' + ' + '.join(variables)
    model = sm.ols(formula=formula, data=train_df).fit()
    return model

def evaluate_model(model):
    return -model.rsquared_adj  # we negate as lower score is better

model, best_variables = exhaustive_search(independent_var, train_model, evaluate_model)
```

backward_elimination

```
def backward_elimination(variables, train_model, score_model, verbose=False):
    """ Variable selection using backward elimination

    Input:
        variables: complete list of variables to consider in model building
        train_model: function that returns a fitted model for a given set of variables
        score_model: function that returns the score of a model; better models have lower
                     scores

    Returns:
        (best_model, best_variables)
    """
    # we start with a model that contains all variables
    best_variables = list(variables)
    best_model = train_model(best_variables)
    best_score = score_model(best_model, best_variables)
    if verbose:
        print('Variables: ' + ', '.join(variables))
        print('Start: score={:.2f}'.format(best_score))

    while len(best_variables) > 1:
        step = [(best_score, None, best_model)]
        for removeVar in best_variables:
            step_var = list(best_variables)
            step_var.remove(removeVar)
            step_model = train_model(step_var)
            step_score = score_model(step_model, step_var)
            step.append((step_score, removeVar, step_model))

        # sort by ascending score
        step.sort(key=lambda x: x[0])

        # the first entry is the model with the lowest score
        best_score, removed_step, best_model = step[0]
        if verbose:
            print('Step: score={:.2f}, remove {}'.format(best_score, removed_step))
        if removed_step is None:
            # step here, as removing more variables is detrimental to performance
            break
        best_variables.remove(removed_step)
    return best_model, best_variables
```

Example use

```
def train_model(variables):
    if len(variables) == 0:
        formula = 'y ~ 1'
    else:
        formula = 'y ~ ' + ' + '.join(variables)
    model = sm.ols(formula=formula, data=train).fit()
    return model
```

```
def evaluate_model(model):
    return model.aic

model, best_variables = backward_selection(independent_var, train_model, evaluate_model)
```

forward_selection

```
def forward_selection(variables, train_model, score_model, verbose=True):
    """ Variable selection using forward selection

    Input:
        variables: complete list of variables to consider in model building
        train_model: function that returns a fitted model for a given set of variables
        score_model: function that returns the score of a model; better models have lower
                     scores

    Returns:
        (best_model, best_variables)
    """
    # we start with a model that contains no variables
    best_variables = []
    best_model = train_model(best_variables)
    best_score = score_model(best_model, best_variables)
    if verbose:
        print('Variables: ' + ', '.join(variables))
        print('Start: score={:.2f}, constant'.format(best_score))
    while True:
        step = [(best_score, None, best_model)]
        for addVar in variables:
            if addVar in best_variables:
                continue
            step_var = list(best_variables)
            step_var.append(addVar)
            step_model = train_model(step_var)
            step_score = score_model(step_model, step_var)
            step.append((step_score, addVar, step_model))
        step.sort(key=lambda x: x[0])

        # the first entry in step is now the model that improved most
        best_score, added_step, best_model = step[0]
        if verbose:
            print('Step: score={:.2f}, add {}'.format(best_score, added_step))
        if added_step is None:
            # stop here, as adding more variables is detrimental to performance
            break
        best_variables.append(added_step)
    return best_model, best_variables
```

stepwise_selection

```
def stepwise_selection(variables, train_model, score_model, verbose=True):
    """ Variable selection using forward and/or backward selection

    Input:
        variables: complete list of variables to consider in model building
        train_model: function that returns a fitted model for a given set of variables
        score_model: function that returns the score of a model; better models have lower
                     scores

    Returns:
        (best_model, best_variables)
    """
    # we start with a model that contains no variables
    best_variables = []
    best_model = train_model(best_variables)
    best_score = score_model(best_model, best_variables)
    if verbose:
        print('Variables: ' + ', '.join(variables))
        print('Start: score={:.2f}, constant'.format(best_score))

    while True:
        step = [(best_score, None, best_model, 'unchanged')]
        for variable in variables:
            if variable in best_variables:
                continue
            step_var = list(best_variables)
            step_var.append(variable)
            step_model = train_model(step_var)
            step_score = score_model(step_model, step_var)
            step.append((step_score, variable, step_model, 'add'))

        for variable in best_variables:
            step_var = list(best_variables)
            step_var.remove(variable)
            step_model = train_model(step_var)
            step_score = score_model(step_model, step_var)
            step.append((step_score, variable, step_model, 'remove'))

        # sort by ascending score
        step.sort(key=lambda x: x[0])

        # the first entry is the model with the lowest score
        best_score, chosen_variable, best_model, direction = step[0]
        if verbose:
            print('Step: score={:.2f}, {} {}'.format(best_score, direction,
                                                      chosen_variable))
        if chosen_variable is None:
            # step here, as adding or removing more variables is detrimental to performance
            break
```

```
        if direction == 'add':
            best_variables.append(chosen_variable)
        else:
            best_variables.remove(chosen_variable)
    return best_model, best_variables
```

printTermDocumentMatrix

```
import pandas as pd

def printTermDocumentMatrix(count_vect, counts):
    """ Print term-document matrix created by the CountVectorizer
    Input:
        count_vect: scikit-learn Count vectorizer
        counts: term-document matrix returned by transform method of counter vectorizer
    """
    shape = counts.shape
    columns = ['S{}'.format(i) for i in range(1, shape[0] + 1)]
    print(pd.DataFrame(data=counts.toarray().transpose(),
                       index=count_vect.get_feature_names(), columns=columns))
```

AIC_score, BIC_score

```
import math
import numpy as np

def AIC_score(y_true, y_pred, model=None, df=None):
    """ calculate Akaike Information Criterion (AIC)
    Input:
        y_true: actual values
        y_pred: predicted values
        model (optional): predictive model
        df (optional): degrees of freedom of model

    One of model or df is requried
    """
    if df is None and model is None:
      raise ValueError('You need to provide either model or df')
    n = len(y_pred)
    p = len(model.coef_) + 1 if df is None else df
    resid = np.array(y_true) - np.array(y_pred)
    sse = np.sum(resid ** 2)
    constant =  n + n * np.log(2*np.pi)
    return n * math.log(sse / n) + constant + 2 * (p + 1)

def BIC_score(y_true, y_pred, model=None, df=None):
    """ calculate Schwartz's Bayesian Information Criterion (AIC)
```

```
    Input:
        y_true: actual values
        y_pred: predicted values
        model: predictive model
        df (optional): degrees of freedom of model
    """
    aic = AIC_score(y_true, y_pred, model=model, df=df)
    p = len(model.coef_) + 1 if df is None else df
    n = len(y_pred)
    return aic - 2 * (p + 1) + math.log(n) * (p + 1)
```

adjusted_r2_score

```
from sklearn.metrics import regression

def adjusted_r2_score(y_true, y_pred, model):
    """ calculate adjusted R2
    Input:
        y_true: actual values
        y_pred: predicted values
        model: predictive model
    """
    n = len(y_pred)
    p = len(model.coef_)
    r2 = regression.r2_score(y_true, y_pred)
    return 1 - (1 - r2) * (n - 1) /(n - p - 1)
```

Index